Test Item File for

CALCULUS: An Applied Approach

FIFTH EDITION

Larson / Edwards

Elizabeth J. Marsch

Houghton Mifflin Company   Boston   New York

Sponsoring Editor: Jack Shira
Managing Editor: Cathy Cantin
Senior Associate Editor: Maureen Ross
Associate Editor: Michael J. Richards
Assistant Editor: Carolyn Johnson
Supervising Editor: Karen Carter
Project Editor: Patty Bergin
Editorial Assistant: Christine E. Lee
Art Supervisor: Gary Crespo
Marketing Manager: Ros Kane
Marketing Assistant: Erin Dionne
Design: Henry Rachlin
Composition and Art: Meridian Creative Group

Calculator Key font used with permission of Texas Instruments Incorporated. Copyright 1990, 1993, 1996.

Printed in the U.S.A.

ISBN: 0-395-93347-1

123456789-EB-02 01 00 99 98

PREFACE

This Test Item File is a supplement for *Calculus: An Applied Approach*, Fifth Edition, by Ron Larson and Bruce H. Edwards. All chapter references refer to this text. The Test Item File is divided into two sections. The first section is a bank of test items and the second section is a compilation of tests and quizzes which may be used to evaluate student performance.

The test item bank is arranged by text section and includes over 2500 multiple-choice and open-ended questions. Each question is followed by a two or three item code line. The first item of the code line indicates the level of difficulty: (1) if routine and (2) if challenging. If the question requires the use of a graphing utility, this is indicated next (T). The last item in the code line is the answer.

The second section consists of tests and corresponding answer keys. There is one mid-chapter quiz in multiple-choice format included for each chapter, and three multiple-choice cumulative exams covering chapters 0–3, 0–7, and 0–10, respectively. None of these tests require a graphing utility. Three final exam forms are included, Forms A and B do not require a graphing utility, with Form A being in multiple-choice format and Form B being open-ended in format. Form C is open-ended in format and does require a graphing utility. There are five chapter test forms included for each chapter. Forms A and B are in multiple-choice format and do not require a graphing utility. These two forms are similar and may be used interchangeably. Test Form C is in open-ended format and does not require a graphing utility. Test Forms D and E both require use of a graphing utility, with Form D being in multiple-choice format and Form E being in open-ended format.

I would like to thank Ann R. Kraus, Gregor Olšavský, and Meredythe M. Burrows for the test items that they provided. Thanks also goes to the staff at Larson Texts, Inc., for preparing this manuscript for publication.

Elizabeth J. Marsch

CONTENTS

Chapter 9   Probability and Calculus

Chapter 10   Series and Taylor Polynomials

Section 2—Quizzes and Tests

CHAPTER 0
A Precalculus Review

Section 0.1   The Real Line and Order

1. In the process of solving an inequality one must pay very close attention when multiplying or dividing both sides of the inequality by a constant. Explain why this is true.

    1—Answer: If you multiply or divide an inequality by a positive number, the order of the inequality remains the same. However, if you multiply or divide by a negative number, the order reverses.

2. Determine which of the following values for x satisfies the inequality $-2 < \dfrac{x+5}{7} < 5$.

    (a) $x = 20$ (b) $x = -19$ (c) $x = 30$

    (d) All of these   (e) None of these

    1—Answer: a

3. Determine which of the following values for x satisfies the inequality $3 \le \dfrac{4-x}{2} < 5$.

    (a) $x = 4$ (b) $x = -2$ (c) $x = -1$

    (d) All of these   (e) None of these

    1—Answer: b

4. Determine which of the following values for x satisfies the inequality $-1 < \dfrac{3-x}{4} < 5$.

    (a) $x = 10$ (b) $x = -8$ (c) $x = 17$

    (d) All of these   (e) None of these

    1—Answer: b

5. Graph the solution: $-16 \le 7 - 2x < 5$.

    1—Answer: $1 < x \le \dfrac{23}{2}$

6. Graph the solution: $3 - 2x < 15$.

    (a)   (b)

    (c)   (d)   (e) None of these

    1—Answer: a

7. Graph the solution: $-6 < 7x + 2 \le 5$.

(a)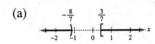

(b)

(c)

(d)

(e) None of these

1—Answer: b

8. Solve the inequality: $14 - 2x \le 5$.

(a) $\left(-\infty, \frac{9}{2}\right)$

(b) $\left(-\infty, \frac{9}{2}\right]$

(c) $\left(\frac{9}{2}, \infty\right)$

(d) $\left[\frac{9}{2}, \infty\right)$

(e) None of these

1—Answer: d

9. Graph the solution: $\frac{1}{2} < 3 - x < 5$.

1—Answer:

10. Solve the inequality: $x^2 - x > 6$.

2—Answer: $(-\infty, -2)$ or $(3, \infty)$

11. Solve for x: $-\frac{2}{3}x > x + 2$.

(a) $\left(-\frac{6}{5}, \infty\right)$

(b) $\left(\frac{6}{5}, \infty\right)$

(c) $\left(\frac{2}{5}, \infty\right)$

(d) $\left(-\infty, -\frac{6}{5}\right)$

(e) None of these

1—Answer: d

12. Solve for x: $3 - 2x \ge 0$.

1—Answer: $x \le \frac{3}{2}$

13. Solve for x: $-\frac{4}{5}x < 4x - 8$.

(a) $\left(-\frac{6}{5}, \infty\right)$

(b) $\left(\frac{5}{3}, \infty\right)$

(c) $\left(\frac{2}{5}, \infty\right)$

(d) $\left(-\infty, -\frac{2}{5}\right)$

(e) None of these

1—Answer: b

14. Solve for x: $-\frac{5}{4}x < 5x - 10$.

(a) $\left(-\infty, \frac{8}{5}\right)$　　　　(b) $x > \frac{8}{5}$　　　　(c) $x < \frac{8}{5}$

(d) $\left[\frac{8}{5}, \infty\right)$　　　　(e) None of these

1—Answer: b

15. Solve for x: $-\frac{3}{2}x < 6x + 12$.

1—Answer: $x > -\frac{8}{5}$

16. Solve for x (accurate to the nearest 0.1): $-x^2 + 5x < -7$.

2—T—Answer: $x < -1.1$ or $x > 6.1$

17. Solve the inequality: $4 \le 3 - 2x < 19$.

1—Answer: $-8 < x \le -\frac{1}{2}$

18. Solve the inequality: $(x - 2)^2 \le 9$.

2—Answer: $[-1, 5]$

19. Solve the inequality: $3x^3 - 6x^2 > 0$.

(a) $(-\infty, 0)$ or $(2, \infty)$　　　　(b) $(0, 2)$　　　　(c) $(-\infty, 0)$

(d) $(2, \infty)$　　　　(e) None of these

2—Answer: d

20. Graph the solution set of $x^2 + 8x + 12 \ge 0$.

(a) 　　　　(b)

(c) 　　　　(d) 　　　　(e) None of these

2—Answer: b

21. Graph the solution set of $x^2 - 6x + 8 \ge 0$.

(a) 　　　　(b)

(c) 　　　　(d) 　　　　(e) None of these

2—Answer: c

22. Solve for x: $-x^2 + 4x - 3 > 0$.

    (a) $(0, 3)$ (b) $[1, 3)$ (c) 2

    (d) $(1, 3)$ (e) $(-\infty, 1)$ or $(3, \infty)$

    2—Answer: d

23. Solve for x: $-x^2 - 3x > 0$.

    (a) $(-3, \infty)$ (b) $(-3, 0)$ (c) $(0, 3)$

    (d) $(-\infty, -3)$ or $(0, \infty)$ (e) None of these

    2—Answer: b

24. Solve for x: $-x^2 + 5x + 6 < 0$.

    2—Answer: $(-\infty, -1)$ or $(6, \infty)$

25. The revenue for selling x units of a product is $R = 79.99x$, and the cost of producing x units of the product is $C = 61x + 1050$. To obtain a profit, the revenue must be greater than the cost. For what values of x will this product return a profit?

    (a) $x \geq 52$ (b) $x \geq 8$ (c) $x \geq 18$ (d) $x \geq 53$ (e) None of these

    1—Answer: e

26. The revenue for selling x units of a product is $R = 69.99x$, and the cost of producing x units of the product is $C = 59x + 855$. To obtain a profit, the revenue must be greater than the cost. For what values of x will this product return a profit?

    (a) $x \geq 78x$ (b) $x \geq 15$ (c) $x \geq 85$ (d) $x \geq 13$ (e) None of these

    1—Answer: a

27. Solve for x: $4 - x^2 \leq 0$.

    (a) $[-2, 2]$ (b) $(-\infty, -2)$ (c) $(-\infty, 2)$

    (d) $(-\infty, -2]$ or $[2, \infty)$ (e) None of these

    2—Answer: d

28. The cost C of manufacturing x compact disks is given by $C = 2000 + 10x + 0.2x^2$, where x is a positive integer or 0. How many compact disks can be produced for less than \$3000?

    1—T—Answer: 49

29. A rural landowner wants to divide some road–front property into 4 rectangular lots of the same width. In order to satisfy local regulations, the size of each lot must be at least 10 acres. If the frontage is 2000 feet, how deep must each lot be? 1 acre = 43,560 sq. ft.

    (a) at least 87.2 feet   (b) at least 217.8 feet   (c) at least 871.2 feet

    (d) no more than 416.3 feet   (e) None of these

    2—T—Answer: c

30. The cost C of manufacturing x radios is given by $C = 400 + 100x + 0.1x^2$. How many radios can be produced for less than $2000?

    (a) $x < 15$ (b) $x > 16$ (c) $x < 14$ (d) $x < 16$ (e) None of these

    2—T—Answer: a

31. The weekly cost of operating a certain manufacturing plant is $C = 0.2x^2 + 11x + 3000$, where x represents the number of units produced. Management wants to produce at least 100 units, but also wants to keep operating costs at less than 10,000 per week. At what values of x can both goals be met?

    2—Answer: $100 \leq x \leq 161$

32. A local trucking company's annual operating cost per truck is given by $C = 1.10m + 9400$, where m is the number of miles traveled by the truck per year. What number of miles will yield an annual operating cost per truck of less than $60,000?

    (a) 63,091 miles   (b) 55,660 miles   (c) 46,000 miles

    (d) 76,340 miles   (e) None of these

    2—T—Answer: c

33. P dollars is invested at a simple interest rate of r. The balance, A, in the account after t years is given by $A = P + Prt$, where the interest rate r is expressed in decimal form. What must the interest rate be in order for an investment of $1000 to grow to at least $1665 in 7 years?

    1—T—Answer: $r \geq 0.095 = 9.5\%$

34. P dollars is invested at a simple interest rate of r. The balance, A, in the account after t years is given by $A = P + Prt$, where the interest rate r is expressed in decimal form. What must the interest rate be in order for an investment of $1500 to grow to at least $2160 in 5 years?

    (a) $0.085 = 8.5\%$ (b) $0.088 = 8.8\%$ (c) $0.09 = 9\%$

    (d) $0.092 = 9.2\%$ (e) None of these

    1—T—Answer: b

35. In addition to fixed overhead costs of $750, the cost of producing x units of a certain item is $1.48 per unit. During one week, the cost of production varied from a high of $2119 to a low of $1860 per day. Find the high and low production levels during the week.

    (a) $750 < x < 925$ (b) $1764 < x < 1939$ (c) $507 < x < 683$

    (d) $1432 < x < 2008$ (e) None of these

    2—T—Answer: a

36. In addition to fixed overhead costs of $250, the cost of producing x units of a certain item is $0.74 per unit. During one month, the cost of production varied from a high of $1149.10 to a low of $927.10 per day. Find the high and low production levels during the month.

    (a) $1003 < x < 1303$ (b) $1502 < x < 1803$ (c) $1591 < x < 1891$

    (d) $915 < x < 1215$ (e) None of these

    2—T—Answer: d

Section 0.2 Absolute Value and Distance on the Real Line

1. Find the midpoint of the interval: $-7 \le x \le 1$.

   (a) -1 (b) -2 (c) -3 (d) -6 (e) None of these

   1—Answer: c

2. Find the midpoint of the interval: $-2 \le x \le 5$.

   (a) 3 (b) $-\frac{1}{2}$ (c) $\frac{3}{2}$ (d) 1 (e) None of these

   1—Answer: c

3. Find the midpoint of the interval: $-17 \le x \le -12$.

   (a) -29 (b) $-\frac{29}{2}$ (c) -5 (d) $-\frac{5}{2}$ (e) None of these

   1—Answer: b

4. Find the directed distance from b to a.

   (a) 4 (b) -4 (c) 2 (d) -2 (e) None of these

   1—Answer: b

5. Find the directed distance from b to a: $a = -6, b = 2$.

   (a) -8 (b) 8 (c) -4 (d) 4 (e) None of these

   1—Answer: a

6. Find the directed distance from b to a: $a = -2, b = 5$.

   (a) 3 (b) -3 (c) 7 (d) -7 (e) None of these

   1—Answer: d

7. Find the distance between a and b: $a = -73, b = 16$.

   1—Answer: 89

8. Find the distance between a and b: $a = -17, b = -56$.

   (a) 73 (b) -73 (c) -39 (d) 39 (e) None of these

   1—Answer: d

9. In a complete sentence, write the meaning of the statement $|x - 2| < 4$, as it refers to two points on a real number line.

   2—Answer: A number x is less than 4 units from the number 2.

10. Use absolute values to describe the interval $[-4, 10]$.

(a) $|x + 3| \geq 7$ (b) $|x - 7| \leq 3$ (c) $|x - 3| \leq 7$

(d) $|x + 7| \geq 3$ (e) None of these

2—Answer: c

11. Use absolute value to define the interval: $-7 \leq x \leq 7$.

1—Answer: $|x| \leq 7$

12. Use absolute value to define the interval: $x < -3$ or $x > 3$.

1—Answer: $|x| > 3$

13. Use absolute value to define the interval: $-7 < x < 3$.

2—Answer: $|x + 2| < 5$

14. Use absolute value to describe the following set: x is less than 5 units from y.

(a) $|y - 5| < x$ (b) $|x - 5| < y$ (c) $|x - y| < 5$

(d) $|x + 5| < y$ (e) None of these

1—Answer: c

15. Use absolute value to describe the following set: x is less than 4 units from y.

(a) $|y - 4| < x$ (b) $|x - 4| < y$ (c) $|x - y| < 4$

(d) $|x + 4| < y$ (e) None of these

1—Answer: c

16. Use absolute value notation to describe: the distance between x and 5 is at least 6.

(a) $|x + 5| > 6$ (b) $|x - 5| > 6$ (c) $|x - 5| \leq 6$

(d) $|6 - x| \geq 5$ (e) None of these

2—Answer: e

17. Use absolute value notation to describe: 6 is at most 3 units from x.

(a) $|x - 3| < 6$ (b) $|x - 6| \leq 3$ (c) $|x - 6| \geq 3$

(d) $|x - 3| \geq 6$ (e) None of these

2—Answer: b

18. Use absolute value notation to describe: the distance between x and 7 is greater than 2.

(a) $|x - 7| \geq 2$

(b) $|x - 2| < 7$

(c) $|x - 7| > 2$

(d) $|x - 2| > 7$

(e) None of these

2—Answer: c

19. Use absolute value notation to describe: y is closer to 5 than y is to -6.

2—Answer: $|y - 5| < |y + 6|$

20. Graph the solution: $|3x - 1| \geq 5$.

(a)

(b)

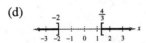

(c)

(d)

(e) None of these

2—Answer: b

21. Solve for x: $|-4x + 8| \geq 12$.

1—Answer: $(-\infty, -1] \cup [5, \infty)$

22. Solve for x: $|-3x + 6| \geq 12$.

(a) $(-\infty, -2] \cup [6, \infty)$

(b) $[-2, 6]$

(c) $x \geq 6$

(d) $x \leq -2$

(e) None of these

1—Answer: a

23. Solve for x: $|2x - 6| < 10$.

1—Answer: $-2 < x < 8$

24. Solve the inequality: $|4 - 2x| < 7$.

(a) $\left(-\frac{11}{2}, \frac{3}{2}\right)$

(b) $\left(-\frac{3}{2}, \frac{11}{2}\right)$

(c) $\left(-\infty, -\frac{11}{2}\right), \left(\frac{3}{2}, \infty\right)$

(d) $\left(-\infty, -\frac{3}{2}\right), \left(\frac{11}{2}, \infty\right)$

(e) None of these

1—Answer: b

25. Graph the solution: $|x + 2| < 9$.

(a)

(b)

(c)

(d)

(e) None of these

2—Answer: a

26. Solve the inequality: $|3x - 1| > 2$.

(a) $\left(-\frac{1}{3}, 1\right)$

(b) $\left[-\frac{1}{3}, 1\right]$

(c) $\left(-\infty, -\frac{1}{3}\right), (1, \infty)$

(d) $\left(-\infty, -\frac{1}{3}\right], [1, \infty)$

(e) None of these

2—Answer: c

27. Graph the solution: $|x + 5| \leq 2$.

2—Answer:

28. Graph the solution: $|3x - 1| > 9$.

2—Answer: $x < -\frac{8}{3}, x > \frac{10}{3}$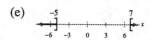

29. Graph the solution: $|2 - x| \leq 5$.

(a)

(b)

(c)

(d)

(e)

2—Answer: a

30. Graph the solution: $|2x - 1| \geq 3$.

(a)

(b)

(c)

(d)

(e) None of these

2—Answer: d

31. Solve the inequality: $\left|1 + \frac{3}{2}x\right| \le 1$.

   2—Answer: $\left[-\frac{4}{3}, 0\right]$

32. A stock market analyst predicts that over the next year the price p of a certain stock will not change from its current price of $\$48\frac{1}{2}$ by more than $\$3$. Use absolute values to write this prediction as an inequality.

   (a) $\left|p - 48\frac{1}{2}\right| \le 3$ (b) $\left|p + 48\frac{1}{2}\right| \ge 3$ (c) $\left|p - 3\right| \le 48\frac{1}{2}$

   (d) $\left|p + 3\right| \ge 48\frac{1}{2}$ (e) None of these

   2—Answer: a

33. A stock market analyst predicts that over the next year the price p of a certain stock will not change from its current price of $\$37\frac{1}{2}$ by more than $\$2$. Use absolute values to write this prediction as an inequality.

   (a) $\left|p + 37\frac{1}{2}\right| \le 2$ (b) $\left|p - 37\frac{1}{2}\right| \le 2$ (c) $\left|p - 2\right| \le 37\frac{1}{2}$

   (d) $\left|p + 2\right| \ge 37\frac{1}{2}$ (e) None of these

   2—Answer: b

Section 0.3 Exponents and Radicals

1. Evaluate $3x^{-4}$ when $x = \frac{1}{2}$.

  (a) $-\frac{3}{16}$ (b) $\frac{81}{16}$ (c) 48   (d) 1296   (e) None of these

  1—Answer: c

2. Evaluate $2x^3 - 4x^2$ when $x = 3$.

  (a) 72   (b) -6 (c) 90   (d) 18   (e) None of these

  1—Answer: d

3. Evaluate the following expression when $x = 3, y = -1, a = -6, b = -3$:

$$-\frac{3x^2y^4}{a^3b^{-3}}.$$

  1—T—Answer: -3.375

4. Evaluate the following expression when $x = 2, y = -1, a = -5, b = -2$:

$$-\frac{3x^2y^4}{a^3b^{-3}}.$$

  (a) -0.768 (b) 0.769   (c) -0.769 (d) 0.768   (e) None of these

  1—T—Answer: a

5. Evaluate: $-\dfrac{x^2}{y^3z}$ if $x = 2, y = 1$, and $z = 3$.

  1—Answer: $-\frac{4}{3}$

6. Evaluate the following expression when $x = 2, y = -1, a = 1, b = -2$:

$$-\frac{2xy^3}{a^2b^3}.$$

  (a) 2   (b) -2 (c) $\frac{1}{2}$ (d) $-\frac{1}{2}$ (e) None of these

  1—Answer: d

7. Evaluate $3x^2y^{-4}$ when $x = -1$ and $y = -2$.

  1—Answer: $\frac{3}{16}$

8. Evaluate: $2x^4 + 3x$ when $x = -3$.

  (a) 1287   (b) 153   (c) -15 (d) 1215   (e) None of these

  1—Answer: b

9. Evaluate $x^{-1/2}$ when $x = \frac{9}{64}$.

(a) $\frac{3}{8}$ (b) $-\frac{3}{8}$ (c) $-\frac{8}{3}$ (d) $\frac{8}{3}$ (e) None of these

1—Answer: d

10. Simplify: $(2x^3)^4(3x^2)^3$.

(a) $432x^{18}$ (b) $279{,}936x^{42}$ (c) $6x^{18}$ (d) $6x^{32}$ (e) None of these

1—Answer: a

11. Simplify: $\dfrac{3x^4}{x^{-2}}$.

(a) $3x^{-8}$ (b) $\dfrac{3}{x^{-8}}$ (c) $3x^6$ (d) $3x^2$ (e) None of these

1—Answer: c

12. Simplify: $\left(\dfrac{x^{-3}y^2}{z}\right)^{-4}$.

(a) $\dfrac{z^4}{x^7y^6}$ (b) $\dfrac{y^2z^4}{x^7}$ (c) $\dfrac{x^{12}z^4}{y^8}$ (d) $\dfrac{x^3z}{y^2}$ (e) None of these

1—Answer: c

13. Simplify: $\left(\dfrac{3x^2y^3}{xw^{-2}}\right)^3$.

(a) $9w^6x^3y^9$ (b) $9w^{-8}x^8y^{27}$ (c) $27w^6x^3y^9$ (d) $3w^6x^3y^9$ (e) None of these

1—Answer: c

14. Simplify: $3x^2(2x)^3(5x^{-1})$.

(a) $30x^{-6}$ (b) $\frac{6}{5}x^6$ (c) $\frac{24}{5}x^4$ (d) $120x^4$ (e) None of these

1—Answer: d

15. Simplify: $\dfrac{7x^{-1/2}y^3z^{-2}}{3x^3y^{-1}z^2}$.

1—Answer: $\dfrac{7y^4}{3z^4x^{7/2}}$

16. Simplify: $\dfrac{4x^{-2}y^2z^3w^{-1}}{64x^2\sqrt{y}z^{-2}w^3}$.

(a) $\dfrac{y^{5/2}z^3}{16x^4w^4}$ (b) $\dfrac{y^{3/2}z^5}{16x^4w^4}$ (c) $\dfrac{y^{3/2}z^3}{16x^2w}$ (d) $\dfrac{y^{5/2}z}{16x^4w^4}$ (e) $\dfrac{y^{3/2}z}{16x^4w^2}$

1—Answer: b

17. Simplify: $(3x^2y^3z)^{-2}(xy^4)$.

1—Answer: $\dfrac{1}{9x^3y^2z^2}$

18. Simplify: $(-2x^2)^5(5x^3)^{-2}$.

1—Answer: $-\dfrac{32x^4}{25}$

19. Simplify: $\dfrac{125x^{-2}y^4z^{-5/2}w^{-1}}{5x^3\sqrt{y}z^{-2}w^{-3}}$.

(a) $\dfrac{25y^{7/2}x^4w^2}{z^{1/2}}$ (b) $\dfrac{25z^{1/2}w^2}{x^5y^{7/2}}$ (c) $\dfrac{25y^{7/2}w^2}{x^5z^{1/2}}$ (d) $\dfrac{25x^5z^{1/2}}{y^{7/2}w^2}$ (e) None of these

1—Answer: c

20. Simplify: $\dfrac{130x^{-3}y^5z^{-7/2}w^{-1}}{5x^4\sqrt{y}z^{-3}w^{-4}}$.

1—Answer: $\dfrac{26y^{9/2}w^3}{x^7z^{1/2}}$

21. Simplify: $\dfrac{100x^{-2}y^3z^{3/2}w^{-1}}{5x^2\sqrt{y}z^{-2}w^{-3}}$.

(a) $\dfrac{20y^{5/2}z^{7/2}w^2}{x^4}$ (b) $\dfrac{20y^{3/2}z^5}{x^4w^4}$ (c) $\dfrac{20y^{3/2}z^3}{x^2w}$ (d) $\dfrac{20y^{5/2}z}{x^4w^4}$ (e) $\dfrac{20y^{3/2}z}{x^4w^2}$

1—Answer: a

22. Simplify: $\sqrt[3]{16x^5y^4}$.

(a) $2xy\sqrt[3]{2x^2y}$ (b) $4x^2y^3\sqrt[3]{2x^2y}$ (c) $2x^3y^3\sqrt[3]{2x^2y}$ (d) $8x^2y^3\sqrt[3]{2xy}$ (e) None of these

1—Answer: a

23. Simplify: $\sqrt{125ab^4c^2}$.

    (a) $5abc\sqrt{5a}$ (b) $25ab^2c\sqrt{5}$ (c) $5b^2c\sqrt{5a}$ (d) $5bc\sqrt{25ab^2c}$ (e) None of these

    1—Answer: c

24. Simplify: $\sqrt[3]{-625x^7y^5}$.

    (a) $5xy\sqrt[3]{-5x^4y^2}$ (b) $-5xy\sqrt[3]{5x^4y^2}$ (c) $-125x^2y\sqrt[3]{5xy^2}$

    (d) $-5x^2y\sqrt[3]{5xy^2}$ (e) None of these

    1—Answer: d

25. Simplify: $\sqrt[3]{16x^4y^7}$.

    1—Answer: $2xy^2\sqrt[3]{2xy}$

26. Simplify: $\sqrt[3]{-128x^9y^6}$.

    1—Answer: $-4x^3y^2\sqrt[3]{2}$

27. Evaluate the following expression when $x = 2, y = -1, a = 1, b = -2$:

$$-\frac{2(xy)^3}{a^2b^3}.$$

    (a) 2   (b) -2 (c) $\frac{1}{2}$ (d) $-\frac{1}{2}$ (e) None of these

    1—Answer: b

28. Find the domain: $\dfrac{1}{\sqrt{x-1}}$.

    (a) $(-\infty, \infty)$ (b) 1   (c) $(1, \infty)$ (d) $(-\infty, 1)$ (e) None of these

    1—Answer: c

29. Find the domain: $\sqrt[3]{1+x}$.

    (a) $(-\infty, \infty)$ (b) $[-1, \infty)$ (c) -1 (d) $(-\infty, -1]$ (e) None of these

    1—Answer: a

30. Find the domain: $\sqrt{3x+2}$.

    1—Answer: $\left[-\frac{2}{3}, \infty\right)$

31. Find the domain of the algebraic expression $\sqrt{x^2+4}$.

    (a) $(-2, 2)$ (b) $x > 2$ (c) $x < -2$

    (d) $x < -2$ or $x > 2$ (e) None of these

    1—Answer: e

32. Find the domain of the algebraic expression $\sqrt{x^2 - 4}$.

   1—Answer: $(-\infty, -2] \cup [2, \infty)$

33. Determine the domain of the algebraic expression $\sqrt{x - 4} + \dfrac{1}{\sqrt{x + 4}}$.

   (a) $(-4, \infty)$ (b) $(-4, 4)$ (c) $(4, \infty)$ (d) $[4, \infty)$ (e) None of these

   2—Answer: d

34. Determine the domain of the algebraic expression $\sqrt{x + 3} + \dfrac{1}{\sqrt{x - 3}}$.

   2—Answer: $(3, \infty)$

35. Find the domain: $\dfrac{4}{\sqrt[3]{2 - x}}$.

   1—Answer: $(-\infty, 2)(2, \infty)$

36. Find the domain: $\dfrac{4}{\sqrt{2 - x}}$.

   (a) $(2, \infty)$ (b) $(-\infty, 2)$ (c) $(-2, \infty)$ (d) $(-\infty, 2)(2, \infty)$ (e) None of these

   1—Answer: b

37. The balance A of an annuity after a total of N payments can be calculated by using the formula
   $A = P\left[\dfrac{(1 + r)^N - 1}{r}\right]$ where P is the amount of each payment and r is the compound interest rate per payment
   period (in decimals). Calculate the balance after five years if \$1000 is deposited annually into an account that pays
   8% interest.

   (a) \$5866.60   (b) \$11,030.67   (c) \$5421.16   (d) \$7247.21   (e) None of these

   1—T—Answer: a

38. The balance A of an annuity after a total of N payments can be calculated by using the formula
   $A = P\left[\dfrac{(1 + r)^N - 1}{r}\right]$ where P is the amount of each payment and r is the compound interest rate per payment
   period (in decimals). Calculate the balance after five years if \$1500 is deposited annually into an account that pays
   8% interest.

   (a) \$11,071.50   (b) \$16,546.01   (c) \$8142.64   (d) \$8799.90   (e) None of these

   1—Answer: d

39. The balance A of an annuity after a total of N payments can be calculated by using the formula $A = P\left[\dfrac{(1 + r)^N - 1}{r}\right]$ where P is the amount of each payment and r is the compound interest rate per payment period (in decimals). Calculate the balance after ten years if $1000 is deposited annually into an account that pays 8% interest.

   1—Answer: $14,486.56

40. A 20-year mortgage for $P = \$56{,}000$ at an annual percentage rate of $r = .07$ requires a monthly payment of $M = \$424.17$. Payments have been made on the loan for 2 years ($N = 24$ monthly payments). Determine the balance B due on the loan if the balance is given by $B = \left(1 + \dfrac{r}{12}\right)^N \left(P - \dfrac{12M}{r}\right) + \dfrac{12M}{r}$.

   2—T—Answer: $53,496.01

41. A 20-year mortgage for $P = \$56{,}000$ at an annual percentage rate of $r = .07$ requires a monthly payment of $M = \$424.17$. Payments have been made on the loan for 3 years ($N = 36$ monthly payments). Determine the balance B due on the loan if the balance is given by $B = \left(1 + \dfrac{r}{12}\right)^N \left(P - \dfrac{12M}{r}\right) + \dfrac{12M}{r}$.

   (a) $53,207.02   (b) $47,492.18   (c) $52,106.68   (d) $40,729.88   (e) None of these

   2—T—Answer: c

42. The daily cost of producing x units of a certain product is given by $C = \sqrt{700 + 0.05x + .002x^2}$. Use a calculator to find the cost, to the nearest penny, of producing 400 units for 7 days.

   (a) $225.74   (b) $32.25   (c) $19.36   (d) $135.55   (e) None of these

   2—T—Answer: a

43. The daily cost of producing x units of a certain product is given by $C = \sqrt{700 + 0.05x + .002x^2}$. Use a calculator to find the cost, to the nearest penny, of producing 300 units for 14 days.

   2—T—Answer: $418.83

44. Use a calculator to find the monthly payment M for an installment loan of two years (rounded to the nearest penny) on a principal P of $1000 if the interest rate is $r = 6\%$ per annum and $n = 12$. The formula for the payment M is

$$M = P\left[\dfrac{\dfrac{r}{n}}{1 - \left(\dfrac{1}{\dfrac{r}{n} + 1}\right)^N}\right] \quad \text{where } N \text{ is the total number of payments.}$$

   1—T—Answer: $44.32

45. Use a calculator to find the *interest accrued* (rounded to the nearest penny) on a principal P of $5000 after two years if the interest rate is $r = 5\%$ per annum and the interest is compounded monthly (i.e., $n = 12$). The formula for the amount A of money in the bank is $A = P\left(1 + \dfrac{r}{n}\right)^{N}$, where N is the number of compoundings.

(a) $5524.71   (b) $7083.33   (c) $524.70   (d) $2083.33   (e) None of these

2—T—Answer: c

Section 0.4   Factoring Polynomials

1. Solve for x: $x^2 - 3x + \frac{3}{2} = 0$.

1—Answer: $\dfrac{3 \pm \sqrt{3}}{2}$

2. Solve for x: $-3x^2 + 4x + 6 = 0$.

1—Answer: $\dfrac{2 \pm \sqrt{22}}{3}$

3. Solve for x: $(x + 2)^2 = -16x$.

(a) $-8 \pm 2\sqrt{15}$ (b) $-10 \pm 4\sqrt{6}$ (c) $-10 \pm 2\sqrt{26}$

(d) $-8 \pm 4\sqrt{15}$ (e) None of these

1—Answer: b

4. Solve for x: $\dfrac{1}{x - 1} + \dfrac{x}{x + 2} = 2$.

1—Answer: $-1 \pm \sqrt{7}$

5. Solve for x: $2x^2 = 162$.

(a) 9   (b) -9 (c) $-9, 9$ (d) 81   (e) None of these

1—Answer: c

6. Solve for x: $5x^2 - 2 = 3x$.

(a) $\frac{2}{5}, -1$ (b) $-\frac{1}{5}, 2$ (c) $-\frac{2}{5}, 1$ (d) $\frac{1}{5}, -2$ (e) None of these

1—Answer: c

7. Solve for x: $2x^2 + 4x = 9x + 18$.

(a) $-2, \frac{9}{2}$ (b) $2, -\frac{9}{2}$ (c) $\frac{9}{2}$ (d) $-\frac{9}{2}$ (e) None of these

1—Answer: a

8. Solve for x: $4x^2 + 12x + 9 = 0$.

1—Answer: $-\frac{3}{2}$

9. Solve for x: $3x^2 + 19x - 14 = 0$.

1—Answer: $-7, \frac{2}{3}$

10. Solve for x: $7(x + 2)^2 = 12$.

     1—Answer: $\frac{1}{7}\left(-14 \pm 2\sqrt{21}\right)$

11. Solve for x: $2x^2 + x = 3$.

     1—Answer: $-\frac{3}{2}, 1$

12. Solve for x: $(x + 7)^2 = 5$.

     1—Answer: $-7 \pm \sqrt{5}$

13. Solve for x: $3x^3 - 27x = 0$.

     (a) 3 (b) $-3, 3$ (c) $-3, 0, 3$ (d) $0, 3i, -3i$ (e) None of these

     1—Answer: c

14. Solve for x: $x^4 + 5x^2 - 36 = 0$.

     (a) $\pm 3, \pm 2$ (b) $9, 4$ (c) $\pm 2, \pm 3i$ (d) $-9, 4$ (e) None of these

     2—Answer: c

15. Solve for x: $3x^3 - 24x^2 + 21x = 0$.

     (a) $7, 1$ (b) $-7, -1$ (c) $0, 1, 7$ (d) $0, -1, -7$ (e) None of these

     1—Answer: c

16. Solve for x: $20x^3 - 500x = 0$.

     1—Answer: $0, \pm 5$

17. Solve for x: $7x^3 = 252x$.

     1—Answer: $\pm 6, 0$

18. Solve for x: $2x^4 - 7x^2 + 5 = 0$.

     1—Answer: $\pm 1, \pm \dfrac{\sqrt{10}}{2}$

19. Solve for x: $x^2 - 2x = 8$.

     1—Answer: $-2, 4$

20. Solve for y: $y^2 + y = 6$.

     (a) $\{8, 3\}$ (b) $\{-4, 3\}$ (c) $\{-1, 0\}$ (d) $\{-3, 4\}$ (e) None of these

     1—Answer: e

21. Solve for y: $(y - 2)(y + 3) = 6$.

    (a) $\{8, 3\}$ (b) $\{-4, 3\}$ (c) $\{-1, 0\}$ (d) $\{-3, 4\}$ (e) None of these

    1—Answer: b

22. Use the quadratic formula to find any real roots: $3x^2 + x - 3 = 0$.

    (a) $\dfrac{-1 \pm \sqrt{37}}{6}$ (b) $\dfrac{1 \pm \sqrt{37}}{6}$ (c) $-\dfrac{7}{6}, \dfrac{5}{6}$ (d) $\dfrac{-1 \pm \sqrt{37}}{3}$ (e) $\dfrac{-1 \pm \sqrt{37}}{2}$

    1—Answer: a

23. Use the quadratic formula to find any real roots: $2x^2 + 4x - 1 = 0$.

    (a) $\dfrac{-1 \pm \sqrt{37}}{6}$ (b) $\dfrac{1 \pm \sqrt{37}}{6}$ (c) $-\dfrac{7}{6}, \dfrac{5}{6}$ (d) $\dfrac{-1 \pm \sqrt{37}}{3}$ (e) None of these

    1—Answer: e

24. Use the quadratic formula and a calculator to estimate the roots of $2x^2 + 5x - 1 = 0$ to the nearest 0.1.

    (a) $-0.2, -2.3$ (b) $-0.4, 5.2$ (c) $-2.7, 0.2$ (d) $0.2, 2.3$ (e) None of these

    1—T—Answer: c

25. Use the quadratic formula and a calculator to estimate the roots of $3x^2 + 5x - 4 = 0$ to the nearest 0.1.

    1—T—Answer: $-2.3, 0.6$

26. Factor: $4x^3 + 6x^2 - 10x$.

    1—Answer: $2x(2x + 5)(x - 1)$

27. Factor: $3x^2 - 13x - 16$.

    (a) $(3x - 16)(x - 1)$ (b) $(3x + 16)(x - 1)$ (c) $(x + 16)(3x - 1)$

    (d) $(x - 16)(3x + 1)$ (e) None of these

    1—Answer: e

28. Factor into linear factors: $6x^3 + 33x^2y - 63xy^2$.

    (a) $3x(2x - 3y)(x + 7y)$ (b) $(6x^2 - 9xy)(x + 7y)$ (c) $3x(2x + 3y)(x + 7y)$

    (d) $(6x^2 + 9xy)(x + 7y)$ (e) None of these

    1—Answer: a

29. Factor completely: $3x^4 - 48$.

    (a) $3(x - 2)^2(x + 2)^2$ (b) $3(x - 2)^4$ (c) $3x^2(x - 4)^2$

    (d) $3(x^2 + 4)(x + 2)(x - 2)$ (e) None of these

    2—Answer: d

30. Factor completely: $x^2(2x + 1)^3 - 4(2x + 1)^2$.

    (a) $(2x + 1)^2(2x^3 - 3)$ (b) $(2x + 1)^2(2x^3 + x^2 - 4)$ (c) $(2x + 1)^3(x^2 - 4)$

    (d) $(2x + 1)^3(x^2 - 8x - 4)$ (e) None of these

    2—Answer: b

31. Factor completely: $35x^2 + 9x - 2$.

    1—Answer: $(5x + 2)(7x - 1)$

32. Factor completely: $(x + 3)^2 - a^2$.

    2—Answer: $(x + 3 - a)(x + 3 + a)$

33. Factor and simplify: $x(x + 1)^{-1/2} + 2(x + 1)^{1/2}$.

    2—Answer: $\dfrac{3x + 2}{\sqrt{x + 1}}$

34. Factor completely: $x^5 - 9x^3 + 8x^2 - 72$.

    2—Answer: $(x - 3)(x + 2)(x + 3)(x^2 - 2x + 4)$

35. Completely factor: $3x^4 - 375x$.

    (a) $3x(x + 5)(x^2 - 5x + 25)$ (b) $3x(x - 5)(x^2 - 5x + 25)$ (c) $3x(x - 5)(x^2 + 5x + 25)$

    (d) $3(x - 5)(x^2 + 5x + 25)$ (e) $3x(x - 5)(x^2 + 10x + 25)$

    1—Answer: c

36. Completely factor: $3x^4 - 24x$.

    (a) $3x(x + 2)(x^2 - 2x + 4)$ (b) $3x(x - 2)(x^2 - 2x + 4)$ (c) $3x(x - 2)(x^2 + 2x + 4)$

    (d) $3(x - 2)(x^2 + 2x + 4)$ (e) None of these

    1—Answer: c

37. Completely factor: $(x - 1)^{-2/3}(x + 2) + (x - 1)^{1/3}$.

    (a) $\dfrac{1 + x}{\sqrt{x + 2}}$ (b) $\dfrac{2(1 + x)}{\sqrt{x + 2}}$ (c) $x\sqrt{x + 2}$ (d) $x^2 + 2x$ (e) None of these

    1—Answer: e

38. Completely factor: $(x + 2)^{1/2} + x(x + 2)^{-1/2}$.

(a) $\dfrac{1 + x}{\sqrt{x + 2}}$ (b) $\dfrac{2(1 + x)}{\sqrt{x + 2}}$ (c) $x\sqrt{x + 2}$ (d) $x^2 + 2x$ (e) $\sqrt{x + 2}(1 + x)$

1—Answer: b

39. Completely factor: $(x - 5)^{-2/3}(3x + 4) - (x - 5)^{1/3}$.

1—Answer: $\dfrac{2x + 9}{(x - 5)^{2/3}}$

40. Completely factor: $(2x - 5)^{-3/4}(x + 2) - (2x - 5)^{1/4}$.

(a) $\dfrac{-x - 3}{(2x - 5)^{3/4}}$ (b) $\dfrac{(7 - x)}{(2x - 5)^{3/4}}$ (c) $\dfrac{3x - 3}{(2x - 5)^{3/4}}$ (d) $\dfrac{-x - 3}{(2x - 5)^{5/4}}$ (e) None of these

2—Answer: b

41. Completely factor: $3rv - 2vt - 6rs + 4st$.

2—Answer: $(v - 2s)(3r - 2t)$

42. Factor: $3x - 24x^4$.

1—Answer: $3x(1 - 2x)(1 + 2x + 4x^2)$

43. Use synthetic division to divide: $(3x^4 + 4x^3 - 2x^2 + 1) \div (x + 2)$.

(a) $3x^3 + 10x^2 + 18x + 37$ (b) $3x^3 - 2x^2 + 2x - \dfrac{3}{x + 2}$

(c) $3x^3 - 2x^2 + 2x - 4 + \dfrac{9}{x + 2}$ (d) $3x^3 + 10x^2 + 18x + 36 + \dfrac{73}{x + 2}$

(e) None of these

1—Answer: c

44. Use synthetic division to divide: $(x^4 + 2x^2 - x + 1) \div (x - 2)$.

1—Answer: $x^3 + 2x^2 + 6x + 11 + \dfrac{23}{x - 2}$

45. Use synthetic division to perform the indicated division:

$$\frac{x^3 - x^2 + 4x - 3}{x + 3}.$$

(a) $x^2 - 4x + 16 + \dfrac{45}{x + 3}$

(b) $x^2 - 4x + 16 + \dfrac{51}{x + 3}$

(c) $x^2 - 4x - 16 - \dfrac{51}{x + 3}$

(d) $x^2 - 4x + 16 - \dfrac{51}{x + 3}$

(e) None of these

1—Answer: d

46. Use synthetic division to find the quotient $\dfrac{x^3 + 2x^2 - 3x - 6}{x + 2}.$

1—Answer: $x^2 - 3$

47. Use synthetic division to perform the indicated division:

$$\frac{x^3 - x^2 - 4x - 5}{x + 2}.$$

1—Answer: $x^2 - 3x + 2 - \dfrac{9}{x + 2}$

48. Use synthetic division to divide: $(5x^4 - 2x^2 + 1) \div (x + 1)$.

(a) $5x^3 - 5x^2 + 3x - 3 + \dfrac{4}{x + 1}$ (b) $5x^2 - 7x + 8$

(c) $5x^2 + 3x + 4$

(d) $5x^3 + 5x^2 + 3x + 3 + \dfrac{4}{x + 1}$ (e) None of these

1—Answer: a

49. Find the interval(s) in which the expression $\sqrt{x^2 - 7x - 8}$ is defined.

(a) $x \le -1, x \ge 8$

(b) $x < -1, x > 8$

(c) $-1 \le x \le 8$

(d) $-1 < x < 8$

(e) None of these

1—Answer: a

50. Find the interval(s) in which the expression $\sqrt{169 - 9x^2}$ is defined.

(a) $\left(-\frac{13}{3}, \frac{13}{3}\right)$

(b) $\left[-\frac{13}{3}, \frac{13}{3}\right]$

(c) $\left(-\infty, -\frac{13}{3}\right], \left[\frac{13}{3}, \infty\right)$

(d) $\left(-\infty, -\frac{13}{3}\right), \left(\frac{13}{3}, \infty\right)$

(e) None of these

1—Answer: b

51. Find the interval(s) in which the expression $\sqrt{180 - 5x^2}$ is defined.

(a) $(-6, 6)$ (b) $[-6, 6]$ (c) $(-\infty, -6], [6, \infty)$

(d) $(-\infty, -6), (6, \infty)$ (e) None of these

1—Answer: b

52. Find the interval in which the expression $\sqrt{36 - x^2}$ is defined.

1—Answer: $[-6, 6]$

53. Find the interval in which the expression $\sqrt{16 - 4x^2}$ is defined.

1—Answer: $[-2, 2]$

54. Find the domain of $\sqrt{-x^2 + 4x - 3}$.

1—Answer: $1 \le x \le 3$

55. Find all of the real zeros of the function: $f(x) = 6x^4 + 32x^3 - 70x^2$.

(a) $0, -1, 5$ (b) $0, -7, \frac{5}{3}$ (c) $\frac{7}{3}, 5$ (d) $0, -1, -7, \frac{5}{3}$ (e) None of these

1—Answer: b

56. Find all of the real zeros of the function: $f(x) = 2x^3 + 14x^2 + 24x$.

1—Answer: $-4, -3, 0$

57. Find all zeros of the polynomial $x^4 + 3x^3 - 4x^2 - 12x$.

1—Answer: $-3, -2, 0, 2$

58. Use the rational zero theorem as an aid to find all real zeros of $2x^3 + 3x^2 - 8x - 12$.

(a) $-1, 0, 2$ (b) $-\frac{3}{2}$ (c) $-1, 0, 4$ (d) $-2, -\frac{3}{2}, 2$ (e) None of these

1—Answer: d

59. Use the rational zero theorem as an aid to find the one rational zero of $3x^3 - 4x^2 - 9x + 12$.

1—Answer: $\frac{4}{3}$

60. Use the rational zero theorem as an aid to find all real zeros of $x^4 - 3x^3 + 4x$.

(a) $\{-1, 0, 2\}$ (b) $\{-2, -1, 0\}$ (c) $\left\{-\frac{1}{2}, 0, 1, 3\right\}$

(d) $\{-1, -1, 0, 2\}$ (e) None of these

2—Answer: a

61. List the possible rational zeros of the function: $f(x) = 3x^5 + 2x^2 - 3x + 2$.

    (a) $\pm 3, \pm 2, \pm\frac{3}{2}, \pm 1, \pm\frac{2}{3}$ (b) $\pm 3, \pm\frac{1}{3}, \pm 2, \pm\frac{1}{2}, \pm 1$ (c) $\pm 2, \pm 1, \pm\frac{2}{3}, \pm\frac{1}{3}$

    (d) $\pm 3, \pm 1, \pm\frac{3}{2}, \pm\frac{1}{2}$ (e) None of these

    1—Answer: c

62. List the possible rational zeros of the function: $f(x) = 3x^5 - 2x^3 + 3x - 5$.

    1—Answer: $\pm\frac{1}{3}, \pm 1, \pm\frac{5}{3}, \pm 5$

63. List the possible rational zeros of the function: $f(x) = 3x^5 + 7x^3 - 3x^2 + 2$.

    1—Answer: $\pm\frac{1}{3}, \pm\frac{2}{3}, \pm 1, \pm 2$

64. Find all of the real zeros of the function: $f(x) = 3x^4 - 27x^3 + 54x^2$.

    (a) $0, 3, 9, 2$ (b) $0, 6, 3$ (c) $0, 9, 2$ (d) $0, 6$ (e) None of these

    1—Answer: b

65. In a complete sentence, give a definition of a rational number.

    1—Answer: A rational number is any real number that can be written as a fraction.

Section 0.5 Functions and Rationalization

1. Subtract, then simplify: $\dfrac{1}{x} - \dfrac{x}{2y}$.

(a) $\dfrac{2y - x}{2xy}$ (b) $\dfrac{1 - x}{2xy}$ (c) $\dfrac{1 - x}{x - 2y}$ (d) $\dfrac{2y - x^2}{2xy}$ (e) None of these

   1—Answer: d

2. Add, then simplify: $\dfrac{2}{x^2 - 9} + \dfrac{5}{x^2 - x - 12}$.

(a) $\dfrac{7}{(x^2 - 9)(x^2 - x - 12)}$ (b) $\dfrac{7x^2 - x - 21}{(x^2 - 9)(x^2 - x - 12)}$ (c) $\dfrac{7x - 7}{(x - 3)(x - 4)(x + 3)}$

(d) $\dfrac{7x - 23}{(x - 3)(x + 3)(x - 4)}$ (e) None of these

   2—Answer: d

3. Subtract, then simplify: $\dfrac{2}{x - 3} - \dfrac{1}{x + 2}$.

(a) $\dfrac{1}{(x - 3)(x + 2)}$ (b) $\dfrac{x - 1}{(x - 3)(x + 2)}$ (c) $\dfrac{x + 7}{(x - 3)(x + 2)}$

(d) $\dfrac{x + 1}{(x - 3)(x + 2)}$ (e) None of these

   1—Answer: c

4. Subtract, then simplify: $\dfrac{3}{x^2 + 2x + 1} - \dfrac{1}{x + 1}$.

(a) $\dfrac{4 - x}{x^2 + 2x + 1}$ (b) $\dfrac{-x^2 + 5x + 2}{(x + 1)(x^2 + 2x + 1)}$ (c) $\dfrac{-x^2 + x + 2}{(x^2 + 2x + 1)(x + 1)}$

(d) $\dfrac{2 - x}{x^2 + 2x + 1}$ (e) None of these

   2—Answer: d

5. Subtract, then simplify: $\dfrac{3}{x} - \dfrac{9}{x + 1}$.

   1—Answer: $\dfrac{3(1 - 2x)}{x(x + 1)}$

6. Subtract, then simplify: $\dfrac{2x}{x^2 + x - 6} - \dfrac{x}{x^2 - x - 2}$.

(a) $\dfrac{x^2 + 5x}{(x + 3)(x - 2)(x + 1)}$

(b) $\dfrac{x}{2x^2 - 8}$

(c) $\dfrac{x^2 + 5x}{(x + 3)(x - 2)^2(x + 1)}$

(d) $\dfrac{x^2 - x}{(x + 3)(x - 2)(x + 1)}$

(e) None of these

2—Answer: d

7. Subtract, then simplify: $\dfrac{3}{x^2 - 1} - \dfrac{2}{1 - x}$.

(a) $\dfrac{2x + 5}{x^2 - 1}$

(b) $\dfrac{2x + 1}{x^2 - 1}$

(c) $\dfrac{2 - 3x - 2x^2}{(x^2 - 1)(1 - x)}$

(d) $\dfrac{1}{x^2 - 1}$

(e) None of these

1—Answer: a

8. Perform the indicated operations and simplify: $\dfrac{A}{x} + \dfrac{B}{x^2} + \dfrac{C}{x + 2}$.

1—Answer: $\dfrac{(A + C)x^2 + (2A + B)x + 2B}{x^2(x + 2)}$

9. Perform the indicated operation: $x - 4 - \dfrac{1}{x - 2}$.

(a) $x - 3$ (b) $\dfrac{x^2 - 6x + 8}{x - 2}$ (c) $\dfrac{x^2 - 6x - 8}{x - 2}$ (d) $\dfrac{x^2 + 6x + 8}{x - 2}$ (e) None of these

1—Answer: e

10. Perform the indicated operation: $x - 5 - \dfrac{1}{x - 3}$.

1—Answer: $\dfrac{x^2 - 8x + 14}{x - 3}$

11. Perform the indicated operation: $x - 2 + \dfrac{3}{x + 1}$.

(a) $\dfrac{x^2 + x + 1}{x + 1}$

(b) $\dfrac{x^2 + x - 1}{x + 1}$

(c) $\dfrac{x^2 - x + 1}{x + 1}$

(d) $\dfrac{x^2 - x - 1}{x + 1}$

(e) $x + 2$

1—Answer: c

A Precalculus Review

12. Perform the indicated operation: $3x - 4 - \dfrac{1}{3x - 2}$.

   (a) $-3(3x - 2)$ (b) $\dfrac{9x^2 - 18x + 8}{3x - 2}$ (c) $\dfrac{9x^2 - 18x - 9}{3x - 2}$

   (d) $\dfrac{9x^2 - 18x + 7}{3x - 2}$ (e) None of these

   1—Answer: d

13. Add and simplify: $-\dfrac{\sqrt{x}}{x - 5} + \dfrac{1}{\sqrt{x}}$.

   (a) $\dfrac{5}{\sqrt{x}(5 - x)}$ (b) $2x - 5$ (c) $\dfrac{1 - \sqrt{x}}{x - 5 + \sqrt{x}}$ (d) $\dfrac{-2\sqrt{x} + 1}{\sqrt{x}(x - 5)}$ (e) None of these

   1—Answer: a

14. Perform the indicated operation and simplify: $\dfrac{-3}{\sqrt{x - 1}} + 4\sqrt{x - 1}$.

   1—Answer: $\dfrac{4x - 7}{\sqrt{x - 1}}$

15. Add and simplify: $-\dfrac{\sqrt{x + 1}}{x} + \dfrac{1}{\sqrt{x + 1}}$.

   (a) $-\dfrac{1}{x\sqrt{x + 1}}$ (b) $\dfrac{x - 1}{x}$ (c) $\dfrac{1}{x\sqrt{x + 1}}$ (d) $-\dfrac{1}{x}$ (e) None of these

   1—Answer: a

16. Multiply, then simplify: $\dfrac{2 - x}{x^2 + 4} \cdot \dfrac{x + 2}{x^2 + 5x - 14}$.

   (a) $-\dfrac{x + 2}{(x^2 + 4)(x + 7)}$ (b) $\dfrac{1}{(x + 2)(x + 7)}$ (c) $\dfrac{x + 2}{(x^2 + 4)(x + 7)}$

   (d) $\dfrac{-1}{(x + 2)(x + 7)}$ (e) None of these

   1—Answer: a

17. Simplify: $\dfrac{\sqrt{1+x} - \left(x/\sqrt{1+x}\right)}{1+x}$.

(a) $\dfrac{1 + 2\sqrt{1+x}}{1+x}$

(b) $\dfrac{-x + \sqrt{1+x}}{(1+x)\sqrt{1+x}}$

(c) $\dfrac{1}{1+x}$

(d) $\dfrac{\sqrt{1+x}}{(1+x)^2}$

(e) None of these

2—Answer: d

18. Simplify: $\dfrac{\sqrt{x} + \left(6/\sqrt{x}\right)}{\sqrt{x}}$.

(a) $\dfrac{6}{x}$

(b) $1 + 6\sqrt{x}$

(c) $\dfrac{x + 6\sqrt{x}}{x}$

(d) $\dfrac{x + 6}{x}$

(e) None of these

2—Answer: d

19. Simplify: $\dfrac{(x+2)^{1/2}}{(x+2)^{1/2} - 4(x+2)^{3/2}}$.

2—Answer: $-\dfrac{1}{4x + 7}$

20. Simplify: $\dfrac{\left(3/\sqrt{x+2}\right) - \sqrt{x+2}}{5\sqrt{x+2}}$.

2—Answer: $\dfrac{1-x}{5(x+2)}$

21. Simplify: $\dfrac{\dfrac{2}{1+x} - \dfrac{2}{x}}{4x}$.

(a) $\dfrac{-1}{2x^2(1+x)}$

(b) $\dfrac{x-1}{2x^2(1+x)}$

(c) -2

(d) $\dfrac{-1}{4x^2(1+x)}$

(e) None of these

1—Answer: a

22. Simplify: $\dfrac{\dfrac{2}{3-x} - \dfrac{2}{x}}{3x^2}$.

1—Answer: $\dfrac{2(2x-3)}{3x^3(3-x)}$

23. Simplify: $\dfrac{3(x + \Delta x)^2 - 4(x + \Delta x) + 5 - (3x^2 - 4x + 5)}{\Delta x}$.

1—Answer: $6x + \Delta x - 4$

24. Simplify: $\dfrac{3(x + 1)^{1/2} - \frac{3}{2}x(x + 1)^{-1/2}}{x + 1}$.

(a) $\dfrac{3\sqrt{x + 1} - 3x}{2(x + 1)^{3/2}}$ (b) $\dfrac{x - 1}{2(x + 1)}$ (c) $\dfrac{3(x + 2)}{2(x + 1)^{3/2}}$

(d) $\dfrac{3 - \frac{3}{2}(x + 1)^{-3/2}}{(x + 1)^{3/2}}$ (e) None of these

2—Answer: c

25. Simplify: $\dfrac{\sqrt{x + 1} - \dfrac{x}{2\sqrt{x + 1}}}{x + 1}$.

(a) $\dfrac{1}{\sqrt{x + 1}}$ (b) $\dfrac{x + 2}{2(x + 1)^{3/2}}$ (c) $\dfrac{1}{2\sqrt{x + 1}}$

(d) $\dfrac{\sqrt{x + 1} - x}{2(x + 1)^{3/2}}$ (e) None of these

2—Answer: b

26. Simplify: $\dfrac{2\sqrt{x} - \dfrac{2x + 1}{2\sqrt{x}}}{x}$.

(a) $\dfrac{1 - 2x}{2\sqrt{x}}$ (b) $\dfrac{2x - 1}{2x^{3/2}}$ (c) $\dfrac{2\sqrt{x} - 2x - 1}{2x^{3/2}}$

(d) $\dfrac{2x + 1}{2x^{3/2}}$ (e) None of these

1—Answer: b

27. Simplify: $\dfrac{\dfrac{\sqrt{x - 1}}{2\sqrt{x + 1}} - \dfrac{\sqrt{x + 1}}{2\sqrt{x - 1}}}{x - 1}$.

(a) $\dfrac{-1}{\sqrt{x + 1}(x - 1)^{3/2}}$ (b) $\dfrac{\sqrt{x - 1} - \sqrt{x + 1}}{2\sqrt{x + 1}(x - 1)^{3/2}}$ (c) $\dfrac{\sqrt{x - 1} - \sqrt{x + 1}}{2\sqrt{x + 1}\sqrt{x - 1}}$

(d) 0   (e) None of these

2—Answer: a

28. Simplify: $\dfrac{\dfrac{2}{x + \Delta x} - \dfrac{2}{x}}{\Delta x}$.

(a) $\dfrac{2}{x(x + \Delta x)}$ (b) $-\dfrac{2}{x + \Delta x}$ (c) 1 (d) $-\dfrac{2}{x(x + \Delta x)}$ (e) $-\dfrac{2}{x^2}$

1—Answer: d

29. Simplify: $\dfrac{\dfrac{5}{3 + x} - \dfrac{5}{x}}{3x}$.

(a) $\dfrac{10x - 15}{3x^2(3 + x)}$ (b) $\dfrac{5}{3x^2(3 + x)}$ (c) -5 (d) $\dfrac{-5}{x^2(3 + x)}$ (e) None of these

1—Answer: d

30. Rationalize the denominator and simplify: $\dfrac{x + 3}{\sqrt{x^2 + x - 6}}$.

(a) $\dfrac{1}{x - 2}$ (b) $\dfrac{(x + 3)\sqrt{x^2 + x - 6}}{x^2 + x - 6}$ (c) $\dfrac{\sqrt{x^3 + 4x^2 - 3x - 18}}{x^2 + x - 6}$

(d) $\dfrac{\sqrt{x^2 + x - 6}}{x - 2}$ (e) None of these

1—Answer: d

31. Rationalize the denominator: $\dfrac{x}{3 - \sqrt{x + 9}}$.

2—Answer: $-\left(3 + \sqrt{x + 9}\right)$

32. Rationalize the denominator and simplify: $\dfrac{3x}{\sqrt{x} - 5}$.

(a) $3x\sqrt{x}$ (b) $\dfrac{3x\sqrt{x} + 15x}{x - 25}$ (c) $\dfrac{3x\sqrt{x} + 15}{x - 25}$ (d) $\dfrac{3x\sqrt{x} + 15x}{x - 5}$ (e) None of these

1—Answer: b

33. Rationalize the numerator and simplify: $\dfrac{\sqrt{x} - 3}{2x}$.

1—Answer: $\dfrac{x - 9}{2x\sqrt{x} + 6x}$

34. Rationalize the denominator: $\dfrac{3}{\sqrt{7}+2}$.

(a) $\sqrt{7}-2$ (b) $\dfrac{3\sqrt{7}-6}{5}$ (c) $\dfrac{3\sqrt{7}-2}{3}$ (d) $\dfrac{3\sqrt{7}-2}{5}$ (e) None of these

1—Answer: a

35. Rationalize the denominator: $\dfrac{5}{7-\sqrt{2}}$.

(a) $\dfrac{35+5\sqrt{2}}{47}$ (b) $\dfrac{35+\sqrt{2}}{47}$ (c) $7+\sqrt{2}$ (d) $\dfrac{35+\sqrt{2}}{3}$ (e) None of these

1—Answer: a

36. Rationalize the numerator: $\dfrac{3-\sqrt{2}}{5}$.

1—Answer: $\dfrac{7}{5\left(3+\sqrt{2}\right)}$

37. Rationalize the denominator: $\dfrac{2}{\sqrt[3]{2x}}$.

(a) $\dfrac{\sqrt[3]{2x}}{x}$ (b) $\dfrac{\sqrt[3]{4x^2}}{x}$ (c) $\dfrac{2\sqrt[3]{2x}}{2x}$ (d) $\sqrt[3]{4x}$ (e) None of these

2—Answer: b

38. Rationalize the numerator and simplify: $\dfrac{3x-\sqrt{6x-1}}{3x-1}$.

2—Answer: $\dfrac{3x-1}{3x+\sqrt{6x-1}}$

39. Rationalize the numerator and simplify: $\dfrac{\sqrt{x}+\sqrt{x+2}}{2}$.

(a) $\dfrac{2}{\sqrt{x}-\sqrt{x+2}}$ (b) $\dfrac{-1}{\sqrt{x}-\sqrt{x+2}}$ (c) $\dfrac{1}{\sqrt{x}-\sqrt{x+2}}$

(d) $\dfrac{x+1}{\sqrt{x}+\sqrt{x+2}}$ (e) None of these

1—Answer: b

40. Rationalize the denominator and simplify: $\dfrac{2}{\sqrt{x+1}+\sqrt{x}}$.

(a) $\dfrac{2}{2x+1}$ (b) $\dfrac{1}{x+1}$ (c) $2\sqrt{2x}$

(d) $2\left(\sqrt{x+1}+\sqrt{x}\right)$ (e) $2\left(\sqrt{x+1}-\sqrt{x}\right)$

1—Answer: e

41. Rationalize the denominator and simplify: $\dfrac{\Delta x}{\sqrt{x+\Delta x}-\sqrt{x}}$.

(a) 1 (b) $\sqrt{x+\Delta x}+\sqrt{x}$ (c) $\sqrt{2x+\Delta x}$

(d) Δx (e) None of these

1—Answer: b

42. Rationalize the denominator and simplify: $\dfrac{4-x}{2+\sqrt{x}}$.

1—Answer: $2-\sqrt{x}$

43. Determine the monthly payment M for an installment loan of $P = \$14,000$ at an annual percentage rate of $7\frac{1}{2}\%$

$(r = 0.075)$ for 5 years $(N = 60$ monthly payments) given the formula $M = P\left[\dfrac{(r/12)}{1-\left(\dfrac{1}{(r/12)+1}\right)^{N}}\right]$.

1—Answer: $\$280.53$

44. Determine the monthly payment M for an installment loan of $P = \$9,000$ at an annual percentage rate of $7\frac{1}{2}\%$

$(r = 0.075)$ for 4 years $(N = 48$ monthly payments) given the formula $M = P\left[\dfrac{(r/12)}{1-\left(\dfrac{1}{(r/12)+1}\right)^{N}}\right]$.

(a) $\$387.43$ (b) $\$172.01$ (c) $\$269.22$ (d) $\$217.61$ (e) None of these

1—Answer: d

CHAPTER 1
Functions, Graphs, and Limits

Section 1.1   The Cartesian Plane and the Distance Formula

1. Find the distance between the points $(3, 17)$ and $(-2, 5)$.

   (a) 13   (b) $\sqrt{145}$ (c) $\sqrt{485}$ (d) $3\sqrt{51}$ (e) None of these

   1—Answer: a

2. Find the distance between the points $(-6, 10)$ and $(12, 2)$.

   (a) $2\sqrt{7}$ (b) $2\sqrt{97}$ (c) 10   (d) $2\sqrt{65}$ (e) None of these

   1—Answer: b

3. Find the distance between the points $(3, -1)$ and $(7, 2)$.

   1—Answer: 5

4. Find the distance between the points $(3, 5)$ and $(-2, -1)$.

   1—Answer: $\sqrt{61}$

5. Calculate the distance between the points $(-1, 5)$ and $(-3, -1)$.

   1—Answer: $2\sqrt{10}$

6. Calculate the distance between the points $(-1, 5)$ and $(3, -1)$.

   1—Answer: $2\sqrt{13}$

7. Calculate the distance between the points $(-1, -6)$ and $(3, -1)$.

   1—Answer: $\sqrt{41}$

8. Find the midpoint of the line segment joining $(3, 7)$ and $(-6, 1)$.

   (a) $\left(-\frac{3}{2}, 4\right)$ (b) $\left(\frac{9}{2}, 3\right)$ (c) $(-3, 6)$ (d) $(-3, 4)$ (e) None of these

   1—Answer: a

9. Find the midpoint of the line segment joining $(-3, 1)$ and $(5, -7)$.

   (a) $(-4, 4)$ (b) $(1, -3)$ (c) $(-4, -3)$ (d) $(1, 4)$ (e) None of these

   1—Answer: b

10. Find the midpoint of the line segment joining $(-2, 1)$ and $(16, 3)$.

    (a) $(7, 2)$ (b) $(9, 1)$ (c) $(14, 4)$ (d) $(-9, -1)$ (e) None of these

    1—Answer: a

11. Find the midpoint of the line segment joining $(6, 9)$ and $(-3, 1)$.

    1—Answer: $\left(\frac{3}{2}, 5\right)$

12. Find the midpoint of the line segment joining $(-6, -2)$ and $(5, -1)$.

    1—Answer: $\left(-\frac{1}{2}, -\frac{3}{2}\right)$

13. Find x so that the point $(x, 4)$ is the midpoint between the points $(2, -6)$ and $(3, 14)$.

    (a) 3 (b) $\frac{5}{2}$ (c) 4 (d) -3 (e) None of these

    1—Answer: b

14. Find x so that the distance between $(x, 1)$ and $(9, -3)$ is 5.

    (a) $x = -1, 1$ (b) $x = 5, 13$ (c) $x = 4, 14$ (d) $x = 6, 12$ (e) None of these

    2—Answer: d

15. Find x so that the distance between $(x, -3)$ and $(-7, -7)$ is 5.

    (a) $x = -10, -4$ (b) $x = -12, -2$ (c) $x = -1, 1$

    (d) $x = -11, -3$ (e) None of these

    2—Answer: a

16. Find x so that the distance between $(x, -4)$ and $(5, -8)$ is 5.

    (a) $x = 1, 9$ (b) $x = 2, 8$ (c) $x = 0, 10$ (d) $x = -1, 1$ (e) None of these

    2—Answer: b

17. Find x so that the distance between $(x, 5)$ and $(5, 1)$ is 5.

    (a) $x = -1, 1$ (b) $x = 1, 9$ (c) $x = 2, 8$ (d) $x = 0, 10$ (e) None of these

    2—Answer: c

18. Find y such that the distance from $(3, y)$ to $(-1, 2)$ is $\sqrt{65}$ units.

    (a) $5, -9$ (b) $\pm 3\sqrt{5}$ (c) $9, -5$ (d) $15, -3$ (e) None of these

    2—Answer: c

19. Find x such that the distance from $(x, -5)$ to $(-1, 2)$ is $\sqrt{65}$ units.

(a) $5, -3$ (b) $\pm\sqrt{15}$ (c) $15, -1$ (d) $-5, 3$ (e) None of these

2—Answer: d

20. Find x so that the distance between the points $(6, -1)$ and $(x, 9)$ is 12.

(a) $2\sqrt{31}$ (b) $6 + 2\sqrt{11}$ (c) $6 + 4\sqrt{10}$

(d) $-6 + 4\sqrt{5}$ (e) None of these

2—Answer: b

21. Find x so that the distance from the origin to the point $(x, 9)$ is 15.

(a) $\pm 3\sqrt{34}$ (b) $\pm 2\sqrt{11}$ (c) ± 9 (d) ± 12 (e) None of these

2—Answer: d

22. Find the point $(x, 0)$ that is equidistant from $(6, 1)$ and $(-2, 5)$.

2—Answer: $\left(\frac{1}{2}, 0\right)$

23. Find the point $(0, y)$ that is equidistant from $(6, 1)$ and $(-1, -2)$.

2—Answer: $\left(0, \frac{16}{3}\right)$

24. Identify the type of triangle that has $(-5, -1)$, $(2, 2)$, and $(0, -3)$ as vertices.

(a) Scalene, not right   (b) Right isosceles   (c) Equilateral

(d) Isosceles, not right   (e) None of these

2—Answer: b

25. Identify the type of triangle that has $(1, 10)$, $(-3, -2)$, and $(3, 16)$ as vertices.

(a) Isosceles, not right   (b) Right isosceles   (c) Scalene, not right

(d) Equilateral   (e) None of these

2—Answer: e

26. For 1984-1990, the number (in thousands) of persons in vocational rehabilitation programs for disabled veterans is given in the table. (*Source:* Statistical Abstract of the U.S. 1992)

1984	1985	1986	1987	1988	1989	1990
29.0	26.9	25.8	24.6	24.7	27.0	27.8

Use a scatter plot to represent the data, then describe any trends that appear.

1—T—Answer:

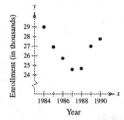

There was a steady decrease in the number of disabled American veterans enrolled in vocational rehabilitation programs between 1984 and 1987. This leveled off for one year then rose substantially in 1989 and leveled off again.

27. From 1985-1990, the amount (in millions of dollars) spent on automotive advertising in magazines in the U.S. is given in the table. (*Source:* Statistical Abstract of the U.S. 1992)

1985	1986	1987	1988	1989	1990
549	597	678	801	881	899

Use a scatter plot to represent the data, then describe any trends that appear.

1—T—Answer:

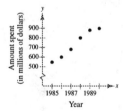

It appears that each year the amount of money spent on advertising increases.

28. A landowner wants to fence in a triangular section of his yard, as shown in the figure. To determine the amount of ornamental fencing required, the landowner needs to find the perimeter of the triangular section. Set up the information on a rectangular coordinate system, then use the distance formula to determine the perimeter.

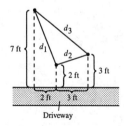

2—T—Answer:

$$d = d_1 + d_2 + d_3 \approx 14.95 \text{ feet.}$$

29. A triangle with the vertices $(2, 8)$, $(4, 1)$, and $(7, 5)$ is translated to a new position in the plane. The vertex $(2, 8)$ is translated to the position $(-4, -1)$. Determine the new vertex corresponding to the point $(4, 1)$.

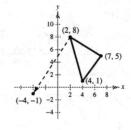

(a) $(-5, -5)$ (b) $(-2, -8)$

(c) $(1, -4)$ (d) $(-1, -2)$ (e) None of these

1—Answer: b

30. A triangle with the vertices $(-2, 6)$, $(1, 2)$, and $(6, 4)$ is translated to a new position in the plane. The vertex $(6, 4)$ is translated to the position $(9, -1)$. Determine the new vertex corresponding to the point $(-2, 6)$.

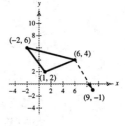

(a) $(-7, 9)$ (b) $(-5, 11)$

(c) $(1, 1)$ (d) $(3, 3)$ (e) None of these

1—Answer: c

Section 1.2 Graphs of Equations

1. Find the center of the circle: $4x^2 + 4y^2 - 2x + 8y - 1 = 0$.

   (a) $(1, -4)$ (b) $(-1, 4)$ (c) $\left(\frac{1}{2}, -2\right)$ (d) $(1, 1)$ (e) None of these

   1—Answer: e

2. Find the center of the circle: $2x^2 + 2y^2 - 4x + 12y + 15 = 0$.

   (a) $(1, -3)$ (b) $(-1, 3)$ (c) $(-1, -3)$ (d) $(1, 3)$ (e) None of these

   1—Answer: a

3. Find the center of the circle: $2x^2 + 2y^2 + 4x - 12y + 24 = 0$.

   (a) $(1, -3)$ (b) $(-1, 3)$ (c) $(-3, 1)$ (d) $(0, 0)$ (e) None of these

   1—Answer: b

4. Find the center and radius of the circle: $x^2 + y^2 - 4x + 12y + 5 = 0$.

   1—Answer: Center: $(2, -6)$, Radius: $\sqrt{35}$

5. Find the center and radius of the circle: $2x^2 + 2y^2 + 12x - 4y + 8 = 0$.

   1—Answer: Center: $(-3, 1)$, Radius: $\sqrt{6}$

6. Find the radius of the circle: $4x^2 + 4y^2 - 2x + 8y - 4 = 0$.

   (a) 1 (b) $\dfrac{1}{2}$ (c) $\dfrac{\sqrt{33}}{4}$ (d) $\dfrac{9}{4}$ (e) None of these

   1—Answer: c

7. Write the given equation of a circle in standard form and give the center and radius:

   $4x^2 + 4y^2 - 24x + 8y + 39 = 0$.

   1—Answer: $(x - 3)^2 + (y + 1)^2 = \frac{1}{4}$; Center: $(3, -1)$; Radius $= \frac{1}{2}$

8. Write the standard form of the equation of the circle which has these endpoints of a diameter:

   $(3, 7)$ and $(5, -1)$.

   1—Answer: $(x - 4)^2 + (y - 3)^2 = 17$

9. Write the equation of the circle with center $(-3, 4)$ and radius $r = \sqrt{3}$ *in general form.*

   (a) $x^2 + y^2 - 6x + 8y + 22 = 0$ (b) $(x + 3)^2 + (y - 4)^2 = 3$ (c) $(x - 3)^2 + (y + 4)^2 = 3$

   (d) $x^2 + y^2 + 6x - 8y + 22 = 0$ (e) None of these

   1—Answer: d

10. Write the equation for the circle with center $(-1, 3)$ and radius $r = 3$. Give your answer in general form.

    1—Answer: $x^2 + y^2 + 2x - 6y + 1 = 0$

11. Write the general equation of the circle with center at $(2, -3)$ and radius of 7.

    (a) $x^2 + y^2 - 4x + 6y + 6 = 0$ (b) $x^2 + y^2 + 4x - 6y + 6 = 0$ (c) $x^2 + y^2 - 4x + 6y - 36 = 0$

    (d) $x^2 + y^2 + 4x - 6y - 36 = 0$ (e) None of these

    1—Answer: c

12. Find the standard equation of the circle: $x^2 + y^2 - 2x + 8y - 20 = 0$.

    (a) $(x - 1)^2 + (y + 4)^2 = 20$ (b) $(x - 1)^2 + (y + 4)^2 = 3$ (c) $(x - 2)^2 + (y + 8)^2 = 48$

    (d) $(x - 1)^2 + (y + 4)^2 = 37$ (e) None of these

    1—Answer: d

13. Find the standard equation of the circle: $x^2 + y^2 - 4x + 2y + 1 = 0$.

    (a) $(x - 4)^2 + (y + 2)^2 = 19$ (b) $(x - 2)^2 + (y + 1)^2 = 4$ (c) $(x + 2)^2 + (y + 1)^2 = 19$

    (d) $(x + 4)^2 + (y + 2)^2 = 21$ (e) None of these

    1—Answer: b

14. Write the equation of the circle with center $(3, -4)$ and radius $r = 5$ in general form.

    1—Answer: $x^2 + y^2 - 6x + 8y = 0$

15. Find the equation of the circle whose diameter has endpoints $(8, -5)$ and $(6, 1)$.

    (a) $(x - 7)^2 + (y + 2)^2 = 10$ (b) $(x - 8)^2 + (y + 5)^2 = 40$ (c) $(x - 8)^2 + (y + 5)^2 = 10$

    (d) $(x - 7)^2 + (y + 2)^2 = 40$ (e) None of these

    2—Answer: a

16. Find the equation of the circle whose diameter has endpoints $(-4, -5)$ and $(-6, 1)$.

    (a) $(x + 4)^2 + (y + 5)^2 = 40$ (b) $(x + 5)^2 + (y + 2)^2 = 10$ (c) $(x + 5)^2 + (y + 2)^2 = 40$

    (d) $(x + 4)^2 + (y + 5)^2 = 10$ (e) None of these

    2—Answer: b

17. Find the equation of the circle whose diameter has endpoints $(5, -4)$ and $(3, 2)$.

    (a) $(x - 5)^2 + (y + 4)^2 = 10$ (b) $(x - 4)^2 + (y + 1)^2 = 40$ (c) $(x - 4)^2 + (y + 1)^2 = 10$

    (d) $(x - 5)^2 + (y + 4)^2 = 40$ (e) None of these

    2—Answer: c

18. Find the equation of the circle whose diameter has endpoints $(3, -2)$ and $(1, 4)$.

    (a) $(x - 2)^2 + (y - 1)^2 = 40$ (b) $(x - 3)^2 + (y + 2)^2 = 10$ (c) $(x - 3)^2 + (y + 2)^2 = 40$

    (d) $(x - 2)^2 + (y - 1)^2 = 10$ (e) None of these

    2—Answer: d

19. Find the equation of the circle whose diameter has endpoints $(-7, -6)$ and $(-9, 0)$.

    (a) $(x + 8)^2 + (y + 3)^2 = 40$ (b) $(x + 8)^2 + (y + 3)^2 = 10$ (c) $(x + 7)^2 + (y + 6)^2 = 10$

    (d) $(x + 7)^2 + (y + 6)^2 = 40$ (e) None of these

    2—Answer: b

20. Sketch the graph of $f(x) = x^2 - 5x + 4$. Be sure to include all intercepts.

    2—Answer:

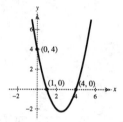

21. Identify the graph of the equation: $y = |x + 7|$.

    (a)

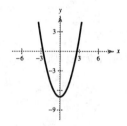

    (b)

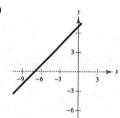

    (c)

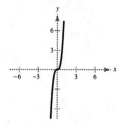

    (d)

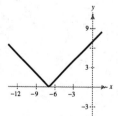

    (e) None of these

    1—Answer: d

22. Identify the graph of the equation: $y = \sqrt{2 - x}$.

(a)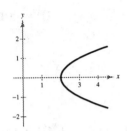

(b)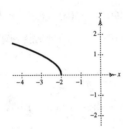

(c)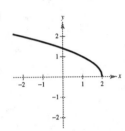

(d)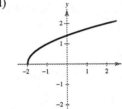

(e) None of these

1—Answer: c

23. Find all x–intercepts of the graph of the function $f(x) = 2x^3 + x^2 - 10x - 5$, accurate to the nearest 0.1.

(a) $-2.2, -0.5, 2.2$ (b) $-0.5, 1.7, 2.2$ (c) $-2.2, 0.5, 2.3$

(d) -0.5 (e) None of these

1—T—Answer: a

24. Find all intercepts of the graph of the equation $y = \dfrac{x^3}{3} - \dfrac{x^2}{2} - 2x + 5$, accurate to the nearest 0.1.

2—T—Answer: $(0, 5), (-2.7, 0)$

25. Find all intercepts of the graph of the equation $y = x^2 + 4x$.

1—Answer: $(0, 0), (-4, 0)$

26. Find all intercepts: $y = -4x^2 + 4x - 1$.

1—Answer: $\left(\frac{1}{2}, 0\right), (0, -1)$

27. Find all intercepts: $y = x^2 - 2x - 3$.

1—Answer: $(-1, 0), (3, 0), (0, -3)$

28. Find all intercepts: $y = \dfrac{x + 2}{x - 3}$.

(a) $(-2, 0)$ (b) $(-2, 0), (3, 0)$ (c) $\left(0, \frac{2}{3}\right), (3, 0)$

(d) $(-2, 0), \left(0, -\frac{2}{3}\right)$ (e) None of these

1—Answer: d

29. Find all intercepts: $y = \dfrac{x-1}{x+3}$.

(a) $(1, 0), \left(0, -\frac{1}{3}\right)$ (b) $(1, 0)$ (c) $(-3, 0), (1, 0)$

(d) $(-3, 0), \left(0, -\frac{1}{3}\right)$ (e) None of these

1—Answer: a

30. Find all intercepts: $y = \dfrac{2x-1}{3-x}$.

1—Answer: $\left(0, -\frac{1}{3}\right), \left(\frac{1}{2}, 0\right)$

31. Find the x–intercept(s): $3x^2 + 2y^2 + 4xy - 12 = 0$.

(a) $\pm\sqrt{6}$ (b) ± 2 (c) 4 (d) 6 (e) None of these

1—Answer: b

32. Find the x–intercept(s): $y = 2x^2 - 1$.

(a) $\dfrac{1}{2}$ (b) -1 (c) $\pm\dfrac{\sqrt{2}}{2}$ (d) $\pm\sqrt{2}$ (e) None of these

1—Answer: c

33. Find the x–intercept(s): $y = x^3(x + 2)(3x - 1)$.

(a) $0, -2, \frac{1}{3}$ (b) 0 (c) $0, 2, -1$ (d) $-2, \frac{1}{3}$ (e) There are no x-intercepts.

1—Answer: a

34. Find all points of intersection of the graphs of $x^2 - 2x - y = 6$ and $x - y = -4$.

(a) $(0, -6), (0, 4)$ (b) $(10, 14), (13, 17)$ (c) $(5, 9), (-2, 2)$

(d) $(-5, -1), (2, 6)$ (e) None of these

1—Answer: c

35. Find all points of intersection of the graphs of $x^2 + 3x - y = 3$ and $x + y = 2$.

(a) $(5, -3), (1, 1)$ (b) $(0, -3), (0, 2)$ (c) $(-5, -3), (1, 1)$

(d) $(-5, 7), (1, 1)$ (e) None of these

1—Answer: d

36. Find all points of intersection: $y = -x^2 + 4x$ and $y = x^2$.

1—Answer: $(0, 0), (2, 4)$

37. Find the points of intersection of the graphs of $y = x$ and $y = -x^2 + 6x$.

(a) $(0, 0), (5, 5)$

(b) $(-1, -1), (6, 6)$

(c) $(1, 1), (-6, -6)$

(d) $(-1, -1), (5, 5)$

(e) None of these

1—Answer: a

38. Determine the points of intersection of the circle $x^2 + y^2 - 4y = 0$ and the line $x + y - 1 = 0$ (accurate to the nearest 0.1).

2—T—Answer: $(0.8, 0.2), (-1.8, 2.8)$

39. Find the points of intersection of the graphs of the equations $y = x^2 + 1$ and $y = 2x + 16$.

(a) $(-5, 6), (3, 22)$

(b) $(5, 26), (-3, 10)$

(c) $(-5, 10), (3, 0)$

(d) $(0, 1), (0, 16)$

(e) None of these

1—Answer: b

40. Find the points of intersection of the graphs of the equations $y = 2x^2 - 1$ and $y = -2x^2 + 3$.

(a) $(0, -1), (0, -3)$

(b) $\left(\frac{1}{\sqrt{2}}, 0\right), \left(-\frac{1}{\sqrt{2}}, 0\right)$

(c) $(1, 0), (-1, 0)$

(d) $(1, 1), (-1, 1)$

(e) None of these

1—Answer: d

41. Find the points of intersection of the graphs of the equations $y = x$ and $y = -x^2 + 4x$.

1—Answer: $(0, 0), (3, 3)$

42. Determine the points of intersection of the circle $x^2 + y^2 + 16y = 0$ and the line $x + y + 3 = 0$ (accurate to the nearest 0.1).

(a) $(-1.2, -4.2)(-3.8, -6.8)$

(b) $(-6.8, -3.8)(-4.2, -1.2)$

(c) $(-2.6, -0.5), (7.6, -10.6)$

(d) $(-0.5, -2.6)(-10.6, 7.6)$

(e) None of these

1—T—Answer: c

43. Find the points of intersection of the graphs of the equations $y = x$ and $y = x^3$.

(a) $(-1, -1), (0, 0), (1, 1)$

(b) $(-1, 1), (0, 0), (1, -1)$

(c) $(-1, 1), (0, 0)$

(d) $(-1, -1), (1, 1)$

(e) None of these

1—Answer: a

44. Find the points of intersection of the graphs of the equations $y = 4x - 2$ and $y = x^2 + 1$.

(a) $(1, 10), (3, 2)$

(b) $(-1, 2), (-3, 10)$

(c) $(1, 2), (3, 9)$

(d) $(1, 2), (3, 10)$

(e) None of these

1—Answer: d

45. On the graph of the cost function $C(x)$ and a revenue function $R(x)$, label the profit and loss regions of the graph and circle the break-even point.

1—Answer:

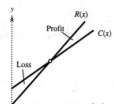

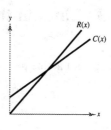

46. If the total cost of running a business is given by the equation $C = 1000x + 75,000$ and the revenue is given by the equation $R = 1250x$, find the sales necessary to break even.

(a) 3000   (b) 34   (c) 300   (d) 30   (e) None of these

2—Answer: c

47. Find the sales necessary to break even if the cost function for a business is $C = 70x + 500$ and the revenue function is $R = 90x$.

1—Answer: 25

48. If the total cost of running a business is given by the equation $C = 450x + 1000$ and the revenue is given by the equation $R = 500x$, find the sales necessary to break even.

(a) 220   (b) 11   (c) 20   (d) 2000   (e) None of these

1—Answer: c

49. Use a graphing utility to find the sales necessary to break even if the cost function for a business is $C = 1000x - 5000$ and the revenue function is $R(x) = -80x^2 + 5000x$.

(a) 1.2   (b) 20.5   (c) 42.8   (d) 51.2   (e) None of these

1—T—Answer: d

50. Use a graphing utility to find the sales necessary to break even if the cost function for a business is $C = 700x - 500$ and the revenue function is $R(x) = -90x^2 + 5000x$.

1—T—Answer: 47.9

Section 1.3   Lines in the Plane and Slope

1. Find the slope of the line passing through $(6, 10)$ and $(-1, 4)$.

   (a) $\frac{7}{6}$ (b) $-\frac{7}{6}$ (c) $\frac{6}{7}$ (d) $-\frac{6}{7}$ (e) None of these

   1—Answer: c

2. Find the slope of the line passing through $(-1, 16)$ and $(4, 2)$.

   (a) $-\frac{5}{14}$ (b) $-\frac{14}{5}$ (c) $\frac{5}{14}$ (d) $\frac{14}{5}$ (e) None of these

   1—Answer: b

3. Find the slope of the line passing through $(3, -2)$ and $(5, 7)$.

   (a) $-\frac{9}{2}$ (b) $\frac{9}{2}$ (c) $\frac{5}{2}$ (d) $\frac{2}{9}$ (e) None of these

   1—Answer: b

4. Find the slope of the line passing through $(5, 9)$ and $(-1, -3)$.

   1—Answer: 2

5. Find the slope of the line passing through $(3, 7)$ and $(-1, -2)$.

   1—Answer: $\frac{9}{4}$

6. What is the slope of a line that is perpendicular to the line given by $2x + 3y + 9 = 0$?

   (a) $\frac{2}{3}$ (b) $-\frac{2}{3}$ (c) $\frac{3}{2}$ (d) $-\frac{3}{2}$ (e) None of these

   1—Answer: c

7. Find the equation of the line that has a slope of $-\frac{3}{4}$ and passes through $(1, 2)$.

   (a) $3x - 4y - 7 = 0$ (b) $3x - 4y - 11 = 0$ (c) $3x + 4y - 11 = 0$

   (d) $3x + 4y + 11 = 0$ (e) None of these

   1—Answer: c

8. Find the equation of the vertical line that passes through $(2, 5)$.

   (a) $y = 2$ (b) $y = 5$ (c) $x = 2$ (d) $x = 5$ (e) None of these

   1—Answer: c

9. Find the equation of the line that passes through $(0, 0)$ and has a slope that is undefined.

   (a) $y = 0$ (b) $x = 0$ (c) $x + y = 0$ (d) $x = y$ (e) None of these

   1—Answer: b

10. Find the equation of the line that passes through $(-1, 5)$ and has a slope of 2.

   1—Answer: $2x - y + 7 = 0$

11. Write the equation of the line having the following data points:

x	-3	0	3	6
y	-11	-5	1	7

   2—Answer: $y = 2x - 5$

12. Find an equation for the straight line passing through the points $(2, -1)$ and $(-6, -1)$.

   (a) $x - 2y - 4 = 0$ (b) $y + 1 = 0$ (c) $x - 4y - 6 = 0$

   (d) $x + 4y = 0$ (e) None of these

   1—Answer: b

13. Find an equation for the straight line passing through the points $(-2, -4)$ and $(2, -1)$.

   1—Answer: $3x - 4y - 10 = 0$

14. Write an equation for the straight line passing through the points $(5, -2)$ and parallel to the line $x = 1$.

   1—Answer: $x = 5$

15. Find an equation for the straight line passing through the points $(2, -1)$ and $(-3, 1)$.

   (a) $2x + 5y + 1 = 0$ (b) $2x - 5y - 9 = 0$ (c) $2x + 5y + 9 = 0$

   (d) $2x - 5y - 1 = 0$ (e) None of these

   1—Answer: a

16. Find an equation for the straight line passing through the point $(4, -1)$ and perpendicular to the line $2x - 3y = 3$.

   (a) $y = \frac{2}{3}x - 1$ (b) $3x + 2y + 2 = 0$ (c) $2x + 3y = 10$

   (d) $3x + 2y = 10$ (e) None of these

   1—Answer: d

17. Find an equation of the line passing through the point $(2, 3)$ and perpendicular to the line whose equation is $2x - 4y + 1 = 0$.

   (a) $2x - y + 3 = 0$ (b) $2x + y - 3 = 0$ (c) $x - 2y - 4 = 0$

   (d) $2x + y - 7 = 0$ (e) None of these

   1—Answer: d

18. Find the equation of the line through $(1, 5)$ perpendicular to the line through $(9, 10)$ and $(11, 7)$.

(a) $y = \frac{2}{3}(x - 1) + 5$ (b) $y = -\frac{3}{2}(x - 1) + 5$ (c) $y = -\frac{3}{2}(x - 9) + 10$

(d) $y = \frac{2}{3}(x - 9) + 10$ (e) None of these

2—Answer: a

19. Find the equation of the line through $(4, 2)$ perpendicular to the line through $(9, 7)$ and $(11, 4)$.

(a) $y = \frac{2}{3}(x - 9) + 7$ (b) $y = -\frac{3}{2}(x - 9) + 7$ (c) $y = -\frac{3}{2}(x - 4) + 2$

(d) $y = \frac{2}{3}(x - 4) + 2$ (e) None of these

2—Answer: d

20. Find the equation of the line through $(2, 4)$ perpendicular to the line through $(6, 10)$ and $(8, 7)$.

(a) $y = -\frac{3}{2}(x - 2) + 4$ (b) $y = -\frac{3}{2}(x - 6) + 10$ (c) $y = \frac{2}{3}(x - 6) + 10$

(d) $y = \frac{2}{3}(x - 2) + 4$ (e) None of these

2—Answer: d

21. Find the equation of the line through $(3, 1)$ perpendicular to the line through $(8, 9)$ and $(10, 6)$.

(a) $y = -\frac{3}{2}(x - 8) + 9$ (b) $y = \frac{2}{3}(x - 3) + 1$ (c) $y - \frac{2}{3}(x - 8) + 9$

(d) $y = -\frac{3}{2}(x - 3) + 1$ (e) None of these

2—Answer: b

22. Find an equation for the line passing through the point $(4, -1)$ and perpendicular to the line $2x - 3y = 3$.

(a) $y = \frac{2}{3}x - 1$ (b) $3x + 2y + 2 = 0$ (c) $2x + 3y = 10$

(d) $3x + 2y = 10$ (e) None of these

2—Answer: d

23. Find an equation in general form for the straight line that passes through the point $(-1, 4)$ and is perpendicular to the line $2x + 3y = 6$.

2—Answer: $3x - 2y + 11 = 0$

24. Write an equation for the line perpendicular to the line $3x + 6y - 10 = 0$, which passes through the point $(2, 0)$. Put the answer in general form.

(a) $2x + y - 4 = 0$ (b) $2x + y + 4 = 0$ (c) $-2x + y + 4 = 0$

(d) $2x - y - 4 = 0$ (e) None of these

1—Answer: d

25. Find an equation of the line passing through the point $(-2, 1)$ and perpendicular to the line whose equation is $3x - 4y + 2 = 0$.

    (a) $-4x + 3y + 5 = 0$ (b) $3x - 4y + 10 = 0$ (c) $4x + 3y - 5 = 0$

    (d) $3x + 4y - 10 = 0$ (e) None of these

    1—Answer: e

26. Write an equation for the line perpendicular to the line $2x + 5y - 6 = 0$, which passes through the point $(2, 0)$. Put the answer in general form.

    1—Answer: $5x - 2y - 10 = 0$

27. Find the equation of the line that passes through $(1, 3)$ and is perpendicular to the line $2x + 3y + 5 = 0$.

    (a) $3x - 2y + 3 = 0$ (b) $2x + 3y - 11 = 0$ (c) $2x + 3y - 9 = 0$

    (d) $3x - 2y - 7 = 0$ (e) None of these

    2—Answer: a

28. Find the equation of the line that passes through $(2, -1)$ and is parallel to the line $2x + 7y = 5$.

    (a) $2x - 7y - 11 = 0$ (b) $2x + 7y + 3 = 0$ (c) $2x + 7y - 12 = 0$

    (d) $7x - 2y - 16 = 0$ (e) None of these

    2—Answer: b

29. Find the equation of the line that passes through $(-3, -2)$ and is parallel to the line $3x + 2y - 5 = 0$.

    2—Answer: $3x + 2y + 13 = 0$

30. Find an equation for the line passing through the point $(4, -1)$ and parallel to the line $2x - 3y = 3$.

    (a) $2x - 3y = 11$ (b) $2x - 3y = -5$ (c) $3x - 2y = -5$

    (d) $y = \frac{2}{3}x - 1$ (e) None of these

    2—Answer: a

31. Find an equation for the straight line that passes through the point $(2, 3)$ and is parallel to $x = 4$.

    1—Answer: $x = 2$

32. A company reimburses its sales representatives \$110 per day for lodging and meals, plus \$0.28 per mile driven. Write a linear equation giving the daily cost C in terms of x, the number of miles driven.

    (a) $C = 110 + 0.28x$ (b) $C = 0.28 + 110x$ (c) $C = 110.28x$

    (d) $C = \dfrac{110x}{0.28}$ (e) None of these

    2—Answer: a

33. A company reimburses its sales representatives $120 per day for lodging and meals, plus $0.25 per mile driven. Write a linear equation giving the daily cost C in terms of x, the number of miles driven.

(a) $C = 0.25 + 120x$ (b) $C = 120.25x$ (c) $C = 120 + 0.25x$

(d) $\dfrac{C}{120} = 0.25x$ (e) None of these

2—Answer: c

34. A local worker earns a base pay of $10.75 per hour plus an additional piecework rate of $0.17 per unit produced. Write a linear equation giving the weekly 40-hour wage W in terms of x, the number of units produced.

(a) $W = 10.92x$ (b) $W = 10.75 + 0.17x$ (c) $W = 1.8275x$

(d) $W = 430 + 0.17x$ (e) None of these

1—Answer: d

35. A local worker earns a base pay of $11.15 per hour plus an additional piecework rate of $0.19 per unit produced. Write a linear equation giving the weekly 40-hour wage W in terms of x, the number of units produced.

(a) $W = 11.34x$ (b) $W = 446 + 0.19x$ (c) $W = 11.15 + 7.6x$

(d) $W = 11.15 + 0.19x$ (e) None of these

1—Answer: b

36. A business had an annual retail sales of $110,000 in 1991 and $224,000 in 1994. Assuming that the annual increase in sales followed a linear pattern, what were the retail sales in 1993?

(a) $182,000   (b) $195,000   (c) $188,000   (d) $186,000   (e) None of these

2—Answer: d

37. A business had an annual retail sales of $100,000 in 1991 and $226,000 in 1994. Assuming that the annual sales followed a linear pattern, what were the retail sales in 1993?

(a) $182,000   (b) $195,000   (c) $184,000   (d) $186,000   (e) None of these

2—Answer: d

38. A business had an annual retail sales of $124,000 in 1993 and $211,000 in 1996. Assuming that the annual increase in sales followed a linear pattern, what were the retail sales in 1995?

(a) $157,000   (b) $182,000   (c) $178,000   (d) $189,250   (e) None of these

1—Answer: b

Section 1.4 Functions

1. Find the domain of the function:

$$y = \frac{1}{x}.$$

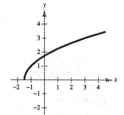

   (a) $(-\infty, \infty)$ (b) $(-\infty, 0)(0, \infty)$ (c) $(-\infty, 0)$

   (d) $(0, \infty)$ (e) None of these

1—Answer: b

2. Find the domain of the function:

$$f(x) = \sqrt{2x + 3}.$$

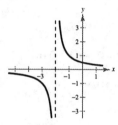

   (a) $[0, \infty)$ (b) $(0, \infty)$ (c) $\left[-\frac{3}{2}, \infty\right)$

   (d) $\left(-\frac{3}{2}, \infty\right)$ (e) None of these

1—Answer: c

3. Find the domain of the function:

$$f(x) = \frac{1}{x + 2}.$$

1—Answer: Domain: $(-\infty, -2), (-2, \infty)$

4. Using a graphing utility, find the domain of the function $f(x) = \sqrt{10 - x - x^3}$.

   (a) $(-\infty, 10.0]$ (b) $(-\infty, -2.1]$ (c) $(-\infty, -0.4]$ (d) $(-\infty, 2.0]$ (e) None of these

1—T—Answer: d

5. What is the domain of the function $y = \sqrt{8 - 4x}$? Use interval notation.

   1—Answer: $(-\infty, 2]$

6. What is the domain of the function $y = \dfrac{3}{\sqrt{4 - 2x}}$? Use interval notation.

   (a) $(2, \infty)$ (b) $[2, \infty)$ (c) $(-\infty, 2)$ (d) $(-\infty, 2]$ (e) None of these

   1—Answer: c

7. What is the domain of the function $y = \sqrt{4 - 3x}$? Use interval notation.

   1—Answer: $\left(-\infty, \frac{4}{3}\right]$

8. What is the domain of the function $y = f(x) = \dfrac{x^2 + 3x - 6}{x^2 - 9}$?

    (a) $(-\infty, -3) \cup (-3, 3) \cup (3, \infty)$ (b) $x > 3$ (c) $x \ne 3$

    (d) $(-3, 3)$ (e) None of these

    1—Answer: a

9. What is the domain of $f(x) = \sqrt{2 - 3x}$?

    1—Answer: $x \le \frac{2}{3}$

10. What is the domain of the function $y = f(x) = \dfrac{x^2 - 3x + 5}{x^2 - 4}$?

    (a) $x < 2$ (b) $(-\infty, -2) \cup (-2, 2) \cup (2, \infty)$ (c) $x \ne 2$

    (d) All real numbers   (e) None of these

    1—Answer: b

11. What is the domain of $f(x) = \dfrac{x - 3}{x + 2}$?

    (a) $x \ne -2$ (b) $x \ne 3, x \ne -2$ (c) $x > 3$

    (d) $\left(0, -\frac{3}{2}\right), (3, 0)$ (e) None of these

    1—Answer: a

12. What is the domain of $f(x) = \dfrac{x - 2}{x + 3}$?

    (a) $x \ne -3$ (b) $x \ne 2, x \ne -3$ (c) $x > 2$

    (d) $(2, 0)$ and $(-3, 0)$ (e) None of these

    1—Answer: a

13. Find the domain of

$$f(x) = \dfrac{1}{\sqrt{3 - 2x}}.$$

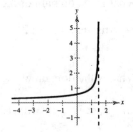

    (a) $\left(-\infty, \frac{3}{2}\right)$ (b) $\left[\frac{3}{2}, \infty\right)$ (c) $\left(\frac{3}{2}, \infty\right)$

    (d) $\left(-\infty, \frac{3}{2}\right) \cup \left(\frac{3}{2}, \infty\right)$ (e) None of these

    1—Answer: a

14. Find the domain of

$$f(x) = \frac{1}{\sqrt{3 + 2x}}.$$

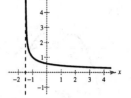

(a) $\left(-\infty, -\frac{3}{2}\right)$ (b) $\left[-\frac{3}{2}, \infty\right)$

(c) $\left(-\frac{3}{2}, \infty\right)$ (d) $\left(-\infty, -\frac{3}{2}\right) \cup \left(-\frac{3}{2}, \infty\right)$

(e) None of these

1—Answer: c

15. Find the domain of:

$$f(x) = \frac{1}{\sqrt{x^2 - 2x - 2}}.$$

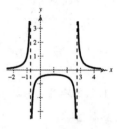

1—Answer: All reals except $1 \pm \sqrt{3}$

16. Find the range of the function:

$$y = \sqrt{9 - x^2}$$

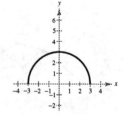

(a) $(-\infty, -3], [3, \infty)$ (b) $[-3, 3]$ (c) $[0, 3]$

(d) $[3, \infty)$ (e) None of these

1—Answer: c

17. Find the domain and range of the function:

$$f(x) = |3 + x|$$

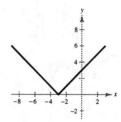

1—Answer: Domain: $(-\infty, \infty)$, Range: $[0, \infty)$

18. Does the graph to the right depict y as a function of x?

(a) y is a function of x.

(b) y is not a function of x.

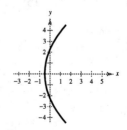

1—Answer: b

19. Use the vertical line test to determine which of the following represent the graphs of functions.

(1)
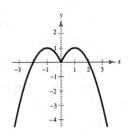

(2
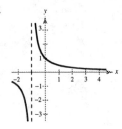

(3)
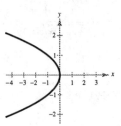

(4)
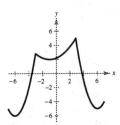

(5)
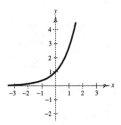

(a) 1, 2, 3, 4, 5   (b) 1, 2, 3, 5   (c) 1, 2, 4, 5   (d) 1, 3, 4, 5   (e) None of these

1—Answer: c

20. Use the vertical line test to determine which of the following represent the graphs of functions.

(1)
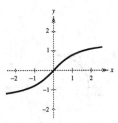

(2)
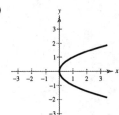

(3)
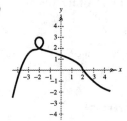

(4)
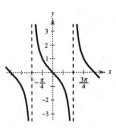

(5)
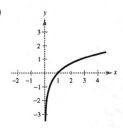

(a) 1, 2, 3   (b) 1, 4, 5   (c) 2, 3   (d) 4, 5   (e) None of these

1—Answer: b

21. Which of the following graphs represent y as a function of x?

(a)

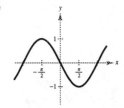

(b)

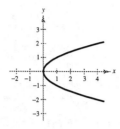

(c)

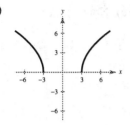

(d)

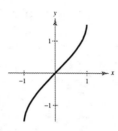

1—Answer: a, c, and d

22. Does the graph at the right depict y as a function of x?

(a) y is a function of x.

(b) y is not a function of x.

1—Answer: a

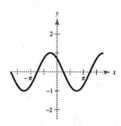

23. In which of the following equations is y a function of x?

(a) $3y + 2x - 9 = 17$ (b) $2x^2y + x = 4y$ (c) Both **a** and **b**

(d) Neither **a** nor **b**   (e) None of these

1—Answer: c

24. In which of the following equations is y a function of x?

(a) $2x + 3y - 1 = 0$ (b) $x^2 + 3y^2 = 7$ (c) $2x^2y = 7$

(d) Both **a** and **b**   (e) Both **a** and **c**

1—Answer: e

25. In which of the following equations is y a function of x?

(a) $3y + 2x - 7 = 0$ (b) $5x^2y = 9 - 2x$ (c) $3x^2 - 4y^2 = 9$

(d) $x = 3y^2 - 1$ (e) None of these

1—Answer: a and b

26. In which of the following equations is y a function of x?

    (a) $y = 3x^2 - 9$ (b) $x^2 + y^2 = 7$ (c) $x^2 - y^2 = 2$

    (d) $3x + 2y = 5$ (e) $|x| = y$

    1—Answer: a, d, and e

27. Which of the following determine y as a function of x?

    (1) $y = x^2$ (2) $x = y^2$ (3) $x^2 + y^2 = 1$ (4) $y^3 = x$

    (a) 2, 3   (b) 2, 3, 4   (c) 1, 4   (d) 1, 2, 3   (e) None of these

    1—T—Answer: c

28. Determine if y is a function of x in the equation $x = \dfrac{2y^2}{2 + x}$.

    1—T—Answer: No

29. Determine if y is a function of x in the equation $y = \dfrac{2x^2}{2 + |x|}$.

    1—T—Answer: Yes

30. Determine if y is a function of x in the equation $y = \dfrac{x}{1 + |x|}$.

    1—T—Answer: Yes

31. Find $f(-1)$ if $f(x) = \dfrac{-4x}{x^2 + 1}$.

    1—Answer: 2

32. Find $f(2)$ if $f(x) = \dfrac{-4x}{x^2 + 1}$.

    1—Answer: $-\dfrac{8}{5}$

33. Find $f(-1)$ for $f(x) = -x^3 - 3x^2 - 2x - 1$.

    (a) 11   (b) 7   (c) 1   (d) -1 (e) None of these

    1—Answer: d

34. Find $f(-1)$ if $f(x) = \dfrac{-10x}{x^2 + 1}$.

    1—Answer: 5

35. Find $f(-1)$ if $f(x) = -x^2 + 3x - 5$.

    (a) -7 (b) -1 (c) -9 (d) -3 (e) None of these

    1—Answer: c

36. Find $f(-2)$ if $f(x) = \dfrac{-4x}{x^2 + 1}$.

(a) $-\dfrac{8}{5}$ (b) $-\dfrac{8}{3}$ (c) $\dfrac{8}{5}$ (d) $\dfrac{8}{3}$ (e) None of these

1—Answer: c

37. Given $f(x) = |3x - 6|$, find $f(0) - f(3)$.

2—Answer: 3

38. Given $f(x) = 3x - 7$, find $f(x + 1) + f(2)$.

2—Answer: $3x - 5$

39. Given $f(x) = x^2 - 3x + 4$, find $f(x + 2) - f(2)$.

(a) $x^2 - 3x + 4$ (b) $x^2 + x$ (c) $x^2 + x - 8$

(d) $x^2 - 3x - 4$ (e) None of these

2—Answer: b

40. Given $f(x) = |x - 3| - 5$, find $f(1) - f(5)$.

(a) 0   (b) -4 (c) 14   (d) -14 (e) None of these

2—Answer: a

41. Given $f(x) = |3x + 1| - 5$, find $f(x + 1) - f(x)$.

(a) 3   (b) -5 (c) $|3x + 4| - |3x + 1| - 10$

(d) $|3x + 4| - |3x + 1|$ (e) None of these

2—Answer: d

42. Find $f(x + \Delta x)$ if $f(x) = -x^2 + 4x + 5$.

1—Answer: $-x^2 - 2x\Delta x - (\Delta x)^2 + 4x + 4\Delta x + 5$

43. Find $f(x + \Delta x)$ if $f(x) = 5x^2 + x$.

1—Answer: $5x^2 + 10x\Delta x + 5(\Delta x)^2 + x + \Delta x$

44. Find $(x + \Delta x)$ if $f(x) = x^2 - 2x - 3$.

(a) $x^2 - x - 3 + \Delta x$ (b) $x^2 + 2x(\Delta x) + (\Delta x)^2 - 2x - 2\Delta x - 3$

(c) $x^2 - 2x - 3 + \Delta x$ (d) 5

(e) None of these

1—Answer: b

45. Find $f(x + \Delta x)$ if $f(x) = 2x^3 + 4$.

    (a) $2x^3 + 6x^2(\Delta x) + 6x(\Delta x)^2 + 2(\Delta x)^3 + 4$ (b) $2x^3 + 2(\Delta x)^3 + 4$

    (c) $6x^2(\Delta x) + 6x(\Delta x)^2 + 2(\Delta x)^3$ (d) $2x^3 + 6x^2(\Delta x) + 6x(\Delta x)^2 + 2(\Delta x)^3$

    (e) None of these

    2—Answer: a

46. Find $f(x + \Delta x)$ if $f(x) = 2x^3 + 3x + 1$.

    (a) $6x^2(\Delta x) + 6x(\Delta x)^2 + 2(\Delta x)^3 + 3\Delta x$

    (b) $6x^2 + 3$

    (c) $x^3 + 3x^2(\Delta x) + 3x(\Delta x)^2 + 3(\Delta x)^3 + 3x + 3\Delta x + 1$

    (d) $2x^3 + 6x^2(\Delta x) + 6x(\Delta x)^2 + 2(\Delta x)^3 + 3x + 3\Delta x + 1$

    (e) None of these

    1—Answer: d

47. Find $f(x + \Delta x)$ if $f(x) = -x^2 + 4x - 3$.

    (a) $-x^2 - 2x\Delta x - (\Delta x)^2 + 4x + 4\Delta x - 3$ (b) $2x\Delta x - (\Delta x)^2 + 4\Delta x$

    (c) $-x^2 + 2x\Delta x + (\Delta x)^2 + 4x + 4\Delta x - 3$ (d) $-x^2 + 2x\Delta x - (\Delta x)^2 - 4x + 4\Delta x - 3$

    (e) None of these

    1—Answer: a

48. Find $f(x + \Delta x)$ if $f(x) = x^3 + 1$.

    (a) $x^3 + 1 + \Delta x$ (b) $x^3 + 3x^2(\Delta x) + 3x(\Delta x)^2 + (\Delta x)^3 + 1$

    (c) $x^3 + (\Delta x)^3 + 1$ (d) $\Delta^3 x^6 + 1$

    (e) None of these

    1—Answer: b

49. Find $f(x + \Delta x)$ if $f(x) = x^2 - 2x - 3$.

    (a) $x^2 - x - 3 + \Delta x$ (b) $x^2 + 2x(\Delta x) + (\Delta x)^2 - 2x - 2\Delta x - 3$

    (c) $x^2 - 2x - 3 + \Delta x$ (d) 5

    (e) None of these

    1—Answer: b

50. If $f(x) = 3 - x^2$, find:

    (a) $f(3)$ (b) $f(-1)$ (c) $f(2 + \Delta x)$

    1—Answer: (a) -6 (b) 2   (c) $-1 - 4\Delta x - (\Delta x)^2$

51. If $g(x) = x^2 + 3x - 1$, find $\dfrac{g(x + \Delta x) - g(x)}{\Delta x}$.

    1—Answer: $2x + \Delta x + 3$

52. Find $\dfrac{f(x + h) - f(x)}{h}$ if $f(x) = 8x^2 + 1$.

    (a) $8h^2 + 1$ (b) $8h + \dfrac{1}{h}$ (c) $16x + 8h$ (d) $16hx + 8h^2$ (e) None of these

    1—Answer: c

53. Find $\dfrac{f(x + h) - f(x)}{h}$ if $f(x) = 9x^2 - 5$.

    (a) $18hx + 9h^2$ (b) $18x + 9h$ (c) $9h - \dfrac{5}{h}$ (d) $9h^2 - 5$ (e) None of these

    1—Answer: b

54. Find $\dfrac{f(x + h) - f(x)}{h}$ if $f(x) = 4x^2 - 2$.

    (a) $8hx + 4h^2$ (b) $8x + 4h$ (c) $4h^2 - 2$ (d) $4h - \dfrac{2}{h}$ (e) None of these

    1—Answer: b

55. Find $\dfrac{f(x + h) - f(x)}{h}$ if $f(x) = 2x^2 + 3$.

    (a) $4x + 2h$ (b) $2h^2 + 3$ (c) $2h + \dfrac{3}{h}$ (d) $4hx + 2h^2$ (e) None of these

    1—Answer: a

56. Which of the following is a sketch of the graph of the equation $f(x) = x^3 + 1$?

(a)

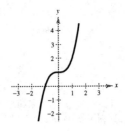

(b)

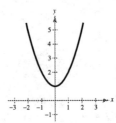

(c)

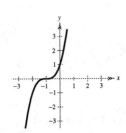

(d)

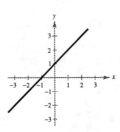

(e) None of these

   1—Answer: a

57. Which of the following is a sketch of the graph of the equation $f(x) = (x - 1)^3$?

(a)

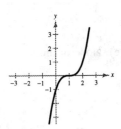

(b)

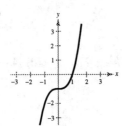

(c)

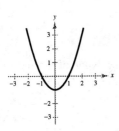

(d)

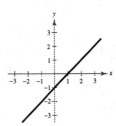

(e) None of these

   1—Answer: c

58. Sketch a graph of $f(x) = x^2 - 3$.

   1—Answer:

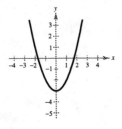

59. Sketch a graph of $f(x) = x^3 - 1$.

   1—Answer:

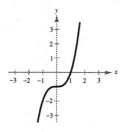

60. Given the graph of $y = x^4$
   sketch the graph of $y = (x - 2)^4 + 6$

   2—Answer:

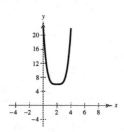 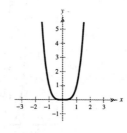

61. Given the graph of $y = x^2$
   sketch the graph of $y = (x + 3)^2 - 1$.

   2—Answer:

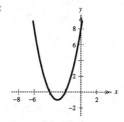 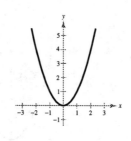

62. Use the graph of $y = x^3$ to find a
   formula for the function $y = f(x)$.

   (a) $y = \left(x - \frac{1}{2}\right)^3$ (b) $y = \left(x + \frac{1}{2}\right)^3$

   (c) $y = x^3 - \frac{1}{2}$ (d) $y = x^3 + \frac{1}{2}$

   (e) None of these

   2—Answer: c

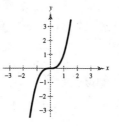 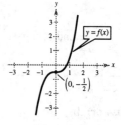

63. Use the graph of $y = x^2$ to find a
formula for the function $y = f(x)$.

(a) $f(x) = (x - 2)^2 + 1$

(b) $f(x) = (x - 1)^2 + 2$

(c) $f(x) = (x + 2)^2 + 1$

(d) $f(x) = (x + 1)^2 - 2$

(e) None of these

2—Answer: a

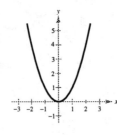
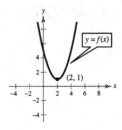

64. Given the graph of $y = x^4$
sketch the graph of $y = (x - 4)^4 + 2$.

2—Answer:

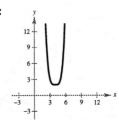
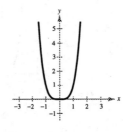

65. Given the graph of $y = x^2$
sketch the graph of $y = (x + 1)^2 - 4$.

2—Answer:

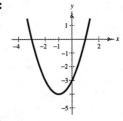
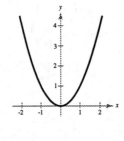

66. If $f(x) = \dfrac{1}{\sqrt{x}}$ and $g(x) = 1 - x^2$, find $f(g(x))$.

(a) $\dfrac{1 - x^2}{\sqrt{x}}$ (b) $\dfrac{1}{\sqrt{1 - x^2}}$ (c) $1 - \dfrac{1}{x}$ (d) $\dfrac{1}{\sqrt{x}} + 1 - x^2$ (e) None of these

1—Answer: b

67. If $f(x) = 1 - x^2$ and $g(x) = \dfrac{1}{\sqrt{x}}$, find $f(g(x))$.

(a) $\dfrac{1 - x^2}{\sqrt{x}}$ (b) $\dfrac{1}{\sqrt{1 - x^2}}$ (c) $1 - \dfrac{1}{x}$ (d) $\dfrac{1}{\sqrt{x}} + 1 - x^2$ (e) None of these

1—Answer: c

68. If $f(x) = \dfrac{1}{\sqrt{x}}$ and $g(x) = x^2 - 5$, find $g(f(x))$.

     1—Answer: $\dfrac{1}{x} - 5$

69. Find $g(f(x))$ if $f(x) = x^2$ and $g(x) = \dfrac{2x}{x + 1}$.

   (a) $\dfrac{4x^2}{(x + 1)^2}$ (b) $\dfrac{2x^2}{x^2 + 1}$ (c) $\dfrac{2x^2}{x + 1}$ (d) $\dfrac{4x^2}{x^4 + 2x^2 + 1}$ (e) None of these

     1—Answer: b

70. Find $g(f(x))$ if $f(x) = x^2$ and $g(x) = \dfrac{x + 1}{x}$.

     1—Answer: $\dfrac{x^2 + 1}{x^2}$

71. Find $f(g(1))$ for $f(x) = x^2 + 5$ and $g(x) = x - 2$.

   (a) 6   (b) 4   (c) $x^2 - 4x + 4$ (d) $x^2 + 3$ (e) None of these

     1—Answer: a

72. Find $f(g(1))$ for $f(x) = x - 2$ and $g(x) = x^2 + 5$.

   (a) $x^2 - 4x + 9$ (b) 6   (c) 4   (d) $x^2 + 3$ (e) None of these

     1—Answer: c

73. If $f(x) = x^2$ and $g(x) = \dfrac{x + 1}{x}$, find $g(f(x))$.

     1—Answer: $\dfrac{x^2 + 1}{x^2}$

74. Given $f(x) = 2x^2 + 1$ and $g(x) = x - 2$, find $f(g(x))$.

   (a) $x^2 - 7$ (b) $2x^2 + x - 1$ (c) $2x^2 - 1$

   (d) $2x^2 - 8x + 9$ (e) None of these

     1—Answer: d

75. Given $f(x) = 2x^2 + 1$ and $g(x) = x + 2$, find $f(g(x))$.

   (a) $2x^2 + 5$ (b) $2x^2 + 3$ (c) $2x^2 + 4x + 5$ (d) $2x^2 + 8x + 9$ (e) None of these

     1—Answer: d

76. Given $f(x) = 7x^2 - 3$ and $g(x) = 9 - 2x$, find $g(f(x))$.

1—Answer: $g(f(x)) = 15 - 14x^2$

77. Given $f(x) = x - 2$ and $g(x) = \dfrac{x + 5}{3}$, find $g(f(x))$.

(a) $\dfrac{x - 1}{3}$
(b) $\dfrac{x + 3}{3}$
(c) $\dfrac{x^2 + 3x - 10}{3}$
(d) $x + 1$
(e) None of these

1—Answer: b

78. Find the functions f and g such that $f(g(x)) = h(x)$: $h(x) = (x - 2)^2 + 1$

(a) $f(x) = x^2 + 1$, $g(x) = x - 2$
(b) $f(x) = x - 2$, $g(x) = x^2 + 1$

(c) $f(x) = (x - 2)^2$, $g(x) = 1$
(d) $f(x) = x^2 - 1$, $g(x) = 6 - 4x$

(e) None of these

2—Answer: a

79. Given $f(x) = 7x + 2$ and $g(x) = x^2 - 9$, find the product $(fg)(x)$.

(a) $7x^3 + 2x^2 - 63x - 18$
(b) $7x^3 - 18$
(c) $2x^2 + 7x - 7$

(d) $7x^2 - 61$
(e) None of these

1—Answer: a

80. Given $f(x) = 6x - 12$ and $g(x) = x^2 - 4$, find $\left(\dfrac{f}{g}\right)(x)$.

(a) $\dfrac{6}{x - 2}$
(b) $\dfrac{6(x - 2)}{x + 2}$
(c) $\dfrac{6}{(x - 2)(x + 2)}$

(d) $\dfrac{6}{x + 2}$
(e) None of these

1—Answer: d

81. Find the functions f and g such that $f(g(x)) = h(x)$: $h(x) = (2x + 1)^2 + 3(2x + 1)$.

2—Answer: $f(x) = x^2 + 3x$, $g(x) = 2x + 1$

82. Determine whether the function is one-to-one: $f(x) = \dfrac{6}{x}$.

1—Answer: f is one-to-one

83. Determine whether the function $f(x) = \dfrac{7}{x + 2}$ is one-to-one. If it is, find its inverse.

(a) Not one-to-one   (b) $f^{-1}(x) = \dfrac{x + 2}{7}$ (c) $f^{-1}(x) = \dfrac{7 - 2x}{x}$

(d) $f^{-1}(x) = -\dfrac{7}{x + 2}$ (e) None of these

     2—Answer: c

84. Determine whether the function $f(x) = \dfrac{1}{x}$ is one-to-one. If it is, find its inverse.

     1—Answer: $f^{-1}(x) = \dfrac{1}{x}$

85. Given $f(x) = 7x + 2$, find $f^{-1}(x)$.

(a) $7x + 2$ (b) $\dfrac{1}{7x + 2}$ (c) $\dfrac{x - 2}{7}$ (d) $\dfrac{x}{7} - 2$ (e) None of these

     1—Answer: c

86. Given $f(x) = \sqrt{2x - 1}$, find $f^{-1}(x)$.

(a) $\sqrt{2y - 1}, y \geq \dfrac{1}{2}$ (b) $x^2 + 1, x \geq 0$ (c) $\dfrac{1}{2}(x^2 + 1), x \geq 0$

(d) $\dfrac{1}{\sqrt{2x - 1}}, x \geq \dfrac{1}{2}$ (e) None of these

     2—Answer: c

87. Given $f(x) = 3x^3 - 1$, find $f^{-1}(x)$.

(a) $\dfrac{1}{3x^3 - 1}$ (b) $3x^{-1} - 1$ (c) $3(x + 1)$ (d) $\sqrt[3]{\dfrac{x + 1}{3}}$ (e) None of these

     1—Answer: d

88. If $f(x) = \dfrac{3}{\sqrt{4 + x}}$, find $f^{-1}(x)$.

(a) $f^{-1}(x) = \dfrac{9 - 4x^2}{x^2}$ (b) $f^{-1}(x) = \dfrac{9 - 4x}{x}$ (c) $f^{-1}(x) = \dfrac{\sqrt{4 + 3x}}{3}$

(d) $f^{-1}(x) = \dfrac{3 - 4x^2}{x^2}$ (e) None of these

     1—Answer: a

89. If $f(x) = \dfrac{3}{\sqrt{2 + x}}$, find $f^{-1}(x)$.

 1—Answer: $\dfrac{9 - 2x^2}{x^2}$

90. If $f(x) = \dfrac{2}{\sqrt{2 - x}}$, find $f^{-1}(x)$.

 1—Answer: $f^{-1}(x) = \dfrac{2x^2 - 4}{x^2}$

91. Find $f^{-1}(x)$ for the function $f(x) = 2x + 4$.

 (a) $\dfrac{x - 4}{2}$ (b) $\dfrac{1}{2}x - 4$ (c) $\dfrac{1}{2x + 4}$ (d) $\dfrac{1}{2}x + 4$ (e) None of these

 1—Answer: a

92. Find $f^{-1}(x)$ for the function $f(x) = \dfrac{3}{4}x + 6$.

 (a) $\dfrac{4}{3}x - 8$ (b) $\dfrac{1}{\frac{3}{4}x + 6}$ (c) $\dfrac{3}{4x + 24}$ (d) $3x + 24$ (e) None of these

 1—Answer: a

93. Find $f^{-1}(x)$ for $f(x) = \dfrac{1}{3}x + 5$.

 (a) $3x + \dfrac{1}{5}$ (b) $\dfrac{1}{\frac{1}{3}x + 5}$ (c) $\dfrac{3}{x + 15}$ (d) $3x + 15$ (e) None of these

 1—Answer: e

94. Find $f^{-1}(x)$ for $f(x) = 4x - 1$.

 (a) $\dfrac{1}{4}x - 1$ (b) $\dfrac{1}{4x - 1}$ (c) $\dfrac{1}{4}x + 1$ (d) $\dfrac{x + 1}{4}$ (e) None of these

 1—Answer: d

95. Given $f(x) = 2x^2 + 1$ for $x \geq 0$, find $f^{-1}(x)$.

 2—Answer: $f^{-1}(x) = \sqrt{\dfrac{x - 1}{2}}$

96. Given $f(x) = \dfrac{2x + 1}{3}$, find $f^{-1}(x)$.

 1—Answer: $f^{-1}(x) = \dfrac{3x - 1}{2}$

97. If $f(x) = \sqrt{x - 1}$, find $f^{-1}(x)$.

1—Answer: $x^2 + 1$

98. To produce x units of a product, there are fixed costs of \$23,000 and a production cost of \$4.78 per unit. Write the total cost C as a function of x.

(a) $C = 4.78x + 23,000$ (b) $C = 23,000 - 4.78x$ (c) $C = \dfrac{4.78}{x} + 23,000$

(d) $C = (23,004.78)x$ (e) None of these

1—Answer: a

99. If an object falls 64 feet in 2 seconds, how long will it take the object to fall to the ground from a height of 96 feet? (Assume that the distance an object falls is directly proportional to the square of the time.)

2—Answer: $\sqrt{6}$ seconds

Section 1.5   Limits

1. Use the graph to find $\lim_{x \to 1} f(x)$ if $f(x) = \begin{cases} 3 - x, & x \neq 1 \\ 1, & x = 1 \end{cases}$.

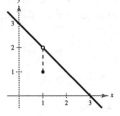

(a) 2

(b) 1

(c) $\frac{3}{2}$

(d) Does not exist

(e) None of these

1—**Answer:** a

2. Use the graph to find $\lim_{x \to -1} f(x)$ if $f(x) = \dfrac{1}{x + 1}$.

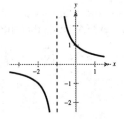

(a) 0

(b) 1

(c) ∞

(d) Does not exist

(e) None of these

1—**Answer:** d

3. Estimate $\lim_{x \to 2} f(x)$.

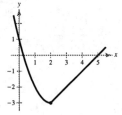

(a) Limit does not exist

(b) 0

(c) -3

(d) 2

(e) None of these

1—**Answer:** c

4. Estimate $\lim_{x \to -1} f(x)$.

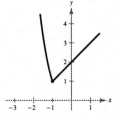

(a) 1

(b) -1

(c) 0

(d) Limit does not exist

(e) None of these

1—**Answer:** a

5. Estimate $\lim_{x \to 1} f(x)$.

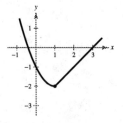

(a) 1

(b) Limit does not exist

(c) -2

(d) 0

(e) None of these

1—**Answer:** c

6. Find $\lim_{x \to 2} (3x^2 + 5)$.

(a) 41

(b) 17

(c) 11

(d) 0

(e) None of these

1—**Answer:** b

7. Find $\lim\limits_{x \to -3} (-2x^2 + 1)$.

    (a) 37   (b) 19   (c) -17 (d) $\pm\sqrt{2}$ (e) None of these

    1—Answer: c

8. Calculate $\lim\limits_{x \to 2} (2x^2 - 6x + 1)$.

    1—Answer: -3

9. Find the limit: $\lim\limits_{x \to 2^-} (x^2 + 4x - 3)$.

    1—Answer: 9

10. Find $\lim\limits_{x \to -1} \dfrac{x^2 + 3x + 2}{x^2 + 1}$.

    (a) 0   (b) ∞ (c) -1 (d) Does not exist   (e)   None of these

    1—Answer: a

11. Find $\lim\limits_{x \to -1} \dfrac{x^2 + 2x + 3}{x^2 + 1}$.

    (a) 0   (b) 1   (c) ∞ (d) Does not exist   (e)   None of these

    1—Answer: b

12. Find $\lim\limits_{x \to 2} \dfrac{x^2 - 4x + 1}{x^2 + 2}$.

    1—Answer: $-\frac{1}{2}$

13. Find the limit: $\lim\limits_{x \to 1} \dfrac{x^2 + x - 2}{x - 3}$.

    1—Answer: 0

14. Find the limit: $\lim\limits_{x \to 1} \dfrac{3x^3 - 4x^2 - 5x + 2}{x^2 - x - 2}$.

    1—Answer: 2

15. Find the limit: $\lim\limits_{x \to 1} \dfrac{x^2 - x - 2}{x - 3}$.

    1—Answer: 1

16. Find $\lim\limits_{x \to 3} \sqrt{x^2 - 4}$.

    (a) 1   (b) 5   (c) -1 (d) $\sqrt{5}$ (e) None of these

    1—Answer: d

17. Find $\lim\limits_{x \to 3^-} \sqrt{9 - x^2}$.

(a) 0   (b) $\sqrt{6}$ (c) $3\sqrt{2}$ (d) Does not exist   (e) None of these

1—Answer: a

18. Find $\lim\limits_{x \to 2} \sqrt{4x^2 + 9}$.

1—Answer: 5

19. Find $\lim\limits_{x \to 1} f(x)$ if $f(x) = \begin{cases} x^2 + 4, & x \neq 1 \\ 2, & x = 1 \end{cases}$.

1—Answer: 5

20. If $\lim\limits_{x \to c} f(x) = -\dfrac{1}{2}$ and $\lim\limits_{x \to c} g(x) = \dfrac{2}{3}$, find $\lim\limits_{x \to c} \dfrac{f(x)}{g(x)}$.

(a) $-\dfrac{1}{3}$ (b) $\dfrac{1}{3}$ (c) $-\dfrac{3}{4}$ (d) -3 (e) None of these

1—Answer: c

21. If $\lim\limits_{x \to c} f(x) = \dfrac{1}{2}$ and $\lim\limits_{x \to c} g(x) = \dfrac{2}{3}$, find $\lim\limits_{x \to c} [f(x)g(x)]$.

(a) $\dfrac{1}{6}$ (b) $-\dfrac{1}{3}$ (c) 1   (d) Does not exist   (e) None of these

1—Answer: b

22. If $\lim\limits_{x \to c} f(x) = -\dfrac{1}{2}$ and $\lim\limits_{x \to c} g(x) = \dfrac{2}{3}$, find $\lim\limits_{x \to c} [f(x) - g(x)]$.

1—Answer: $-\dfrac{7}{6}$

23. Find $\lim\limits_{x \to 2} \dfrac{x - 2}{x^2 - 4}$.

(a) 0   (b) $\dfrac{1}{4}$ (c) ∞ (d) 1   (e) None of these

1—Answer: b

24. Find $\lim\limits_{x \to -1} \dfrac{x^2 - 5x - 6}{x + 1}$.

(a) 0   (b) -7 (c) $-\infty$ (d) ∞ (e) None of these

1—Answer: b

25. Find $\lim\limits_{x \to -2} \dfrac{x + 2}{x^3 + 8}$.

1—Answer: $\frac{1}{12}$

26. Find the limit: $\lim\limits_{x \to -9} \dfrac{x^2 + 6x - 27}{x + 9}$.

    (a) -12 (b) Limit does not exist   (c) -3

    (d) 0   (e) None of these

    1—Answer: a

27. Find the limit: $\lim\limits_{x \to 4} \dfrac{x^2 - 5x - 4}{x - 4}$.

    (a) 0   (b) -1 (c) 3

    (d) Limit does not exist   (e) None of these

    1—Answer: c

28. Find the limit: $\lim\limits_{x \to -4} \dfrac{x^2 + 11x + 28}{x + 4}$.

    (a) 7   (b) 3   (c) 0

    (d) Limit does not exist   (e) None of these

    1—Answer: b

29. Find the limit: $\lim\limits_{x \to 5} \dfrac{x^2 - 3x - 10}{x - 5}$.

    (a) 2   (b) Limit does not exist   (c) 0

    (d) 7   (e) None of these

    1—Answer: d

30. Find $\lim\limits_{x \to 0} \dfrac{1 - \cos^2 x}{x}$.

    (a) 1   (b) 0   (c) ∞ (d) Does not exist   (e) None of these

    1—Answer: b

31. Find the limit: $\lim\limits_{x \to 1} \dfrac{x^2 + x - 2}{x - 1}$.

    1—Answer: 3

32. Find the limit: $\lim\limits_{x \to 2} \dfrac{3x^3 - 4x^2 - 5x + 2}{x^2 - x - 2}$.

1—Answer: 5

33. Find $\lim\limits_{x \to 3} \dfrac{x - 3}{|x - 3|}$.

(a) 0   (b) 1   (c) 3   (d) Does not exist   (e) None of these

2—Answer: d

34. Find $\lim\limits_{x \to 2} \dfrac{x - 2}{|x - 2|}$.

(a) 0   (b) 1   (c) 2   (d) Does not exist   (e) None of these

2—Answer: d

35. Find $\lim\limits_{x \to 1} \dfrac{x - 1}{|x - 1|}$.

2—Answer: Does not exist

36. Find $\lim\limits_{x \to 0} \dfrac{\sqrt{x + 4} - 2}{x}$.

(a) 0   (b) $\frac{1}{4}$ (c) ∞ (d) 1   (e) None of these

1—Answer: b

37. Find $\lim\limits_{x \to 0} \dfrac{\sqrt{x + 9} - 3}{x}$.

(a) 0   (b) 1   (c) ∞ (d) $\frac{1}{3}$ (e) None of these

1—Answer: e

38. Find the limit: $\lim\limits_{x \to 1} \dfrac{1 - \sqrt{2x^2 - 1}}{x - 1}$.

1—Answer: -2

39. Find $\lim\limits_{\Delta x \to 0} \dfrac{\sqrt{x + \Delta x} - \sqrt{x}}{\Delta x}$.

1—Answer: $\dfrac{1}{2\sqrt{x}}$

40. Evaluate the limit: $\lim\limits_{x \to 3} \dfrac{x + 3}{x^2 - 9}$.

    (a) Limit does not exist   (b) 0   (c) $\frac{1}{6}$

    (d) $-\frac{1}{6}$ (e) None of these

    1—Answer: a

41. Find $\lim\limits_{x \to -2} \dfrac{x - 2}{x^2 - 9}$.

    1—Answer: $\frac{4}{5}$

42. Find $\lim\limits_{x \to 3} \dfrac{x^2 - 9}{x^2}$.

    1—Answer: 0

43. Find $\lim\limits_{x \to 2} \dfrac{x - 2}{x^2 - x - 2}$.

    1—Answer: $\frac{1}{3}$

44. Find $\lim\limits_{x \to -3} \dfrac{x^2 + 2x - 3}{x - 3}$.

    (a) -2 (b) 4   (c) 0   (d) Does not exist   (e) None of these

    1—Answer: c

45. Find $\lim\limits_{x \to -1} \dfrac{x^2 - 3x - 4}{x - 1}$.

    (a) -5 (b) -3 (c) Does not exist   (d) 0   (e) None of these

    1—Answer: d

46. Find $\lim\limits_{x \to 2^+} \dfrac{|x - 2|}{x - 2}$.

    (a) -1 (b) 1   (c) 0   (d) ∞ (e) None of these

    1—Answer: b

47. Find $\lim\limits_{x \to 2^-} \dfrac{|x - 2|}{x - 2}$.

    (a) -1 (b) 1   (c) 0   (d) ∞ (e) None of these

    1—Answer: a

48. Find $\lim\limits_{x \to 0} \dfrac{\sqrt{x+3} - \sqrt{3}}{x}$.

(a) $\dfrac{1}{2\sqrt{3}}$ (b) $\dfrac{1}{3\sqrt{3}}$ (c) $\dfrac{1}{3}$ (d) Does not exist   (e) None of these

1—Answer: a

49. Evaluate: $\lim\limits_{x \to 0} \dfrac{x}{\sqrt{x+4} - 2}$.

(a) 2   (b) 8   (c) 0   (d) Does not exist   (e) None of these

1—Answer: e

50. Find $\lim\limits_{x \to 3^-} \dfrac{|x-3|}{x-3}$.

(a) ∞ (b) 0   (c) -1 (d) Does not exist   (e) None of these

1—T—Answer: c

51. Find $\lim\limits_{x \to 2^-} \sqrt{2x-3}$.

(a) $1, -1$ (b) 1   (c) -1 (d) $\dfrac{1}{2}$ (e) None of these

1—Answer: b

52. Find $\lim\limits_{x \to 3^+} \sqrt{2x-5}$.

(a) 1   (b) 0   (c) $2i$ (d) Does not exist   (e) None of these

1—Answer: a

53. Find $\lim\limits_{x \to 2^+} \sqrt{2x-1}$.

1—Answer: $\sqrt{3}$

54. Find $\lim\limits_{x \to 1^+} \sqrt{x-1}$.

1—Answer: 0

55. Find $\lim\limits_{x \to 0} \dfrac{\sqrt{x+2} - \sqrt{2}}{x}$.

(a) Does not exist   (b) $\dfrac{1}{2}$ (c) $\dfrac{1}{2\sqrt{2}}$

(d) 2   (e) None of these

1—Answer: c

56. Find $\lim\limits_{x \to 4^-} \dfrac{|x - 4|}{x - 4}$.

(a) Does not exist   (b) -1 (c) 0

(d) ∞ (e) None of these

1—Answer: b

57. Find the limit: $\lim\limits_{x \to 1^-} \sqrt{x - 1}$.

1—Answer: Does not exist

58. Find the limit: $\lim\limits_{x \to 7^-} \dfrac{|8x - 56|}{7 - x}$.

(a) 8   (b) -1 (c) 1   (d) -8 (e) None of these

2—Answer: a

59. Find the limit: $\lim\limits_{x \to 6^-} \dfrac{|3x - 18|}{6 - x}$.

(a) -1 (b) 1   (c) 3   (d) -3 (e) None of these

2—Answer: c

60. Find the limit: $\lim\limits_{x \to 5^-} \dfrac{|3x - 15|}{5 - x}$.

(a) -3 (b) 3   (c) -1 (d) 1   (e) None of these

2—Answer: b

61. Find the limit: $\lim\limits_{x \to 8^-} \dfrac{|8x - 56|}{8 - x}$.

(a) -1 (b) 7   (c) 1   (d) -7 (e) None of these

2—Answer: b

62. Find $\lim\limits_{\Delta x \to 0} \dfrac{2(x + \Delta x) - 3 - (2x - 3)}{\Delta x}$.

(a) 0   (b) ∞ (c) 2   (d) Does not exist   (e) None of these

1—Answer: c

63. Find $\lim\limits_{\Delta x \to 0} \dfrac{3(x + \Delta x) + 4 - (3x + 4)}{\Delta x}$.

1—Answer: 3

64. Find $\lim\limits_{\Delta x \to 0} \dfrac{2(x + \Delta x)^2 + 1 - (2x^2 + 1)}{\Delta x}$.

(a) 0 (b) $4x$ (c) ∞ (d) $4x + 1$ (e) None of these

1—Answer: b

65. Find $\lim\limits_{\Delta x \to 0} \dfrac{2(x + \Delta x) + 3 - (2x - 3)}{\Delta x}$.

(a) 0 (b) ∞ (c) 2 (d) Does not exist (e) None of these

1—Answer: c

66. Evaluate $\lim\limits_{\Delta x \to 0} \dfrac{3(x + \Delta x) + 7 - (3x + 7)}{\Delta x}$.

1—Answer: 3

67. Evaluate $\lim\limits_{\Delta x \to 0} \dfrac{2(x + \Delta x) + 5 - (2x + 5)}{\Delta x}$.

1—Answer: 2

68. Evaluate $\lim\limits_{\Delta x \to 0} \dfrac{f(x + \Delta x) - f(x)}{\Delta x}$ if $f(x) = x^2 - 3$.

(a) $2x$ (b) $2x - 3$ (c) $2x + \Delta x$

(d) Limit does not exist (e) None of these

1—Answer: a

69. Find the limit: $\lim\limits_{h \to 0} \dfrac{\sqrt{(x + h) - 8} - \sqrt{x - 8}}{h}$.

(a) $\sqrt{x - 8}$ (b) 0 (c) None of these (d) $\dfrac{1}{2\sqrt{x - 8}}$

1—Answer: d

70. Find the limit: $\lim\limits_{h \to 0} \dfrac{\sqrt{(x + h) + 2} - \sqrt{x + 2}}{h}$.

(a) $\sqrt{x + 2}$ (b) None of these (c) 0 (d) $\dfrac{1}{2\sqrt{x + 2}}$

1—Answer: d

71. Find the limit: $\lim\limits_{h \to 0} \dfrac{\sqrt{(x + h) - 9} - \sqrt{x - 9}}{h}$.

(a) 0 (b) $\sqrt{x - 9}$ (c) $\dfrac{1}{2\sqrt{x - 9}}$ (d) None of these

1—Answer: c

72. Sketch the graph of $f(x) = \dfrac{x^2 - 3x + 2}{x - 2}$.

2—Answer:

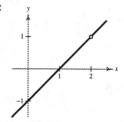

73. Sketch the graph of $f(x) = \dfrac{x^2 - x - 2}{x + 1}$.

2—Answer:

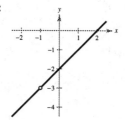

74. Match the graph with the correct function.

(a) $f(x) = \dfrac{x + 3}{x - 1}$

(b) $f(x) = x + 3$

(c) $f(x) = \dfrac{x - 1}{x^2 + 2x - 3}$

(d) $f(x) = \dfrac{x^2 + 2x - 3}{x - 1}$

(e) None of these

1—Answer: d

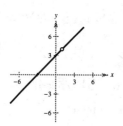

Section 1.6 Continuity

1. Find the intervals in which the function is continuous: $f(x) = \dfrac{(x + 1)(x - 3)}{x - 2}$.

   (a) $(-\infty, 2)(2, \infty)$

   (b) $(-\infty, -1)(-1, 2)(2, \infty)$

   (c) $(-\infty, 1)(1, \infty)$

   (d) $(-\infty, -1)\left(-1, \frac{3}{2}\right)\left(\frac{3}{2}, 2\right)(2, 3)(3, \infty)$

   (e) None of these

   1—Answer: a

2. Find the intervals in which the function is continuous: $f(x) = \dfrac{x - 4}{(x - 2)(x + 1)}$.

   (a) $(-\infty, 4)(4, \infty)$

   (b) $(-\infty, -1)(-1, 2)(2, 4)(4, \infty)$

   (c) $(-\infty, -1)(-1, 2)(2, \infty)$

   (d) $(-\infty, -2)(-2, -1)(-1, 2)(2, \infty)$

   (e) None of these

   1—Answer: c

3. Let $f(x) = \dfrac{1}{x + 1}$ and $g(x) = x^2 - 5$. Find the intervals on which $f(g(x))$ is continuous.

   (a) $(-\infty, -1)(-1, \infty)$

   (b) $(-\infty, -1)\left(-1, \sqrt{5}\right)\left(\sqrt{5}, \infty\right)$

   (c) $\left(-\infty, \sqrt{5}\right)\left(\sqrt{5}, \infty\right)$

   (d) $(\infty, -2)(-2, 2)(2, \infty)$

   (e) None of these

   1—Answer: d

4. Let $f(x) = \dfrac{1}{\sqrt{x}}$ and $g(x) = x - 1$. Find the intervals on which $f(g(x))$ is continuous.

   (a) $(-\infty, 0)(0, \infty)$

   (b) $(-\infty, 1)(1, \infty)$

   (c) $(-\infty, 0)(0, 1)(1, \infty)$

   (d) $(-\infty, -1)(-1, 1)(1, \infty)$

   (e) None of these

   1—Answer: e

5. Let $f(x) = \dfrac{5}{x - 1}$ and $g(x) = x^4$.

   (a) Find $f(g(x))$.

   (b) Find the intervals on which $f(g(x))$ is continuous.

   1—Answer: (a) $\dfrac{5}{x^4 - 1}$ **(b)** $(-\infty, -1)(-1, 1)(1, \infty)$

6. Sketch the graph of the function. Then use the graph to describe the intervals on which the function is continuous:

$$f(x) = \begin{cases} x^2 + 3, & x < 1 \\ 2x + 1, & x \geq 1 \end{cases}.$$

2—T—Answer: $(-\infty, 1)(1, \infty)$

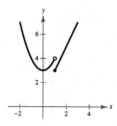

7. Sketch the graph of the function. Then use the graph to describe the intervals on which the function is continuous:

$$f(x) = \frac{x^2 - 9}{x + 3}.$$

2—T—Answer: $(-\infty, -3)(-3, \infty)$

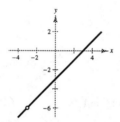

8. Find the intervals on which the function is continuous: $f(x) = \dfrac{3x}{x^2 + 1}$.

(a) $(-\infty, -1)(-1, \infty)$ (b) $(-\infty, \infty)$ (c) $(-\infty, -1)(-1, 0)(0, \infty)$

(d) $(-\infty, 0)(0, \infty)$ (e) None of these

1—Answer: b

9. Sketch the graph then describe the intervals on which the function is continuous: $f(x) = [\![x]\!] + x$.

2—Answer: $[c, c + 1)$, c is an integer

10. Find all values of x that make the function $f(x) = \begin{cases} x^2 + 1, & x \geq 3 \\ 4x + 2, & x < 3 \end{cases}$ discontinuous.

1—Answer: 3

11. Find all values of x that make the function $f(x) = \begin{cases} x^2 + 3, & x \geq 0 \\ 2x + 5, & x < 0 \end{cases}$ discontinuous.

1—Answer: 0

12. Find all values of x that make the function $f(x) = \begin{cases} x^2 + 3, & x \geq 1 \\ 2x + 2, & x < 1 \end{cases}$ discontinuous.

(a) $x = 1$ (b) $x = 0$ and $x = 1$ (c) $x = 3$

(d) $x = -1$ (e) None of these

1—Answer: e

13. Find any points of discontinuity for $f(x) = |9 - x^2|$.

(a) $x = -3, x = 3$ (b) $x = -3$

(c) $x = 3$ (d) $x = 0$

(e) Graph has no points of discontinuity

1—Answer: e

14. At what value(s) of x is the function $f(x) = \dfrac{(x + 1)(x - 3)}{x - 2}$ discontinuous?

(a) 2   (b) $-1, 2, 3$ (c) 1   (d) $-1, \frac{3}{2}, 2, 3$ (e) None of these

1—Answer: a

15. At what value(s) of x is the function $f(x) = \dfrac{x - 4}{x^2 - x - 2}$ discontinuous?

(a) 4   (b) $-1, 2, 4$ (c) $-1, 2$ (d) $-1, 2, 4, -2$ (e) None of these

1—Answer: c

16. Find all values of x for which $f(x) = \dfrac{x^3 - 2x^2 - 3x}{x^2 + x}$ has removable discontinuities.

(a) $-1, 0$ (b) 0   (c) $-1, 0, 3$

(d) $-3, -1, 0$ (e) None of these

1—Answer: b

17. At which value(s) of x is the function $f(x) = \dfrac{x - 1}{x^2 + x - 2}$ discontinuous? Further classify each discontinuity as removable or nonremovable.

(a) $x = -2$ removable, $x = 1$ nonremovable   (b) $x = -2$ nonremovable, $x = 1$ removable

(c) $x = -2$ nonremovable   (d) $x = 1$ nonremovable

(e) None of these

1—Answer: b

18. Find any points of discontinuity of $f(x) = \dfrac{|x|}{x}$. Are they removable or nonremovable?

2—Answer: $x = 0$, <u>non</u>removable

19. Find any points of discontinuity of $f(x) = \dfrac{x^2 - 6x + 5}{x - 6}$. Are they removable or nonremovable?

1—Answer: $x = 6$, <u>non</u>removable

20. Find the value(s) of x for which $f(x) = \dfrac{x - 2}{x^2 - 4}$ is discontinuous and label these discontinuities as removable or nonremovable.

1—Answer: $x = 2$, removable; $x = -2$, nonremovable

21. Find the value(s) of x for which the function $f(x) = \dfrac{x - 3}{x^2 - 5x + 6}$ has a removable discontinuity.

(a) 2, 3   (b) 2   (c) −3   (d) 0   (e) None of these

1—Answer: e

22. Find the value(s) of x for which the function $f(x) = \dfrac{x^3 - 5x^2 + 6x}{x^2 + 7x}$ has a removable discontinuity.

(a) −7, 0   (b) −7   (c) 0   (d) −7, 0, 2   (e) None of these

1—Answer: c

23. At which value(s) of x is the function $f(x) = \dfrac{x + 3}{x^2 + 2x - 3}$ discontinuous? Label each discontinuity removable or nonremovable.

1—Answer: −3 removable; 1 nonremovable

24. Find any value(s) of x for which $f(x) = \dfrac{x - 1}{x^2 + x - 2}$ has removable discontinuities.

(a) 1, −2   (b) −1, 2   (c) 0   (d) 1   (e) None of these

1—Answer: d

25. At which value(s) of x is the function $f(x) = \dfrac{x + 3}{x^2 + x - 6}$ discontinuous? Label each discontinuity removable or nonremovable.

1—Answer: −3 removable; 2 nonremovable

26. At which value(s) of x is the function $f(x) = \dfrac{x + 3}{x^2 + 4x + 3}$ discontinuous? Label each discontinuity removable or nonremovable.

1—Answer: −1 removable; −3 nonremovable

27. Determine any value(s) of x at which the function is not continuous: $f(x) = \dfrac{x^2 + 3x}{x}$.

(a) $x = 0$ (b) $x = 0, -3$ (c) $x = -3$

(d) Continuous for all values of x (e) None of these

1—Answer: a

28. Determine any value(s) of x at which the function is not continuous: $f(x) = \dfrac{x - 2}{x - 1}$.

(a) Continuous for all values of x (b) $x = 1, 2$ (c) $x = 1$

(d) $x = 2$ (e) None of these

1—Answer: c

29. Determine any value(s) of x at which the function is not continuous: $f(x) = [\![x - 2]\!]$.

2—T—Answer: Discontinuous at $x = c$, where c is any integer

30. Determine which of the following functions have nonremovable discontinuities at $x = 2$.

(a) $f(x) = \dfrac{x - 2}{x^2 - 3x + 2}$ (b) $f(x) = \begin{cases} 3x + 1, & x < 2 \\ 2x^2 - 1, & x > 2 \end{cases}$ (c) $f(x) = \dfrac{1}{x - 2}$

(d) All of these   (e) None of these

1—T—Answer: c

31. Determine which of the following functions have nonremovable discontinuities at $x = 1$.

(a) $f(x) = \dfrac{1}{x - 1}$ (b) $f(x) = \begin{cases} x^2, & x < 1 \\ 2x - 1, & x > 1 \end{cases}$ (c) $f(x) = \dfrac{x^2 - 3x + 2}{x - 1}$

(d) All of these   (e) None of these

1—T—Answer: a

32. Determine which of the following functions have removable discontinuities at $x = 2$.

(a) $f(x) = [\![x]\!]$ (b) $f(x) = \begin{cases} 2x + 1, & x < 2 \\ x^2, & x > 2 \end{cases}$ (c) $f(x) = \dfrac{1}{x - 2}$

(d) All of these   (e) None of these

2—T—Answer: e

33. Determine which of the following functions have removable discontinuities at $x = 1$.

(a) $f(x) = \dfrac{x^2 - 2x + 1}{x - 1}$ (b) $f(x) = \dfrac{x - 1}{x^2 - 1}$ (c) $f(x) = \begin{cases} 2x + 1, & x < 1 \\ x^2 + 2, & x > 1 \end{cases}$

(d) All of these   (e) None of these

1—T—Answer: d

34. A local fuel company charges $0.63 per CCF for the first 50 CCF of gas used and $0.60 for each additional CCF. Using the greatest integer function, write the charge C for x CCF's of gas used.

1—Answer: $C = \begin{cases} 0.63x, & 0 < x \leq 50 \\ 31.50 + 0.60[\![x - 49]\!], & x > 50 \end{cases}$

35. Determine the value of c so that $f(x)$ is continuous on the entire real line when

$$f(x) = \begin{cases} x - 2, & x \leq 5 \\ cx - 3, & x \geq 5 \end{cases}.$$

(a) 0   (b) $\frac{6}{5}$ (c) 1   (d) $\frac{5}{6}$ (e) None of these

2—Answer: b

36. Determine the value of c so that $f(x)$ is continuous on the entire real line when

$$f(x) = \begin{cases} x + 3, & x \leq -1 \\ 2x - c, & x > -1 \end{cases}.$$

(a) -4 (b) 4   (c) 0   (d) -1 (e) None of these

2—Answer: ap

37. Determine the value of c so that $f(x)$ is continuous on the entire real line if $f(x) = \begin{cases} x^2, & x \leq 3 \\ \dfrac{c}{x} & x > 3 \end{cases}$

2—Answer: 27

38. State in a complete sentence the definition for continuity of a function at the point $x = a$.

1—Answer: Answers will vary.

39. State in at least one complete sentence the difference between a removable discontinuity and a nonremovable discontinuity.

2—Answer: Answers will vary.

40. Use a graphing utility to locate (accurate to the nearest 0.1) any nonremovable discontinuities of the function

$$f(x) = \frac{x - 2}{x^3 - 2x^2 - 5x + 10}.$$

(a) $x = 2.0$ (b) $x = -2.3$ (c) $x = -1.5, x = 1.5$

(d) $x = -1.7, 1.6$ (e) None of these

1—T—Answer: c

CHAPTER 2
Differentiation

Section 2.1   The Derivative and the Slope of a Curve

1. Determine whether the slope at the indicated point is positive, negative, or zero.

   (a) Zero

   (b) No slope

   (c) Positive

   (d) Negative

   (e) None of these

   1—Answer: d

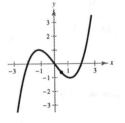

2. Determine whether the slope at the indicated point is positive, negative, or zero.

   (a) No slope

   (b) Positive

   (c) Negative

   (d) Zero

   (e) None of these

   1—Answer: b

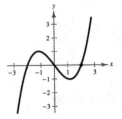

3. Determine whether the slope at the indicated point is positive, negative, or zero.

   (a) Positive

   (b) Zero

   (c) Negative

   (d) No Slope

   (e) None of these

   1—Answer: a

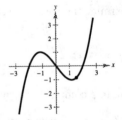

4. Determine whether the slope at the indicated point is positive, negative, or zero.

   (a) Negative

   (b) Positive

   (c) No slope

   (d) Zero

   (e) None of these

   1—Answer: b

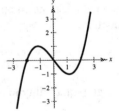

5. The graph represents the cost C in cents per mile of owning and operating an automobile from 1990 through 1995. (Source: Statistical Abstract of the United States, 1997). Estimate the slope of the graph in 1990.

   1—Answer: 2.7

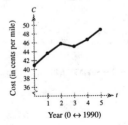

6. The graph represents the cost C in cents per mile of owning and operating an automobile from 1990 through 1995. (Source: Statistical Abstract of the United States, 1997). Estimate the slope of the graph in 1992.

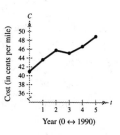

1—Answer: -2.1

7. If $f(x) = 2x^2 + 4$, which of the following will calculate the derivative of $f(x)$?

(a) $\dfrac{[2(x + \Delta x)^2 + 4] - (2x^2 + 4)}{\Delta x}$

(b) $\displaystyle\lim_{\Delta x \to 0} \dfrac{(2x^2 + 4 + \Delta x) - (2x^2 + 4)}{\Delta x}$

(c) $\displaystyle\lim_{\Delta x \to 0} \dfrac{[2(x + \Delta x)^2 + 4] - (2x^2 + 4)}{\Delta x}$

(d) $\dfrac{(2x^2 + 4 + \Delta x) - (2x^2 + 4)}{\Delta x}$

(e) None of these

1—Answer: c

8. If $f(x) = -x^2 + x$, which of the following will calculate the derivative of $f(x)$?

(a) $\displaystyle\lim_{\Delta x \to 0} \dfrac{(-x^2 + x + \Delta x) - (-x^2 + x)}{\Delta x}$

(b) $\displaystyle\lim_{\Delta x \to 0} \dfrac{[-(x + \Delta x)^2 + (x + \Delta x)] - (-x^2 + x)}{\Delta x}$

(c) $\dfrac{[-(x + \Delta x)^2 + (x + \Delta x)] - (-x^2 + x)}{\Delta x}$

(d) $\dfrac{(-x^2 + x + \Delta x) - (-x^2 + x)}{\Delta x}$

(e) None of these

1—Answer: b

9. Use the definition of a derivative to calculate the derivative of $f(x) = \dfrac{1}{x}$.

1—Answer: $-\dfrac{1}{x^2}$

10. Use the definition of a derivative to calculate the derivative of $f(x) = x^2 + x$.

1—Answer: $2x + 1$

11. Use the definition of a derivative to calculate the derivative of $f(x) = -x^2 + 2$.

1—Answer: $-2x$

12. Use the definition of a derivative to calculate the derivative of $f(x) = \dfrac{2}{x}$.

    1—Answer: $-\dfrac{2}{x^2}$

13. Use the definition of a derivative to calculate the derivative of $\sqrt{x}$.

    1—Answer: $\dfrac{1}{2\sqrt{x}}$

14. Use the definition of a derivative to calculate the derivative of $2\sqrt{x}$.

    1—Answer: $\dfrac{1}{\sqrt{x}}$

15. Find the derivative of $y = 2$.

    (a) 0   (b) 1   (c) 2   (d) None of these

    1—Answer: a

16. Find the derivative of $y = -1$.

    (a) 1   (b) -1 (c) None of these   (d) 0

    1—Answer: d

17. Find the derivative of $y = -4$.

    (a) -4 (b) 0   (c) 1   (d) None of these

    1—Answer: b

18. Find the slope of the tangent line to the graph of $f(x) = -2x + 4$ when $x = 2$.

    2—Answer: -2

19. Find the slope of the tangent line to the graph of $f(x) = 3x - 1$ when $x = -1$.

    2—Answer: 3

20. Find the slope of the tangent line to the graph of $f(x) = -x + 3$ when $x = 2$.

    2—Answer: -1

21. Find an equation of the line tangent to $f(x) = 2x^2 - 4$ at the point $(3, 14)$.

    (a) $y = 8x - 10$ (b) $y = 8x + 8$ (c) $y = 12x + 50$ (d) $y = 12x - 22$ (e) None of these

    1—Answer: d

22. Find an equation of the line tangent to $f(x) = 3x^2 + 1$ at the point $(2, 13)$.

    (a) $y = 12x - 11$ (b) $y = 12x - 154$ (c) $y = 3x + 7$

    (d) $y = 3x + 37$ (e) None of these

    1—Answer: a

23. If $f(2) = 3$ and $f'(2) = -1$, find an equation of the tangent line when $x = 2$.

    (a) $y - 3 = 2(x + 1)$ (b) $y - 2 = 3(x + 1)$ (c) $y - 3 = -1(x - 2)$

    (d) $y + 1 = 2(x - 2)$ (e) None of these

    2—Answer: c

24. If $f(1) = 4$ and $f'(1) = 2$, find an equation of the tangent line when $x = 1$.

    (a) $y - 4 = 2(x - 1)$ (b) $y + 4 = 2(x + 1)$ (c) $y - 1 = 4(x - 2)$

    (d) $y - 2 = 4(x - 1)$ (e) None of these

    2—Answer: a

25. Find an equation of the tangent line to the curve $f(x) = x^2$, parallel to the line $y = -2x + 5$.

    (a) $y = -2x + 3$ (b) $y = -2x - 3$ (c) $y = -2x - 1$

    (d) $y = 2x + 1$ (e) None of these

    2—Answer: c

26. Find an equation of the tangent line to the curve $f(x) = x^2$, parallel to the line $y = 6x + 2$.

    (a) $y = 6x$ (b) $y = 6x - 9$ (c) $y = -6x - 72$

    (d) $y = 6x - 27$ (e) None of these

    2—Answer: b

27. Determine where the function is not differentiable.

    (a) $(-\infty, 2)(2, \infty)$

    (b) $x = 2$

    (c) The function is differentiable everywhere.

    (d) $y = \sqrt[3]{4}$

    (e) None of these

    1—Answer: b

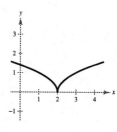

28. Determine where the function is not differentiable.

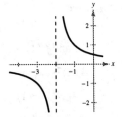

    (a) $(-\infty, 0)(0, \infty)$

    (b) $y = 0$

    (c) $(-\infty, 1)(1, \infty)$

    (d) $x = 1$

    (e) None of these

    1—Answer: d

29. Determine where the function is not differentiable.

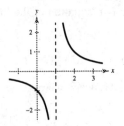

    (a) $(-\infty, 0)(0, \infty)$

    (b) $y = 0$

    (c) $(-\infty, -2)(-2, \infty)$

    (d) $x = -2$

    (e) None of these

    1—Answer: d

Section 2.2   Some Rules for Differentiation

1. Find $f'(x)$: $f(x) = 4x^4 - 5x^3 + 2x - 3$.

   (a) $f'(x) = 4x^3 - 5x^2 + 2$ (b) $f'(x) = 16x^3 - 15x^2 + 2$

   (c) $f'(x) = 16x^3 - 15x^2 + 2x - 3$ (d) $f'(x) = 4x^4 - 5x^3 + 2x$

   (e) None of these

   1—Answer: b

2. Find $f'(x)$: $f(x) = 3x^4 - 6x^3 + 3x - 2$.

   (a) $f'(x) = 3x^3 - 6x^2 + 3$ (b) $f'(x) = 12x^3 - 18x^2 + 3x - 2$

   (c) $f'(x) = 12x^3 - 18x^2 + 3$ (d) $f'(x) = 3x^4 - 6x^3 + 3x$

   (e) None of these

   1—Answer: c

3. Find $f'(x)$: $f(x) = \dfrac{1}{x^2}$.

   (a) $f'(x) = -\dfrac{1}{x^3}$ (b) $f'(x) = \dfrac{1}{x}$ (c) $f'(x) = -\dfrac{2}{x^3}$ (d) $f'(x) = \dfrac{2}{x}$ (e) None of these

   1—Answer: c

4. Find $f'(x)$: $f(x) = \dfrac{1}{x}$.

   (a) $f'(x) = -\dfrac{1}{x^2}$ (b) $f'(x) = \dfrac{1}{x}$ (c) $f'(x) = \dfrac{1}{x^2}$ (d) $f'(x) = -\dfrac{1}{x}$ (e) None of these

   1—Answer: a

5. Find $f'(x) = f(x) = \dfrac{x^2 - 4x}{\sqrt{x}}$.

   (a) $f'(x) = \dfrac{3}{2}x^{1/2} - \dfrac{2}{x^{1/2}}$ (b) $f'(x) = \dfrac{2x - 4}{\sqrt{x}}$ (c) $f'(x) = \dfrac{2x - 4}{1/(2\sqrt{x})}$

   (d) $f'(x) = x^{3/2} - 4x^{1/2}$ (e) None of these

   2—Answer: a

6. Find $f'(x)$: $f(x) = \dfrac{x^2 - 3x}{x^2}$.

(a) $f'(x) = \dfrac{2x - 3}{x^2}$

(b) $f'(x) = \dfrac{2x - 3}{2x}$

(c) $f'(x) = 1 - \dfrac{3}{x}$

(d) $f'(x) = \dfrac{3}{x^2}$

(e) None of these

2—Answer: d

7. Find the derivative of x^{-8}.

(a) $-8x^{-9}$ (b) x^{-9} (c) $-8x^{-7}$ (d) -8 (e) None of these

1—Answer: a

8. Find the derivative of x^{-9}.

(a) $-9x^{-10}$ (b) -9 (c) $-9x^{-8}$ (d) x^{-10} (e) None of these

1—Answer: a

9. Find the derivative of x^{-3}.

(a) -3 (b) x^{-4} (c) $-3x^{-4}$ (d) $-3x^{-2}$ (e) None of these

1—Answer: c

10. Find the derivative of y with respect to x if $y = 4\sqrt{x}(2x + 3)$.

(a) $\dfrac{6(2x + 1)}{\sqrt{x}}$

(b) $\dfrac{3}{2\sqrt{x}}$

(c) $12\sqrt{x} + 6$

(d) $\dfrac{9}{2}\sqrt{x} - \dfrac{1}{2\sqrt{x}}$

(e) None of these

1—Answer: a

11. Find the derivative of y with respect to x if $y = 4\sqrt[3]{x}(2x + 3)$.

1—Answer: $\dfrac{4(8x + 3)}{3x^{2/3}}$

12. Find the derivative of y with respect to x if $y = 4x(2x + 3)$.

(a) $16x + 12$ (b) $20x$ (c) $8x + 12$ (d) $4x + 6$ (e) None of these

1—Answer: a

13. Find $\dfrac{dy}{dx}$ for $y = \sqrt{x}(3x - 1)$.

    (a) $\dfrac{9x - 1}{2\sqrt{x}}$ (b) $\dfrac{9}{2}\sqrt{x} - 1$ (c) $3\sqrt{x}$ (d) $\dfrac{3}{2\sqrt{x}}$ (e) None of these

    1—Answer: a

14. Take the derivative of each of the following.

    (a) $y = \dfrac{2x^3}{3}$ (b) $f(x) = \dfrac{7}{x^2}$ (c) $y = \dfrac{1 - x}{x}$ (d) $g(x) = \dfrac{4}{\sqrt{x}}$

    1—Answer: **(a)** $2x^2$ **(b)** $\dfrac{14}{x^3}$ **(c)** $\dfrac{-1}{x^2}$ **(d)** $\dfrac{-2}{x^{3/2}}$

15. Find the first derivative of $f(x) = \dfrac{7}{x^3}$.

    1—Answer: $\dfrac{-21}{x^4}$

16. Differentiate: $y = \dfrac{1 - 2x}{x}$.

    1—Answer: $\dfrac{-1}{x^2}$

17. Find y' if $y = \dfrac{8}{\sqrt{x}}$.

    1—Answer: $\dfrac{-4}{x^{3/2}}$

18. Find $\dfrac{dy}{dx}$ if $y = \dfrac{2x^4}{4}$.

    1—Answer: $2x^3$

19. Let $g(x) = -7f(x)$ and let $f'(-7) = -9$. Use the Constant Multiple Rule to find $g'(-7)$.

    (a) -7 (b) -9 (c) 0 (d) 63 (e) None of these

    1—Answer: d

20. Let $g(x) = 3f(x) + 5$ and let $f'(4) = 2$. Use the Constant and Constant Multiple Rules to find $g'(4)$.

    (a) 11 (b) 7 (c) 6 (d) 17 (e) None of these

    1—Answer: c

21. Let $g(x) = 2f(x) - 3$ and let $f'(4) = 2$. Use the Constant and Constant Multiple Rules to find $g'(4)$.

(a) 1   (b) 4   (c) 5   (d) 7   (e) None of these

1—Answer: b

22. Let $g(x) = -5f(x)$ and let $f'(-7) = 6$. Use the Constant Multiple Rule to find $g'(-7)$.

(a) 6   (b) 0   (c) -30 (d) -5 (e) None of these

1—Answer: c

23. $f'(2) = 4$, $g'(2) = -7$, and $h'(2) = 2$. Choose the statement that is <u>not</u> true.

(a) $g'(2) + h'(2) = -5$ (b) $f'(2) - g'(2) = 11$ (c) $f'(2) + g'(2) - h'(2) = -5$

(d) $f'(2) + h'(2) = -3$ (e) None of these

1—Answer: d

24. $f'(2) = 3$, $g'(2) = -9$, and $h'(2) = 2$. Choose the statement that is <u>not</u> true.

(a) $g'(2) + h'(2) = -7$ (b) $f'(2) + h'(2) = -6$ (c) $f'(2) - g'(2) = 12$

(d) $f'(2) + g'(2) - h'(2) = -8$ (e) None of these

1—Answer: b

25. $f'(2) = 4$, $g'(2) = -4$, and $h'(2) = 4$. Choose the statement that is <u>not</u> true.

(a) $f'(2) + h'(2) = 0$ (b) $f'(2) - g'(2) = 8$ (c) $f'(2) + g'(2) - h'(2) = -4$

(d) $g'(2) + h'(2) = 0$ (e) None of these

1—Answer: a

26. Let $g(x) = 9f(x)$ and let $f'(-6) = -6$. Find $g'(-6)$.

(a) -54 (b) 0   (c) -6 (d) 9   (e) None of these

1—Answer: a

27. Find the value of the derivative of $f(x) = 1 + \sqrt{x}$ at the point $(9, 4)$.

(a) 3   (b) $\frac{1}{6}$ (c) $\frac{9}{2}$ (d) $\frac{7}{6}$ (e) None of these

1—Answer: b

28. Find the value of the derivative of $f(x) = 3 + \sqrt{x}$ at the point $(4, 5)$.

(a) $\frac{1}{4}$ (b) 5   (c) 1   (d) $\frac{13}{4}$ (e) None of these

1—Answer: a

29. Find the slope of the tangent line to the graph of $y = 3\sqrt[4]{x} - 1$ at the point $(1, 2)$.

(a) 2   (b) 11   (c) $-\frac{1}{4}$ (d) $\frac{3}{4}$ (e) None of these

1—Answer: d

30. Find the slope of the tangent line to the graph of $y = 3.1t^2 - 0.2t$ when $t = 1$.

(a) 2.9   (b) 0   (c) 6.2   (d) 6   (e) None of these

1—Answer: d

31. Find the point(s) on the graph of the function $f(x) = x^3 - 2$ where the slope is 3.

(a) $(1, 3), (-1, 3)$ (b) $(1, -1), (-1, -3)$ (c) $\left(\sqrt[3]{2}, 0\right)$

(d) $(1, 3)$ (e) None of these

2—Answer: b

32. Find the values of x for all points on the graph of $f(x) = x^3 - 2x^2 + 5x - 16$ at which the slope of the tangent line is 4.

2—Answer: $\frac{1}{3}$, 1

33. Find the point on the graph of the function $f(x) = 2x^2 - 2x - 9$ where the slope is 10.

(a) $(3, 10)$ (b) $(1, -9)$ (c) $(10, 171)$ (d) $(3, 3)$ (e) None of these

2—Answer: d

34. Write the equation of the tangent line, in general form, to the graph of $y = \dfrac{-3}{x^4} + 4x - 3$ at the point $(1, -2)$.

2—Answer: $16x - y - 18 = 0$

35. Find an equation for the tangent line to the graph of $f(x) = 2x^2 - 2x + 3$ at the point where $x = 1$.

(a) $y = 2x - 2$ (b) $y = 4x^2 - 6x + 5$ (c) $y = 2x + 1$

(d) $y = 4x^2 - 6x + 2$ (e) None of these

1—Answer: c

36. Find an equation for the tangent line to the graph of $f(x) = -2x^2 + 2x + 3$ at the point where $x = 1$.

(a) $y = -4x + 2$ (b) $2x + y - 1 = 0$ (c) $y = -4x^2 + 2x + 1$

(d) $2x + y = 5$ (e) None of these

1—Answer: d

37. Find an equation of the tangent line to the graph of $f(x) = 3x^3 + 2x$ when $x = 1$.

1—Answer: $y = 11x - 6$

38. Write the equation of the tangent line, in slope–intercept form, to the graph of $y = -3x^4 + 4x - 3$ at the point $(1, -2)$.

    (a) $y = -8x + 10$ (b) $y = 8x - 6$ (c) $y = -8x - 10$

    (d) $y = -8x + 6$ (e) None of these

    2—Answer: d

39. Find the equation of the tangent line to the graph of $f(x) = x^2 - 5x + 2$ at the point $(2, -4)$.

    (a) $y = -x - 4$ (b) $y = 2x^2 - 9x + 6$ (c) $x + y + 6 = 0$

    (d) $x + y + 2 = 0$ (e) None of these

    2—Answer: d

40. Find an equation for the tangent line, in slope–intercept form, to the curve $y = f(x) = 4 - 3x + x^3$ at the point $(1, 2)$.

    2—Answer: $y = 2$

41. Find the equation of the tangent line to the graph of $f(x) = 2x^3 - 4x^2 - 1$ at the point $(1, -3)$.

    (a) $2x + y + 5 = 0$ (b) $2x + y + 1 = 0$ (c) $6x^3 - 14x^2 + 8x - y - 3 = 0$

    (d) $y = -2x - 3$ (e) None of these

    1—Answer: b

42. Write the equation of the tangent line, in slope–intercept form, to the the graph of $f(x) = -3x^3 + 5x^2 - 3$ at the point $(2, -7)$.

    (a) $y = 16x + 39$ (b) $y = -16x + 39$ (c) $8x + y + 10 = 0$

    (d) $y = -16x + 25$ (e) None of these

    2—Answer: d

43. Find an equation for the tangent line of the function $f(x) = -x^2 + 3x + 1$ at the point $(0, 1)$.

    1—Answer: $y = 3x + 1$

44. Find an equation of the tangent line to the graph of $f(x) = 3x^3 + 4x^2 - 1$ at the $x = 2$.

    2—Answer: $y = -20x + 31$

45. Write the equation of the tangent line, in general form, to the graph of $y = -3x^4 + 4x - 4$ at the point $(1, -3)$.

    (a) $8x + y - 5 = 0$ (b) $8x - y - 5 = 0$ (c) $y = -8x - 10$

    (d) $y = -8x - 5$ (e) None of these

    2—Answer: a

46. Use a graphing utility to find all points at which the graph of $f(x) = x^4 - 4x + 5$ has horizontal tangent lines.

(a) $(2, 0)$ (b) $(1, 0)$ (c) $(1, 2)$

(d) $(1, 2), (-1, 10)$ (e) None of these

1—T—Answer: c

47. Find all points at which the graph of $f(x) = -x^3 + 3x^2 - 2$ has horizontal tangent lines.

(a) $(0, -2), (2, 2)$ (b) $(0, -2)$ (c) $(1, 0) (0, -2)$

(d) $(2, 2)$ (e) None of these

2—Answer: a

48. Find all points at which the graph of $f(x) = x^3 - 3x$ has horizontal tangent lines.

2—Answer: $(1, -2), (-1, 2)$

49. Find the points at which the graph of the function $f(x) = 2x^3 + 3x^2 - 12x + 1$ has horizontal tangent lines.

2—Answer: $(1, -6), (-2, 21)$

50. Find all points at which the graph of $y = -2x^3 + 6x + 5$ has horizontal tangent lines.

1—Answer: $(-1, 1), (1, 9)$

Section 2.3   Rates of Change: Velocity and Marginals

1. Find the average rate of change of y with respect to x on the interval $[1, 4]$, where $y = x^2 + x + 1$.

   1—Answer: 6

2. Find the average rate of change of y with respect to x on the interval $[2, 3]$, where $y = x^3 + 2$.

   1—Answer: 19

3. Find the average rate of change of y with respect to x on the interval $[-1, 1]$, where $y = 2x^3 + 4x$.

   1—Answer: 6

4. Find the average rate of change of y with respect to x on the interval $[0, 5]$, where $y = 2x^2 + x - 3$.

   1—Answer: 11

5. The velocity function for an object is given by $s'(t) = -10t^2 + 4$, where s is measured in feet and t is measured in seconds. What is the instantaneous velocity when $t = 2$?

   (a) -10 ft/sec.   (b) -40 ft/sec.   (c) -36 ft/sec.

   (d) 44 ft/sec.   (e) None of these

   1—Answer: c

6. The velocity function for an object is given by $s'(t) = -8t^2 + 6$, where s is measured in feet and t is measured in seconds. What is the instantaneous velocity when $t = 2$?

   (a) -32 ft/sec.   (b) 262 ft/sec.   (c) -8 ft/sec.

   (d) -26 ft/sec.   (e) None of these

   1—Answer: d

7. For the function $y = f(x) = -x^2 + 4x$, find the average rate of change on $[2, 3]$ and the instantaneous rate of change at $x = 2$.

   2—Answer: Average rate of change: -1, instantaneous rate of change: 0

8. In at least one complete sentence, describe the difference between the average velocity of a particle and the instantaneous velocity of a particle.

   1—Answer: Answers will vary.

9. Find the instantaneous rate of change of y with respect to x when $x = 36$ for the function $y = 3 - 2x$.

   (a) 36   (b) -69 (c) -2 (d) 3   (e) None of these

   1—Answer: c

10. Find the instantaneous rate of change of w with respect to z for the function $w = \dfrac{1}{z} + \dfrac{z}{2}$.

   (a) $2\dfrac{1}{2}$
   (b) -2
   (c) $\dfrac{z^2 - 2}{2z^2}$
   (d) $\dfrac{-1}{z^2}$
   (e) None of these

   1—Answer: c

11. Find the instantaneous rate of change of y with respect to x when $x = 20$ for the function $y = x - x^2$.

   (a) -380
   (b) -39
   (c) -19
   (d) -20
   (e) None of these

   1—Answer: b

12. Find the instantaneous rate of change of y with respect to x when $x = 12$ for the function $y = 3x^2 - x$.

   (a) 71
   (b) 420
   (c) 432
   (d) 60
   (e) None of these

   1—Answer: a

13. Find the instantaneous rate of change of w with respect to z for the function $w = \dfrac{7}{3z^2}$.

   (a) $\dfrac{7}{6z}$
   (b) $\dfrac{14}{3}z$
   (c) $-\dfrac{14}{3z}$
   (d) $-\dfrac{14}{3z^3}$
   (e) None of these

   1—Answer: d

14. Suppose the position equation for a moving object is given by $s(t) = 3t^2 - 2t + 5$ where s is measured in meters and t is measured in seconds. Find the velocity of the object when $t = 2$.

   (a) 13 m/sec.
   (b) 6 m/sec.
   (c) 10 m/sec.
   (d) 14 m/sec.
   (e) None of these

   1—Answer: c

15. Suppose the position equation for a moving object is given by $s(t) = 4t^2 + 2t + 8$ where s is measured in meters and t is measured in seconds. Find the velocity of the object when $t = 3$.

   (a) 50 m/sec.
   (b) 36 m/sec.
   (c) 32 m/sec.
   (d) 26 m/sec.
   (e) None of these

   1—Answer: d

16. If the movement of a particle is given by the position equation

$$s(t) = 2t^2 + \frac{1}{t}$$

where s is measured in meters and t is measured in seconds, find the velocity at $t = 2$.

   1—Answer: $\frac{31}{4}$ m/sec.

17. Find the instantaneous rate of change of w with respect to z if $w = \dfrac{1}{z} + \dfrac{z^2}{2}$.

   (a) $\dfrac{5}{2}$
   (b) 0
   (c) $\dfrac{z^3 - 2}{2z^3}$
   (d) $-\dfrac{1}{z^3}$
   (e) None of these

   1—Answer: e

18. Find the instantaneous rate of change of w with respect to z if $w = \dfrac{8}{3z^2}$.

    (a) $\dfrac{4}{3z}$ (b) $\dfrac{16z}{3}$ (c) $\dfrac{-16}{3z}$ (d) $\dfrac{-16}{3z^3}$ (e) None of these

    1—Answer: d

19. Suppose the position equation for a moving particle is given by

    $$s = \frac{3t^2 - 4t + 10}{5}, \, t \geq 0,$$

    where s is measured in meters and t in seconds. Find the time when the particle has velocity zero.

    (a) 1 sec   (b) $\frac{3}{2}$ sec   (c) $\frac{2}{3}$ sec   (d) 0 sec   (e) None of these

    1—Answer: c

20. Suppose the position equation for a moving particle is given by

    $$s = \frac{3t^2 + 4t - 1}{4}, \, t \geq 0,$$

    where s is measured in meters and t in seconds. Find the velocity and acceleration of the particle when $t = 3$ seconds.

    (a) $v = 5.5$ m/sec., $a = 1.5$ m/sec.^{2} (b) $v = 22$ m/sec., $a = 6$ m/sec.^{2}

    (c) $v = 5.25$ m/sec., $a = 1.25$ m/sec.^{2} (d) $v = 9.5$ m/sec., $a = 5.5$ m/sec.^{2}

    (e) None of these

    2—T—Answer: a

21. The height s (in feet) of an object fired straight up from ground level with an initial velocity of 150 feet per second is given by $s = -16t^2 + 150t$, where t is the time in seconds. How fast is the object moving after 2 seconds?

    (a) 236 ft/sec.   (b) 86 ft/sec.   (c) 150 ft/sec.   (d) 0 ft/sec.   (e) None of these

    1—Answer: b

22. The height s (in feet) of an object fired straight up from ground level with an initial velocity of 150 feet per second is given by $s = -16t^2 + 150t$, where t is the time in seconds. How fast is the object moving after 5 seconds?

    (a) 0 ft/sec.   (b) 350 ft/sec.   (c) -160 ft/sec.   (d) -10 ft/sec.   (e) None of these

    1—Answer: d

23. The demand and cost functions for a given product are $p = 100 - 0.1x^2$ and $C = 20x + 100,000$. Use a graphing utility to estimate at what production level (i.e., at what value of x) the marginal profit is zero.

    (a) 16.3   (b) 800   (c) 82.95   (d) 30.7   (e) None of these

    2—Answer: a

24. A manufacturer determines that the profit derived from selling x units of a certain item is given by $P = 4x^3 - 15x^2 - 120x - 10$. Use a graphing utility to locate (to the nearest 0.1) any positive values of x where the tangent line is horizontal.

(a) 2.3   (b) 2.6   (c) 4.7   (d) 3.7   (e) None of these

1—T–Answer: c

25. Use the marginal Cost function to estimate the additional cost if the production level is increased from 50 to 51 units: $C(x) = 2.4\sqrt{x} + 400$.

(a) \$0.15   (b) \$0.17   (c) \$0.20   (d) \$0.23   (e) None of these

1—T—Answer: b

26. The demand and cost functions for a given product are $p = 100 - 0.1x^2$ and $C = 40x + 20{,}000$. Use a graphing utility to estimate at what production level (i.e., at what value of x) the marginal profit is zero.

1—T—Answer: 14.1

27. A manufacturer determines that the cost of producing x units of a certain item is given by $C(x) = 120\sqrt[3]{x} - 3.6x$. Use a graphing utility to locate (to the nearest 0.1) any positive values of x where the marginal cost is zero.

1—T—Answer: 37.0

28. Use the marginal Cost function to estimate the additional cost if the production level is increased from 50 to 51 units: $C(x) = 3.7\sqrt{x} + 400$.

1—T—Answer: \$0.26

29. A manufacturer determines that the profit derived from selling x units of a certain item is given by $P = -0.05x^2 + 200x - 20$. Find the marginal profit for a production level of 50 units.

(a) \$9855   (b) \$195   (c) \$205   (d) \$225   (e) None of these

1—Answer: b

30. A manufacturer determines that the profit derived from selling x units of a certain item is given by $P = 0.025x^2 + 20x - 20$. Find the marginal profit for a production level of 100 units.

(a) \$25   (b) \$50   (c) \$10   (d) \$20.50   (e) None of these

1—T—Answer: a

31. The demand function for a particular commodity is given by $p = 600 - 3x$. Find the marginal revenue when $x = 30$.

(a) \$15,300.00   (b) \$420.00   (c) \$510.00   (d) \$3.00   (e) None of these

1—Answer: b

32. The demand function and cost function for x units of a product are $p = \dfrac{60}{\sqrt{x}}$ and $C = .65x + 400$. Find the marginal profit when $x = 81$.

2—T—Answer: \$2.68

33. The demand function and cost function for x units of a product are $p = \dfrac{60}{\sqrt{x}}$ and $C = .65x + 400$. Find the marginal profit when $x = 100$.

   (a) $193.50   (b) $4.58   (c) $2.35   (d) $87.35   (e) None of these

   2—T—Answer: c

34. The demand function for a particular commodity is given by $p = 500 - 2x$. Find the marginal revenue when $x = 30$.

   (a) $380.00   (b) $2.00   (c) $440.00   (d) $13,200.00   (e) None of these

   1—Answer: a

35. The demand function for a particular commodity is given by $p = 40 - 0.02x$. Find the marginal revenue when $x = 30$.

   (a) $0.02   (b) $1182.00   (c) $39.40   (d) $38.80   (e) None of these

   1—Answer: d

36. A manufacturer determines that the profit derived from selling x units of a certain item is given by $P = 0.003x^2 + 10x$. Find the marginal profit for a production level of 50 units.

   (a) $507.50   (b) $10.30   (c) $13.00   (d) $10.03   (e) None of these

   1—Answer: b

37. A manufacturer determines that the profit derived from selling x units of a certain item is given by $P = -x^2 + 101x$. Find the marginal profit for a production level of 50 units.

   (a) $2550.00   (b) $1.00   (c) $201.00   (d) $20.10   (e) None of these

   1—Answer: b

38. A manufacturer determines that the profit derived from selling x units of a certain item is given by $P = -2x^2 + 400x$. Find the marginal profit for a production level of 50 units.

   (a) $15,000.00   (b) $25,000.00   (c) $200.00   (d) $600.00   (e) None of these

   1—Answer: c

39. The demand function and cost function for x units of a product are $p = \dfrac{40}{\sqrt{x}}$ and $C = 0.5x + 400$. Find the revenue as a function of x.

   (a) $R = 40\sqrt{x}$ (b) $R = \dfrac{40}{\sqrt{x}} - 0.5x - 400$ (c) $R = \dfrac{40}{\sqrt{x}} + 0.5x + 400$

   (d) $R = \dfrac{40}{\sqrt{x}}(0.5x + 400)$ (e) None of these

   1—Answer: a

40. The demand function and cost function for x units of a product are $p = \dfrac{60}{\sqrt{x}}$ and $C = 0.65x + 400$. Find the revenue as a function of x.

(a) $R = \dfrac{60}{\sqrt{x}} - 0.65x - 400$ (b) $R = 60\sqrt{x} - 0.65x + 400$ (c) $R = \dfrac{60}{\sqrt{x}}(0.65x + 400)$

(d) $R = 60\sqrt{x}$ (e) None of these

1—Answer: a

41. The cost (in dollars) of producing x units of a product is given by $C = 5.46\sqrt{x} + 3600$. Find the additional cost when the number of units produced is increased from 12 to 13 units.

(a) $0.91   (b) $0.79   (c) $0.77   (d) $0.76   (e) None of these

1—Answer: c

42. The cost (in dollars) of producing x units of a product is given by $C = 5.46\sqrt{x} + 3600$. Find the additional cost when the number of units produced is increased from 30 to 31 units.

(a) $0.50   (b) $0.48   (c) $0.77   (d) $0.49   (e) None of these

1—Answer: d

43. The cost (in dollars) of producing x units of a product is given by $C = 5.46\sqrt{x} + 3600$. Find the marginal cost when $x = 9$.

1—Answer: $0.91

44. The cost (in dollars) of producing x units of a product is given by $C = 5.46\sqrt{x} + 3600$. Find the marginal cost when $x = 25$.

(a) $0.54   (b) $0.55   (c) $0.56   (d) $0.57   (e) None of these

1—Answer: b

45. Use a graphing utility to find the point on the graph of the function $C(x) = \dfrac{2x^2 - 2x + 9}{\sqrt{x}}$, $x \geq 0$ where the marginal cost is 0.

(a) 0.8   (b) 1.4   (c) 3.5   (d) 5.3   (e) None of these

1—T—Answer: b

46. Use a graphing utility to find all points on the graph of $C(x) = x^5 - 6x^2 + 10$ where the marginal cost function is zero.

1—T—Answer: 0.0, 1.3

47. Use a graphing utility to find the point(s) on the graph of the function $P(x) = -0.3x^2 + 5.6x + 9$ where the marginal profit is zero.

1—T—Answer: 9.3

48. A certain particle moves so that its position as a function of time is given by $s(t) = \dfrac{3t^2 + 4}{t}$, where s is measured in meters and t in seconds. Find the velocity when $t = 4$ seconds.

1—Answer: 2.75 m/sec.

Section 2.4 The Product and Quotient Rules

1. Differentiate: $y = \dfrac{x^2}{3x - 1}$.

(a) $\dfrac{2x}{3}$ (b) $-2x$ (c) $\dfrac{x(3x - 2)}{(3x - 1)^2}$ (d) $\dfrac{2x - 3x^2}{(3x - 1)^2}$ (e) None of these

1—Answer: c

2. Let $y = \dfrac{x^2}{x^2 + 2}$. Use the quotient rule to find y' and simplify.

1—Answer: $\dfrac{4x}{(x^2 + 2)^2}$

3. Find $\dfrac{dy}{dx}$ if $y = \dfrac{4x}{1/x + 3}$.

1—Answer: $\dfrac{12x^2 + 8x}{(1 + 3x)^2}$

4. Differentiate: $y = \dfrac{x^2}{3x^2 - 1}$.

(a) $\dfrac{2x}{(3x^2 - 1)^2}$ (b) $\dfrac{2x(6x^2 + 1)}{(3x^2 - 1)^2}$ (c) $\dfrac{-2x}{(3x^2 - 1)^2}$ (d) $\dfrac{2x(6x^2 - 1)}{(3x^2 - 1)^2}$ (e) None of these

1—Answer: c

5. Differentiate: $y = \dfrac{3x}{x^2 + 1}$.

(a) $\dfrac{3}{1 + x^2}$ (b) $\dfrac{3}{2x}$ (c) $\dfrac{3x^2 - 3}{(1 + x^2)^3}$ (d) $\dfrac{3(1 - x^2)}{(1 + x^2)^2}$ (e) None of these

1—Answer: d

6. Differentiate: $y = \dfrac{2x}{1 - 3x^2}$.

1—Answer: $\dfrac{6x^2 + 2}{(1 - 3x^2)^2}$

7. Differentiate: $f(x) = \dfrac{x^2 - 1}{x^2 + 1}$.

1—Answer: $\dfrac{4x}{(x^2 + 1)^2}$

8. Differentiate: $f(x) = \dfrac{x^2 - 2}{x^2 + 2}$.

1—Answer: $\dfrac{8x}{(x^2 + 2)^2}$

9. Differentiate: $y = (3x^3 - 4x)(x^2 + 1)$.

   (a) $15x^4 - 3x^2 - 4$ (b) $-3x^4 - 13x^2 + 4$ (c) $x^2(9x^2 + 6x + 1)$

   (d) $x^2(15x^2 + 1)$ (e) None of these

   1—Answer: a

10. Differentiate: $y = (3 - 2x^2)(x^4 + x)$.

    (a) $-3(4x^5 - 4x^3 + 2x^2 - 1)$ (b) $4x^5 - 12x^3 - 2x^2 - 3$ (c) $-2(5x^4 - 6x^3 + 1)$

    (d) $-4x^5 + 12x^3 + 2x^2 + 3$ (e) None of these

    1—Answer: a

11. Differentiate: $(x + 2)(x^2 - 5x + 1)$.

    (a) $3x^2 - 6x - 9$ (b) $x^2 + 4x - 11$ (c) $x^2 - 6x - 9$

    (d) $2x - 5$ (e) None of these

    1—Answer: a

12. Differentiate: $(3x - 4)(x^2 - 2x + 1)$.

    (a) $3x^2 - 8x + 5$ (b) $6x - 6$ (c) $3x^2 - 20x + 11$

    (d) $9x^2 - 20x + 11$ (e) None of these

    1—Answer: d

13. Differentiate: $(2x + 5)(x^2 - 3x + 1)$.

    (a) $4x - 6$ (b) $2x^2 + 10x - 17$ (c) $6x^2 - 2x - 13$

    (d) $2x^2 - 2x - 13$ (e) None of these

    1—Answer: c

14. Let $y = (x^2 + 1)(2 - x)$. Use the product rule to find $\dfrac{dy}{dx}$ and simplify.

    1—Answer: $-3x^2 + 4x - 1$

15. Let $y = (x^3 + 4x)(4 - 3x)$. Use the product rule to find $\dfrac{dy}{dx}$ and simplify.

    1—Answer: $-4(3x^3 - 3x^2 + 6x - 4)$

16. Find the derivative of $x^2 f(x)$.

    (a) $x[xf'(x) + 2f(x)]$ (b) $2xf'(x)$ (c) $x[xf(x) + 2f'(x)]$

    (d) $x^2 f'(x)$ (e) None of these

    2—Answer: a

17. Find the derivative of $9x^2 f(x)$.

(a) $9x^2 f'(x)$ (b) $9x[xf(x) + 2f'(x)]$ (c) $18xf'(x)$

(d) $9x[xf'(x) + 2f(x)]$ (e) None of these

2—Answer: d

18. Let $f(7) = 0$, $f'(7) = 14$, $g(7) = 1$ and $g'(7) = \frac{1}{7}$. Find $h'(7)$ if $h(x) = f(x)/g(x)$.

(a) 98   (b) -14 (c) -2 (d) 14   (e) None of these

2—Answer: d

19. Let $f(-5) = 0$, $f'(-5) = -10$, $g(-5) = 1$ and $g'(-5) = -\frac{1}{5}$. Find $h'(-5)$ if $h(x) = f(x)/g(x)$.

(a) 10   (b) -2 (c) -10 (d) 50   (e) None of these

2—Answer: c

20. Let $f(3) = 0$, $f'(3) = 6$, $g(3) = 1$ and $g'(3) = \frac{1}{3}$. Find $h'(3)$ if $h(x) = f(x)/g(x)$.

(a) 18   (b) 6   (c) -6 (d) -2 (e) None of these

2—Answer: b

21. Find the value of the derivative of $f(x) = \dfrac{x}{x + 2}$ at the point $\left(1, \dfrac{1}{3}\right)$.

(a) $\frac{2}{3}$ (b) $\frac{2}{9}$ (c) $-\frac{2}{9}$ (d) $\frac{1}{2}$ (e) None of these

1—Answer: b

22. Find the value of the derivative of $f(x) = (x^2 + 1)(2x + 3)$ at the point $(1, 10)$.

(a) 14   (b) -6 (c) -2 (d) 4   (e) None of these

1—Answer: a

23. Find the value of the derivative of $f(x) = \dfrac{x + 2}{x + 1}$ at the point $\left(1, \dfrac{3}{2}\right)$.

(a) $\frac{1}{4}$ (b) $-\frac{1}{4}$ (c) 2   (d) $\frac{3}{4}$ (e) None of these

1—Answer: b

24. Find the slope of the line tangent to the curve $y = \dfrac{x - 1}{x + 3}$ at the point $(-1, -1)$.

1—T—Answer: 1

25. Find all points at which the graph of $f(x) = \dfrac{x^2}{x + 2}$ has a slope of $\dfrac{5}{9}$.

2—Answer: $\left(1, \frac{1}{3}\right)\left(5, \frac{-25}{3}\right)$

26. Using the graph of $f'(x)$ at the right, which of the following statements about $f(x)$ is true?

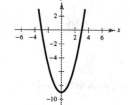

(a) $f(x)$ decreases $(-3, 3)$.

(b) $f(x)$ increases $(-\infty, -3)$.

(c) $f(x)$ increases $(3, \infty)$.

(d) All are true.

(e) All are false.

2—Answer: d

27. Using the graph of $f'(x)$ at the right, which of the following statements about $f(x)$ is true?

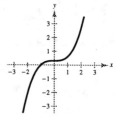

(a) $f(x)$ increases $(-1, \infty)$.

(b) $f(x)$ is always increasing.

(c) $f(x)$ decreases $(-\infty, 0)$.

(d) All are true.

(e) All are false.

2—Answer: a

28. Find an equation of the tangent line to the graph of $f(x) = \dfrac{(x-1)}{(x+1)}$ when $x = 1$.

(a) $y = \dfrac{2}{(x+1)^2}(x-1)$

(b) $x - 2y = 1$

(c) $y - 1 = \dfrac{1}{2}x$

(d) $y = 2(x-1)$

(e) None of these

2—Answer: b

29. Find an equation of the tangent line to the graph of $f(x) = \dfrac{2x}{x+5}$ at $x = -3$.

2—Answer: $5x - 2y + 9 = 0$

30. Find an equation of the tangent line to the graph of $f(x) = \dfrac{x-1}{x+1}$ when $x = 0$.

2—Answer: $2x - y - 1 = 0$

31. If y changes in relation to x according to the formula $y = \dfrac{30x}{x+2}$, at what rate is y changing when $x = 0$?

1—Answer: 15 units of y per unit of x

32. If y changes in relation to x according to the formula $y = \dfrac{20x}{x+1}$, at what rate is y changing when $x = 1$?

1—Answer: 5 units of y per unit of x

33. If y changes in relation to x according to the formula $y = \dfrac{20x}{x+2}$, at what rate is y changing when $x = 0$?

1—Answer: 10 units of y per unit of x

34. A population of bacteria is introduced into a culture. The number of bacteria P can be modeled by

$$P = 200\left(1 + \frac{2t}{40 + t^2}\right)$$

where t is the time (in hours). Find the rate of change of the population when $t = 2$.

2—T—Answer: 7.4

35. A population of bacteria is introduced into a culture. The number of bacteria P can be modeled by

$$P = 200\left(1 + \frac{2t}{40 + t^2}\right)$$

where t is the time (in hours). Find the rate of change of the population when $t = 3$.

(a) 551.1   (b) 224.5   (c) 63.1   (d) 5.2   (e) None of these

2—T—Answer: d

Section 2.5 The Chain Rule

1. Find $f'(x)$ for $f(x) = (2x^2 + 5)^7$.

   (a) $7(4x)^6$

   (b) $(4x)^7$

   (c) $28x(2x^2 + 5)^6$

   (d) $7(2x^2 + 5)^6$

   (e) None of these

   1—Answer: c

2. Find the derivative of $y = \sqrt[3]{x^2 + x}$.

   1—Answer: $\frac{1}{3}(x^2 + x)^{-2/3}(2x + 1)$

3. Find the derivative of $y = (x^2 + 2x + 5)^6$.

   1—Answer: $6(2x + 2)(x^2 + 2x + 5)^5$

4. Differentiate: $\sqrt[3]{x^3 + 12x^2 - 3}$.

   (a) $\dfrac{-9x(x + 8)}{(x^3 + 12x^2 - 3)^4}$

   (b) $\dfrac{x(x - 8)}{(x^3 + 12x^2 - 3)^{2/3}}$

   (c) $1 + \dfrac{8}{\sqrt[3]{x}}$

   (d) $\dfrac{1}{3(3x^2 + 2x)^{2/3}}$

   (e) None of these

   1—Answer: b

5. Differentiate: $2(4 - 2x^4)^5$.

   (a) $10(-8x^3)^4$

   (b) $(4 - 2x^4)(-80x^3 + 1)$

   (c) $-80x^3(4 - 2x^4)^4$

   (d) $-80x^{12}$

   (e) None of these

   1—Answer: c

6. Find $f'(x)$ for $f(x) = (4 - x^2)^5$.

   (a) $80x^4$

   (b) $-10x(4 - x^2)^4$

   (c) $10x(x^2 - 4)^4$

   (d) $5(4 - x^2)^4$

   (e) None of these

   1—Answer: b

7. Differentiate: $y = 5(x^4 - 3x)^{-2}$.

   1—Answer: $\dfrac{-10(4x^3 - 3)}{(x^4 - 3x)^3}$

8. Differentiate: $y = 3(x^3 - 1)^4$.

   1—Answer: $36x^2(x^3 - 1)^3$

9. Differentiate: $x^3 \sqrt{x^2 - 4}$.

(a) $x^3(x - 2)$

(b) $\dfrac{4x^2(x^2 - 3)}{\sqrt{x^2 - 4}}$

(c) $\dfrac{x^4 + 3x \sqrt[2]{x^2 - 4}}{\sqrt{x^2 - 4}}$

(d) $\dfrac{6x^3}{\sqrt{x^2 - 4}}$

(e) None of these

1—Answer: b

10. Differentiate: $x^2(3 - 2x^2)^3$.

(a) $-36x^3(3 - 2x^3)$

(b) $3x^2(3 - 2x^2)^2$

(c) $2x(3 - 4x^2)$

(d) $2x(3 - 2x^2)^2(3 - 8x^2)$

(e) None of these

1—Answer: d

11. Differentiate: $\dfrac{3}{(1 - 4x^3)^2}$.

1—Answer: $\dfrac{72x^2}{(1 - 4x^3)^3}$

12. Differentiate: $\dfrac{2x}{\sqrt{4 + 3x}}$.

(a) $\dfrac{3x + 8}{(3x + 4)^{3/2}}$

(b) $\dfrac{5x + 8}{3x + 4}$

(c) $\dfrac{-2(6x^2 + 12x - 1)}{\sqrt{3x + 4}}$

(d) $\frac{4}{3}\sqrt{4 + 3x}$

(e) None of these

1—Answer: a

13. Differentiate: $\dfrac{2x + 1}{(1 - x^2)^3}$.

1—Answer: $\dfrac{2(5x^2 + 3x + 1)}{(1 - x^2)^4}$

14. Differentiate: $\dfrac{3x}{g(x)}$.

(a) $\dfrac{3}{g'(x)}$

(b) $\dfrac{3x}{g'(x)}$

(c) $\dfrac{3xg'(x) - 3g(x)}{(g(x))^2}$

(d) $\dfrac{3g(x) + 3xg'(x)}{(g(x))^2}$

(e) None of these

1—Answer: e

15. Find the derivative: $f(x) = \sqrt{4 - 3x + x^2}$.

(a) $\sqrt{2x - 3}$

(b) $\dfrac{1}{2\sqrt{4 - 3x + x^2}}$

(c) $\dfrac{2x - 3}{2\sqrt{4 - 3x + x^2}}$

(d) $\dfrac{1}{2\sqrt{2x - 3}}$

(e) None of these

1—**Answer:** c

16. Find the derivative: $f(x) = \sqrt{x^2 - 2x + 5}$.

(a) $\sqrt{2x - 2}$

(b) $\dfrac{1}{2\sqrt{x^2 - 2x + 5}}$

(c) $\dfrac{1}{2\sqrt{2x - 2}}$

(d) $\dfrac{x - 1}{\sqrt{x^2 - 2x + 5}}$

(e) None of these

1—**Answer:** d

17. Find the derivative of y with respect to x if $y = x^2\sqrt{2x - 5}$.

(a) $\dfrac{5x(x - 2)}{\sqrt{2x - 5}}$

(b) $\dfrac{x(x + 2)}{\sqrt{2x - 5}}$

(c) $\dfrac{x(9x - 20)}{2\sqrt{2x - 5}}$

(d) $\dfrac{2x}{\sqrt{2x - 5}}$

(e) None of these

1—**Answer:** a

18. Find $\dfrac{dy}{dx}$ for $y = x^3\sqrt{x + 1}$.

(a) $\dfrac{3x^2}{2\sqrt{x + 1}}$

(b) $\dfrac{x^2(7x + 6)}{2\sqrt{x + 1}}$

(c) $3x^2\sqrt{x + 1}$

(d) $\dfrac{7x^3 + x^2}{2\sqrt{x + 1}}$

(e) None of these

1—**Answer:** b

19. Find $\dfrac{dy}{dx}$ for $y = \sqrt{x}(3x - 1)$.

(a) $\dfrac{9x - 1}{2\sqrt{x}}$

(b) $\tfrac{9}{2}\sqrt{x} - 1$

(c) $3\sqrt{x}$

(d) $\dfrac{3}{2\sqrt{x}}$

(e) None of these

1—**Answer:** a

20. Find $\dfrac{dy}{dx}$ for $y = \sqrt{2x + 1}\,(x^3)$.

1—**Answer:** $\dfrac{x^2(7x + 3)}{\sqrt{2x + 1}}$

21. Find the derivative of $f(x) = -4(1 - x)^2 - 7(1 - x) + 3$.

(a) $8(1 - x) + 7$

(b) $-8(1 - x) + 7$

(c) $-8x + 8$

(d) $15(1 - x)$

(e) None of these

1—**Answer:** a

22. Find the derivative of $f(x) = 2(1 - x)^2 + 9(1 - x) + 6$.

    (a) $4(1 - x) - 9$ (b) $-13(1 - x)$ (c) $-4(1 - x) - 9$

    (d) $4x - 4$ (e) None of these

    1—Answer: c

23. Find the derivative of $f(x) = -8(1 - x)^2 + 7(1 - x) + 2$.

    (a) $-16x + 16$ (b) $16(1 - x) - 7$ (c) $9(1 - x)$

    (d) $-16(1 - x) - 7$ (e) None of these

    1—Answer: b

24. Find the slope of the equation of the tangent line to the curve $f(x) = \dfrac{2}{(3x - 1)^3}$ at the point $\left(1, \dfrac{1}{4}\right)$.

    1—T—Answer: $-\dfrac{9}{8}$

25. Find the slope of the equation of the tangent line to the curve $\dfrac{-1}{(3 - 2x^2)^3}$.

    (a) -1 (b) -12 (c) -4 (d) $\dfrac{\sqrt{6}}{2}$ (e) None of these

    1—T—Answer: b

26. Find an equation of the tangent line to the curve $y = \dfrac{x}{\sqrt{x - 2}}$ at the point $(3, 3)$.

    (a) $y = -\frac{1}{2}x + \frac{9}{2}$ (b) $y = 3x - 9$ (c) $y = -\frac{3}{2}x + \frac{9}{2}$

    (d) $y = -3x - \frac{9}{2}$ (e) None of these

    2—T—Answer: a

27. Find an equation of the tangent line to the curve $y = \dfrac{8x}{(3x - 1)^3}$ at the point $(1, 1)$.

    2—T—Answer: $y = -\frac{7}{2}x + \frac{9}{2}$

28. Find an equation of the tangent line to the graph of $f(x) = \sqrt{x + 1}$ at the point where $x = 3$.

    2—Answer: $x - 4y = -5$

29. A manufacturer determines that the revenue derived from selling x units of a certain product is given by $R = \dfrac{20x}{\sqrt{x - 1}}$. Find the marginal revenue when $x = 5$.

    2—Answer: $3.75

30. A manufacturer determines that the revenue derived from selling x units of a certain product is given by $R = 13\sqrt{8x + 1}$. Find the marginal revenue when $x = 21$.

2—**Answer:** \$4.00

31. A manufacturer determines that the revenue derived from selling x units of a certain item is given by $R = 300x - \sqrt{x^2 + 81}$. Find the marginal revenue when $x = 40$.

2—**Answer:** \$299.02

32. The revenue from selling a certain product is given by $R(x) = \dfrac{20x}{\sqrt{x - 1}}$. Find the marginal revenue when five units are sold.

2—T—**Answer:** \$3.75

33. The revenue from selling a certain product is given by $R(x) = 300x - \sqrt{x^2 + 81}$. Find the marginal revenue when 40 units are sold.

(a) \$119.59   (b) \$312.69   (c) \$299.02   (d) \$432.17   (e) None of these

2—T—**Answer:** c

34. The daily profit a company earns from producing x items is given by $P(x) = \sqrt{1200x - x^3}$. What is the marginal profit when the production level is 10 units per day?

(a) \$4.29   (b) \$17.01   (c) \$61.42   (d) \$104.89   (e) None of these

2—T—**Answer:** a

35. An assembly plant produces bushings to install in one of its products. The estimated cost per bushing over the next five years is given by $C = 4(1.52t + 10)^{1.5}$, where t is time in years. Find the rate of change of the cost per bushing for the fifth year.

2—T—**Answer:** \$38.26

36. Find the rate of change in the supply q of a product when the price p is \$150 and the supply function is given by $q = 10\sqrt{(p - 100)^2 + 25}$.

2—T—**Answer:** \$9.95

Section 2.6 Higher Order Derivatives

1. Find $\dfrac{d^2y}{dx^2}$ for $y = \dfrac{x+3}{x-1}$.

   (a) 0
   (b) $\dfrac{-8}{(x-1)^3}$
   (c) $\dfrac{-4}{(x-1)^3}$
   (d) $\dfrac{8}{(x-1)^3}$
   (e) None of these

   1—Answer: d

2. Find $\dfrac{d^2y}{dx^2}$ for $y = \dfrac{x+2}{x-3}$.

   (a) $\dfrac{10}{(x-3)^3}$
   (b) 0
   (c) $\dfrac{-10}{(x-3)^3}$
   (d) $\dfrac{2}{(x-3)^3}$
   (e) None of these

   1—Answer: a

3. Calculate $\dfrac{d^2y}{dx^2}$ if $y = \dfrac{1-x}{2-x}$.

   1—Answer: $\dfrac{-2}{(2-x)^3}$

4. Calculate $\dfrac{d^2y}{dx^2} : y = 2\sqrt{3-2x^3}$.

   (a) $2\sqrt{12x}$
   (b) $2\sqrt{-6x^2}$
   (c) $\dfrac{6x(x^3-6)}{(3-2x^3)^{3/2}}$
   (d) 0
   (e) None of these

   1—Answer: c

5. Find $f''(x) : f(x) = \dfrac{4}{\sqrt[3]{2-3x^2}}$.

   (a) $\dfrac{8(5x^2+2)}{(2-3x^2)^{7/3}}$
   (b) $\dfrac{-8x}{(2-3x^2)^{2/3}}$
   (c) $\dfrac{-8(x^2+2)}{(2-3x^2)^{5/3}}$
   (d) 0
   (e) None of these

   1—Answer: a

6. Find $f''(x) : f(x) = 4\sqrt[3]{2-3x^2}$.

   (a) 0
   (b) $\dfrac{-8(x^2+2)}{(2-3x^2)^{5/3}}$
   (c) $\dfrac{8x}{(2-3x^2)^{4/3}}$
   (d) $\dfrac{8(5x^2+2)}{(2-3x^2)^{7/3}}$
   (e) None of these

   1—Answer: b

7. Find $h''(x)$ if $h(x) = f(x)g'(x)$.

   1—Answer: $h''(x) = f(x)g'''(x) + 2f'(x)g''(x) + f''(x)g'(x)$

8. Find y''' : $y = 4x^5 + 2x^{-1}$.

(a) $240x^2 - \dfrac{12}{x^4}$ (b) $4x^2 + \dfrac{1}{x^4}$ (c) $240x^2$ (d) 0 (e) None of these

1—**Answer:** a

9. Find y''' : $y = 3x^3 - 2x^{-2}$.

(a) 0 (b) 18 (c) $18 + \dfrac{48}{x^5}$ (d) $\dfrac{1}{48x^5}$ (e) None of these

1—**Answer:** c

10. Find $f'''(x)$: $f(x) = 2x^4 - 3x^{-2} + 5$

(a) $24x^2 + 6$ (b) $48x$ (c) $48x + \dfrac{72}{x^5}$ (d) 0 (e) None of these

1—**Answer:** c

11. Find $f''(x)$: $f(x) = (1 + x^2)^3$.

1—**Answer:** $6(5x^2 + 1)(x^2 + 1)$

12. Find $f^{(4)}(x)$ if $f'(x) = \dfrac{2}{3x^2}$.

(a) $\dfrac{-16}{x^5}$ (b) 0 (c) $\dfrac{-12}{x}$ (d) $\dfrac{36}{x^3}$ (e) None of these

1—**Answer:** a

13. Find the second derivative of y with respect to x if $y = \dfrac{x - 5}{x + 3}$.

(a) $\dfrac{16}{(x + 3)^3}$ (b) $\dfrac{8}{(x + 3)^2}$ (c) $\dfrac{-16}{(x + 3)^4}$ (d) 0 (e) None of these

2—**Answer:** e

14. Find the second derivative of y with respect to x if $y = \dfrac{x^2 - 3}{x}$.

1—**Answer:** $\dfrac{-6}{x^3}$

15. Find $\dfrac{d^2y}{dx^2}$ if $y = \sqrt{x^2 + 1}$.

1—**Answer:** $\dfrac{1}{(x^2 + 1)^{3/2}}$

16. Find the second derivative of y with respect to x if $y = \dfrac{x + 3}{x - 4}$.

(a) $\dfrac{-14}{(x - 4)^3}$ (b) $\dfrac{-7}{(x - 4)^2}$ (c) $\dfrac{14}{(x - 4)^3}$ (d) 0   (e) None of these

2—Answer: c

17. If $f''(x) = 3x^2 + 6x + 4$, find $f^{(4)}(x)$.

(a) 0   (b) 6   (c) $6x + 6$ (d) None of these

1—Answer: b

18. If $f''(x) = 5x^2 + 9x + 8$, find $f^{(4)}(x)$.

(a) 10   (b) $10x + 9$ (c) 0   (d) None of these

1—Answer: a

19. If $f''(x) = -2x^2 + 7x - 2$, find $f^{(4)}(x)$.

(a) 0   (b) -4 (c) $-4x + 7$ (d) None of these

1—Answer: b

20. Solve the equation $f''(x) = 0$ for $f(x) = 2x^3 - 6x^2 + 10$.

(a) 1   (b) -7 (c) $\frac{1}{2}$ (d) 4   (e) None of these

1—Answer: a

21. Solve the equation $f''(x) = 0$ for $f(x) = \frac{1}{2}x^3 - 2x^2 + 4x$.

(a) $\frac{2}{3}$ (b) $\frac{4}{3}$ (c) 1   (d) -1 (e) None of these

1—Answer: b

22. Solve the equation $f''(x) = 0$ for $f(x) = (6x + 1)^{7/3}$.

(a) 0   (b) $-\frac{1}{216}$ (c) $\frac{56}{3}$ (d) $-\frac{1}{6}$ (e) None of these

1—Answer: d

23. Evaluate $f''(x)$ at $x = 6$: $f(x) = \frac{1}{12}x^4 + x^2 - 1$.

(a) 2   (b) 84   (c) 38   (d) ± 2 (e) None of these

2—Answer: c

24. Evaluate $f''(x)$ at $x = 0$: $f(x) = \frac{1}{4}x^4 - 6x^2 + 4x$.

(a) -12 (b) 0   (c) ± 2 (d) -8 (e) None of these

2—Answer: a

25. Evaluate $f''(x)$ at $x = 2$: $f(x) = \frac{1}{3}x^3 + 5x^2 - 1$.

  (a) $\pm\dfrac{\sqrt{5}}{2}$ (b) 24   (c) 14   (d) -4 (e) None of these

  2—Answer: c

26. $f(x)$ is a polynomial function. Compare the graphs in a, b, c, and d. One of them is the graph of $f(x)$, one of $f'(x)$, one of $f''(x)$ and one of $f'''(x)$. Which is the graph of $f(x)$, of $f'(x)$, of $f''(x)$ and of $f'''(x)$? How did you determine this?

(a)

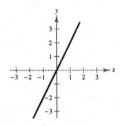

(b)

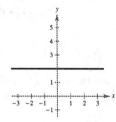

(c)

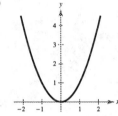

(d)

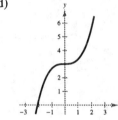

  2—Answer: (a) $f''(x)$ (b) $f'''(x)$ (c) $f'(x)$ (d) $f(x)$

           In general, the degree of the successive derivatives of a polynomial function decreases by one. For $f'''(x)$ to be a constant function, $f(x)$ would have to be cubic (d), $f'(x)$ a quadratic (c), and $f''(x)$ a linear function.

27. An object is propelled straight up from the ground level with an initial velocity of 216 ft/sec.

  (a) Write the position function of the object.

  (b) Find the velocity function.

  (c) Find the acceleration.

  1—Answer: (a) $s(t) = -16t^2 + 216t$

             (b) $v(t) = s'(t) = -32t + 216$

             (c) $a(t) = s''(t) = -32$

28. The position equation for the movement of a particle is given by $s = (t^2 - 1)^3$ when s is measured in feet and t is measured in seconds. Find the acceleration at two seconds.

    (a) 342 units/sec^2 (b) 18 units/sec^2 (c) 288 units/sec^2

    (d) 90 units/sec^2 (e) None of these

    2—Answer: a

29. A particle moves along the curve given by $y = \sqrt{x^3 + 1}$. Find the acceleration at 2 seconds.

    (a) 3 units/sec^2 (b) $\frac{2}{3}$ units/sec^2 (c) $-\frac{1}{108}$ units/sec^2

    (d) $-\frac{1}{9}$ units/sec^2 (e) None of these

    2—Answer: b

30. The position equation for the movement of a particle is given by $s = (t^3 + 1)^2$ where s is measured in feet and t is measured in seconds. Find the acceleration of this particle at 1 second.

    2—Answer: 42 ft/sec^2

Section 2.7 Implicit Differentiation

1. Find y' if $y^2 - 3xy + x^2 = 7$.

(a) $\dfrac{2x + y}{3x - 2y}$ (b) $\dfrac{3y - 2x}{2y - 3x}$ (c) $\dfrac{2x}{3 - 2y}$ (d) $\dfrac{2x}{y}$ (e) None of these

1—Answer: b

2. Find y' if $x^2 + y^2 = 2xy$.

(a) $\dfrac{x}{1 - y}$ (b) $\dfrac{y + x}{y - x}$ (c) 1   (d) $-\dfrac{x}{y}$ (e) None of these

1—Answer: c

3. Find y' if $y = \dfrac{x}{x + y}$.

1—Answer: $\dfrac{y}{(x + y)^2 + x}$

4. Find $\dfrac{dy}{dx}$ for $2x^2 + xy + 3y^2 = 0$.

(a) $-\dfrac{4x + y}{x + 6y}$ (b) $-\dfrac{4x + y}{6y}$ (c) $4x + y + 6y$ (d) $\dfrac{4x + 6y}{-x}$ (e) None of these

1—Answer: a

5. Find $\dfrac{dy}{dx}$ for $5x^2 - 2xy + 7y^2 = 0$.

(a) $\dfrac{10x + 14y}{2x}$ (b) $-\dfrac{10x - 2y}{14y}$ (c) $10x - 2y + 14y$

(d) $-\dfrac{10x - 2y}{-2x + 14y}$ (e) None of these

1—Answer: d

6. Find $\dfrac{dy}{dx}$ for $7x^2 + 6xy + 9y^2 = 0$.

(a) $-\dfrac{14x + 6y}{18y}$ (b) $-\dfrac{14x + 6y}{6x + 18y}$ (c) $\dfrac{14x + 18y}{-6x}$

(d) $14x + 6y + 18y$ (e) None of these

1—Answer: b

7. Find $\dfrac{dy}{dx}$ if $xy^2 - y = x^2$.

    (a) $\dfrac{2x - y^2}{2xy - 1}$ (b) $\dfrac{2x}{2y - 1}$ (c) $2x - y^2$ (d) y (e) None of these

    1—Answer: a

8. Use implicit differentiation to get $\dfrac{dy}{dx}$ for $x^2 + xy + y^2 = 5$.

    1—Answer: $\dfrac{-2x - y}{x + 2y}$

9. Find $\dfrac{dy}{dx}$ if $x\sqrt{y} + y^2 = x$.

    1—Answer: $\dfrac{2\sqrt{y} - 2y}{2y\sqrt{y} + x}$

10. Find $\dfrac{dy}{dx}$ if $x^2y + y^2 = x$.

    (a) $\dfrac{1}{2x + 2y}$ (b) $\dfrac{1 - 2xy - 2y}{x^2}$ (c) $\dfrac{1 - 2xy}{x^2 + 2y}$ (d) $\dfrac{1}{x}$ (e) None of these

    1—Answer: c

11. Find y' for $xy^2 + y = x^2$.

    (a) $\dfrac{2x - y^2}{2xy + 1}$ (b) $\dfrac{2x}{2y + 1}$ (c) $2x - y^2$ (d) y (e) None of these

    1—Answer: a

12. Use implicit differentiation to find $\dfrac{dy}{dx}$: $x^2 + xy + y^2 = 5$.

    1—Answer: $\dfrac{-2x - y}{x + 2y}$

13. Find y' for $x^2y + y^2 = x$.

    (a) $\dfrac{1}{2x + 2y}$ (b) $\dfrac{1 - 2xy - 2y}{x^2}$ (c) $\dfrac{1 - 2xy}{x^2 + 2y}$ (d) $\dfrac{1}{x}$ (e) None of these

    1—Answer: c

14. Find $\dfrac{dy}{dx}$ for the equation $x^3 - 2x^2y + 3xy^2 = 38$.

    1—Answer: $\dfrac{3x^2 - 4xy + 3y^2}{2x^2 - 6xy}$

15. Find $\dfrac{dy}{dx}$ for the equation $x^3 - 2x^2y + 4xy^2 = 20$.

1—Answer: $\dfrac{3x^2 - 4xy + 4y^2}{2x^2 - 8xy}$

16. Find $\dfrac{dy}{dx}$, then evaluate the derivative at the point $(0, 2)$: $x^2 - 2xy = y^2 - 4$.

(a) -1 (b) 3 (c) 1 (d) $\frac{1}{2}$ (e) None of these

1—Answer: a

17. Find $\dfrac{dy}{dx}$, then evaluate the derivative at the point $(0, 2)$: $x^2 - 2xy^2 = y^3 - 8$.

(a) 1 (b) $-\frac{5}{4}$ (c) $\frac{2}{3}$ (d) -1 (e) None of these

1—Answer: c

18. Find $\dfrac{dy}{dx}$, then evaluate the derivative at the point $(0, 2)$: $5x^2 - 3xy + y = 2$.

(a) -2 (b) $-\frac{5}{4}$ (c) 0 (d) 6 (e) None of these

1—Answer: d

19. Find $\dfrac{dy}{dx}$, then evaluate the derivative at the point $(0, 0)$: $2x - 5x^3y^2 + 4y = 0$.

(a) 3 (b) $-\frac{1}{2}$ (c) undefined   (d) 6 (e) None of these

1—Answer: b

20. Find $\dfrac{dy}{dx}$, then evaluate the derivative at the point $(1, -1)$: $x^4 + 4x^2y^3 + y^2 = 2y$.

(a) 3 (b) 0 (c) undefined   (d) $\frac{1}{2}$ (e) None of these

1—Answer: d

21. Find $\dfrac{dy}{dx}$, then evaluate the derivative at the point $(0, -2)$: $x^2 - y^2 - 2x - 4y - 4 = 0$.

(a) 3 (b) 0 (c) undefined   (d) $\frac{1}{2}$ (e) None of these

1—Answer: c

22. Find the slope of the line tangent to the graph of $4y^2 - xy = 3$ at the point $(-1, -1)$.

(a) $\frac{2}{3}$ (b) $\frac{1}{7}$ (c) 0 (d) undefined (e) None of these

1—Answer: b

23. Find the slope of the line tangent to the graph of $4y^2 - xy = 3$ at the point $\left(-1, \frac{3}{4}\right)$.

(a) $\frac{3}{28}$ (b) $\frac{1}{7}$ (c) $\frac{4}{71}$ (d) undefined (e) None of these

1—Answer: a

24. Find the slope of the line tangent to the graph of $y^3 - 2xy^2 = x^2$ at the point $(-1, -1)$.

(a) $\frac{3}{28}$ (b) $\frac{4}{71}$ (c) undefined (d) 0 (e) None of these

1—Answer: d

25. Find the slope of the curve $y^4 - xy^2 = x$ at the point $\left(\frac{1}{2}, 1\right)$.

1—Answer: $\frac{2}{3}$

26. Find an equation of the tangent line to the graph of $x^2 + 2y^2 = 3$ at the point $(1, 1)$.

(a) $y - 1 = -\frac{x}{zy}(x - 1)$ (b) $y + 1 = -\frac{1}{2}(x + 1)$ (c) $y - 1 = \frac{1}{2}(x - 1)$

(d) $x + 2y = 3$ (e) None of these

2—Answer: d

27. Find an equation of the tangent line to the graph of $x^2 + 3y^2 = 4$ at the point $(1, 1)$.

(a) $y + 1 = -\frac{1}{3}(x + 1)$ (b) $y - 1 = \frac{x}{3y}(x - 1)$ (c) $x + 3y = 2$

(d) $y - 1 = -\frac{1}{3}(x - 1)$ (e) None of these

2—Answer: d

28. Find an equation of the line tangent to the curve $x^2 + y^2 = 9$ at the point $(3, 0)$.

(a) $x = -1$ (b) $x = 3$ (c) $y = 0$ (d) $y = x - 3$ (e) None of these

2—Answer: b

29. Find an equation of the tangent to the curve $2x^2 - y^2 = 1$ at the point $(5, 7)$.

2—Answer: $y = \frac{10}{7}x - \frac{1}{7}$

30. Find an equation of the tangent to the curve $2y^2 - x^2 = 1$ at the point $(7, -5)$.

2—Answer: $y = -\frac{7}{10}x - \frac{17}{2}$

31. The demand for a certain product is given by $x^3 + p^3 = 1200$. Find the rate of change of price when $x = 5$ units.

   1—Answer: -0.2382

32. The air pollution y (in parts per million) x miles away from the source is given by $y + 2xy + x^2y = 600$. Find the rate of pollution 10 miles away from the source.

   (a) 3.0924 parts per million   (b) -0.9016 parts per million   (c) 1.0020 parts per million

   (d) -1.997 parts per million   (e) None of these

   1—Answer: b

33. In a complete sentence, explain the difference between an explicit function and an implicit function.

   1—Answer: Answers will vary.

Section 2.8   Related Rates

1. Assume x and y are both differentiable functions of t. Find $\dfrac{dy}{dt}$ given $x = 3$ and $\dfrac{dx}{dt} = 2 : y = x^2 + 5x$.

   (a) 11   (b) 22   (c) 6   (d) $\frac{1}{2}$ (e) None of these

   1—Answer: b

2. Assume x and y are both differentiable functions of t. Find $\dfrac{dy}{dt}$ given $x = 5$ and $\dfrac{dx}{dt} = 2 : y = x^2 - x$.

   (a) 15   (b) $\frac{9}{2}$ (c) 9   (d) 18   (e) None of these

   1—Answer: d

3. Assume x and y are both differentiable functions of t. Find $\dfrac{dy}{dt}$ given $x = 2$ and $\dfrac{dx}{dt} = 6 : 2x^2 - y^3 = 16$.

   (a) -4 (b) $\frac{2}{3}$ (c) $\frac{1}{9}$ (d) 4   (e) None of these

   1—Answer: d

4. Assume x and y are both differentiable functions of t. Find $\dfrac{dy}{dt}$ given $x = 2$ and $\dfrac{dx}{dt} = 9 : x^2 - 3y^3 = 1$.

   (a) $\frac{35}{9}$ (b) 4   (c) $\frac{2}{9}$ (d) $\frac{4}{81}$ (e) None of these

   1—Answer: b

5. Assume x and y are both differentiable functions of t. Find $\dfrac{dx}{dt}$ given $x = 2$ and $\dfrac{dy}{dt} = 60 : y = 3x^3 - 6x + 4$.

   (a) 2   (b) 4   (c) 30   (d) $\frac{1}{2}$ (e) None of these

   1—Answer: a

6. Assume x and y are both differentiable functions of t. Find $\dfrac{dx}{dt}$ given $x = 9$ and $\dfrac{dy}{dt} = 8 : y = 4\sqrt{x}$.

   (a) -24 (b) 6   (c) 12   (d) $\frac{2}{3}$ (e) None of these

   1—Answer: c

7. Assume x and y are both differentiable functions of t. Find $\dfrac{dx}{dt}$ given $y = -1$ and $\dfrac{dy}{dt} = 12 : 2x^3 + y^2 = 3$.

   1—Answer: $\dfrac{dx}{dt} = 4$

8. Assume x and y are both differentiable functions of t. Find $\dfrac{dx}{dt}$ given $y = 1$ and $\dfrac{dy}{dt} = \dfrac{1}{9} : 3x^2 + 2y^3 = 57$.

   (a) -1 (b) $\frac{1}{3}$ (c) 6   (d) -54 (e) None of these

   1—Answer: a

9. A point moves along the curve $y = 2x^2 + 1$ in such a way that the y value is decreasing at the rate of 2 units per second. At what rate is x changing when $x = \frac{3}{2}$?

   1—Answer: Decreasing at 6 units/sec

10. A particle moves on the curve $y = \dfrac{4}{3 - x^2}$ such that $\dfrac{dy}{dt} = 6$. Find the instantaneous rate of change of x with respect to t when $x = 5$.

    1—T—Answer: 72.6

11. A particle moves on the curve $y = \dfrac{3}{x^2 + 4}$ such that $\dfrac{dy}{dt} = 6$. Find the instantaneous rate of change of x with respect to t when $x = 2$.

    (a) -128 (b) -32 (c) 32   (d) 128   (e) None of these

    1—Answer: b

12. A point moves along the curve $y = \dfrac{-x^2 + 4x - 3}{10}$ so that the y value is decreasing at a rate of 3 units per second. Find the instantaneous rate of change of x with respect to time at the point on the curve where $x = 5$.

    1—Answer: 5 units/sec

13. The side of a square is increasing at the rate of 2 ft/min. Find the rate at which the area is increasing when the side is 7 feet.

    (a) 28 ft²/min   (b) 49 ft²/min   (c) 14 ft²/min   (d) 28π ft²/min   (e) None of these

    2—Answer: a

14. A machine is rolling a metal cylinder under pressure. The radius of the cylinder is decreasing at a constant rate of 0.05 inches per second and the volume V is 128π cubic inches. At what rate is the length h changing when the radius r is 1.8 inches? [Hint: $V = \pi r^2 h$]

    (a) -2.195 in./sec   (b) 39.51 in./sec   (c) 2.195 in./sec

    (d) -43.90 in./sec   (e) None of these

    1—Answer: c

15. A machine is rolling a metal cylinder under pressure. The radius of the cylinder is decreasing at a constant rate of 0.05 inches per second and the volume V is 128π cubic inches. At what rate is the length h changing when the radius r is 2.5 inches? [Hint: $V = \pi r^2 h$]

(a) 20.48 in./sec   (b) -0.8192 in./sec   (c) -16.38 in./sec

(d) 0.8192 in./sec   (e) None of these

1—Answer: d

16. A machine is rolling a metal cylinder under pressure. The radius of the cylinder is decreasing at a constant rate of 0.05 inches per second and the volume V is 128π cubic inches. At what rate is the length h changing when the radius r is 1.5 inches? [Hint: $V = \pi r^2 h$]

(a) -75.85 in./sec   (b) 56.89 in./sec   (c) 3.793 in./sec

(d) -3.793 in./sec   (e) None of these

1—Answer: c

17. As a balloon in the shape of a sphere is being blown up, the volume is increasing at the rate of 4 in³/sec. At what rate is the radius increasing when the radius is 1 in.?

1—Answer: $\dfrac{1}{\pi}$ in./sec

18. The radius of a circle is increasing at the rate of 5 inches per minute. At what rate is the area increasing when the radius is 10 inches?

1—Answer: 100π in.²/min

19. Sand is falling off a conveyor onto a conical pile at the rate of 15 cubic feet per minute. The diameter of the base of the cone is approximately twice the altitude. At what rate is the height of the pile changing when it is 10 feet high?

1—T—Answer: 0.04775 ft/min

20. A spherical balloon is inflated at the rate of 16 cubic feet per minute. How fast is the radius of the balloon changing at the instant the radius is 2 feet?

(a) 4π ft/min   (b) $\dfrac{32}{3}\pi$ ft/min   (c) $\dfrac{1}{\pi}$ ft/min   (d) 2π ft/min   (e) None of these

2—Answer: c

21. A spherical balloon is inflated at the rate of 12 cubic feet per minute. How fast is the radius of the balloon changing at the instant the radius is 3 feet?

(a) $\dfrac{1}{3\pi}$ ft/min   (b) $\dfrac{3}{\pi}$ ft/min   (c) 27π ft/min   (d) 3π ft/min   (e) None of these

2—Answer: a

22. A metal cube contracts when it is cooled. If the edge of the cube is decreasing at a rate of 0.2 cm/hr, how fast is the volume changing when the edge is 60 cm?

2—T—Answer: -36.0 cm^3/hr

23. A 5–meter–long ladder is leaning against the side of a house. The foot of the ladder is pulled away from the house at a rate of 0.4 m/sec. Determine the rate of change of the position of the top of the ladder when the foot of the ladder is 3 meters from the house.

   (a) 1.2 m/sec.   (b) -1.2 m/sec.   (c) 0.3 m/sec.   (d) -0.3 m/sec.   (e) None of these

1—Answer: d

24. Two boats leave the same port at the same time with one boat traveling north at 15 knots per hour and the other traveling west at 12 knots per hour. How fast is the distance between the two boats changing after 2 hours?

   (a) 19.2 knots/hr   (b) 26.8 knots/hr   (c) 17.7 knots/hr

   (d) 38.4 knots/hr   (e) None of these

2—Answer: a

25. Two boats leave the same port at the same time with one boat traveling north at 35 knots per hour and the other traveling east at 40 knots per hour. How fast is the distance between the two boats changing after 2 hours?

   (a) 106.4 knots/hr   (b) 429.4 knots/hr   (c) 53.2 knots/hr

   (d) 57.9 knots/hr   (e) None of these

2—Answer: c

26. The area of a circle is decreasing at a rate of 2 square centimeters/minute. Find the rate of change of the radius with respect to time when the radius is 4 cm.

   (a) $\dfrac{1}{4\pi}$ cm/min   (b) $-\dfrac{1}{8\pi}$ cm/min   (c) $-\dfrac{1}{2\pi}$ cm/min   (d) $-\dfrac{1}{4\pi}$ cm/min   (e) None of these

2—Answer: e

27. The height of a cylinder with a radius of 4 cm is increasing at a rate of 2 cm/min. Find the rate of change of the volume of the cylinder with respect to time when the height is 10 cm.

   (a) 16π cm^3/min   (b) $\dfrac{1}{16\pi}$ cm^3/min   (c) $\dfrac{5}{8\pi}$ cm^3/min   (d) 160π cm^3/min   (e) None of these

2—Answer: e

28. The radius of a circle is increasing at the rate of 2 ft/min. Find the rate at which the area is increasing when the radius is 7 feet.

   (a) 28 ft^2/min   (b) 49π ft^2/min   (c) 14π ft^2/min   (d) 28π ft^2/min   (e) None of these

2—Answer: d

29. The profit for a product is increasing at a rate of $4000 per month. Find the rate of change of sales with respect to time when the monthly sales are $x = 300$ units, if profit is given by $P = 178x - 0.01x^2 - 200$.

    2—Answer: 23 units/month

30. The profit for a product is increasing at a rate of $5000 per month. Find the rate of change of sales with respect to time when the monthly sales are $x = 300$ units, if profit is given by $P = 178x - 0.01x^2 - 200$.

    (a) 23 units/month   (b) 29 units/month   (c) 35 units/month

    (d) 41 units/month   (e) None of these

    2—Answer: b

31. A company is increasing its production of a certain product at the rate of 50 units per week. The weekly demand function is given by

    $$p = 100 - \frac{x}{1000}.$$

    Find the rate of change of the revenue with respect to time (in weeks) when the weekly production is 1500.

    1—Answer: $4850.00/week

32. A company is increasing its production of a certain product at the rate of 100 units per month. The monthly demand function is given by

    $$p = 100 - \frac{x}{800}.$$

    Find the rate of change of the revenue with respect to time (in months) when the monthly production is 4000.

    1—Answer: $9000.00/month

CHAPTER 3
Applications of the Derivative

Section 3.1 Increasing and Decreasing Functions

1. Find all critical numbers: $f(x) = \dfrac{x - 1}{x + 3}$.

    (a) 1   (b) $1, -3$ (c) -3 (d) $1, -1$ (e) None of these

    1—Answer: e

2. Find all critical numbers: $f(x) = (9 - x^2)^{3/5}$.

    (a) 0   (b) 3   (c) $-3, 3$ (d) $-3, 0, 3$ (e) None of these

    1—Answer: d

3. Find all critical numbers: $f(x) = x\sqrt{2x + 1}$.

    1—Answer: $-\dfrac{1}{3}, -\dfrac{1}{2}$

4. Find the critical numbers of $f(x) = 3x^4 - 4x^3$.

    1—Answer: $x = 0, 1$

5. Find the critical numbers of $f(x) = x^3 - 12x^2$.

    1—Answer: $x = 0, x = 8$

6. Find all critical numbers for $f(x) = 5\sqrt[3]{4 - x^2}$.

    (a) 0   (b) $-2, 2$ (c) $-2, 0, 2$ (d) 2   (e) None of these

    1—Answer: c

7. Find all critical numbers for $f(x) = \dfrac{x^2 - 1}{x^3}$.

    (a) 0   (b) $-\sqrt{3}, 0, \sqrt{3}$ (c) $-\sqrt{3}, \sqrt{3}$ (d) $-1, 1$ (e) None of these

    1—Answer: b

8. Find all critical numbers for the function $f(x) = x + \dfrac{36}{x}$.

    1—Answer: $6, -6$

9. Find all critical numbers: $2x\sqrt{x-5}$.

   (a) $\frac{10}{3}, 5$ (b) $1, 5$ (c) -2 (d) $0, 5$ (e) None of these

   1—Answer: a

10. Find all critical numbers: $6x\sqrt[3]{x+1}$.

   (a) $0, -1$ (b) $3, -1$ (c) $-1, -\frac{3}{4}$ (d) 3 (e) None of these

   1—Answer: c

11. Find all critical numbers: $f(x) = x^3 - 3x^2$.

   (a) -2 (b) $0, 3$ (c) $0, 2$ (d) $0, 2, 3$ (e) None of these

   1—Answer: c

12. Find all critical numbers: $f(x) = 3x^2 + 5x - 2$.

   (a) $\frac{1}{3}, -2$ (b) $-\frac{5}{6}$ (c) $-\frac{1}{3}, 2$ (d) $-\frac{6}{5}$ (e) None of these

   1—Answer: b

13. Find all critical numbers: $5x^2 + x - 18$.

   (a) $-\frac{1}{10}$ (b) -10 (c) $\frac{9}{5}, -2$ (d) $-\frac{9}{5}, 2$ (e) None of these

   1—Answer: a

14. Find all intervals on which $y = \dfrac{x-1}{x^2+3}$ is increasing.

   (a) $(-1, 3)$ (b) $(3, \infty)$ (c) $(-\infty, -1)$ (d) $(-3, 1)$ (e) None of these

   1—Answer: a

15. Find all intervals on which $y = f(x) = \dfrac{x+1}{x^2+3}$ is increasing.

   1—Answer: $(-3, 1)$

16. Find all open intervals on which $f(x) = \dfrac{x^2}{x^2+4}$ is decreasing.

   (a) $(0, \infty)$ (b) $(-2, 2)$ (c) $(-\infty, 0)$ (d) $(-\infty, \infty)$ (e) None of these

   1—Answer: c

17. Find all open intervals on which the function $f(x) = \sqrt[3]{x^2 - 1}$ is decreasing.

   1—Answer: $(-\infty, 0)$

18. Find all open intervals on which the function is increasing: $f(x) = 2x\sqrt{4-x}$.

　1—T—Answer: $\left(-\infty, \frac{8}{3}\right)$

19. Find all open intervals on which the function is increasing: $f(x) = (3x + 1)\sqrt[3]{x + 2}$.

　(a) $\left(-2, \frac{1}{3}\right)$　　(b) $(-2.8, -1.58)$　(c) $(-1.58, \infty)$　　(d) $(-2.8, \infty)$　　(e) None of these

　1—T—Answer: c

20. Find all open intervals on which the function is decreasing: $f(x) = \dfrac{x^2}{x^2 - 9}$.

　(a) $(-3, 3)$　　　　　　　(b) $(0, \infty)$　　　　　　　(c) $(-\infty, -3), (3, \infty)$

　(d) $(0, 3), (3, \infty)$　　　　(e) None of these

　1—T—Answer: d

21. Find all open intervals on which the function is increasing: $f(x) = 3x\sqrt{x + 2}$.

　1—Answer: $\left(-\frac{4}{3}, \infty\right)$

22. Find all open intervals on which the function is decreasing: $f(x) = 3x\sqrt{2 - x}$.

　1—T—Answer: $\left(-\infty, \frac{4}{3}\right)$

23. Find all open intervals on which $f(x) = \dfrac{x}{x^2 + x - 2}$ is decreasing.

　(a) $(-\infty, \infty)$　　　　　　　(b) $(-\infty, 0)$

　(c) $(-\infty, -2)$ and $(1, \infty)$　　　(d) $(-\infty, -2), (-2, 1)$ and $(1, \infty)$

　(e) None of these

　1—Answer: d

24. Find the open intervals on which $f(x) = \dfrac{1}{x^2}$ is increasing or decreasing.

　1—Answer: Increasing: $(-\infty, 0)$; Decreasing: $(0, \infty)$

25. Find the open intervals on which $f(x) = x^3 - 3x^2$ is increasing or decreasing.

　1—Answer: Increasing: $(-8, 0)$ and $(2, \infty)$; Decreasing: $(0, 2)$

26. Find the open intervals on which $f(x) = x^2 - 2x$ is increasing or decreasing.

　1—Answer: Increasing: $(1, \infty)$; Decreasing: $(-\infty, 1)$

27. Find all open intervals on which the function is increasing: $f(x) = \begin{cases} x^2 + 3x + 2, & x \le 0 \\ x + 2, & x > 0 \end{cases}$.

    1—Answer: $\left(-\frac{3}{2}, \infty\right)$

28. Find all open intervals on which the function is increasing: $f(x) = \begin{cases} 3 - 2x^2, & x < 1 \\ 3x - 2, & x \ge 1 \end{cases}$.

    1—T—Answer: $(-\infty, 0), (1, \infty)$

29. Find all open intervals on which the function is increasing: $f(x) = \begin{cases} 7 - x^2, & x < 3 \\ 2x - 8, & x \ge 3 \end{cases}$.

    (a) $(-\infty, 0), (3, \infty)$ (b) $(-\infty, 7), (-2, \infty)$ (c) $(0, 2)$

    (d) $(-\infty, \infty)$ (e) None of these

    1—T—Answer: a

30. Which of the following statements is true of $f(x) = -x^3 - 6x^2 - 9x - 2$?

    (a) f is decreasing on $(-3, -1)$ (b) f is increasing on $(-3, -1)$

    (c) f is increasing on $(-\infty, -3)$ (d) f is increasing on $(-2, \infty)$

    (e) None of these

    1—Answer: b

31. Which of the following statements is true of $f(x) = -x^3 + 18x^2 - 105x + 198$?

    (a) f is decreasing on $(6, \infty)$ (b) f is decreasing on $(5, 7)$

    (c) f is increasing on $(-\infty, 5)$ (d) f is increasing on $(5, 7)$

    (e) None of these

    1—Answer: d

32. Which of the following statements is true of $f(x) = -x^3 + 9x^2 - 24x + 18$?

    (a) f is decreasing on $(2, 4)$ (b) f is increasing on $(3, \infty)$

    (c) f is increasing on $(2, 4)$ (d) f is increasing on $(-\infty, 2)$

    (e) None of these

    1—Answer: c

33. Suppose the total cost of producing a shipment of a certain product is

$$C = 50x + \frac{1000}{x},$$

where x is the number of machines used in production. Over what interval does the cost decrease and over what interval does the cost increase?

    2—T—Answer: Decreasing on $(0, 10)$ and increasing on $(10, \infty)$

Section 3.2   Extrema and the First-Derivative Test

1. Find the absolute maximum and absolute minimum of f on $(0, 3]$. $f(x) = \dfrac{x^3 - 4x^2 + 7x}{x}$.

   (a) Maximum: None; Minimum: $(3, 4)$ (b) Maximum: $(0, 7)$; Minimum: $(3, 4)$

   (c) Maximum: None; Minimum: $(2, 3)$ (d) Maximum: $(0, 7)$; Minimum: $(2, 3)$

   (e) None of these

   2—Answer: c

2. Find the absolute maximum and absolute minimum of f on $(-1, 2]$. $f(x) = \dfrac{x^3 - x^2 - 3x - 1}{x + 1}$.

   (a) Maximum: $(-1, 2)$; Minimum: $(2, -1)$ (b) Maximum: None; Minimum: $(1, -2)$

   (c) Maximum: $(-1, 2)$; Minimum: $(1, -2)$ (d) Maximum: None; Minimum: $(2, -1)$

   (e) None of these

   2—Answer: b

3. Find the absolute maximum and absolute minimum of f on $(1, 4]$. $f(x) = \dfrac{x^3 - 7x^2 + 12x - 6}{x - 1}$.

   (a) Maximum: None; Minimum: $(3, -3)$ (b) Maximum: $(1, 1)$; Minimum: $(4, -2)$

   (c) Maximum: $(1, 1)$; Minimum: $(3, -3)$ (d) Maximum: None; Minimum: $(4, -2)$

   (e) None of these

   2—Answer: a

4. Find the absolute maximum and absolute minimum of f on $(-4, -1]$. $f(x) = \dfrac{x^3 + 8x^2 + 19x + 12}{x + 4}$.

   (a) Maximum: None; Minimum: $(-2, -1)$ (b) Maximum: $(-4, 3)$; Minimum: $(-1, 0)$

   (c) Maximum: $(-4, 3)$; Minimum: $(-2, -1)$ (d) Maximum: None; Minimum: $(-1, 0)$

   (e) None of these

   2—Answer: a

5. Find the absolute minimum and absolute maximum for $f(x) = \dfrac{10}{(x^2 + 1)}$ on the interval $[-1, 2]$.

   2—Answer: Maximum at $(0, 10)$; Minimum at $(2, 2)$

6. Find the absolute minimum and absolute maximum values of $f(x) = x^2 - 2x + 1$ on the interval $[0, 3]$.

   2—Answer: Minimum at $(1, 0)$; Maximum at $(3, 4)$

7. Find the absolute extrema on the interval $[0, 2]$: $f(x) = \dfrac{2x}{x^2 + 1}$.

(a) Maximum: $(1, 1)$; Minimum: $(0, 0)$

(b) Maximum: $(1, 3)$; Minimum: $(0, 1)$

(c) Maximum: $\left(2, \frac{4}{5}\right)$; Minimum: $(-1, -1)$

(d) Maximum: $\left(2, \frac{4}{5}\right)$; Minimum: $(0, 0)$

(e) None of these

1—Answer: a

8. Find the absolute extrema on the interval $\left[\dfrac{3}{2}, 2\right]$: $f(x) = \dfrac{2x}{x^2 - 1}$.

1—Answer: Maximum: $\left(\frac{3}{2}, \frac{12}{5}\right)$; Minimum: $\left(2, \frac{4}{3}\right)$

9. Find the absolute extrema on the interval $[-1, 0]$: $f(x) = \frac{2}{3}x^3 - \frac{9}{2}x^2 - 5x + 2$.

(a) Maximum: $\left(-\frac{1}{2}, 5\right)$; Minimum: $(0, 0)$

(b) Maximum: $(0, 2)$; Minimum: $\left(-1, \frac{11}{6}\right)$

(c) Maximum: $\left(-1, \frac{11}{6}\right)$; Minimum: $\left(5, -\frac{313}{6}\right)$

(d) Maximum: $\left(-\frac{1}{2}, \frac{79}{24}\right)$; Minimum: $(0, 2)$

(e) None of these

1—Answer: d

10. Find the absolute minimum of the function on the interval $[-1, 0]$: $f(x) = \frac{2}{3}x^3 - \frac{9}{2}x^2 - 5x + 2$.

1—Answer: $(0, 2)$

11. Use a graphing utility to find the absolute extrema of the function on the closed interval $[0, 2]$: $y = 0.3x^3 - 0.7x^2 - 1$.

1—T—Answer: Maximum: $(0, -1)$; Minimum $(1.6, -1.6)$

12. Use a graphing utility to find the absolute extrema of the function on the closed interval $[-1, 1]$: $y = 0.3x^3 - 0.7x^2 - 1$.

(a) Maximum: $(0, -1)$; Minimum: $(1, -1.4)$

(b) Maximum: $(0, -1)$; Minimum: $(1.6, -1.6)$

(c) Maximum: $(1, 1.4)$; Minimum: $(-1, -2)$

(d) Maximum: $(0, -1)$; Minimum: $(-1, -2)$

(e) None of these

1—T—Answer: d

13. Use a graphing utility to find the absolute extrema of the function on the closed interval $[-1, 1]$: $f(x) = -0.2x^5 + 0.9x^2 - 4$.

1—T—Answer: Maximum: $(-1, -2.9)$; Minimum: $(0, -4)$

14. Find all relative extrema: $f(x) = 2x^3 + x^2 - 4x + 3$.

(a) Relative minimum: $(1, 2)$; Relative maximum: $\left(-\frac{3}{2}, \frac{9}{2}\right)$

(b) Relative minimum: $(-1.9, 0)$; Relative maximum: $(-1, 6)$

(c) Relative minimum: $\left(\frac{2}{3}, \frac{37}{27}\right)$; Relative maximum: $(-1, 6)$

(d) Relative minimum: $(-2, -1)$; Relative maximum: $\left(-1, \frac{50}{37}\right)$

(e) None of these

1—Answer: c

15. Find all relative extrema: $f(x) = \frac{2x^3}{3} + \frac{3x^2}{2} - 2x - 1$.

(a) Relative minimum: $\left(-\frac{1}{2}, \frac{7}{24}\right)$; Relative maximum: $\left(2, \frac{19}{3}\right)$

(b) Relative minimum: $\left(\frac{1}{2}, -\frac{37}{24}\right)$; Relative maximum: $\left(-2, \frac{11}{3}\right)$

(c) Relative minimum: $\left(\frac{1}{2}, -\frac{37}{4}\right)$; Relative maximum: $(-2, 22)$

(d) Relative minimum: $\left(1, -\frac{5}{6}\right)$; Relative maximum: $\left(-1, \frac{11}{6}\right)$

(e) None of these

1—Answer: b

16. Find all relative extrema: $f(x) = x^5 - 5x^3 - 20x + 4$.

(a) Relative minimum: $(2, -44)$; Relative maximum: $(-2, 52)$

(b) Relative minimum: $(1, -20)$; Relative maximum: $(-1, 28)$

(c) Relative minima: $(-1, 28)$, $(2, -44)$; Relative maxima: $(-2, 52)$, $(1, -20)$

(d) Relative maximum: $(5, 2404)$

(e) None of these

1—Answer: a

17. Find all relative extrema: $f(x) = 3x^5 - 25x^3 + 60x + 2$.

1—T—Answer: Relative minima: $(2, 18)$, $(-1, -36)$; Relative maxima: $(-2, -14)$, $(1, 40)$

18. Find the maximum value of $|f''(x)|$ on the interval $[0, 1]$: $f(x) = \frac{1}{12}x^4 - 2x^2 + 3x - 1$.

(a) -3 (b) 2 (c) 0 (d) 4 (e) None of these

2—Answer: d

19. Find the maximum value of $|f''(x)|$ on the interval $[0, 2]$: $f(x) = 3x^5 - 10x^3 + 9x - 1$.

2—Answer: $\dfrac{40\sqrt{3}}{3}$

Applications of the Derivative

20. Find the maximum value of $|f''(x)|$ on the interval $[0, 2]$: $f(x) = x^4 - 2x^3 - 12x^2$.

(a) 48   (b) 27   (c) $\frac{51}{16}$ (d) 9   (e) None of these

2—Answer: b

21. The concentration C in milligrams per cubic centimeter of a particular drug in a patient's bloodstream is given by

$$C = \frac{0.16t}{t^2 + 4t + 4},$$

where t is the number of hours after the drug is taken. For what values of t is C increasing and what is the maximum concentration of the drug in the patient's bloodstream?

1—Answer: C is increasing on $0 < t < 2$, since time is not negative: Maximum concentration is 0.02 milligrams per cubic centimeter.

22. Find the values of x that give relative extrema for the function $f(x) = 3x^5 - 5x^3$.

(a) Relative maximum: $x = 0$; Relative minimum: $x = \sqrt{5/3}$

(b) Relative maximum: $x = -1$; Relative minimum: $x = 1$

(c) Relative maxima: $x = \pm 1$; Relative minimum: $x = 0$

(d) Relative maximum: $x = 0$; Relative minima: $x = \pm 1$

(e) None of these

2—Answer: b

23. Find the values of x that give relative extrema for the function $f(x) = (x + 1)^2(x - 2)$.

(a) Relative maximum: $x = -1$; Relative minimum: $x = 1$

(b) Relative maxima: $x = 1, x = 3$; Relative minimum: $x = -1$

(c) Relative minimum: $x = 2$

(d) Relative maximum: $x = -1$; Relative minimum: $x = 2$

(e) None of these

2—Answer: a

24. Find the extrema of $y = \frac{2x}{(x + 4)^3}$.

2—Answer: $\left(2, \frac{1}{54}\right)$, relative maximum

25. Find the relative minimum and relative maximum for $f(x) = 2x^3 + 3x^2 - 12x$.

2—Answer: Relative maximum: $(-2, 20)$; Relative minimum: $(1, -7)$

26. Find the point(s) of relative extrema for the graph of the function $f(x) = x(x - 4)^3$.

1—Answer: Relative minimum: $(1, -27)$

27. Use calculus to locate the actual relative extrema for $f(x) = 4.5x^4 + 2x^3 - 18x^2 - 12x + 5$.

    (a) Relative minimum at $x = -\frac{1}{3}$; Relative maxima at $x = \sqrt{2}$

    (b) Relative maximum at $x = \frac{1}{3}$; Relative minimum at $x = \sqrt{2}$

    (c) Relative maximum at $x = -\frac{1}{3}$; Relative minimum at $x = \pm\sqrt{2}$

    (d) Relative minima at $x = \pm\sqrt{3}$

    (e) None of these

    1—Answer: c

28. Use a graphing utility to estimate the x-values of the relative extrema of the function

    $$f(x) = 4.5x^4 + 3x^3 - 1.8x^2 - 12x + 10.$$

    1—T—Answer: Relative minimum: $(0.8, 2.6)$

29. Use a graphing utility to estimate the x-values of the relative extrema of the function

    $$f(x) = 4.5x^4 + 2x^3 - 18x^2 - 12x + 5.$$

    (a) Relative minimum at $x = \pm 1.4$; Relative maximum at $x = 0.3$

    (b) Relative maximum at $x = \pm 1.4$; Relative minimum at $x = -0.3$

    (c) Relative maximum at $x = -0.3$

    (d) Relative minimum at $x = \pm 1.4$

    (e) None of these

    1—T—Answer: b

30. Given that $f(x) = -x^2 + 18x - 78$ has an absolute maximum at $x = 9$, choose the correct statement.

    (a) f' is negative on the interval $(-\infty, 9)$

    (b) f' is negative on the interval $(9, \infty)$

    (c) f' is positive on the interval $(-\infty, \infty)$

    (d) f' is positive on the interval $(9, \infty)$

    (e) None of these

    1—Answer: b

31. Given that $f(x) = -x^2 + 12x - 28$ has an absolute maximum at $x = 6$, choose the correct statement.

    (a) f' is negative on the interval $(-\infty, 6)$

    (b) f' is positive on the interval $(-\infty, \infty)$

    (c) f' is negative on the interval $(6, \infty)$

    (d) f' is positive on the interval $(6, \infty)$

    (e) None of these

    1—Answer: c

32. Given that $f(x) = -x^2 + 12x - 34$ has an absolute maximum at $x = 6$, choose the correct statement.

(a) f' is positive on the interval $(6, \infty)$

(b) f' is positive on the interval $(-\infty, \infty)$

(c) f' is negative on the interval $(6, \infty)$

(d) f' is negative on the interval $(-\infty, 6)$

(e) None of these

1—Answer: c

33. Explain in a complete sentence the significance of the sign of the derivative of a function $y = f(x)$ with respect to the increasing or decreasing behavior of the function $y = f(x)$.

1—Answer: Answers will vary.

34. In a complete sentence, explain what must be true for a function $y = f(x)$ to have a maximum point at the point (a, c) if $f(x)$ is differentiable on an open interval containing $x = a$.

2—Answer: Answers will vary.

Section 3.3   Concavity and the Second-Derivative Test

1. Find all intervals on which the function is concave upward: $f(x) = \dfrac{x^2 + 1}{x^2}$.

    (a) $(-\infty, \infty)$ (b) $(-\infty, -1)$ and $(1, \infty)$ (c) $(-\infty, 0)$ and $(0, \infty)$

    (d) $(1, \infty)$ (e) None of these

    1—Answer: c

2. Find all intervals on which the function is concave upward: $f(x) = \dfrac{x - 1}{x + 3}$.

    (a) $(-\infty, \infty)$ (b) $(-\infty, -3)$ (c) $(1, \infty)$ (d) $(-3, \infty)$ (e) None of these

    1—Answer: b

3. Find all intervals for which the function $y = 8x^3 - 2x^4$ is concave downward.

    1—Answer: $(-\infty, 0)$ and $(2, \infty)$

4. Find the intervals on which $f(x) = x^4 - 4x^3 + 2$ is concave upward or downward. Then find all points of inflection for the function.

    1—Answer: Concave Up: $(-\infty, 0)$, $(2, \infty)$;

                        Concave Down: $(0, 2)$;

                        Points of Inflection: $(0, 2)$ and $(2, -14)$

5. Given that $f(x) = \dfrac{-8}{x}$, choose the correct statement.

    (a) f is concave up on the interval $(0, \infty)$ (b) f is concave up on the interval $(-\infty, 0)$

    (c) f is concave down on the interval $(-\infty, 0)$ (d) f is concave up on the interval $(-\infty, \infty)$

    (e) None of these

    1—Answer: b

6. Given that $f(x) = \dfrac{-6}{x}$, choose the correct statement.

    (a) f is concave up on the interval $(-\infty, 0)$ (b) f is concave down on the interval $(-\infty, 0)$

    (c) f is concave up on the interval $(-\infty, \infty)$ (d) f is concave up on the interval $(0, \infty)$

    (e) None of these

    1—Answer: a

7. Given that $f(x) = \dfrac{4}{x}$, choose the correct statement.

   (a) f is concave up on the interval $(-\infty, 0)$ (b) f is concave down on the interval $(-\infty, 0)$

   (c) f is concave down on the interval $(-\infty, \infty)$ (d) f is concave down on the interval $(0, \infty)$

   (e) None of these

   1—Answer: b

8. Find all intervals on which $y = \dfrac{x^2 - 1}{x^3}$ is concave up.

   (a) $\left(-\sqrt{6}, 0\right)$ and $\left(\sqrt{6}, \infty\right)$ (b) $\left(-\sqrt{3}, \sqrt{3}\right)$ (c) $\left(-\infty, -\sqrt{6}\right)$ and $\left(\sqrt{6}, \infty\right)$

   (d) $\left(-\sqrt{6}, 0\right)$ and $\left(0, \sqrt{6}\right)$ (e) None of these

   1—Answer: a

9. Find all intervals on which $y = \dfrac{4x^2 - x}{x^4}$ is concave up.

   1—Answer: $(-\infty, 0), \left(\frac{1}{2}, \infty\right)$

10. Find all intervals on which $y = \dfrac{x - 3}{x + 4}$ is concave down.

    (a) $(-\infty, -4)$ (b) $(-4, \infty)$ (c) $(0, \infty)$ (d) $(-\infty, \infty)$ (e) None of these

    1—Answer: b

11. Determine any x values (to the nearest 0.1) where the graph of

    $$f(x) = \frac{x^5}{20} - \frac{x^4}{6} + \frac{7}{6}x^3 - 7x^2$$

    has any points of inflection by using a graphing utility to find the zeros of the second derivative.

    (a) $x = -2.6$ (b) $x = 2.6$ (c) $x = 2.0$

    (d) $x = -2.6, 2.0, 2.6$ (e) None of these

    1—T—Answer: c

12. Given that $f(x) = -\dfrac{4}{x + 2}$, find the intervals where y is concave up or down and any inflection points.

    1—Answer: Concave upward: $(-\infty, -2)$; Concave downward: $(-2, \infty)$; No inflection points

13. Find all inflection points for the graph of the function $f(x) = x^4 - 4x^3 + 16x + 8$.

    1—Answer: $(0, 8)$ and $(2, 24)$

14. Given $f(x) = 3x^4 - 4x^3 - 18x^2$, find any critical numbers and use the Second-Derivative Test to determine which of these critical numbers, if any, give a relative maximum.

   2—Answer: Critical numbers: $0, \dfrac{\sqrt{13}}{2} + \dfrac{1}{2}, \dfrac{1}{2} - \dfrac{\sqrt{13}}{2}$; Relative maximum at $x = 0$

15. Find all points of inflection of the function $f(x) = x^4 + x^3$.

   (a) $(0, 0)$ and $\left(-\frac{1}{2}, -\frac{1}{16}\right)$ (b) $\left(-\frac{1}{2}, -\frac{1}{16}\right)$ (c) $(0, 0)$

   (d) $(0, 0)$ and $\left(-\frac{3}{4}, -\frac{27}{256}\right)$ (e) None of these

   1—Answer: a

16. Find the point of inflection of $f(x) = x^3 - 3x^2 - x + 7$.

   1—Answer: $(1, 4)$

17. Find all points of inflection: $f(x) = \frac{1}{12}x^4 - 2x^2 + 15$.

   (a) $(2, 0)$ (b) $(2, 0), (-2, 0)$ (c) $(0, 15)$

   (d) $\left(2, \frac{25}{3}\right), \left(-2, \frac{25}{3}\right)$ (e) None of these

   1—Answer: d

18. Find all points of inflection: $f(x) = x^3 - 12x$.

   (a) $(0, 0), \left(\pm\sqrt{12}, 0\right)$ (b) $(0, 0)$ (c) $(2, 0), (-2, 0)$

   (d) $(2, -16), (-2, 16)$ (e) None of these

   1—Answer: b

19. Find all points of inflection: $f(x) = 2x(x - 4)^3$.

   1—Answer: $(4, 0), (2, -32)$

20. Find all points of inflection of the function $f(x) = x^4 - x^3$.

   (a) $(0, 0)$ and $\left(\frac{3}{4}, -\frac{27}{256}\right)$ (b) $(0, 0)$ (c) $(0, 0)$ and $\left(\frac{1}{2}, -\frac{1}{16}\right)$

   (d) $\left(\frac{1}{2}, -\frac{1}{16}\right)$ (e) None of these

   1—Answer: c

21. Find all points of inflection of the function $f(x) = x^4 - 6x^3$.

   (a) $(0, 0)$ (b) $(0, 0)$ and $\left(\frac{9}{2}, -\frac{2187}{16}\right)$ (c) $(3, -81)$

   (d) $(0, 0)$ and $(3, -81)$ (e) None of these

   1—Answer: d

22. Determine any x values, to the nearest 0.1, where the graph of $f(x) = 3x^5 - 10x^4 + 70x^3 - 420x^2$ has any points of inflection by using a graphing utility to find the zeros of the second derivative.

    1—T—Answer: $x = 2$

23. Let $f''(x) = 3x^2 - 2x - 3$ and let $f(x)$ have critical numbers $x = -1$ and $x = \sqrt{3}$. Use the Second-Derivative Test to determine which of these critical numbers, if any, give a relative maximum.

    (a) $x = -1$ (b) $x = \sqrt{3}$ (c) Both

    (d) Neither   (e) Second-Derivative Test fails

    1—Answer: d

24. Let $f''(x) = 4x^3 - 2x$ and let $f(x)$ have critical numbers $-1, 0,$ and 1. Use the Second-Derivative Test to determine which critical numbers, if any, give a relative maximum.

    (a) -1 (b) 0 (c) 1 (d) -1 and 1 (e) None of these

    2—Answer: a

25. Let $f''(x) = 3x^2 - 4$ and let $f(x)$ have critical numbers $-2, 0,$ and 2. Use the Second-Derivative Test to determine which critical numbers, if any, gives a relative maximum.

    (a) -2 (b) 2 (c) 0 (d) -2 and 2 (e) None of these

    2—Answer: c

26. Let $f(x) = x^3 - x^2 + 3$. Use the Second-Derivative Test to determine which critical numbers, if any, give relative extrema.

    2—Answer: $x = 0$, relative maximum; $x = \frac{2}{3}$, relative minimum

27. Give the sign of the second derivative of f at the indicated point.

    (a) Negative   (b) Positive

    (c) Zero   (d) The sign cannot be determined

    (e) None of these

    1—Answer: b

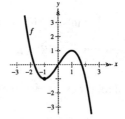

28. Given that $f(x) = -\dfrac{3}{x + 2}$, choose the correct statement.

    (a) The graph of $f(x)$ is concave down on $(-\infty, -2)$.

    (b) The graph of $f(x)$ is concave down on $(-2, \infty)$.

    (c) The graph of $f(x)$ is concave up on $(-2, \infty)$.

    (d) The graph of $f(x)$ is concave up on $(-\infty, \infty)$.

    (e) None of these

    1—Answer: b

29. The graph of the function $y = x^3 - 3x + 4$ has:

    (a) One relative extremum and one inflection point.   (b) Two relative extrema and one inflection point.

    (c) One relative extremum and two inflection points.   (d) No extrema and two inflection points.

    (e) None of these

    1—Answer: b

30. The graph of the function $y = x^3 - 4x + 5$ has:

    (a) Two relative extrema and one inflection point.   (b) One relative extremum and one inflection point.

    (c) One relative extremum and two inflection points.   (d) No extrema and two inflection points.

    (e) None of these

    1—Answer: a

31. Give the sign of the second derivative of f at the indicated point.

    (a) Positive   (b) Negative

    (c) Zero   (d) The sign cannot be determined

    (e) None of these

    1—Answer: b

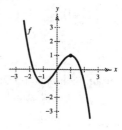

32. Give the sign of the second derivative of f at the indicated point.

    (a) Zero   (b) Negative

    (c) Positive   (d) The sign cannot be determined

    (e) None of these

    1—Answer: a

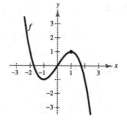

33. Which statement is <u>not</u> true of the graph of $f(x) = (x + 3)(x - 4)^2$?

    (a) f has a relative minimum at $(4, 0)$.   (b) f has a point of inflection at $(4, 0)$.

    (c) f has a relative maximum at $\left(-\frac{2}{3}, \frac{1372}{27}\right)$.   (d) f has an intercept at $(4, 0)$.

    (e) None of these

    1—Answer: b

34. Which statement is <u>not</u> true of the graph of $f(x) = (x + 1)(x - 3)^2$?

    (a) f has a relative maximum at $\left(\frac{1}{3}, \frac{256}{27}\right)$.   (b) f has a point of inflection at $(3, 0)$.

    (c) f has an intercept at $(3, 0)$.   (d) f has a relative minimum at $(3, 0)$.

    (e) None of these

    1—Answer: b

35. Which statement is <u>not</u> true of the graph of $f(x) = (x + 2)(x - 1)^2$?

    (a) f has a relative minimum at $(1, 0)$.   (b) f has an intercept at $(1, 0)$.

    (c) f has a relative maximum at $(-1, 4)$.   (d) f has a point of inflection at $(1, 0)$.

    (e) None of these

    1—Answer: d

36. The cost function for a manufacturer to produce x items is $C = x^2 + 3x + 3x + 400$. Determine the production level that will minimize the average cost of the product. $\left(\overline{C} = \dfrac{C}{x} \right)$

    (a) 10   (b) 15   (c) 20   (d) 25   (e) None of these

    2—Answer: c

37. The cost function for a manufacturer to produce x items is $C = \frac{1}{9}x^2 - 2x + 100$. Determine the production level that will minimize the average cost of the product. $\left(\overline{C} = \dfrac{C}{x} \right)$

    2—Answer: 30 items

38. A certain manufacturer finds the revenue derived from selling x items is determined by using the function $R = -4x^3 + 84x^2$. Find the point of diminishing returns.

    (a) $(7, 2744)$ (b) $(9, 3888)$ (c) $(11, 4840)$ (d) $(15, 5400)$ (e) None of these

    2—Answer: a

39. A certain manufacturer finds the revenue derived from selling x items is determined by using the function $R = -\frac{2}{3}x^3 + 18x^2$. Find the point of diminishing returns.

    2—Answer: $(9, 972)$

Section 3.4 Optimization Problems

1. Three rectangular pens of the same size are to be built beside an existing pasture. Each pen is to contain 1200 ft². What dimensions will use the least amount of new fencing? No new fencing is required along the pasture.

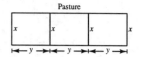

  (a) $x = 26.5, y = 45.3$ (b) $x = 30.0, y = 40.0$

  (c) $x = 34.6, y = 34.6$ (d) $x = 45.3, y = 26.5$

  (e) None of these

1—T—Answer: b

2. Three rectangular pens of the same size are to be built beside an existing pasture. Each pen is to contain 700 ft². What dimensions will use the least amount of new fencing? No new fencing is required along the pasture.

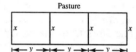

  (a) $x = 22.9, y = 30.6$ (b) $x = 30.0, y = 25.0$

  (c) $x = 34.6, y = 20.2$ (d) $x = 26.5, y = 26.5$

  (e) None of these

1—T—Answer: a

3. A person has 400 feet of fencing to enclose two adjacent rectangular regions of the same size. What dimensions should each region be so that the enclosed area will be a maximum?

  (a) $x = 40.0, y = 17.5$ (b) $x = 70.0, y = 32.1$

  (c) $x = 57.1, y = 57.1$ (d) $x = 66.7, y = 50.0$

  (e) None of these

1—T—Answer: d

4. A dog owner has 25 ft of fencing to use for a rectangular dog run. If he puts the run next to the garage he only needs to use the wire for three sides. What dimensions will yield the maximum area?

1—T—Answer: $x = 6.25$ ft, $y = 12.5$ ft

5. A page is to contain 45 in.² of print. The margins at the top and bottom of the page are each $1\frac{1}{2}$ in. wide. The margins on each side are 1 in. What should be the dimensions of print so that a minimum amount of paper is used?

2—Answer: $\sqrt{30}$ in. by $\dfrac{3\sqrt{30}}{2}$ in.

Applications of the Derivative

6. A page is to contain 60 in.^{2} of print. The margins at the top and bottom of the page are each $1\frac{1}{2}$ in. wide. The margins on each side are 1 in. What should be the dimensions of print so that a minimum amount of paper is used?

(a) 6.3 in. by 9.5 in. (b) 5.9 in. by 10.2 in. (c) 5.8 in. by 10.3 in.

(d) 5.3 in. by 11.3 in. (e) None of these

2—T—Answer: a

7. Two equal rectangular lots are to be made by fencing in a rectangular lot and putting a fence across the middle. If each lot is to contain 1875 ft^2, what size lots require the minimum amount of fence and what is the minimum amount of fence needed?

2—Answer: 50 ft by 37.5 ft for a minimum amount of 300 ft of fence

8. The amount of material required to make an open top box with a square base that contains 108 in.^{3} is given by

$$M = x^2 + \frac{432}{x},$$

where x is the length of a side of the base. Find the length of a side of the base that minimizes the amount of material used.

1—Answer: $x = 6$ in.

9. An open box is to be made from a 3 ft by 4 ft rectangular piece of material by cutting equal squares from each corner and turning up the sides. Find the volume of the largest box that can be made in this manner.

(a) 4.01 ft^3 (b) 3.92 ft^3 (c) 3.03 ft^3 (d) 2.08 ft^3 (e) None of these

1—T—Answer: c

10. An open box is to be made from a 3 ft by 5 ft rectangular piece of material by cutting equal squares from each corner and turning up the sides. Find the volume of the largest box that can be made in this manner.

(a) 5.2 ft^3 (b) 4.1 ft^3 (c) 7.5 ft^3 (d) 3.3 ft^3 (e) None of these

1—T—Answer: b

11. An open box is constructed from cardboard by cutting out squares of equal size in the corners and then folding up the sides. If the cardboard is 5 in. by 10 in., determine the volume of the largest box which can be so constructed.

(a) 24.0 in.^{3} (b) 1.1 in.^{3} (c) 14.7 in.^{3} (d) 3.4 in.^{3} (e) None of these

2—T—Answer: a

12. An open box is to be constructed from cardboard by cutting out squares of equal size in the corners and then folding up the sides. If the cardboard is 6 in. by 11 in., determine the volume of the largest box which can be so constructed.

2—T—Answer: 37.2 in.^{3}

13. Find the positive number such that the sum of the number and its reciprocal is a minimum.

(a) 3   (b) $\frac{1}{2}$ (c) $\frac{1}{3}$ (d) 1   (e) None of these

1—Answer: d

14. The management of a large store has 1,600 ft. of fencing to fence in a rectangular storage yard using the building as one side of the yard. If the fencing is used for the remaining three sides, find the area of the largest possible yard.

2—Answer: 320,000 ft^2

15. An open box is to be made from a rectangular piece of material by cutting equal squares from each corner and turning up the sides. Find the dimensions of the box of maximum volume if the material has dimensions 6 in by 6 in.

2—Answer: 4 in. by 4 in. by 1 in.

16. An open box is to be made from a square piece of material, 12 in. on each side, by cutting equal squares from each corner and turning up the sides. Find the volume of the largest box that can be made in this manner.

2—Answer: $8^2(2) = 128$ in.^{3}

17. Find two positive integers whose product is a maximum of all sets of two numbers whose sum is 56.

(a) 52 and 4   (b) 32 and 24   (c) 29 and 27   (d) 28 and 28   (e) None of these

2—Answer: d

18. Find two positive integers whose sum is a minimum of all sets of two numbers whose product is 36.

(a) 3 and 12   (b) 4 and 9   (c) 2 and 18   (d) 6 and 6   (e) None of these

1—Answer: d

19. A rectangular field is to be fenced in so that the resulting perimeter is 250 meters. Find the dimensions of that field for which the area is maximum.

2—Answer: 62.5 meters by 62.5 meters

20. Find the x value, accurate to the nearest 0.1, of the point on the graph of $y = x^3$ that lies closest to the point $(2, 0)$.

(a) $(1.2, 1.728)$ (b) $(0.8, 0.512)$ (c) $(1.8, 5.832)$ (d) $(1, 1)$ (e) None of these

1—T—Answer: b

21. Find the x value, accurate to the nearest 0.1, of the point on the graph of $y = x^3$ that lies closest to the point $(1, 0)$.

1—T—Answer: $(0.7, 0.3)$

22. A rectangular field has a river on one side and is to be fenced on the other three sides. If the perimeter of the rectangle (not including the side on the river) is 300 meters, find the dimensions of the field for which the area is a maximum.

1—T—Answer: 75 meters by 150 meters

23. The product of two positive numbers is 588. Minimize the sum of the first and three times the second.

(a) Both numbers are $14\sqrt{3}$ (b) 42 and 14

(c) 28 and 21 (d) None of these

1—Answer: b

24. The product of two positive numbers is 675. Minimize the sum of the first and three times the second.

(a) 30 and $\frac{45}{2}$ (b) Both numbers are $15\sqrt{3}$

(c) None of these (d) 45 and 15

1—Answer: d

25. The product of two positive numbers is 363. Minimize the sum of the first and three times the second.

(a) 33 and 11 (b) Both numbers are $11\sqrt{3}$

(c) 22 and $\frac{33}{2}$ (d) None of these

1—Answer: a

26. A rancher has 300 ft of fencing to enclose a pasture bordered on one side by a river. The river side of the pasture needs no fence. Find the dimensions that will produce a pasture with a maximum area.

1—Answer: 75 ft by 150 ft

27. A farmer has 160 ft of fencing to enclose two adjacent rectangular pig pens. What dimensions should be used for each pig pen so that the enclosed area will be a maximum?

(a) $4\sqrt{15}$ ft by $\frac{8}{5}\sqrt{15}$ ft (b) 40 ft by $\frac{80}{3}$ ft (c) 20 ft by $\frac{80}{3}$ ft

(d) 40 ft by 40 ft (e) None of these

1—Answer: c

28. The management of a large store wishes to add a fenced–in rectangular storage yard of 20,000 ft^2, using the building as one side of the yard. Find the minimum amount of fencing that must be used to enclose the remaining three sides of the yard.

(a) 400 ft (b) 200 ft (c) 20,000 ft (d) 500 ft (e) None of these

2—Answer: a

29. Find two positive numbers whose product is a maximum if the sum of the numbers is 10.

(a) 1, 9 (b) 2, 8 (c) 3, 7 (d) 5, 5 (e) None of these

1—Answer: d

Section 3.5   Business and Economic Applications

1. The cost of producing x units of a certain product is given by $C = 10{,}000 + 5x + \frac{1}{9}x^2$. Find the value of x that gives the minimum average cost.

   (a) 30,000   (b) 300   (c) 3000   (d) 30   (e) None of these

   1—Answer: b

2. The marketing research department for a computer company used a large city to test market their new product. They found that the demand equation was $p = 1296 - 0.12x^2$. If the cost equation is $C = 830 + 396x$, find the number of units that will produce maximum profit.

   (a) 16.5   (b) 17   (c) 50   (d) 500   (e) None of these

   1—Answer: c

3. A certain item sells for $30. If the cost of producing this item is given by $C = 0.05x^3 + 100$, find the marginal profit when $x = 10$.

   1—Answer: $15

4. Find the price per unit p that produces the maximum profit P if the cost function is $C = 2400x + 5200$ and the demand function is $6000 - 0.4x^2$.

   1—Answer: $4800

5. Find the number of units x that produces a maximum revenue for the revenue function $R = 600x^2 - 0.02x^3$.

   1—Answer: 20,000 units

6. The cost of producing x units of a product is given by $C = 0.05x^2 + 25x + 400$.

   (a) Find the additional cost if production is increased from 1000 to 1001 units.

   (b) Find the marginal cost of production when 1000 units are produced.

   2—Answer: (a) $125.05/unit   (b) $125.00/unit

7. Find the number of units, x, that will minimize the average cost function if the total cost function is $C = 3x^2 + 7x + 75$.

   1—Answer: 5

8. A given commodity has a demand function given by $p = 200 - x$ and a total cost function given by $C = 100x + 1000$. Find the maximum profit.

   2—Answer: $1500

9. Find the number of units, x, that will minimize the average cost function if the total cost function is $C = 3x^2 + 12x + 75$.

   1—Answer: 5

10. A nursery has determined that the demand in June for potted plants is

$$p = 2.00 - \frac{x}{43,000}.$$

The cost of growing x plants is $C = 2000 + 0.20x$, $0 \le x \le 100,000$. Find the marginal profit.

(a) $1.8 - \dfrac{x}{21,500}$

(b) $1.8x - \dfrac{x^2}{43,000} - 2000$

(c) $-\dfrac{8601}{43,000}$

(d) $\dfrac{77,399}{43,000}$

(e) None of these

2—Answer: a

11. A nursery has determined that the demand in June for potted plants is

$$p = 2.00 - \frac{x}{21,000}.$$

The cost of growing x plants is $C = 2000 + 0.20x$, $0 \le x \le 100,000$. Find the marginal profit.

(a) $1.8 - \dfrac{x}{10,500}$

(b) $-\dfrac{4201}{21,000}$

(c) $\dfrac{37,799}{21,000}$

(d) $1.8x - \dfrac{x^2}{21,000} - 2000$

(e) None of these

1—Answer: a

12. A nursery has determined that the demand in June for potted plants is

$$p = 2.00 - \frac{x}{30,000}.$$

The cost of growing x plants is $C = 2000 + 0.20x$, $0 \le x \le 100,000$. Find the marginal profit.

(a) $\dfrac{53,999}{30,000}$

(b) $1.8 - \dfrac{x}{15,000}$

(c) $1.8x - \dfrac{x^2}{30,000} - 2000$

(d) $-\dfrac{6001}{30,000}$

(e) None of these

1—Answer: b

13. The demand for a certain product is given by the model

$$p = \frac{53}{\sqrt{x}}.$$

The fixed costs are \$608 and the cost per unit is \$0.53. Find the production x that yields the maximum profit in the range $0 \le x \le 7530$.

(a) 14   (b) 2500   (c) 7530   (d) 50   (e) None of these

1—Answer: b

14. The demand for a certain product is given by the model

$$p = \frac{43}{\sqrt{x}}.$$

The fixed costs are \$782 and the cost per unit is \$0.43. Find the production x that yields the maximum profit in the range $0 \le x \le 5791$.

(a) 50   (b) 14   (c) 5791   (d) 2500   (e) None of these

1—Answer: d

15. Find the number of units, x, that will minimize the average cost function if the total cost function is $C = \frac{1}{2}x^2 - 5x + 5000$.

(a) 100   (b) 5   (c) 1000   (d) 50   (e) None of these

1—Answer: a

16. If the cost function is $C = 100x - 2x^3$ and the demand function is $p = \$1000 - 75x$, find the price p that produces maximum profit.

(a) \$80   (b) \$250   (c) \$10   (d) \$15   (e) None of these

1—Answer: b

17. Find the number of units, x, that will minimize the average cost function if the total cost function is $C = \frac{1}{4}x^2 - 3x + 400$.

(a) 6   (b) 40   (c) 400   (d) 1612   (e) None of these

1—Answer: b

18. If the cost function is $C = 600x - 2x^3$ and the demand function is $p = 2400 - 105x$, find the price p that produces maximum profit.

(a) \$300   (b) \$15   (c) \$825   (d) \$2.29   (e) None of these

1—Answer: c

19. Given the revenue function $R(x) = 40x^3 - 2x^4 - 100x^2 + 4000x$ and the cost function $C = 1000x + 2000$; find the number of units x to produce in order to maximize the profit.

(a) 10.2   (b) 20.7   (c) 100.6   (d) 15.0   (e) None of these

1—Answer: d

20. If the cost function is $C = 100 + 40x$ and the demand function is $p = 200 - 10x$, find the price p that maximizes the profit.

(a) \$8   (b) \$120   (c) \$20   (d) \$540   (e) None of these

2—Answer: b

21. Given the demand function $p(x) = \sqrt{16 - x}$ and the cost function $C = 0.2x + 1.0$; find the number of units x to produce in order to maximize the profit by using a graphing utility to draw the graph of the profit function.

     1—T—Answer: 10 units

22. If the cost function is $C = 100 + 40x$ and the revenue function is $R = 200x - 10x^2$, find the price p that maximizes the profit.

     (a) \$8   (b) \$120   (c) \$20   (d) \$540   (e) None of these

     2—Answer: b

23. Find the x–coordinate of the point of diminishing returns for the revenue function

$$R(x) = \frac{300x^2 - x^3}{10,000},$$

where R is the revenue (in thousands of dollars) and x is the amount spent on advertising (in thousands of dollars).

     1—Answer: $x = 100$

24. The demand for a certain product is given by the model

$$p = \frac{45}{\sqrt{x}}.$$

The fixed costs are \$574 and the cost per unit is \$0.45. Find the production x that yields the maximum profit in the range $0 \le x \le 7223$.

     (a) 2550   (b) 50   (c) 14   (d) 7223   (e) None of these

     1—Answer: a

25. For what values of η is $p = 57x^{-1/\eta}$ elastic? $(\eta > 0)$

     (a) $0 < \eta < 1$ (b) p is never elastic   (c) p is always elastic

     (d) $\eta > 1$ (e) None of these

     1—Answer: d

26. For what values of η is $p = 76x^{-1/\eta}$ elastic? $(\eta > 0)$

     (a) p is never elastic   (b) $\eta > 1$ (c) $0 < \eta < 1$

     (d) p is always elastic   (e) None of these

     1—Answer: b

27. For what values of η is $p = 45x^{-1/\eta}$ elastic? $(\eta > 0)$

     (a) p is always elastic   (b) p is never elastic   (c) $0 < \eta < 1$

     (d) $\eta > 1$ (e) None of these

     1—Answer: d

28. If the demand function for a product is $p = 20 - 4x^2$, determine the elasticity of demand and whether the demand function is elastic or inelastic at the price of \$2.

(a) 1; neither elastic or inelastic   (b) $\frac{1}{2}$; elastic   (c) $\frac{1}{2}$; inelastic

(d) $-\frac{1}{8}$; inelastic   (e) None of these

2—Answer: d

29. The demand function for a particular commodity is given by

$$p = 2.44x - \frac{x^2}{200} - 50.$$

Find the price elasticity of demand, η, when $x = 200$.

(a) 238.00   (b) 1.19   (c) 0.61   (d) 1.94   (e) None of these

1—Answer: c

30. The demand function for a particular commodity is given by

$$p = 2.44x - \frac{x^2}{200} - 50.$$

Find the price elasticity of demand, η, when $x = 300$.

(a) 0.77   (b) 0.56   (c) 232.00   (d) -1.38 (e) None of these

1—Answer: d

31. The demand function for a particular commodity is given by

$$p = \frac{1000 - x}{400}.$$

Find the price elasticity of demand, η, when $x = 500$.

(a) -500.00 (b) 0.44   (c) -1 (d) 1.25   (e) None of these

1—Answer: c

32. The demand function for a particular commodity is given by

$$p = \frac{1500 - x}{300}.$$

Find the price elasticity of demand, η, when $x = 700$.

1—Answer: $\eta = -1.14$

Section 3.6 Asymptotes

1. Find $\lim\limits_{x \to 2} \dfrac{1}{(x-2)^2}$.

    (a) ∞ (b) $-\infty$ (c) 0 (d) $\frac{1}{4}$ (e) None of these

    1—Answer: a

2. Find $\lim\limits_{x \to 0} \left(2 + \dfrac{5}{x^2}\right)$.

    (a) 7 (b) 2 (c) ∞ (d) $-\infty$ (e) None of these

    1—Answer: c

3. Find $\lim\limits_{x \to 2^-} \dfrac{1}{x-2}$.

    (a) ∞ (b) $-\infty$ (c) 0 (d) $-\frac{1}{4}$ (e) None of these

    1—Answer: b

4. Find $\lim\limits_{x \to 0^+} \dfrac{1}{x}$.

    (a) ∞ (b) 0 (c) $-\infty$ (d) Does not exist   (e) None of these

    1—Answer: a

5. Find $\lim\limits_{x \to 1} \dfrac{5}{(x-1)^2}$.

    (a) 0 (b) $-\infty$ (c) $\frac{5}{4}$ (d) ∞ (e) None of these

    1—Answer: d

6. Find $\lim\limits_{x \to 1} \left(2 - \dfrac{5}{(x-1)^2}\right)$.

    (a) $-\infty$ (b) ∞ (c) -3 (d) 2 (e) None of these

    1—Answer: a

7. Find $\lim\limits_{x \to -1^-} \dfrac{1}{x+1}$.

    1—Answer: $-\infty$

8. Find $\lim\limits_{x \to 3} \dfrac{3}{x^2 - 6x + 9}$.

    1—Answer: ∞

9. Find $\lim\limits_{x \to 0} \left(3x + 2 + \dfrac{1}{x^2} \right)$.

1—Answer: ∞

10. Find the limit: $\lim\limits_{x \to 3^-} \dfrac{1}{x - 3}$.

1—Answer: $-\infty$

11. Find the limit: $\lim\limits_{x \to 1^+} \dfrac{x^2 - x - 2}{x - 1}$.

1—Answer: $-\infty$

12. Find all vertical asymptotes of $f(x) = \dfrac{x - 3}{x + 2}$.

    (a) $x = -2, x = 3$ (b) $x = -2$ (c) $x = 3$

    (d) $x = 1$ (e) None of these

1—Answer: b

13. Find all vertical asymptotes of $g(x) = \dfrac{x + 1}{x^2 - 1}$.

    (a) $x = -1, x = 1$ (b) $x = -1$ (c) $x = 1$

    (d) $y = 1$ (e) None of these

1—Answer: c

14. Find all vertical asymptotes of $f(x) = \dfrac{2x - 1}{x + 3}$.

    (a) $x = 2$ (b) $x = \frac{1}{2}, x = -3$ (c) $x = -3$

    (d) $x = \frac{1}{2}$ (e) None of these

1—Answer: c

15. Determine the vertical asymptote(s) for the graph of $f(x) = \dfrac{x^2 + 1}{(x - 2)(x + 1)}$.

    (a) $x = -1, x = 2$ (b) $x = -1, x = 1, x = 2$ (c) $x = -1, x = 1$

    (d) $x = 2$ (e) None of these

1—Answer: a

Applications of the Derivative

16. Determine the vertical asymptote(s) for the graph of $f(x) = \dfrac{x^2 + 4}{x^2 - 4x - 12}$.

(a) $x = -2$ (b) $x = 6$ (c) $x = -2, x = 6$

(d) $x = -6$ (e) None of these

1—Answer: c

17. Determine the vertical asymptote(s) for the graph of $f(x) = \dfrac{x^2 + 2x}{x^2 - 4x}$.

(a) $x = -4$ (b) $x = 0, x = 4$ (c) $x = -2, x = 0$

(d) $x = 4$ (e) None of these

1—Answer: d

18. Use a graphing utility to locate any vertical asymptotes for the function $y = \dfrac{3x + 2}{2x^3 - 4x^2 + 14x - 28}$.

1—T—Answer: $x = 2$

19. Use a graphing utility to locate any vertical asymptotes for the function $y = \dfrac{x^2 + 3x + 2}{x^3 + x^2 - 5x - 5}$.

(a) $x = -2.2$ (b) $x = -2.2, x = 2.2$ (c) $x = -2.2, x = -1.0\ x = 2.2$

(d) $x = -1.0$ (e) None of these

1—T—Answer: b

20. Find any vertical and/or horizontal asymptotes for the function $f(x) = \dfrac{3x^2}{x^2 + 4}$.

1—Answer: Horizontal asymptote: $y = 3$. No vertical asymptotes.

21. Find all vertical and horizontal asymptotes for the graph of the function $f(x) = \dfrac{5x^2}{1 - x^2}$.

1—Answer: Vertical asymptotes: $x = 1, x = -1$. Horizontal asymptotes: $y = -5$.

22. Find all vertical asymptotes of $f(x) = \dfrac{x - 2}{x^2 - 4}$.

(a) $x = -2, x = 2$ (b) $x = -2$ (c) $x = 0$

(d) $x = 2$ (e) None of these

1—Answer: b

23. Find the vertical asymptote: $f(x) = \dfrac{7}{x + 2}$.

(a) $x = -2$ (b) $x = 2$ (c) $(0, -2)$ (d) $y = 0$ (e) None of these

1—Answer: a

24. Find the vertical aysmptote(s): $f(x) = \dfrac{1}{(x + 2)(x - 5)}$.

    (a) $x = -2, x = 5$ (b) $y = 1$ (c) $y = 0$

    (d) $y = 1, y = 0$ (e) None of these

    1—Answer: a

25. Find all vertical asymptotes of $f(x)$ if $f(x) = \dfrac{x^2 + 3x - 1}{x + 7}$.

    1—Answer: $x = -7$

26. Find all vertical asymptotes of $f(x)$ if $f(x) = \dfrac{2x - 2}{(x - 1)(x^2 + x - 1)}$.

    1—Answer: $x = \dfrac{-1 - \sqrt{5}}{2}, x = \dfrac{-1 + \sqrt{5}}{2}$

27. Determine the vertical asymptotes for the graph of $f(x) = \dfrac{x^2 + x}{x(x - 3)}$.

    (a) $x = 0, x = 3$ (b) $x = 0, x = -1$ (c) $y = 1$

    (d) $x = -1, x = 3$ (e) None of these

    1—Answer: a

28. Find all horizontal and vertical asymptotes for the graph of the function $f(x) = \dfrac{6x^2}{8 - x^3}$.

    1—Answer: Vertical asymptote: $x = 2$. Horizontal asymptote: $y = 0$.

29. The function $f(x) = \dfrac{3x^2}{x^2 + 4}$ has:

    (a) A horizontal asymptote at $y = 3$ (b) A vertical asymptote at $x = 2$

    (c) No vertical asymptotes   (d) Both **(a)** and **(c)**

    (e) Both **(a)** and **(b)**

    1—Answer: d

30. Find all horizontal asymptotes: $f(x) = \dfrac{2}{x - 3} - \dfrac{x}{x + 2}$.

    1—Answer: $y = -1$

31. Find the horizontal asymptote: $f(x) = \dfrac{7}{x - 4}$.

    (a) $x = 4$ (b) $y = 7$ (c) $y = 0$ (d) $x = 0$ (e) None of these

    1—Answer: c

32. Find the horizontal asymptote: $f(x) = \dfrac{3x^2 + 2x - 16}{x^2 - 7}$.

(a) $x = \pm\sqrt{7}$ (b) $y = 3$ (c) $y = 3x + 7$ (d) $y = 0$ (e) None of these

1—Answer: b

33. Find the horizontal asymptote for $f(x) = \dfrac{2x^2 + x - 7}{x^2 - 1}$.

1—Answer: $y = 2$

34. Find the horizontal asymptote for $f(x) = \dfrac{2x - 7}{x^2 - 1}$.

1—Answer: $y = 0$

35. Find all horizontal asymptotes of $f(x) = \dfrac{4x}{\sqrt{x^2 + 9}}$.

(a) $y = \pm 1$ (b) $y = 4$ (c) $y = \pm 4$ (d) $y = 0$ (e) None of these

1—Answer: c

36. Find all horizontal asymptotes of $f(x) = \dfrac{5x}{\sqrt{x^2 + 3}}$.

(a) $y = 0$ (b) $y = \pm 5$ (c) $y = 5$ (d) $y = \pm 1$ (e) None of these

1—Answer: b

37. Find all horizontal asymptotes of $f(x) = \dfrac{6x}{\sqrt{x^2 - 3}}$.

(a) $y = \pm 1$ (b) $y = \pm 6$ (c) $y = 6$ (d) $y = 0$ (e) None of these

1—Answer: b

38. Which of the following functions has a horizontal asymptote at $y = 2$?

(a) $\dfrac{x - 2}{3x - 5}$ (b) $\dfrac{2x}{\sqrt{x - 2}}$ (c) $\dfrac{2x^2 - 6x + 1}{1 + x^2}$ (d) $\dfrac{2x - 1}{x^2 + 1}$ (e) None of these

1—Answer: c

39. Which of the following functions has a horizontal asymptote at $y = -\dfrac{1}{2}$?

(a) $\dfrac{x^3}{1 - 2x^3}$ (b) $\dfrac{x}{\sqrt{2x + 1}}$ (c) $\dfrac{2x^2 - 6x + 1}{1 + x^2}$ (d) $\dfrac{x - 1}{2x^2 + 1}$ (e) None of these

1—Answer: a

40. Find the horizontal asymptote, if any, for the function $y = \dfrac{x^2 + 1}{x - 2}$.

(a) $x = 2$　　(b) $y = 1$　　(c) $y = -\frac{1}{2}$　　(d) $x = 1$　　(e) None of these

1—Answer: e

41. Find the horizontal asymptote, if any, for the graph of $y = \dfrac{2x}{x^2 - 4}$.

(a) $y = 0$　　(b) $y = 1$　　(c) $y = 2$　　(d) $x = 2$　　(e) None of these

1—Answer: a

42. Find the horizontal asymptote, if any, for the function $y = \dfrac{2x^2}{x^2 - 4}$.

(a) $y = 0$　　(b) $y = 1$　　(c) $y = 2$　　(d) $x = 2$　　(e) None of these

1—Answer: b

43. Find $\displaystyle\lim_{x \to \infty} \dfrac{2x^3 + 6x^2 + 5}{x^3 + 3}$

(a) $\frac{2}{3}$　　(b) ∞　　(c) 1　　(d) 2　　(e) None of these

1—Answer: d

44. Find $\displaystyle\lim_{x \to \infty} \dfrac{2x^3 + 6x^2 + 5}{3 + x^2}$

(a) 2　　(b) ∞　　(c) 0　　(d) $\frac{2}{3}$　　(e) None of these

1—Answer: b

45. Evaluate: $\displaystyle\lim_{x \to \infty} \dfrac{6 + x^2}{x^2 + 2x + 3}$.

(a) 6　　(b) 1　　(c) 0　　(d) ∞　　(e) None of these

1—Answer: b

46. Find $\displaystyle\lim_{x \to -\infty} \dfrac{2x^2 + 6x + 5}{4x^3 + 3}$.

(a) $\frac{1}{2}$　　(b) $-\infty$　　(c) 0　　(d) $-\frac{1}{2}$　　(e) None of these

1—Answer: c

47. Find $\displaystyle\lim_{x \to \infty} \dfrac{2x^2 + 6x + 5}{3 + x^3}$.

(a) $\frac{2}{3}$　　(b) ∞　　(c) 1　　(d) 2　　(e) None of these

1—Answer: e

48. Find $\lim\limits_{x\to\infty} \dfrac{7 - x^2}{x^2 + 2x + 2}$.

    (a) -1 (b) 7 (c) 0 (d) ∞ (e) None of these

    1—Answer: a

49. Evaluate: $\lim\limits_{x\to-\infty} \dfrac{6x - x^3}{x^2 + 2x + 3}$.

    (a) ∞ (b) $-\infty$ (c) -1 (d) 0 (e) None of these

    1—Answer: a

50. Find $\lim\limits_{x\to\infty} \dfrac{5x}{x^2 - 1}$.

    1—Answer: 0

51. Find $\lim\limits_{x\to\infty} \left(\dfrac{2x}{x + 2} + \dfrac{x}{x - 1} \right)$.

    1—Answer: 3

52. Evaluate: $\lim\limits_{x\to\infty} \dfrac{10 + x^3}{-x^2 + 2x + 3}$.

    1—Answer: $-\infty$

53. Evaluate: $\lim\limits_{x\to\infty} \dfrac{6x}{x^3 + 3}$.

    1—Answer: 0

54. Find $\lim\limits_{x\to\infty} \dfrac{3x^2 + 7x + 5}{6x^3 + 3}$.

    1—Answer: 0

55. Evaluate: $\lim\limits_{x\to\infty} \dfrac{6 + x^3}{-x^2 + 2x + 3}$.

    (a) -6 (b) -1 (c) 0 (d) ∞ (e) None of these

    1—Answer: e

56. Find $\lim\limits_{x\to\infty} \dfrac{\sqrt{4x^2 - 1}}{x^2}$.

    (a) 4 (b) 0 (c) 2 (d) ∞ (e) None of these

    1—Answer: b

57. Find $\lim\limits_{x\to-\infty} \dfrac{\sqrt{4x^2 - 1}}{x^2}$.

1—Answer: 0

58. $f(x)$ decreases without bound as x approaches what value from the right? $f(x) = \dfrac{7}{(x - 1)(7 - x)}$

    (a) $x\to 1^-$ (b) $x\to 1^+$ (c) $x\to 7^+$ (d) $x\to 7^-$ (e) None of these

2—Answer: c

59. $f(x)$ decreases without bound as x approaches what value from the right? $f(x) = \dfrac{4}{(x - 3)(5 - x)}$

    (a) $x\to 5^+$ (b) $x\to 3^-$ (c) $x\to 5^-$ (d) $x\to 3^+$ (e) None of these

2—Answer: a

60. $f(x)$ decreases without bound as x approaches what value from the right? $f(x) = \dfrac{9}{(x - 4)(9 - x)}$

    (a) $x\to 9^-$ (b) $x\to 4^+$ (c) $x\to 9^+$ (d) $x\to 4^-$ (e) None of these

2—Answer: c

61. $f(x)$ decreases without bound as x approaches what value from the right? $f(x) = \dfrac{6}{(x - 2)(7 - x)}$

    (a) $x\to 2^-$ (b) $x\to 7^-$ (c) $x\to 2^+$ (d) $x\to 7^+$ (e) None of these

2—Answer: d

Section 3.7   Curve Sketching: A Summary

1. Which of the following is the correct sketch of the graph of the function $f(x) = \dfrac{1}{(x-2)^2}$?

(a) 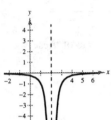   (b) 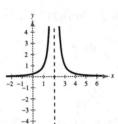   (c) 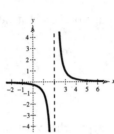   (d) 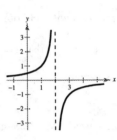   (e) None of these

1—Answer: b

2. Which of the following is the correct sketch of the graph of the function $f(x) = x^3 - 6x^2 + 9x + 2$?

(a) 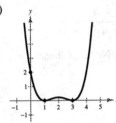   (b)    (c) 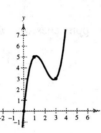   (d)    (e) None of these

1—Answer: b

3. Which of the following is the correct sketch of the graph of the function $y = x^3 - 12x + 20$?

(a) 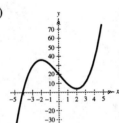   (b) 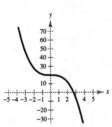   (c) 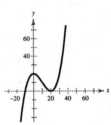   (d) 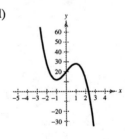   (e) None of these

1—Answer: a

4. Which of the following is the correct sketch of the graph of the function $f(x) = x^3 - 12x$?

(a) 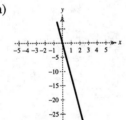   (b) 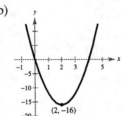   (c) 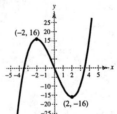   (d) 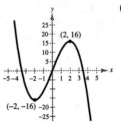   (e) None of these

1—Answer: c

5. Which of the following is the correct sketch of the graph of the function $f(x) = \dfrac{x-1}{x+2}$?

(a)   (b)   (c)   (d)   (e) None
of these

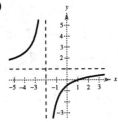

1—Answer: a

6. Which of the following is the correct sketch of the graph of the function $y = 8x^3 - 2x^4$?

(a)   (b)   (c)   (d)   (e) None
of these

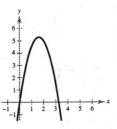 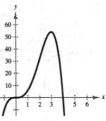 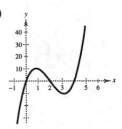

1—Answer: c

7. Sketch the graph of $f(x) = \dfrac{x^2 - 3x + 6}{x - 2}$?

(a)   (b)   (c)   (d) None of these

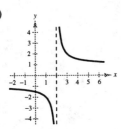 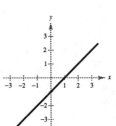 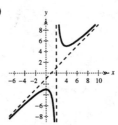

1—Answer: c

8. Sketch the graph of $f(x) = \dfrac{x^2 - 5x + 8}{x - 3}$?

(a)   (b) None of these   (c)   (d)

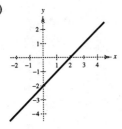 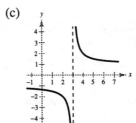 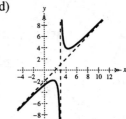

1—Answer: d

9. Determine where the graph of $y = x(x^2 - 12)$ is increasing/decreasing, if it has any relative extrema, where it is concave up/down and whether it has any points of inflection. Then draw a rough sketch of the graph of $f(x)$.

   1—Answer: Increasing on $(-\infty, -2), (2, \infty)$
   Decreasing on $(-2, 2)$
   Concave up on $(0, \infty)$
   Concave down on $(-\infty, 0)$
   Relative maximum at $(-2, 16)$
   Relative minimum at $(2, -16)$
   Inflection point at $(0, 0)$

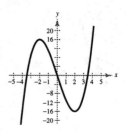

10. Sketch the graph of $f(x) = \dfrac{x^2 - 7x + 13}{x - 4}$.

   (a)    (b) 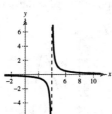   (c) None of these   (d)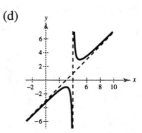

   1—Answer: d

11. Sketch the graph of $y = \dfrac{3}{(1 - x)^2}$.

   1—Answer:

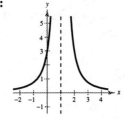

12. Use the techniques learned in this chapter to sketch a graph of $y = f(x) = \dfrac{1}{x^3}$.

   1—Answer:

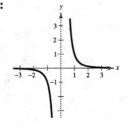

13. Sketch the graph of $y = x^3 - 3x + 1$.

    1—Answer:

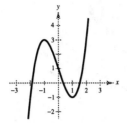

14. Sketch the graph of $f(x) = 3x^{2/3} - x^2$.

    1—Answer:

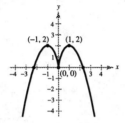

15. Sketch the graph of $f(x) = \dfrac{x^2}{x - 1}$.

    1—Answer:

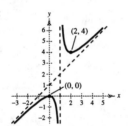

16. Use the techniques learned in this chapter to sketch a graph of $y = x(x^2 - 12)$.

    1—Answer:

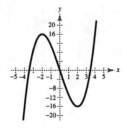

17. Use the techniques learned in this chapter to sketch a graph of $y = \dfrac{1}{x^2}$.

1—Answer:

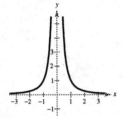

18. Sketch the graph of the function $f(x) = x^5 + 2$.

2—Answer:

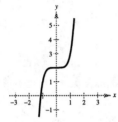

19. Sketch the graph of the function $f(x) = 2x^3 - 3x^2$.

2—Answer:

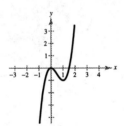

20. Sketch the graph of the function $f(x) = x^3 + x^2 - 6x$.

2—Answer:

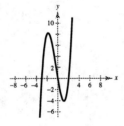

21. Sketch the graph of $f(x) = \dfrac{x^2 + 4}{x - 2} = x + 2 + \dfrac{8}{x - 2}$.

1—Answer:

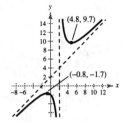

22. Sketch the graph of the function $f(x) = 2x^4 - 8x^2$.

2—Answer:

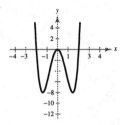

23. Sketch the graph of $f(x) = x^3 - 3x + 2$.

2—Answer:

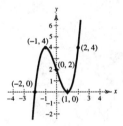

24. Identify the graph below that satisfies the following characteristics:

$$f(x) = 3 \qquad f'(x) > 0, \quad -\infty < x < 2$$
$$f(0) = -5 \qquad f'(x) > 0, \quad 2 < x < \infty$$
$$f'(2) = 0$$

(a) 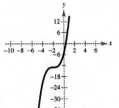   (b) 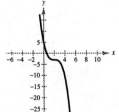   (c) 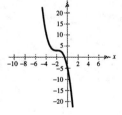   (d) 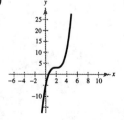   (e) None of these

2—Answer: d

25. Identify the graph below that satisfies the following characteristics:

$$f'(x) > 0, \quad -\infty < x < -2$$

$$f''(x) < 0, \quad -\infty < x < \frac{-2\sqrt{3}}{3}$$

(a)
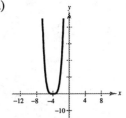

(b)
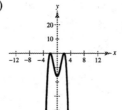

(c)
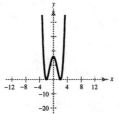

(d)
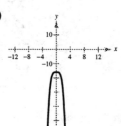

(e) None of these

2—Answer: b

Section 3.8   Differentials and Marginal Analysis

1. Find Δy for $y = 6x^2 - 2$, $x = 15$ and $\Delta x = 1$.

(a) -180 (b) 180 (c) -186 (d) 186 (e) None of these

1—Answer: d

2. Find Δy for $\dfrac{2}{x^2 + 1}$, $x = 3$ and $\Delta x = -0.5$.

(a) -0.0759 (b) 0.0759 (c) -0.0600 (d) 0.0600 (e) None of these

1—Answer: b

3. Find Δy for $\sqrt{6 - 2x}$, $x = 1$ and $\Delta x = -1$.

(a) -0.500 (b) 0.500 (c) 0.499 (d) -0.449 (e) None of these

1—Answer: c

4. Find Δy for $y = \dfrac{x^3}{2x^2 + 4}$ as x changes from 0.5 to 0.4

(a) -0.013 (b) 0.013 (c) 0.015 (d) -0.011 (e) None of these

1—T—Answer: a

5. Find dy for $\dfrac{x^3}{2x^3 + 1}$.

1—Answer: $\dfrac{3x^2}{(2x^3 + 1)^2}dx$

6. Find dy for $\dfrac{x^2}{4x^2 + 1}$.

1—Answer: $\dfrac{2x}{(4x^2 + 1)^2}dx$

7. Find dy for $\dfrac{x^2}{4x^2 + 1}$ as x changes from 0.5 to 0.6.

(a) 0.250 (b) 2.50 (c) 0.0250 (d) 0.0225 (e) None of these

1—T—Answer: c

8. Evaluate Δy and dy for $y = 4 - x^2$ as x changes from 3 to 3.1.

(a) $dy = -6, \Delta y = 0.61$ (b) $dy = -0.6, \Delta y = -0.61$ (c) $dy = -0.62, \Delta y = -0.6$

(d) $dy = 0.1, \Delta y = -0.1$ (e) None of these

1—T—Answer: b

    Applications of the Derivative

9. Evaluate Δy and dy for $y = x^4 + 2x$ as x changes from 3 to 2.98.

   (a) $dy = 2.157, \Delta y = 2.178$ (b) $dy = -2.157, \Delta y = -2.178$ (c) $dy = 2.200, \Delta y = 2.178$

   (d) $dy = -2.200, \Delta y = -2.178$ (e)   None of these

   1—T—Answer: d

10. Calculate the differential of p for the demand function $p(x) = \sqrt{100 - x}$.

   (a) $dp = \dfrac{dx}{2\sqrt{100 - x}}$ (b) $dp = \dfrac{-1}{2\sqrt{100 - x}}$ (c) $dp = \dfrac{-1}{2\sqrt{100 - x}}\, dx$

   (d) $dp = \dfrac{-dx}{\sqrt{100 - x}}$ (e)   None of these

   1—T—Answer: c

11. Calculate the differential of p for the demand function $p(x) = \sqrt{200 - 3x}$.

   1—Answer: $dp = \dfrac{-3dx}{2\sqrt{200 - 3x}}$

12. Find the differential dy if $y = \dfrac{x - 2}{x + 3}$.

   1—Answer: $dy = \dfrac{5}{(x + 3)^2}\, dx$

13. Calculate the differential dy for the function $y = x^4 - x^2$.

   (a) $dy = 4x^3 - 2x$ (b) $dy = (2x^2 - 1)\, dx$ (c) $dy = (4x^3 - 2x)\, dx$

   (d) $y' = (4x^3 - 2x)\, dx$ (e)   None of these

   1—Answer: c

14. Calculate the differential dy for the function $y = (x^2 + 1)^{3/2}$.

   (a) $dy = \frac{3}{2}(x^2 + 1)^{1/2}dx$ (b) $dy = 3(x^2 + 1)^{1/2}dx$ (c) $y' = 3x\sqrt{x^2 + 1}$

   (d) $dy = 3x\sqrt{x^2 + 1}\, dx$ (e)   None of these

   1—Answer: d

15. For the function $y = f(x) = 2x^3 - 10x^2$, compare the actual change in y on $[1, 2]$ with the value of the differential of y when $x = 1$ and $dx = 1$.

   2—T—Answer: $dy = -14, \Delta y = -16$

16. Using a graphing utility, graph the function $y = x^3 - 2x^2 + 3$ and its tangent line at $x = 1$. Determine the approximate discrepancy between dy at $x = 1$ and Δy on $[1, 2]$.

(a) $dy = 1, \Delta y = 1$ (b) $dy = -1, \Delta y = 1$ (c) $dy = -1, \Delta y = -1$

(d) $dy = 1, \Delta y = -1$ (e) None of these

2—T—Answer: b

17. Find Δx, dx, Δy, and dy for $y = x^3 + 5x$ as x changes from 2 to 1.99.

1—T—Answer: $\Delta x = dx = -0.1, \Delta y = -0.1694, dy = -0.17$

18. The demand, x, for a product depends on its price p (in dollars) according to

$$x = \frac{800}{\sqrt{p}} - 2 \text{ for } p > 0.$$

Approximate, using differentials, the change in demand if the price changes from $30 to $33.

1—T—Answer: -7 units

19. Use the differential of C to approximate the change in cost if the cost function is

$$C(x) = \frac{10,000x}{50 - x},$$

and production is increased from 100 to 101 units.

1—T—Answer: $200

20. The side of a cube is measured to be 3.0 inches. If the measurement is correct to within 0.01 inch, use differentials to estimate the propagated error in the volume of the cube.

(a) ± 0.000001 in.^{3} (b) ± 0.06 in.^{3} (c) ± 0.027 in.^{3}

(d) ± 0.27 in.^{3} (e) None of these

1—Answer: d

21. The radius of a sphere is measured to be 3.0 inches. If the measurement is correct to within 0.01 inch, use differentials to estimate the propagated error in the volume of the sphere.

(a) ± 0.000001 in.^{3} (b) $\pm 0.36\pi$ in.^{3} (c) $\pm 0.036\pi$ in.^{3}

(d) ± 0.06 in.^{3} (e) None of these

1—Answer: b

22. The volume of a cube is claimed to be 27 in.^{3}, correct to within 0.027 in.^{3}. Use differentials to estimate the propagated error in the measurement of the side of the cube.

1—Answer: ± 0.001 in.

23. Find the values of dy and Δy for $y = x^3 - 2x$ when $x = 2$ and $\Delta x = 0.1$.

1—Answer: $dy = 1 \quad \Delta y = 1.061$

24. Use differentials to approximate the change in revenue as the number of items sold increases from 7 to 8.
$R = -x^3 + 21x^2$

   (a) $144   (b) $146   (c) $147   (d) $149   (e) None of these

   1—Answer: c

25. Use differentials to approximate the change in revenue as the number of items sold increases from 15 to 16.
$R = -\frac{1}{3}x^3 + 25x^2$

   (a) $525.00   (b) $534.67   (c) $544.00   (d) $552.33   (e) None of these

   1—Answer: a

26. Use differentials to approximate the change in revenue as the number of items sold increases from 150 to 155.
$R = -x^2 + 700x$

   (a) $1950   (b) $1975   (c) $2000   (d) $2025   (e) None of these

   1—Answer: c

CHAPTER 4
Exponential and Logarithmic Functions

Section 4.1   Exponential Functions

1. Evaluate: $\left(\frac{1}{64}\right)^{2/3}$.

   (a) $\frac{1}{16}$ (b) $\frac{1}{96}$ (c) 96   (d) $\frac{1}{2}$ (e) None of these

   1—Answer: a

2. Solve for x: $\left(\frac{1}{2}\right)^{x-1} = 32$.

   (a) 4   (b) 6   (c) 7   (d) -4 (e) None of these

   1—Answer: d

3. Evaluate: $\left(\frac{7}{2}\right)^{3/2}$.

   (a) 3.726   (b) 6.548   (c) 5.328   (d) 4.269   (e) None of these

   1—T—Answer: b

4. Evaluate: $\left(\frac{1}{16}\right)^{3/4}$.

   (a) $\frac{3}{64}$ (b) $\frac{1}{8}$ (c) 12   (d) $\frac{1}{12}$ (e) None of these

   1—Answer: b

5. Evaluate: $\left(\frac{8}{27}\right)^{-4/3}$.

   1—Answer: $\frac{81}{16}$

6. Solve for x: $4^{3x+1} = \frac{1}{16}$.

   (a) $-\frac{1}{3}$ (b) $\frac{1}{3}$ (c) $-\frac{1}{2}$ (d) -1 (e) None of these

   1—Answer: d

7. Solve for x: $4^{7x-4} = \frac{1}{64}$.

   (a) $\frac{3}{7}$ (b) $\frac{1}{7}$ (c) $\frac{6}{7}$ (d) $-\frac{1}{7}$ (e) None of these

   1—Answer: b

8. Solve for x: $(2x + 1)^{3/2} = 64$.

   (a) $\frac{511}{2}$ (b) $\frac{15}{2}$ (c) $\frac{3}{2}$ (d) $\frac{7}{2}$ (e) None of these

   1—Answer: b

9. Identify the correct sketch of the graph of $y = e^x$.

(a) 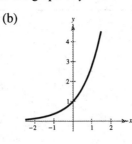 (b) 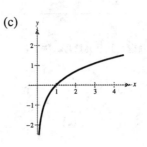 (c) 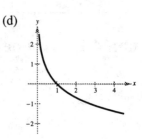 (d)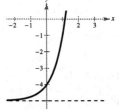

1—Answer: b

10. Match the graph shown with the correct function.

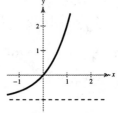

(a) $f(x) = 4^x - 5$ (b) $f(x) = 4^x + 5$

(c) $f(x) = 4^{-x} + 5$ (d) $f(x) = 4^{-x} - 5$

(e) None of these

1—Answer: a

11. Match the graph shown with the correct function.

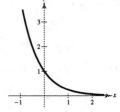

(a) $y = 3^{x-1}$ (b) $y = 3^x - 1$

(c) $y = 3^{1-x}$ (d) $y = 3^{-x} - 1$

(e) None of these

1—Answer: b

12. Match the graph shown with the correct function.

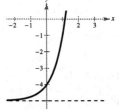

(a) $f(x) = \left(\frac{1}{2}\right)^x - 1$ (b) $f(x) = 3^{-x^2} - 1$

(c) $f(x) = 3^{x+1}$ (d) $f(x) = 4^{-x}$

(e) None of these

1—Answer: d

13. Sketch the graph: $f(x) = 3^x - 5$.

1—Answer:

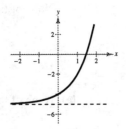

14. Match the graph shown with the correct function.

(a) $f(x) = e^x + 1$ (b) $f(x) = e^{(x-1)}$

(c) $f(x) = e^{-x} + 1$ (d) $f(x) = e^{-(x-1)}$

(e) None of these

2—Answer: c

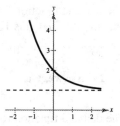

15. Match the graph shown with the correct function.

(a) $f(x) = e^{(x+3)}$ (b) $f(x) = e^{-x} - 3$

(c) $f(x) = e^x - 3$ (d) $f(x) = e^{-(x+3)}$

(e) None of these

2—Answer: b

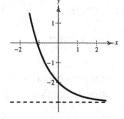

16. Sketch a graph of $y = e^{-x}$.

1—Answer:

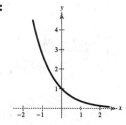

17. Solve for x: $\left(\frac{1}{3}\right)^{2x-1} = 81$.

(a) $\frac{3}{2}$ (b) $-\frac{3}{2}$ (c) $\frac{5}{2}$ (d) $-\frac{5}{2}$ (e) None of these

1—Answer: b

18. Solve for x: $3^{2x+1} = 243$.

(a) 40   (b) 3   (c) 2   (d) 5   (e) None of these

1—Answer: c

19. Solve for x: $4^{3x+1} = 256$.

(a) 1   (b) 2   (c) $\frac{1}{2}$ (d) 21   (e) None of these

1—Answer: a

20. The number of fish in a lake is modeled using

$$P(t) = \frac{20{,}000}{1 + 19e^{-(t/10)}},$$

where $t \geq 0$, where t is the time since the lake was stocked (in months). Use a graphing utility to determine if the population is increasing or decreasing after one year.

1—T—Answer: Increasing

21. The demand function for a certain product is given by $p = 750 - 0.5e^{0.002x}$. Find the price of the product if the quantity demanded is 1200.

    (a) $749.45   (b) $746.90   (c) $744.49   (d) $742.12   (e) None of these

    1—T—**Answer:** c

22. The demand function for a certain product is given by $p = 750 - 0.5e^{0.002x}$. Find the price of the product if the quantity demanded is 1500.

    (a) $739.96   (b) $745.10   (c) $760.04   (d) $747.71   (e) None of these

    1—T—**Answer:** a

23. The demand function for a certain product is given by $p = 750 - 0.5e^{0.002x}$. Find the price of the product if the quantity demanded is 2500.

    1—T—**Answer:** $675.79

24. Find an expression that is equivalent to $\dfrac{4^x + 4^{x+y}}{9^x}$.

    (a) $\left(\dfrac{4}{9}\right)^x + \left(\dfrac{4^y}{9}\right)^x$ (b) $4(9^{-x}) + 4^y$ (c) $\dfrac{2(4^x) + 4^y}{9x}$

    (d) $4^x 9^{-x}(1 + 4^y)$ (e) None of these

    1—**Answer:** d

25. Find an expression that is equivalent to $\dfrac{3^x + 3^{x+y}}{2^x}$.

    (a) $\left(\dfrac{3}{2}\right)^x + \left(\dfrac{3^y}{2}\right)^x$ (b) $\dfrac{2(3^x) + 3^y}{2^x}$ (c) $3(2^{-x}) + 3^y$

    (d) $3^x 2^{-x}(1 + 3^y)$ (e) None of these

    1—**Answer:** d

26. Find an expression that is equivalent to $\dfrac{6^x + 6^{x+y}}{5^x}$.

    (a) $\dfrac{2(6^x) + 6^y}{5^x}$ (b) $\left(\dfrac{6}{5}\right)^x + \left(\dfrac{6^y}{5}\right)^x$ (c) $6(5^{-x}) + 6^y$

    (d) $6^x 5^{-x}(1 + 6^y)$ (e) None of these

    1—**Answer:** d

27. Find the amount of an investment of $5000 invested at a rate of 5% for three years if the interest is compounded monthly.

    1—T—**Answer:** $5807.36

28. Find the amount of an investment of $2000 invested at a rate of $8\frac{1}{2}\%$ for ten years if the interest is compounded daily.

1—T—Answer: $4678.83

29. Find the amount of an investment of $1000 invested at a rate of 6% for three years if the interest is compounded quarterly.

(a) $2000(1 + 0.06)^{12}$

(b) $1000\left(1 + \frac{0.06}{4}\right)^{12}$

(c) $1000\left(1 + \frac{0.06}{4}\right)^{3}$

(d) $1000\left(1 + \frac{0.06}{3}\right)^{12}$

(e) None of these

1—Answer: b

30. Find the amount of an investment of $1000 invested at a rate of 11% for two years if the interest is compounded quarterly.

(a) $220.00   (b) $1242.38   (c) $1220.00   (d) $1246.08   (e) None of these

1—T—Answer: b

31. Find the amount of an investment of $1000 invested at an annual rate of 6% for three years if the interest is compounded continuously.

1—T—Answer: $1000e^{0.018} = \$1197.22$

32. Find the amount of an investment of $1000 invested at a rate of 9% for three years if the interest is compounded monthly.

(a) $270.00   (b) $1270.00   (c) $1309.96   (d) $1308.65   (e) None of these

1—T—Answer: d

33. Find the amount of an investment of $2000 invested at a rate of 4% for three years if the interest is compounded monthly.

(a) $2000(1 + 0.04)^{36}$

(b) $2000\left(1 + \frac{0.04}{12}\right)^{36}$

(c) $200\left(1 + \frac{0.04}{12}\right)^{3}$

(d) $2000\left(1 + \frac{0.04}{3}\right)^{36}$

(e) None of these

1—T—Answer: b

Section 4.2 Derivatives of Exponential Functions

1. Find $f'(x)$ for $f(x) = \sqrt{4 + e^{2x}}$.

(a) $\dfrac{e^{2x}}{\sqrt{4 + e^{2x}}}$ (b) $\dfrac{1}{2\sqrt{2e^{2x}}}$ (c) $\dfrac{xe^{2x-1}}{\sqrt{x + e^{2x}}}$ (d) e^x (e) None of these

1—Answer: a

2. Find $f'(x)$ for $f(x) = \dfrac{2}{2x + e^{2x}}$.

(a) 0   (b) $\dfrac{1}{1 + e^{2x}}$ (c) $\dfrac{-4(1 + e^{2x})}{(2x + e^{2x})^2}$ (d) $\dfrac{1 + xe^{2x-1}}{(2x + e^{2x})^2}$ (e) None of these

1—Answer: c

3. Find y': $y = e^{1/x}$.

1—Answer: $-\dfrac{e^{1/x}}{x^2}$

4. Find $\dfrac{dy}{dx}$: $y = (e^x + e^{3x})^4$.

1—Answer: $4(e^x + 3e^{3x})(e^x + e^{3x})^3$

5. Find $\dfrac{dy}{dx}$ if $y = x^e e^x$.

1—Answer: $e^x x^{e-1}(x + 1)$

6. Differentiate with respect to x: $y = e^{7-(3/x)}$.

(a) $\dfrac{dy}{dx} = e^{3/x^2}$ (b) $\dfrac{dy}{dx} = \dfrac{3}{x^2} e^{7-(3/x)}$ (c) $\dfrac{dy}{dx} = e^{7-(3/x)}$

(d) $\dfrac{dy}{dx} = -e^{7-(3/x)}$ (e) None of these

1—Answer: b

7. Differentiate with respect to x: $y = e^{7-(5/x)}$.

(a) $\dfrac{dy}{dx} = -e^{7-(5/x)}$ (b) $\dfrac{dy}{dx} = e^{7-(5/x)}$ (c) $\dfrac{dy}{dx} = \dfrac{5}{x^2} e^{7-(5/x)}$

(d) $\dfrac{dy}{dx} = e^{5/x^2}$ (e) None of these

1—Answer: c

8. Differentiate with respect to x: $y = e^{5-(2/x)}$.

   (a) $\dfrac{dy}{dx} = e^{2/x^2}$

   (b) $\dfrac{dy}{dx} = e^{5-(2/x)}$

   (c) $\dfrac{dy}{dx} = \dfrac{2}{x^2} e^{5-(2/x)}$

   (d) $\dfrac{dy}{dx} = -e^{5-(2/x)}$

   (e) None of these

   1—Answer: c

9. Find y' if $xe^y + 1 = xy$.

   (a) 0

   (b) $\dfrac{y - e^y}{xe^y - x}$

   (c) $\dfrac{y}{e^y - x}$

   (d) $\dfrac{e^y}{xe^y - 1}$

   (e) None of these

   1—Answer: b

10. Find y' if $ye^x - x = y^2$.

   1—Answer: $\dfrac{1 - ye^x}{e^x - 2y}$

11. Find the derivative $\dfrac{dy}{dx}$ if $y = e^{-x^3}$.

   (a) $-x^3 e^{-x^3-1}$

   (b) $-3x^2 e^{-x^3}$

   (c) $\dfrac{1}{x^3 e^{-x^3-1}}$

   (d) e^{-3x^2}

   (e) None of these

   1—Answer: b

12. Find the derivative $\dfrac{dy}{dx}$ if $y = e^{x^2+4x}$.

   (a) $(2x)e^{x^2+4x}$

   (b) $(2x + 4)e^{x^2+4x}$

   (c) $\dfrac{1}{(2x + 4)e^{x^2+4x}}$

   (d) e^{-2x}

   (e) None of these

   1—Answer: b

13. Find $\dfrac{dy}{dx}$ if $y = \dfrac{10}{1 + e^{-(1/x)}}$.

   (a) $\dfrac{dy}{dx} = \dfrac{-10e^{-(1/x)}}{x^2(1 + e^{-(1/x)})^2}$

   (b) $\dfrac{dy}{dx} = \dfrac{-10}{(1 + e^{-(1/x)})^2}$

   (c) $\dfrac{dy}{dx} = \dfrac{-10e^{-(1/x)}}{x^2(1 + e^{-(1/x)})^2}$

   (d) $\dfrac{dy}{dx} = \dfrac{10e^{-(1/x)}}{(1 + e^{-(1/x)})^2}$

   (e) None of these

   1—Answer: a

14. Find $f'(x)$ if $f(x) = \sqrt[3]{x + e^{-4x}}$.

(a) $\dfrac{1 + e^{-4x}}{3\sqrt[3]{x + e^{-4x}}}$

(b) $\dfrac{1 - 4e^{-4x}}{\sqrt[3]{x + e^{-4x}}}$

(c) $\dfrac{1}{3\sqrt[3]{1 + 4e^{-4x}}}$

(d) $\dfrac{1 - 4e^{-4x}}{3(x + e^{-4x})^{2/3}}$

(e) None of these

1—Answer: d

15. Find the derivative: $y = e^{\sqrt{x}}$.

1—Answer: $\dfrac{e^{\sqrt{x}}}{2\sqrt{x}}$

16. Find $f'(x)$ if $f(x) = xe^{3x}$.

1—Answer: $e^{3x}(3x + 1)$

17. Find $f'(x)$ if $f(x) = \dfrac{e^x + e^{-x}}{2x}$.

1—Answer: $\dfrac{x(e^x - e^{-x}) - (e^x + e^{-x})}{2x^2}$

18. Find $f'(x)$ if $f(x) = \sqrt{x + e^{-2x}}$.

(a) $\dfrac{1 + e^{-2x}}{2\sqrt{x + e^{-2x}}}$
(b) $\dfrac{1 - 2e^{-2x}}{\sqrt{x + e^{-2x}}}$
(c) $\dfrac{1}{2\sqrt{1 - 2e^{-2x}}}$
(d) $\dfrac{1 - 2e^{-2x}}{2\sqrt{x + e^{-2x}}}$
(e) None of these

1—Answer: d

19. Find $f'(x)$ if $f(x) = \dfrac{3}{4x - e^{3x}}$.

(a) $\dfrac{3}{(4x - e^{3x})^2}$
(b) $\dfrac{3(3e^{3x} - 4)}{(e^{3x} - 4x)^2}$
(c) $\dfrac{3}{4 - 3e^{3x}}$
(d) $\dfrac{(4 + 3e^{3x})}{(4x - e^{3x})^2}$
(e) None of these

1—Answer: b

20. Find $\dfrac{dy}{dx}$ if $y = \dfrac{10}{x + e^{-2x}}$.

1—Answer: $\dfrac{10(2e^{-2x} - 1)}{(x + e^{-2x})^2}$

21. Find the derivative: $y = e^{3-x}$.

(a) $(3 - x)e^{2-x}$
(b) e^{x-3}
(c) $-e^{3-x}$
(d) $\dfrac{1}{e}$
(e) None of these

1—Answer: c

22. Find $f'(x)$ if $f(x) = \dfrac{1}{\sqrt[4]{x + e^{3x}}}$.

  1—Answer: $\dfrac{-(1 + 3e^{3x})}{4(x + e^{3x})^{5/4}}$

23. Find the derivative: $y = e^{-x^2}$.

  (a) $-x^2 e^{-x^2-1}$ (b) $-2xe^{-x^2}$ (c) $\dfrac{1}{x^2 e^{x^2-1}}$ (d) e^{-2x} (e) None of these

  1—Answer: b

24. Find the second derivative of the function: $f(x) = (x + 7x^2)e^{2x}$.

  (a) $(14x^2 + 16x + 1)e^{2x}$ (b) $2(14x^2 + 30x + 9)e^{2x}$ (c) $2x(1 + 14x)e^{2x-1}$

  (d) $(7x^2 + 29x + 16)e^{2x}$ (e) None of these

  1—Answer: b

25. Find the second derivative of the function: $f(x) = (3 + 9x)e^{-3x^2}$.

  (a) $(81x - 27)e^{-3x^2}$ (b) $9e^{-3x^2}$ (c) $18(18x^3 + 6x^2 - 9x - 1)e^{-3x^2}$

  (d) $-9(6x^2 + 2x - 1)e^{-3x^2}$ (e) None of these

  1—Answer: c

26. Find the second derivative of the function: $f(x) = e^{-7x^3}$.

  (a) $21x(21x^3 - 2)e^{-7x^3}$ (b) $-21x^2 e^{-7x^3}$ (c) $7x^3(7x^3 + 1)e^{-7x^3-2}$

  (d) $-7x^3 e^{-7x^3-1}$ (e) None of these

  1—Answer: a

27. Find the second derivative of the function: $f(x) = e^{2x-x^2}$.

  (a) $2(1 - x)e^{2x-x^2}$ (b) $(2x - x^2)e^{2x-x^2-2}$ (c) $2(2x^2 - 4x + 1)e^{2x-x^2}$

  (d) $(2 - 2x)e^x$ (e) None of these

  1—Answer: c

28. Find the second derivative of the function: $f(x) = e^{1/x}$.

  1—Answer: $\dfrac{(2x + 1)e^{1/x}}{x^4}$

29. Use a graphing utility to find the number of units which maximizes the profit for a product whose demand function is

$$p = \frac{1000}{1 + e^{-x}}$$

and cost function is $C = e^x + 100$.

  2—T—Answer: $x = 6.9$

30. Use a graphing utility to find the number of units which maximizes the profit for a product whose demand function is $p = 1000(\frac{2}{3})^x$ and cost function is $C = 40x + 100$.

    (a) 30.1   (b) 24.3   (c) 2.3   (d) 23.5   (e) None of these

    2—T—Answer: c

31. Find the price per unit that will maximize the revenue function if the demand function for a certain product is $p = 42e^{-0.002x}$.

    (a) \$15.45   (b) \$500.00   (c) \$7725.47   (d) \$4321.22   (e) None of these

    2—T—Answer: a

32. Find the price per unit that will maximize the revenue function if the demand function for a certain product is $p = 46e^{-0.003x}$.

    2—T—Answer: \$16.92

33. Find the instantaneous rate of change of y with respect to x for the curve described implicitly by $xe^y + x = xy$.

    1—Answer: $\dfrac{y - 1 - e^y}{xe^y - x}$

34. Find any critical numbers for the function: $y = \dfrac{e^x}{x}$.

    1—Answer: $x = 1$

35. Find the slope of the curve $y = e^{4 - 3/x}$ at the point where $x = 3$.

    1—Answer: $\frac{1}{3}e^3$

36. Determine where the graph of $f(x) = \dfrac{e^x}{x^3}$ is increasing.

    1—Answer: $(3, \infty)$

37. Determine where the graph of $f(x) = e^{-(1/2)x^2}$ has any inflection points.

    1—Answer: $-1, 1$

38. Determine where the graph of $f(x) = \dfrac{e^x}{x^2}$ is increasing.

    (a) $(-\infty, 0), (2, \infty)$ (b) $(0, 2)$ (c) $(-\infty, 2)$

    (d) $(2, \infty)$ (e) None of these

    1—Answer: a

39. Determine where the graph of $f(x) = e^{-x^2}$ is concave up.

(a) $\left(-\dfrac{\sqrt{2}}{2}, \dfrac{\sqrt{2}}{2}\right)$ (b) $\left(-\infty, -\dfrac{\sqrt{2}}{2}\right), \left(\dfrac{\sqrt{2}}{2}, \infty\right)$ (c) $(-8, 0)$

(d) $(0, \infty)$ (e) None of these

2—Answer: b

40. Determine where the graph of $f(x) = e^{-(1/2)x^2}$ is concave down.

(a) $(-1, 1)$ (b) $(-\infty, -1), (1, \infty)$ (c) $(-\infty, 0)$

(d) $(0, \infty)$ (e) None of these

2—Answer: a

41. Explain in a complete sentence how to differentiate a function of the form $y = f(x) = e^u$ if $u = g(x)$.

1—Answer: The derivative of $y = e^u$ where $u = g(x)$ is the function e^u times the derivative of the exponent.

Section 4.3   Logarithmic Functions

1. Find the domain of the function: $f(x) = \ln(3x + 1)$.

(a) $(-\infty, \infty)$ (b) $\left(-\frac{1}{3}, \infty\right)$ (c) $(0, \infty)$ (d) $\left(\frac{1}{3}, \infty\right)$ (e) None of these

1—Answer: b

2. Find the domain of the function: $f(x) = 3\ln(5x - 2)$.

(a) $(-\infty, \infty)$ (b) $(0, \infty)$ (c) $\left(\frac{2}{5}, \infty\right)$ (d) $(0.064, \infty)$ (e) None of these

1—Answer: c

3. Find the domain of the function: $f(x) = 3 + \ln(x - 1)$.

(a) $(-\infty, \infty)$ (b) $(0, \infty)$ (c) $(1, \infty)$ (d) $(3, \infty)$ (e) None of these

1—Answer: c

4. Find the domain of the function: $f(x) = 3 - \ln(x^2 - 1)$.

2—Answer: $(-\infty, -1), (1, \infty)$

5. Find the domain of the function: $f(x) = \ln(x^2 - 4)$.

2—Answer: $(-\infty, -2), (2, \infty)$

6. Match the graph with the correct function.

(a) $f(x) = e^x$ (b) $f(x) = e^{x-1}$

(c) $f(x) = \ln x$ (d) $f(x) = \ln(x - 1)$

(e) None of these

1—Answer: d

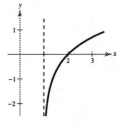

7. Sketch the graph: $f(x) = \ln|x|$.

2—Answer:

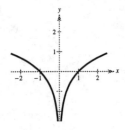

8. Sketch the graph: $f(x) = 1 + \log_5 x$.

    2—Answer:

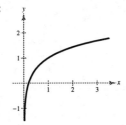

9. Match the graph with the correct function.

    (a) $f(x) = -3 + \ln x$ (b) $f(x) = 3 + \ln x$

    (c) $f(x) = \ln(x - 3)$ (d) $f(x) = \ln(x + 3)$

    (e) None of these

    1—Answer: d

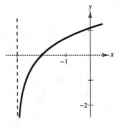

10. Match the graph with the correct function.

    (a) $f(x) = 3 + \log x$ (b) $f(x) = \log(x + 3)$

    (c) $f(x) = \frac{1}{3} \log x$ (d) $f(x) = 3 \log x$

    (e) None of these

    1—Answer: a

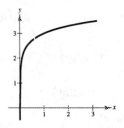

11. Identify the correct sketch of the graph of $y = \ln x$.

    (a) 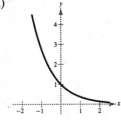   (b) 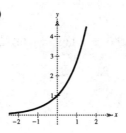   (c) 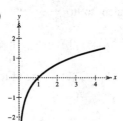   (d)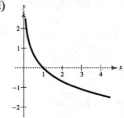

    (e) None of these

    1—Answer: c

12. Sketch a graph of $y = f(x) = \ln(x - 2)$.

    1—Answer:

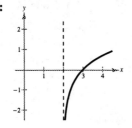

13. Write as a single logarithm: $2 \ln(x) - 3 \ln(x - 2) - 5 \ln(x + 1)$.

1—Answer: $\ln \dfrac{x^2}{(x - 2)^3(x + 1)^5}$

14. Write the given expression as a single logarithm: $\frac{1}{2} \ln x - \ln(x + 1) - \ln(x - 1)$.

1—Answer: $\ln \dfrac{\sqrt{x}}{x^2 - 1}$

15. Choose the expression equivalent to $\ln \dfrac{3x^2}{7y}$.

    (a) $\dfrac{\ln 3 + \ln x^2}{\ln 7 + \ln y}$ (b) $\ln(3x^2) + \ln(7y)$ (c) $\ln 3 - \ln 7 + 2 \ln x - \ln y$

    (d) $2 \ln(3x) - \ln(7y)$ (e) None of these

    1—Answer: c

16. Choose the expression equivalent to $\ln \dfrac{8x^2}{3y}$.

    (a) $\ln 8 - \ln 3 + 2 \ln x - \ln y$ (b) $\dfrac{\ln 8 + \ln x^2}{\ln 3 + \ln y}$ (c) $\ln(8x^2) + \ln(3y)$

    (d) $2 \ln(8x) - \ln(3y)$ (e) None of these

    1—Answer: a

17. Choose the expression equivalent to $\ln \dfrac{9x^2}{2y}$.

    (a) $\ln(9x^2) + \ln(2y)$ (b) $\ln 9 - \ln 2 + 2 \ln x - \ln y$ (c) $2 \ln(9x) - \ln(2y)$

    (d) $\dfrac{\ln 9 + \ln x^2}{\ln 2 + \ln y}$ (e) None of these

    1—Answer: b

18. Solve for x: $4^{2x+1} = 10$.

    1—T—Answer: 0.3305

19. Solve for x: $\ln(5x + 1) + \ln x = \ln 4$.

    (a) $-1, \frac{4}{5}$ (b) $\frac{4}{5}$ (c) $\frac{3}{5}, 4$ (d) $e^4, e^{3/5}$ (e) None of these

    1—Answer: b

20. Solve for x: $\ln(5x - 1) - \ln x = 3$.

    1—Answer: $\dfrac{1}{5 - e^3}$

21. Solve for x: $2^{3x-1} = 5$.

(a) $\frac{1}{3}\ln 10$ (b) $\frac{7}{6}$ (c) $\frac{1}{3}[\ln 2.5 + 1]$ (d) $\frac{1}{3}\left[\frac{\ln 5}{\ln 2} + 1\right]$ (e) None of these

1—Answer: d

22. Simplify: $e^{\ln(3x+1)}$.

(a) $\ln(3x + 1)$ (b) $3x + 1$ (c) $e^{(3x+1)}$.   (d) $-\frac{1}{3}$ (e) None of these

1—Answer: b

23. Simplify: $\ln e^4$.

(a) 4   (b) e^4 (c) $\ln 4$ (d) 0   (e) None of these

1—Answer: a

24. Simplify: $6 - \ln e^0$.

1—Answer: 6

25. Solve for x: $3 \ln x = 12$.

(a) $\ln 4$ (b) $\sqrt[3]{12}$ (c) 4   (d) e^4 (e) None of these

1—Answer: d

26. Solve for x: $2^{3x+1} = 10$.

(a) 0.774   (b) 1.246   (c) 0.891   (d) -0.713 (e) None of these

1—T—Answer: a

27. Solve for x: $7 \ln x = 21$.

(a) 3   (b) e^3 (c) $\sqrt[7]{21}$ (d) $\ln 3$ (e) None of these

1—Answer: b

28. Solve for x: $4 \ln x = 20$.

1—Answer: e^5

29. A deposit of \$1000 is made into a fund with an annual interest rate of 9%. Find the time required for the investment to double if the interest is compounded continuously. $A = Pe^{rt}$

1—Answer: 7.7 years

30. A deposit of \$1000 is made into a fund with an annual interest rate of 8%. Find the time required for the investment to triple if the interest is compounded continuously. $A = Pe^{rt}$

1—Answer: 13.7 years

31. A deposit of $3000 is made into a fund with an annual interest rate of 6%. Find the time required for the investment to double if the interest is compounded continuously. $A = Pe^{rt}$

(a) 11.55 years   (b) 3.51 years   (c) 10.41 years   (d) 133.44 years   (e) None of these

1—Answer: a

32. A deposit of $1000 is made into a fund with an annual interest rate of 10%. Find the time (in years) necessary for the investment to double if the interest is compounded continuously. Round your answer to two decimal places.

(a) 10 years   (b) 7.23 years   (c) 6.93 years   (d) 20 years   (e) None of these

1—T—Answer: c

33. A deposit of $2000 is made into a fund with an annual interest rate of 10%. Find the time (in years) necessary for the investment to amount to $10,000 if the interest is compounded continuously. Round your answer to two decimal places.

1—T—Answer: 16.09 years

34. A deposit of $1000 is made into a fund with an annual interest rate of 10%. Find the time (in years) necessary to triple the investment if the interest is compounded continuously. Round your answer to two decimal places.

(a) 30 years   (b) 15 years   (c) 10.99 years   (d) 11.12 years   (e) None of these

1—T—Answer: c

Section 4.4 Derivatives of Logarithmic Functions

1. Find $\dfrac{dy}{dx}$ for $y = \ln\sqrt{x^2 + 4}$.

    (a) $\dfrac{x}{\sqrt{x^2 + 4}}$ (b) $\dfrac{2x}{\sqrt{x^2 + 4}}$ (c) $\dfrac{x}{x^2 + 4}$ (d) $\dfrac{1}{x}$ (e) None of these

    1—Answer: c

2. Take the derivative: $f(x) = \ln\dfrac{\sqrt{x^2 + 1}}{x(2x^3 - 1)^2}$.

    (a) $\dfrac{x}{x^2 + 1} - \dfrac{1}{x} + \dfrac{12x^2}{2x^3 - 1}$ (b) $\dfrac{x}{x^2 + 1} - \dfrac{1}{x} + \dfrac{6x^2}{2x^3 - 1}$ (c) $\dfrac{1}{(x^2 + 1)^{1/2}(4x^2)(2x^3 - 1)}$

    (d) $\dfrac{x}{x^2 + 1} - \dfrac{1}{x} - \dfrac{12x^2}{2x^3 - 1}$ (e) None of these

    1—Answer: d

3. Find $\dfrac{dy}{dx}$ for $y = \ln(5 - x)^6$.

    (a) $\dfrac{1}{(5 - x)^6}$ (b) $\dfrac{6}{x - 5}$ (c) $-6(5 - x)^5$ (d) $6(5 - x)^5$ (e) None of these

    1—Answer: e

4. Take the derivative: $f(x) = \ln\dfrac{x^2\sqrt{4x + 1}}{(x^3 + 5)^3}$.

    (a) $\dfrac{x}{9x^2(x^3 + 5)^2\sqrt{4x + 1}}$ (b) $\dfrac{2}{x} + \dfrac{2}{4x + 1} - \dfrac{9x^2}{x^3 + 5}$ (c) $\dfrac{2}{x} + \dfrac{1}{2(4x + 1)} - \dfrac{3}{x^3 + 5}$

    (d) $\dfrac{2}{x} - \dfrac{2}{4x + 1} - \dfrac{9x^2}{x^3 + 5}$ (e) None of these

    1—Answer: b

5. Find $\dfrac{dy}{dx}$ if $y = \ln\dfrac{\sqrt{x}}{5 - x}$.

    1—Answer: $\dfrac{1}{2x} + \dfrac{1}{5 - x}$

6. Find $\dfrac{dy}{dx}$ if $y = \ln\sqrt{x^2 + 4}$.

    1—Answer: $\dfrac{x}{x^2 + 4}$

Exponential and Logarithmic Functions

7. Take the derivative: $f(x) = \ln(x^3 + 3x)^3$.

   1—Answer: $\dfrac{9(x^2 + 1)}{x(x^2 + 3)}$

8. Find the derivative of $f(x) = \ln\dfrac{x(x^2 + 2)}{\sqrt{x^3 - 7}}$.

   (a) $\dfrac{x^2 + 2}{x} + \dfrac{2x^2}{x^2 + 2} + \dfrac{3x^2}{2(x^3 - 7)}$ (b) $\dfrac{1}{x} + \dfrac{2x}{x^2 + 2} - \dfrac{3x^2}{2(x^3 - 7)}$ (c) $\dfrac{x^2 + 2}{x} + \dfrac{2x^2}{x^2 + 2} - \dfrac{3x^2}{2(x^3 - 7)}$

   (d) $\dfrac{1}{x} + \dfrac{2x}{x^2 + 2} + \dfrac{3x^2}{2(x^3 - 7)}$ (e) None of these

   1—Answer: b

9. Find the derivative of $f(x) = \ln\dfrac{x(x^2 + 1)}{\sqrt{x^3 - 1}}$.

   (a) $\dfrac{1}{x} + \dfrac{2x}{x^2 + 1} + \dfrac{3x^2}{2(x^3 - 1)}$ (b) $\dfrac{1}{x} + \dfrac{2x}{x^2 + 1} - \dfrac{3x^2}{2(x^3 - 1)}$ (c) $\dfrac{x^2 + 1}{x} + \dfrac{2x^2}{x^2 + 1} - \dfrac{3x^2}{2(x^3 - 1)}$

   (d) $\dfrac{x^2 + 1}{x} + \dfrac{2x^2}{x^2 + 1} + \dfrac{3x^2}{2(x^3 - 1)}$ (e) None of these

   1—Answer: b

10. Find the derivative of $f(x) = \ln\dfrac{x(x^2 + 5)}{\sqrt{x^3 - 5}}$.

   (a) $\dfrac{1}{x} + \dfrac{2x}{x^2 + 5} - \dfrac{3x^2}{2(x^3 - 5)}$ (b) $\dfrac{x^2 + 5}{x} + \dfrac{2x^2}{x^2 + 5} - \dfrac{3x^2}{2(x^3 - 5)}$ (c) $\dfrac{x^2 + 5}{x} + \dfrac{2x^2}{x^2 + 5} + \dfrac{3x^2}{2(x^3 - 5)}$

   (d) $\dfrac{1}{x} + \dfrac{2x}{x^2 + 5} + \dfrac{3x^2}{2(x^3 - 5)}$ (e) None of these

   1—Answer: a

11. Find $\dfrac{dy}{dx}$ for $y = x^2 10^{2x}$.

    1—Answer: $2x(1 + x \ln 10)10^{2x}$

12. Find $\dfrac{dy}{dx}$ for $y = \ln\sqrt{x^3 + 4e^x}$.

    (a) $\dfrac{3x^2 + 4e^x}{2(x^3 + 4e^x)}$ (b) $\dfrac{1}{2\sqrt{x^3 + 4e^x}}$ (c) $\dfrac{3x^2 + 4e^x}{(x^3 + 4e^x)}$ (d) $\dfrac{3}{x} + 1$ (e) None of these

    1—Answer: a

13. Find $\dfrac{dy}{dx}$ if $y = \ln(x^2 + 1)$.

(a) $\dfrac{dy}{dx} = \dfrac{2x}{x^2 + 1}$

(b) $\dfrac{dy}{dx} = \dfrac{1}{x^2 + 1}$

(c) $\dfrac{dy}{dx} = \dfrac{1}{(x^2 + 1)\ln^2(x^2 + 1)}$

(d) $\dfrac{dy}{dx} = \dfrac{2x}{(x^2 + 1)\ln^2(x^2 + 1)}$

(e) None of these

1—**Answer:** a

14. Find $\dfrac{dy}{dx}$ if $y = \ln(x^3 + 1)$.

(a) $\dfrac{dy}{dx} = \dfrac{1}{x^3 + 1}$

(b) $\dfrac{dy}{dx} = \dfrac{3x^2}{x^3 + 1}$

(c) $\dfrac{dy}{dx} = \dfrac{1}{(x^3 + 1)\ln^2(x^3 + 1)}$

(d) $\dfrac{dy}{dx} = \dfrac{3x^2}{(x^3 + 1)\ln^2(x^3 + 1)}$

(e) None of these

1—**Answer:** b

15. Find $\dfrac{dy}{dx}$ if $y = \ln\dfrac{(x)(x + 1)}{x - 2}$.

1—**Answer:** $\dfrac{x^2 - 4x - 2}{x^3 - x^2 - 2x}$

16. Find y' if $\ln xy = x + y$.

(a) $-\dfrac{y}{x}$

(b) e^{x+y}

(c) $\dfrac{xy}{1 - xy}$

(d) $\dfrac{xy - y}{x - xy}$

(e) None of these

2—**Answer:** d

17. Use implicit differentiation to find $\dfrac{dy}{dx}$: $\ln y = y + e^2$.

(a) $\dfrac{ye^x}{1 - y}$

(b) $\dfrac{1}{y} - e^x$

(c) $y(1 + e^x)$

(d) $\dfrac{1}{y} - xe^{x-1}$

(e) None of these

1—**Answer:** a

18. Find $\dfrac{dy}{dx}$ using implicit differentiation: $\ln\sqrt{y} + e^x = \ln(2y) + 4x$.

(a) $\dfrac{dy}{dx} = 2y(e^x - 4)$

(b) $\dfrac{dy}{dx} = 2y(e^2 + 4)$

(c) $\dfrac{e^x + 4}{2y}$

(d) $\dfrac{dy}{dx} = \dfrac{e^x - 4}{2y}$

(e) None of these

1—**Answer:** a

19. Find $\dfrac{dy}{dx}$ using implicit differentiation: $y^3 + \dfrac{1}{e^y} = \ln\sqrt{x} + 4x$.

1—Answer: $\dfrac{1 + 8x}{6xy^2 - 2xe^{-y}}$

20. Find $\dfrac{dy}{dx}$ using implicit differentiation: $y^2 + e^y = \ln x^2 + 4$.

(a) $\dfrac{2 - xe^y}{2xy}$ (b) $\dfrac{2x - 2yx}{xe^y}$ (c) $\dfrac{\dfrac{2}{x} - e^y}{2y}$ (d) $\dfrac{2}{2xy + xe^y}$ (e) None of these

1—Answer: d

21. Find $\dfrac{dy}{dx}$ using implicit differentiation: $y^2 + e^y = \ln x^2 + 4x$.

(a) $\dfrac{2 + 4x - xe^y}{2xy}$ (b) $\dfrac{2 + 4x - 2yx}{xe^y}$ (c) $\dfrac{\dfrac{2}{x} + 4 - e^y}{2y}$ (d) $\dfrac{2 + 4x}{2xy + xe^y}$ (e) None of these

1—Answer: d

22. Use implicit differentiation to find $\dfrac{dy}{dx}$: $e^y = y + \ln x$.

(a) $e^y - \dfrac{1}{x}$ (b) $\dfrac{x + 1}{xe^y}$ (c) $ye^{y-1} - \dfrac{1}{x}$ (d) $\dfrac{1}{x(e^y - 1)}$ (e) None of these

1—Answer: d

23. Find the slope of the tangent line to the graph of $y = \ln x^2$ at the point where $x = e^2$.

2—Answer: $\dfrac{2}{e^2}$

24. Find the slope of the tangent line to the graph of $y = (\ln x)e^x$ at the point where $x = 2$.

(a) $\tfrac{1}{2}e^2$ (b) $e^2\left(\ln 2 + \tfrac{1}{2}\right)$ (c) e (d) $e(2\ln 2 + 1)$ (e) None of these

1—Answer: b

25. Find the slope of the tangent line to the graph of $y = \ln(xe^x)$ at the point where $x = 3$.

(a) $\ln 3 + 3$ (b) $e^3 + \ln 3$ (c) $\tfrac{4}{3}$ (d) $\tfrac{1}{3}$ (e) None of these

1—Answer: c

26. Find the slope of the tangent line to the curve $y = (\ln x)e^x$ at the point where $x = e$.

(a) 6.70   (b) 20.73   (c) 2.72   (d) 8.69   (e) None of these

1—T—Answer: b

27. Find any critical numbers for the function $f(x) = x^2 \ln x$.

(a) $x = -\dfrac{1}{\sqrt{e}}$

(b) $x = \dfrac{1}{\sqrt{e}}$

(c) $x = 0$

(d) $x = -\dfrac{1}{\sqrt{e}}, 0, \dfrac{1}{\sqrt{e}}$

(e) None of these

1—Answer: b

28. Find any critical numbers for the function $f(x) = x^2 - \ln x$.

(a) $x = \pm\sqrt{2}$

(b) $x = 0$

(c) $x = \sqrt{2}$

(d) $x = -\sqrt{2}, 0, \sqrt{2}$

(e) None of these

1—Answer: c

29. Write the equation of the tangent line to the curve $y = \ln\left(\dfrac{4}{e^{3x}}\right)$ at the point $(0, \ln 4)$.

2—Answer: $y = -3x + \ln 4$

30. Write the equation of the tangent line to the curve $y = \ln\left(\dfrac{2}{e^{2x}}\right)$ at the point $(0, \ln 2)$.

(a) $2x + y + \ln 2 = 0$

(b) $2x - y + \ln 2 = 0$

(c) $2x + y - \ln 2 = 0$

(d) $2x - y - \ln 2 + 0$

(e) None of these

2—Answer: c

31. Find the instantaneous rate of change of the demand function $x = \ln\left(\dfrac{100}{p^2 + 1}\right)$ when the price p is \$10.

(a) Decreasing $\frac{10}{101}$ (b) Increasing $\frac{10}{101}$ (c) Increasing $\frac{20}{101}$ (d) Decreasing $\frac{20}{101}$ (e) None of these

2—Answer: d

32. Find the instantaneous rate of change of the demand function $x = \ln\left(\dfrac{200}{p^3 + 10}\right)$ when the price p is \$10.

2—Answer: $-\frac{30}{101}$

33. The temperature T in degrees Fahrenheit at which water boils at selected pressures p (in pounds per square inch) can be modeled by the equation

$$T = 87.97 + 34.96 \ln p + 7.91\sqrt{p}.$$

Find the rate of change of the temperature, accurate to the nearest 0.01, when the pressure is 50 pounds per square inch.

(a) 1.26 degrees/pound

(b) 12.6 degrees/pound

(c) 140.63 degrees/pound

(d) 280.67 degrees/pound

(e) None of these

2—Answer: a

34. The temperature T in degrees Fahrenheit at which water boils at selected pressures p (in pounds per square inch) can be modeled by the equation

$$T = 87.97 + 34.96 \ln p + 7.91\sqrt{p}.$$

Find the rate of change of the temperature, accurate to the nearest 0.01, when the pressure is 65 pounds per square inch.

(a) 146.43 degrees/pound   (b) 12.60 degrees/pound   (c) 2.06 degrees/pound

(d) 1.03 degrees/pound   (e) None of these

2—Answer: a

35. The temperature T in degrees Fahrenheit at which water boils at selected pressures p (in pounds per square inch) can be modeled by the equation

$$T = 87.97 + 34.96 \ln p + 7.91\sqrt{p}.$$

Find the rate of change of the temperature, accurate to the nearest 0.01, when the pressure is 55 pounds per square inch.

2—Answer: 1.17 degrees/pound

Section 4.5   Exponential Growth and Decay

1. A deposit of $1000 is made into a fund with an annual interest rate of 10 percent. Find the time (in years) necessary for the investment to double if the interest is compounded continuously. Round your answer to 2 decimal places.

   (a) 10.00 years   (b) 7.23 years   (c) 6.93 years   (d) 20.00 years   (e) None of these

   1—Answer: c

2. A deposit of $1000 is made into a fund with an annual interest rate of 10 percent. Find the time (in years) necessary for the investment to triple if the interest is compounded continuously. Round your answer to 2 decimal places.

   (a) 30.00 years   (b) 15.00 years   (c) 10.99 years   (d) 11.12 years   (e) None of these

   1—Answer: c

3. In 1970 the population of a town was 21,000 and in 1980 it was 20,000. Assuming the population decreases continuously at a constant rate proportional to the existing population, estimate the population in the year 2000.

   (a) 17,619   (b) 18,000   (c) 19,048   (d) 18,141   (e) None of these

   1—Answer: d

4. A certain type of bacteria increases continuously at a rate proportional to the number present. If there are 500 present at a given time and 1000 present 2 hours later, how many will there be 5 hours from the initial time given?

   (a) 1750   (b) 2828   (c) 3000   (d) 2143   (e) None of these

   1—Answer: b

5. A certain type of bacteria increases continuously at a rate proportional to the number present. If there are 500 present at a given time and 1000 present 2 hours later, how many hours (from the initial given time) will it take for the numbers to be 2,500? Round your answer to 2 decimal places.

   1—Answer: 4.64

6. A mold culture doubles its mass every three days. Find the growth model for a plate seeded with 1.2 grams of mold. [Hint: Use the model $y = Ce^{kt}$ where t is time in days and y is grams of mold.]

   (a) $y = 1.2e^{0.54931t}$ (b) $y = 1.2e^{0.23105t}$ (c) $y = 1.2e^{0.10034t}$

   (d) $y = 12e^{0.23856t}$ (e) None of these

   1—Answer: b

7. A mold culture doubles its mass every three days. Find the growth model for a plate seeded with 1.6 grams of mold. [Hint: Use the model $y = Ce^{kt}$ where t is time in days and y is grams of mold.]

   (a) $y = 1.6e^{0.23856t}$ (b) $y = 1.6e^{0.54931t}$ (c) $y = 1.6e^{0.10034t}$

   (d) $y = 1.6e^{0.23105t}$ (e) None of these

   1—Answer: d

8. A mold culture doubles its mass every three days. Find the growth model for a plate seeded with 0.3 grams of mold. [Hint: Use the model $y = Ce^{kt}$ where t is time in days and y is grams of mold.]

    (a) $y = 0.3e^{0.10034t}$ (b) $y = 0.3e^{0.23856t}$ (c) $y = 0.3e^{0.54931t}$

    (d) $y = 0.3e^{0.23105t}$ (e) None of these

    1—Answer: d

9. The balance in an account triples in 21 years. Assuming that interest is compounded continuously, what is the annual percentage rate?

    (a) 4.27% (b) 3.30% (c) 5.23% (d) 10.15% (e) None of these

    1—Answer: c

10. The balance in an account triples in 13 years. Assuming that interest is compounded continuously, what is the annual percentage rate?

    (a) 6.89% (b) 8.45% (c) 8.55% (d) 5.33% (e) None of these

    1—Answer: b

11. The balance in an account triples in 20 years. Assuming that interest is compounded continuously, what is the annual percentage rate?

    (a) 9.99% (b) 4.48% (c) 5.49% (d) 3.47% (e) None of these

    1—Answer: c

12. A radioactive element has a half–life of 50 days. What percentage of the original sample is left after 60 days?

    (a) 43.53% (b) 49.56% (c) 37.50% (d) 25.00% (e) None of these

    1—Answer: a

13. A radioactive element has a half–life of 50 days. What percentage of the original sample is left after 85 days?

    (a) 37.50% (b) 30.78% (c) 25.00% (d) 24.06% (e) None of these

    1—Answer: b

14. A radioactive element has a half–life of 40 days. What percentage of the original sample is left after 48 days?

    (a) 49.56% (b) 43.53% (c) 25.00% (d) 37.50% (e) None of these

    1—Answer: b

15. Find the constant k so that the exponential function $y = 3e^{kt}$ passes through the points given on the graph.

    2—T—Answer: $k = \frac{1}{3} \ln \frac{5}{3} \approx 0.1703$

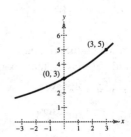

16. The population P of a city is given by $P = 2000e^{kt}$. Let $t = 0$ correspond to the year 1960 and suppose the population in 1950 was 1500. Find the value of k (to 3 decimal places) and then predict the population in 1990.

    2—T—Answer: $k = 0.029$, In 1990, $P = 4774$

17. The number N of bacteria in a culture is given by $N = 200e^{kt}$. If $N = 300$ when $t = 4$ hours, find k (to the nearest tenth) and then determine approximately how long it will take for the number of bacteria to triple in size.

    2—T—Answer: $k = 0.1$, $t \approx 11$ hours

18. Write an equation for the amount Q of a radioactive substance with a half-life of 30 days, if 10 grams are present when $t = 0$.

    2—Answer: $Q(t) = 10e^{-0.0231t}$

19. The number of fruit flies increases according to the law of exponential growth. If initially there are 10 fruit flies and after 8 hours there are 30, find the number of fruit flies after t hours.

    1—Answer: $y = 10e^{[(\ln 3)/8]t}$

20. The number of fruit flies increases according to the law of exponential growth. If initially there are 10 fruit flies and after 6 hours there are 24, find the number of fruit flies after t hours.

    (a) $y = 10e^{[\ln(12/5)](t/6)}$ (b) $y = 10e^{[\ln(12/5)]t}$ (c) $y = 10e^{[-\ln(12/5)](t/6)}$

    (d) $y = 10e^{(\ln 12)(t/6)}$ (e) None of these

    1—Answer: a

21. The number of fruit flies increases according to the law of exponential growth. If initially there are 10 fruit flies and after 7 hours there are 24, find the number of fruit flies after t hours.

    (a) $y = 10e^{[\ln(12/5)]t}$ (b) $y = 10e^{[\ln(12/5)](t/7)}$ (c) $y = 10e^{[-\ln(12/5)](t/7)}$

    (d) $y = 10e^{(\ln 12)(t/7)}$ (e) None of these

    1—Answer: b

22. The number of fruit flies increases according to the law of exponential growth. If initially there are 10 fruit flies and after 5 hours there are 24, find the number of fruit flies after t hours.

    (a) $y = 10e^{[\ln(12/5)]t}$ (b) $y = 10e^{[\ln(12/5)](t/5)}$ (c) $y = 10e^{[-\ln(12/5)](t/5)}$

    (d) $y = 10e^{(\ln 12)(t/5)}$ (e) None of these

    1—Answer: b

23. A radioactive isotope has a half–life of 20 years. At $t = 0$, there are 100 grams of this substance. Find the amount of this isotope present at time t using an exponential model of decay.

    (a) $y = 100e^{(\ln 2)t/20}$ (b) $y = 100e^{-[\ln(1/2)]t/20}$ (c) $y = 20e^{-(\ln 2)t/100}$

    (d) $y = 100e^{-(\ln 2)t/20}$ (e) None of these

    1—Answer: d

24. A radioactive isotope has a half–life of 40 years. At $t = 0$, there are 200 grams of this substance. Find the amount of this isotope present at time t using an exponential model of decay.

(a) $y = 200e^{(\ln 2)t/40}$ (b) $y = 200e^{-[\ln(1/2)]t/40}$ (c) $y = 200e^{-(\ln 2)t/40}$

(d) $y = 40e^{-(\ln 2)t/200}$ (e) None of these

1—Answer: c

25. A radioactive isotope has a half–life of 3 years. At $t = 0$, there are 100 grams of this substance. Find the amount of this isotope present at time t using an exponential model of decay.

1—Answer: $y = 100e^{-t(\ln 2)/3}$

26. A radioactive isotope has a half–life of 30 years. At $t = 0$, there are 100 grams of this substance. Find the amount of this isotope present at time t using an exponential model of decay.

(a) $y = 100e^{(\ln 2)t/30}$ (b) $y = 100e^{-[\ln(1/2)]t/30}$ (c) $y = 30e^{-(\ln 2)t/100}$

(d) $y = 100e^{-(\ln 2)t/30}$ (e) None of these

1—Answer: d

27. A radioactive isotope has a half–life of 50 years. At $t = 0$, there are 200 grams of this substance. Find the amount of this isotope present at time t using an exponential model of decay.

1—Answer: $y = 200e^{-t(\ln 2)/50}$

28. In a complete sentence, describe how the rate of change of a quantity y which grows exponentially is related to the amount of the quantity itself.

2—Answer: The rate of change of the quantity is the multiple of a constant, a power of e, and the quantity itself.

CHAPTER 5
Integration and its Applications

Section 5.1 Antiderivatives and Indefinite Integrals

1. Evaluate the integral: $\int 6\,dx$.

   (a) $6 + C$ (b) $6x + C$ (c) $0 + C$ (d) $x + 6 + C$ (e) None of these

   1—Answer: b

2. Evaluate the integral: $\int 8\,dx$.

   (a) $0 + C$ (b) $8x + C$ (c) $x + 8 + C$ (d) $8 + C$ (e) None of these

   1—Answer: b

3. Evaluate $\int (3x^3 - 2x^2 + 5)\,dx$.

   (a) $9x^2 - 4x + C$
   (b) $\frac{3}{4}x^4 - \frac{2}{3}x^3 + 5x + C$
   (c) $\frac{3}{4}x^4 - \frac{2}{3}x^3 + C$
   (d) $9x^4 - 8x^3 + 60x + C$
   (e) None of these

   1—Answer: b

4. Evaluate $\int (2x^4 + 3x^2 - 2x)\,dx$.

   (a) $\frac{3}{8}x^8 + C$
   (b) $8x^3 + 6x - 2 + C$
   (c) $\frac{2}{5}x^5 + x^3 - x^2 + C$
   (d) $2x^5 + 5x^3 - 5x^2 + C$
   (e) None of these

   1—Answer: c

5. Evaluate $\int (3x^2 - 2x + 5)\,dx$.

   1—Answer: $x^3 - x^2 + 5x + C$

6. Evaluate $\int \frac{1}{x^4}\,dx$.

   (a) $-\dfrac{1}{3x^3}$ (b) $\dfrac{5}{x^5}$ (c) $\dfrac{1}{5x^5} + C$ (d) $-\dfrac{1}{3x^3} + C$ (e) None of these

   1—Answer: d

7. Evaluate $\int \frac{1}{t^6}\, dt$.

(a) $-\frac{1}{5t^5} + C$ (b) $-\frac{6}{t^7} + C$ (c) $\frac{7}{t^7} + C$ (d) $\frac{1}{6t^7} + C$ (e) None of these

1—Answer: a

8. Evaluate $\int \frac{3}{x^2}\, dx$.

1—Answer: $-\frac{3}{x} + C$

9. Evaluate $\int \sqrt[3]{t}\, dt$.

(a) $\frac{3}{4}t^{4/3} + C$ (b) $\sqrt[3]{\frac{1}{2}t^2} + C$ (c) $\frac{3}{2}t^{2/3} + C$ (d) $\frac{1}{3t^{2/3}} + C$ (e) None of these

1—Answer: a

10. Evaluate $\int \sqrt[5]{x^2}\, dx$.

(a) $\sqrt[5]{\frac{x^3}{3}} + C$ (b) $\frac{5}{7}x^{7/5} + C$ (c) $-\frac{1}{9x^9} + C$ (d) $-\frac{1}{4x^8} + C$ (e) None of these

1—Answer: b

11. Evaluate $\int \sqrt{x^3}\, dx$.

1—Answer: $\frac{2}{5}x^{5/2} + C$

12. Evaluate $\int \frac{6}{x^3}\, dx$.

1—Answer: $\frac{-3}{x^2} + C$

13. Evaluate $\int \frac{x^3 + x}{x}\, dx$.

(a) $x^3 + 3x + C$ (b) $2x + C$ (c) $\frac{x^3}{3} + x + C$ (d) $\frac{2x^3 + x - 1}{x^2}$ (e) None of these

1—Answer: c

14. Evaluate $\int \dfrac{x^4 - x^3}{x^2}\, dx$.

    (a) $2x^3 - 3x^2 + C$ (b) $\dfrac{x^3}{3} - \dfrac{x^2}{2} + C$ (c) $2x - 1 + C$

    (d) $\dfrac{3}{20}(4x^2 - 5x) + C$ (e) None of these

    1—Answer: b

15. Evaluate $\int \dfrac{x^3 - x^2}{x^2}\, dx$.

    1—Answer: $\dfrac{x^2}{2} - x + C$

16. Evaluate the integral: $\int \dfrac{3 + 4x^{3/2}}{\sqrt{x}}\, dx$.

    (a) $\frac{3}{2}\sqrt{x} + 2x^2 + C$ (b) $-\frac{3}{2}x^{-3/2} + 4 + C$ (c) $\frac{3}{2}x^{-3/2} + 2x^2 + C$

    (d) $6\sqrt{x} + 2x^2 + C$ (e) None of these

    2—Answer: d

17. Evaluate the integral: $\int \dfrac{4 + 5x^{3/2}}{\sqrt{x}}\, dx$.

    (a) $2x^{-3/2} + \frac{5}{2}x^2 + C$ (b) $8\sqrt{x} + \frac{5}{2}x^2 + C$ (c) $-2x^{-3/2} + 5 + C$

    (d) $2\sqrt{x} + \frac{5}{2}x^2 + C$ (e) None of these

    2—Answer: b

18. Evaluate the integral: $\int \dfrac{7 + 3x^{3/2}}{\sqrt{x}}\, dx$.

    (a) $\frac{7}{2}\sqrt{x} + \frac{3}{2}x^2 + C$ (b) $14\sqrt{x} + \frac{3}{2}x^2 + C$ (c) $-\frac{7}{2}x^{-3/2} + 3 + C$

    (d) $\frac{7}{2}x^{-3/2} + \frac{3}{2}x^2 + C$ (e) None of these

    2—Answer: b

19. Evaluate $\int 5x\sqrt{x}\, dx$.

    (a) $\frac{5}{3}x^{7/2} + C$ (b) $\frac{5}{2}x^2 + C$ (c) $5x^{5/2} + C$ (d) $2x^{5/2} + C$ (e) None of these

    1—Answer: d

20. Evaluate $\int (x - 1)x^2 \, dx$.

(a) $3x^4 - 4x^3 + C$ (b) $\frac{1}{4}x^4 - \frac{1}{3}x^3 + C$ (c) $\frac{1}{6}x^3(x - 1)^2 + C$

(d) $3x^2 - 2x + C$ (e) None of these

1—Answer: b

21. Evaluate $\int \frac{1}{(3t)^2} \, dt$.

(a) $-\frac{1}{3t} + C$ (b) $-\frac{1}{3(3t)^3} + C$ (c) $\frac{1}{9}(3t)^3 + C$ (d) $-\frac{1}{9t} + C$ (e) None of these

1—Answer: d

22. Evaluate $\int \frac{x^3 + 1}{x^2} \, dx$.

(a) $\frac{3x^3 + 12}{4x^2} + C$ (b) $\frac{x^2}{2} - \frac{1}{3x^3} + C$ (c) $\frac{x^2}{2} - \frac{1}{x} + C$

(d) $\frac{x^2}{2} + \frac{1}{3x^3} + C$ (e) None of these

1—Answer: a

23. Evaluate $\int \frac{x^3 - x^2}{x} \, dx$.

(a) $\frac{1}{6}(3x^2 - 4x) + C$ (b) $x^2 - x + C$ (c) $\frac{1}{3}x^3 - \frac{1}{2}x^2 + C$

(d) $\frac{1}{4}x^4 - \frac{1}{3}x^3 + C$ (e) None of these

1—Answer: c

24. Evaluate $\int \frac{2}{\sqrt{x}} \, dx$.

1—Answer: $4\sqrt{x} + C$

25. Evaluate $\int x(3x^2) \, dx$.

1—Answer: $\frac{3}{4}x^4 + C$

26. Evaluate $\int \dfrac{t+1}{t^3}\,dt.$

   1—Answer: $-\dfrac{2t+1}{2t^2}+C$

27. Evaluate $\int \dfrac{4}{x^3}\,dx.$

   (a) $\dfrac{1}{x^4}+C$ (b) $\dfrac{-2}{x^2}+C$ (c) $\dfrac{16}{x^3}+C$ (d) $\dfrac{-2}{x}+C$ (e) None of these

   1—Answer: b

28. Evaluate $\int \dfrac{3x^4-6}{x^2}\,dx.$

   (a) $3x^3-\dfrac{6}{x}+C$ (b) $x^3+\dfrac{6}{x}+C$ (c) $x^3+\dfrac{3}{x}+C$ (d) $x^3+\dfrac{2}{x^3}+C$ (e) None of these

   1—Answer: b

29. Evaluate $\int x(4x^3)\,dx.$

   1—Answer: $\frac{4}{5}x^5+C$

30. Evaluate $\int 4(x^3+5)x^4\,dx.$

   (a) $x^5(x^3+5)^2+C$ (b) $4x^5(x^3+5)^2+C$ (c) $4x^8+20x^5+C$

   (d) $\dfrac{x^8}{2}+4x^5+C$ (e) None of these

   1—Answer: d

31. Evaluate $\int \dfrac{5}{x^2}\,dx.$

   (a) $-\dfrac{5}{x}+C$ (b) $\dfrac{5}{3x^3}+C$ (c) $\dfrac{15}{x^3}+C$ (d) $-\dfrac{5}{2x}+C$ (e) None of these

   1—Answer: a

32. Evaluate $\int \dfrac{3x^4 - 5}{x^2}\,dx$.

   (a) $x^3 + \dfrac{5}{x} + C$ (b) $3x^3 + \dfrac{5}{x} + C$ (c) $x^3 - \dfrac{5}{x} + C$

   (d) $x^3 - \dfrac{5}{3x^3} + C$ (e) None of these

   1—Answer: a

33. Evaluate $\int (4x^3 + 5)^2\,dx$.

   (a) $\dfrac{(4x^3 + 5)^3}{3} + C$ (b) $16x^7 + 20x^4 + 25x + C$ (c) $16x^7 - 80x^4 + 25x + C$

   (d) $\dfrac{16}{7}x^7 + 10x^4 + 25x + C$ (e) None of these

   1—Answer: d

34. Find an equation for the function f whose graph passes through the point $(1, 5)$ with slope given by $f'(x) = 4x^3 - 1$.

   2—Answer: $y = x^4 - x + 5$

35. Find $y = f(x)$ if $f''(x) = x^{1/\sqrt{x}}$, $f'(0) = 3$, and $f(1) = 4$.

   (a) $\frac{4}{3}x^{3/2} + 3x + 4$ (b) $x^{-1/2} + 7$ (c) $\frac{4}{3}x^{3/2} + 3x - \frac{1}{3}$

   (d) $4x^{3/2} + 9x - 1$ (e) None of these

   2—Answer: c

36. Find $y = f(x)$ if $f''(x) = x$, $f'(0) = -5$, and $f(1) = 4$.

   (a) $x^3 - 30x + 5$ (b) $x - 9$ (c) $\dfrac{x^3}{6} - 5x + \dfrac{5}{6}$

   (d) $\dfrac{x^3}{6} - 5x - 4$ (e) None of these

   2—Answer: c

37. Find the particular solution of the equation $f'(x) = 2x^{-1/2}$ that satisfies the condition $f(1) = 6$.

   (a) $4\sqrt{x} + 2$ (b) $4\sqrt{x} + C$ (c) $\sqrt{2x} + 6 - \dfrac{2}{\sqrt{2}}$

   (d) $2\sqrt{x} + 4$ (e) None of these

   1—Answer: a

38. Find the particular solution of the equation $f'(x) = 4x^{-1/2}$ that satisfies the condition $f(1) = 12$.

(a) $8\sqrt{x} + C$ (b) $2\sqrt{x} + 10$ (c) $\frac{1}{2}\sqrt{4x} + 11$ (d) $8\sqrt{x} + 4$ (e) None of these

1—Answer: d

39. Find $y = f(x)$ if $f''(x) = x^2$, $f'(0) = 7$ and $f(0) = 2$.

(a) $x^2 + 9$

(b) $\frac{1}{12}x^4 + 7x + 2$

(c) $x^2 + 7x + 2$

(d) $x^4 + 84x + 24$

(e) None of these

2—Answer: b

40. Find $y = f(x)$ if $f''(x) = x + 2$, $f'(0) = 3$ and $f(0) = -1$.

(a) $\frac{1}{6}x^3 + x^2 + 3x - 1$

(b) $\frac{x^3}{6} + 2x^2 + C$

(c) $x^3 + 6x^2 + 18x - 6$

(d) $\frac{1}{6}x^3 + x^2 + \frac{21}{2}x + \frac{61}{6} + C$ (e) None of these

2—Answer: a

41. Find the function, $y = f(x)$, if $y' = 2x - 1$ and $f(1) = 3$.

2—Answer: $y = x^2 - x + 3$

42. Find the cost function if the marginal cost function is $\dfrac{dC}{dx} = \dfrac{1}{10\sqrt{x}} + 2$ and fixed costs are \$560.

1—Answer: $\frac{1}{5}\sqrt{x} + 2x + 560$

43. Find the cost function if the marginal cost function is $\dfrac{dC}{dx} = 2x + 50$ and fixed costs are \$150.

(a) $C = 2x^2 + 50x + 150$ (b) $C = x^2 + 50x + 150$ (c) $C = 2x^2 + 50x - 150$

(d) $x^2 + 50x - 150$ (e) None of these

1—Answer: b

44. If the marginal cost function is $\dfrac{dC}{dx} = 2x - 15$ and fixed costs are \$75, find the total cost function.

(a) $C = x^2 - 15x + 75$ (b) $C = 2x + 60$ (c) $C = x^2 - 15x$

(d) $C = x^2 + 160x$ (e) None of these

2—Answer: a

45. If the marginal cost function is $\dfrac{dC}{dx} = x + 65$ and fixed costs are \$125, find the total cost function.

(a) $C = \frac{1}{2}x^2 + 65x$ (b) $C = x + 190$ (c) $C = \frac{1}{2}x^2 + 65x + 125$

(d) $C = \frac{1}{2}x^2 + 190x$ (e) None of these

1—Answer: c

46. Find the cost function if the marginal cost function is $\dfrac{dC}{dx} = 0.03x^2 + 0.6x$ and fixed costs are \$3000.

    (a) $C = 0.06x + 0.6 + \dfrac{3000}{x}$ (b) $C = 0.01x^3 + 0.3x^2 - 3000$ (c) $C = 0.03x + 0.6 - \dfrac{3000}{x}$

    (d) $C = 0.01x^3 + 0.3x^2 + 3000$ (e) None of these

    1—Answer: d

47. A company produces a product for which the marginal cost of producing x units is

$$\frac{dC}{dx} = 0.12x + 8$$

and fixed costs are \$1500. Find the average cost of producing 50 units.

    2—Answer: \$41

48. A company produces a product for which the marginal cost of producing x units is

$$\frac{dC}{dx} = 0.12x + 8$$

and fixed costs are \$1500. Find the average cost of producing 100 units.

    2—Answer: \$29

49. A company produces a product for which the marginal cost of producing x units is

$$\frac{dC}{dx} = 0.6x - 2$$

and fixed costs are \$250. Find the average cost of producing 50 units.

    (a) \$18   (b) \$30   (c) \$90   (d) \$900   (e) None of these

    2—Answer: a

50. If the marginal cost function is $\dfrac{dC}{dx} = \dfrac{400}{3x + 4}$ and the fixed costs are \$160, find the total cost function.

    1—T—Answer: $C = \frac{400}{3} \ln|3x + 4| - 24.84$

Section 5.2   The General Power Rule

1. Evaluate $\int x^2(x^3 + 5)^6 \, dx$.

(a) $\frac{1}{21}(x^3 + 5)^7 + C$

(b) $\frac{1}{7}(x^3 + 5)^7 + C$

(c) $\frac{x^3(x^3 + 5)^7}{27} + C$

(d) $\frac{x^3}{3}\left(\frac{x^4}{4} + 5x\right)^6 + C$

(e) None of these

1—Answer: a

2. Evaluate $\int x(x^2 - 1)^4 \, dx$.

(a) $\frac{1}{10}(x^2)(x^2 - 1)^5$

(b) $\frac{1}{10}(x^2 - 1)^5 + C$

(c) $\frac{1}{5}(x^3 - x)^5 + C$

(d) $\frac{1}{5}(x^2 - 1)^5 + C$

(e) None of these

1—Answer: b

3. Use the general power rule to evaluate the integral: $\int x\sqrt{8 - 4x^2} \, dx$.

(a) $\frac{2}{3}(8 - 4x^2)^{3/2} + C$

(b) $-\frac{1}{8}(8 - 4x^2)^{3/2} + C$

(c) $-\frac{1}{12}(8 - 4x^2)^{3/2} + C$

(d) $-\frac{1}{3}(8 - 4x^2)^{3/2} + C$

(e) None of these

1—Answer: c

4. Use the general power rule to evaluate the integral: $\int x\sqrt{4 - 9x^2} \, dx$.

(a) $-\frac{1}{27}(4 - 9x^2)^{3/2} + C$

(b) $-\frac{1}{18}(4 - 9x^2)^{3/2} + C$

(c) $\frac{2}{3}(4 - 9x^2)^{3/2} + C$

(d) $-\frac{4}{27}(4 - 9x^2)^{3/2} + C$

(e) None of these

1—Answer: a

5. Use the general power rule to evaluate the integral: $\int x\sqrt{3 - 7x^2} \, dx$.

(a) $-\frac{1}{21}(3 - 7x^2)^{3/2} + C$

(b) $-\frac{4}{21}(3 - 7x^2)^{3/2} + C$

(c) $-\frac{1}{14}(3 - 7x^2)^{3/2} + C$

(d) $\frac{2}{3}(3 - 7x^2)^{3/2} + C$

(e) None of these

1—Answer: a

6. Use the general power rule to evaluate the integral: $\int x\sqrt{9 - 5x^2} \, dx$.

(a) $-\frac{1}{10}(9 - 5x^2)^{3/2} + C$

(b) $-\frac{1}{15}(9 - 5x^2)^{3/2} + C$

(c) $\frac{2}{3}(9 - 5x^2)^{3/2} + C$

(d) $-\frac{4}{15}(9 - 5x^2)^{3/2} + C$

(e) None of these

1—Answer: b

7. Evaluate: $\int \dfrac{1}{\sqrt{2x + 1}}\, dx$.

(a) $\sqrt{x^2 + x} + C$ (b) $\dfrac{1}{\sqrt{x^2 + x}} + C$ (c) $\sqrt{2x + 1} + C$

(d) $\dfrac{1}{2}\sqrt{2x + 1} + C$ (e) None of these

1—Answer: c

8. Find the indefinite integral: $\int \left(x - \dfrac{1}{x}\right)^2 dx$.

1—Answer: $\dfrac{x^3}{3} - 2x - \dfrac{1}{x} + C$

9. Evaluate: $\int \dfrac{x + 1}{\sqrt{x^2 + 2x + 3}} + C$

2—Answer: $\sqrt{x^2 + 2x + 3} + C$

10. Evaluate: $\int \dfrac{6x^2 + 30}{(x^3 + 15x)^3}\, dx$.

2—Answer: $\dfrac{-1}{(x^3 + 15x)^2} + C$

11. Evaluate: $\int (x + 1)\sqrt{x^2 + 2x - 7}\, dx$.

2—Answer: $\frac{1}{3}(x^2 + 2x - 7)^{3/2} + C$

12. Evaluate: $\int \sqrt{1 - x}\, dx$.

1—Answer: $-\frac{2}{3}(1 - x)^{3/2} + C$

13. Evaluate: $\int \dfrac{3x^2}{(x^3 - 1)^4}\, dx$.

1—Answer: $-\dfrac{1}{3(x^3 - 1)^3}$

14. Evaluate: $\int 5y(2y^2 + 1)^3\, dy$.

1—Answer: $\frac{5}{16}(2y^2 + 1)^4 + C$

15. Evaluate: $\int 5y(2y^2 - 3)^6 \, dy$.

(a) $\dfrac{5}{28}(2y^2 - 3)^7 + C$

(b) $\dfrac{5}{14}y^2(2y^2 - 3)^7 + C$

(c) $\dfrac{5}{7}(2y^2 - 3)^7 + C$

(d) $-\dfrac{5(2y^2 - 3)^7}{28} + C$

(e) None of these

1—Answer: a

16. Evaluate: $\int (2t^2 + 1)^2 \, dt$.

(a) $\dfrac{4}{5}t^5 + \dfrac{4}{3}t^3 + t + C$

(b) $\dfrac{(2t^3 + 1)^3}{3} + C$

(c) $4t^5 + 4t^3 + t + C$

(d) $12t^5 - 20t^3 + 15t + C$

(e) None of these

1—Answer: a

17. Evaluate: $\int \sqrt{4 - x} \, dx$.

(a) $2x - \dfrac{2}{3}x^{3/2} + C$

(b) $(4 - x)^{3/2} + C$

(c) $-\dfrac{2}{3}(4 - x)^{3/2} + C$

(d) $-\dfrac{3}{2}(4 - x)^{3/2} + C$

(e) None of these

1—Answer: c

18. Evaluate: $\int 3x^2(x^3 + 5)^4 \, dx$.

(a) $\dfrac{1}{5}x^3(x^3 + 5)^5 + C$

(b) $\dfrac{3}{5}(x^5 + 5x^2)^5 + C$

(c) $\dfrac{1}{5}(x^3 + 5)^5 + C$

(d) $6x(7x^2 + 5)(x^3 + 5)^3 + C$

(e) None of these

1—Answer: c

19. Evaluate: $\int \dfrac{3y}{\sqrt{y^2 + 1}} \, dy$.

(a) $\dfrac{3}{4}\sqrt{y^2 + 1} + C$

(b) $6\sqrt{y^3 + y} + C$

(c) $\dfrac{3}{4}y^2\sqrt{y^2 + 1} + C$

(d) $3\sqrt{y^2 + 1} + C$

(e) None of these

1—Answer: d

20. Evaluate: $\int 3x^2(x^3 - 1)^5 \, dx$.

(a) $\frac{1}{6}x^3(x^3 - 1)^6 + C$ (b) $\frac{1}{2}x^6 - x^3 + C$ (c) $\frac{1}{2}(x^5 - x^2)^6 + C$

(d) $\frac{1}{6}(x^3 - 1)^6 + C$ (e) None of these

1—Answer: d

21. Evaluate: $\int \frac{1}{\sqrt{1 + x}} \, dx$.

(a) $\dfrac{-1}{2(1 + x)^{3/2}}$ (b) $\ln|1 + x| + C$ (c) $-\dfrac{1}{2}\sqrt{1 + x} + C$

(d) $2\sqrt{x + 1} + C$ (e) None of these

1—Answer: d

22. Evaluate: $\int \frac{5y}{\sqrt[3]{4 - y^2}} \, dy$.

(a) $\dfrac{-15(4 - y^2)^{2/3}}{2}$ (b) $\dfrac{15(4 - y^2)^{2/3}}{4}$ (c) $\dfrac{-15(4 - y^2)^{4/3}}{8}$

(d) $\dfrac{-15(4 - y^2)^{2/3}}{4}$ (e) None of these

1—Answer: d

23. Evaluate: $\int \frac{3}{\sqrt{2 + 3x}} \, dx$.

1—Answer: $\frac{2}{3}\sqrt{2 + 3x} + C$

24. Evaluate: $\int 10y(3y^2 + 4)^5 \, dy$.

1—Answer: $\frac{5}{18}(3y^2 + 4)^6 + C$

25. Evaluate: $\int \sqrt[3]{2 - 3x} \, dx$.

1—Answer: $-\frac{1}{4}(2 - 3x)^{4/3} + C$

26. For a family of four, the marginal propensity to consume income x can be modeled by

$$\frac{dQ}{dx} = \frac{0.96}{(x - 11,999)^{0.4}}, \quad x \geq 12,000.$$

Find Q, the propensity to consume, if 100% of the income is consumed when the income is \$12,000.

2—Answer: $Q = (x - 11,999)^{0.96} + 11,999$

27. For a family of four, the marginal propensity to consume income x can be modeled by

$$\frac{dQ}{dx} = \frac{0.96}{(x - 12{,}499)^{0.4}}, \quad x \geq 12{,}500.$$

Find Q, the propensity to consume, if 100% of the income is consumed when the income is \$12,500.

2—Answer: $Q = (x - 12{,}499)^{0.96} + 12{,}499$

28. For a family of four, the marginal propensity to consume income x can be modeled by

$$\frac{dQ}{dx} = \frac{0.97}{(x - 14{,}999)^{0.3}}, \quad x \geq 15{,}000.$$

Find Q, the propensity to consume, if 100% of the income is consumed when the income is \$154,000.

2—Answer: $Q = (x - 14{,}999)^{0.97} + 14{,}999$

Section 5.3   Exponential and Logarithmic Integrals

1. Evaluate $\displaystyle\int \frac{e^{1/(x+1)}}{(x+1)^2}\, dx$.

   (a) $\dfrac{e^{1/(x+1)}}{2(x+1)} + C$

   (b) $\dfrac{e^{-x/(x+1)}}{(x+1)^2} + C$

   (c) $-e^{1/(x+1)} + C$

   (d) $\dfrac{e^{-x/(x+1)}}{(x+1)^2}$

   (e) None of these

   1—Answer: c

2. Evaluate $\displaystyle\int \frac{e^{\sqrt{x}}}{\sqrt{x}}\, dx$.

   (a) $2e^{\sqrt{x}} + C$

   (b) $\frac{1}{2}e^{\sqrt{x}} + C$

   (c) $\sqrt{x}\, e^{\sqrt{x}} + C$

   (d) $\sqrt{x}\, e^{\sqrt{x}+1} + C$

   (e) None of these

   1—Answer: a

3. Evaluate $\displaystyle\int 19e^{-t/5}\, dt$.

   1—Answer: $-95\, e^{-t/5} + C$

4. Evaluate $\displaystyle\int \frac{e^x}{\sqrt{e^x + 1}}\, dx$.

   1—Answer: $2\sqrt{e^x + 1} + C$

5. Evaluate the indefinite integral: $\displaystyle\int \frac{1}{x^2 e^{2/x}}\, dx$.

   (a) $\frac{1}{2}xe^{-2/x} + C$

   (b) $\frac{1}{2}xe^{2/x} + C$

   (c) $\frac{1}{2}e^{2/x} + C$

   (d) $\frac{1}{2}e^{-2/x} + C$

   (e) None of these

   1—Answer: d

6. Evaluate the indefinite integral: $\displaystyle\int \frac{1}{x^2 e^{5/x}}\, dx$.

   (a) $\frac{1}{5}e^{5/x} + C$

   (b) $\frac{1}{5}xe^{5/x} + C$

   (c) $\frac{1}{5}e^{-5/x} + C$

   (d) $\frac{1}{5}xe^{-5/x} + C$

   (e) None of these

   1—Answer: c

7. Evaluate the indefinite integral: $\int \frac{1}{x^2 e^{3/x}} \, dx$.

(a) $\frac{1}{3} x e^{-3/x} + C$

(b) $\frac{1}{3} e^{-3/x} + C$

(c) $\frac{1}{3} x e^{3/x} + C$

(d) $\frac{1}{3} e^{3/x} + C$

(e) None of these

1—**Answer:** b

8. Evaluate $\int \frac{e^{\sqrt{x+1}}}{\sqrt{x+1}} \, dx$.

(a) $\frac{2 e^{\sqrt{x+1}+1}}{\sqrt{x+1}+1} + C$

(b) $\frac{1}{2} e^{\sqrt{x+1}} + C$

(c) $e^x + C$

(d) $2 e^{\sqrt{x+1}} + C$

(e) None of these

1—**Answer:** d

9. Evaluate $\int \frac{2x}{3x^2 + 4} \, dx$.

(a) $\frac{2(4 - 9x^2)}{(3x^2 + 4)^2} + C$

(b) $\frac{x}{x^2 + 4} + C$

(c) $\frac{1}{3} \ln(3x^2 + 4) + C$

(d) $\frac{1}{6}(3x^2 + 4)^2 + C$

(e) None of these

1—**Answer:** c

10. Evaluate $\int \frac{x + 2}{x + 1} \, dx$.

(a) $\frac{x^2 + 4x}{x^2 + 2x} + C$

(b) $2x + C$

(c) $x + C$

(d) $x + \ln|x + 1| + C$

(e) None of these

1—**Answer:** d

11. Evaluate $\int e^x \sqrt{1 - e^x} \, dx$.

(a) $-\frac{2}{3}(1 - e^x)^{3/2} + C$

(b) $e^x + \frac{2}{3}(1 - e^x)^{3/2} + C$

(c) $\frac{2}{3}(e^x - e^{2x})^{3/2} + C$

(d) $\frac{2}{3} e^x (1 - e^x)^{3/2} + C$

(e) None of these

1—**Answer:** a

12. Evaluate $\displaystyle\int \frac{2x + 1}{x + 1}\, dx.$

(a) $2x - \ln|x + 1| + C$ (b) $2x + C$ (c) $x^2 + \ln|x + 1| + C$

(d) $\dfrac{2x^2 + 2x}{x^2 + 2x} + C$ (e) None of these

1—Answer: a

13. Evaluate $\displaystyle\int e^{5t}\, dt.$

1—Answer: $\dfrac{e^{5t}}{5} + C$

14. Evaluate $\displaystyle\int (4x^2 - 1)e^{4x^3 - 3x}\, dx.$

1—Answer: $\frac{1}{3}e^{4x^3 - 3x} + C$

15. Evaluate $\displaystyle\int \frac{3x^2}{x^3 + 1}\, dx.$

1—Answer: $\ln|x^3 + 1| + C$

16. Evaluate $\displaystyle\int \frac{3x^2}{\sqrt{x^3 + 1}}\, dx.$

1—Answer: $2\sqrt{x^3 + 1} + C$

17. Evaluate $\displaystyle\int \frac{x - 3}{x + 1}\, dx.$

1—Answer: $x - 4\ln|x + 1| + C$

18. Evaluate the integral: $\displaystyle\int \frac{3x^2 + 3x + 3}{x^2 + 1}\, dx.$

(a) $3x + 3\ln(x^2 + 1) + C$ (b) $3 + \frac{3}{2}\ln(x^2 + 1) + C$ (c) $3x + \frac{3}{2}\ln(x^2 + 1) + C$

(d) $3 + 3\ln(x^2 + 1) + C$ (e) None of these

2—Answer: c

19. Evaluate the integral: $\int \dfrac{8x^2 + 9x + 8}{x^2 + 1}\, dx$.

(a) $8 + \frac{9}{2} \ln(x^2 + 1) + C$ (b) $8x + 9 \ln(x^2 + 1) + C$ (c) $8 + 9 \ln(x^2 + 1) + C$

(d) $8x + \frac{9}{2} \ln(x^2 + 1) + C$ (e) None of these

2—Answer: d

20. Evaluate the integral: $\int \dfrac{9x^2 - 9x + 9}{x^2 + 1}\, dx$.

(a) $9x - \frac{9}{2} \ln(x^2 + 1) + C$ (b) $9 - \frac{9}{2} \ln(x^2 + 1) + C$ (c) $9x - 9 \ln(x^2 + 1) + C$

(d) $9 - 9 \ln(x^2 + 1) + C$ (e) None of these

2—Answer: a

21. Evaluate $\int x e^{5x^2}\, dx$.

(a) $\dfrac{1}{10} e^{5x^2} + C$ (b) $\dfrac{x^2 e^{5x^2 + 1}}{2(5x^2 + 1)} + C$ (c) $10 e^{5x^2} + C$

(d) $e^{5x^2}(10x^2 + 1) + C$ (e) None of these

1—Answer: a

22. Evaluate $\int \dfrac{x^2}{1 - x^3}\, dx$.

(a) $-\frac{1}{6}(1 - x^3)^2 + C$ (b) $-\frac{1}{3} \ln|1 - x^3| + C$ (c) $\ln(1 - x^3) + C$

(d) $\frac{1}{3}x^3 - \ln|x| + C$ (e) None of these

1—Answer: b

23. Evaluate $\int \dfrac{e^x}{(1 + e^x)^2}\, dx$.

(a) $\ln(1 + e^x)^2 + C$ (b) $\dfrac{3e^x}{(1 + e^x)^3} + C$ (c) $\frac{1}{3}e^x(1 + e^x)^3 + C$

(d) $-\dfrac{1}{1 + e^x} + C$ (e) None of these

1—Answer: d

24. Evaluate $\int \dfrac{x^2 + x + 1}{x^2 + 1}\, dx$.

1—Answer: $x + \frac{1}{2} \ln(x^2 + 1) + C$

25. Evaluate $\int \dfrac{7y^2}{4 - y^3}\, dy$.

(a) $\dfrac{-7}{6(4 - y^3)^2} + C$

(b) $\dfrac{7}{3} \ln|4 - y^3| + C$

(c) $-\dfrac{7}{3} \ln|4 - y^3| + C$

(d) $-7 \ln|4 - y^3| + C$

(e) None of these

1—Answer: c

26. Evaluate $\int \dfrac{x^2}{x^3 - 1}\, dx$.

1—Answer: $\frac{1}{3} \ln|x^3 - 1| + C$

27. Evaluate $\int \left(\dfrac{4x^5 - 7x^2}{x^3} + e^x \right) dx$.

1—Answer: $\frac{4}{3} x^3 - 7 \ln|x| + e^x + C$

28. Evaluate $\int x e^{-x^2}\, dx$.

1—Answer: $-\frac{1}{2} e^{-x^2} + C$

29. Evaluate $\int \dfrac{15y^3}{6 + y^4}\, dy$.

1—Answer: $\frac{15}{4} \ln(6 + y^4) + C$

30. Evaluate $\int \dfrac{10y^2}{5 + y^3}\, dy$.

(a) $\dfrac{-10}{3(5 + y^3)^2} + C$

(b) $-\dfrac{10}{3} \ln|5 + y^3| + C$

(c) $\dfrac{10}{3} \ln|5 + y^3| + C$

(d) $10 \ln|5 + y^3| + C$

(e) None of these

1—Answer: c

31. Evaluate $\int \left(\dfrac{2}{x} + 3 \right)^2 dx$.

(a) $-\dfrac{4}{x} + 9x + C$

(b) $\dfrac{4}{x} + 12 \ln x + 9x + C$

(c) $\dfrac{4}{x^3} - \dfrac{12}{x^2} + 9x + C$

(d) $-\dfrac{4}{x} + 12 \ln x + 9x + C$

(e) None of these

1—Answer: d

32. Evaluate $\int \left(\dfrac{3}{x} + 4\right)^2 dx.$

    1—Answer: $-\dfrac{9}{x} + 24 \ln|x| + 16x + C$

33. Evaluate $\int \dfrac{3x^4 - 5x}{x^2} dx.$

    (a) $x^3 - \ln x^5 + C$ (b) $3x^3 + \dfrac{5}{x} + C$ (c) $x^3 - \dfrac{5}{x} + C$

    (d) $x^3 - \dfrac{5}{3x^3} + C$ (e) None of these

    1—Answer: a

34. Find $y = f(x)$ if $f''(x) = \dfrac{1}{e^x} + 2, f'(0) = 3,$ and $f(0) = 1.$

    (a) $f(x) = -e^{-x} + 2x^2 + 4x$ (b) $f(x) = -e^{-x} + 2x + 4$ (c) $f(x) = e^{-x} + x^2 + 4x$

    (d) $f(x) = -e^{-x} - x^2 + 4x + 3$ (e) None of these

    2—Answer: c

35. Find $y = f(x)$ if $\dfrac{dy}{dx} = xe^{-x^2}$ and $f(0) = 2.$

    2—Answer: $f(x) = -\dfrac{1}{2}e^{-x^2} + \dfrac{5}{2}$

36. Find y as a function of x if the slope of the graph is given by

$$\dfrac{dy}{dx} = \dfrac{2}{(x + 1)}$$

and the graph passes through the point $(0, 1)$.

    1—Answer: $2 \ln|x + 1| + 1$

Section 5.4   Area and the Fundamental Theorem of Calculus

1. Use the Fundamental Theorem of Calculus to evaluate $\int_{1}^{4} \sqrt{x} \, dx$.

   (a) 1   (b) $-\frac{14}{3}$ (c) 7   (d) $\frac{14}{3}$ (e) None of these

   1—Answer: d

2. Use the Fundamental Theorem of Calculus to evaluate $\int_{-1}^{2} (2x - 1) \, dx$.

   (a) 4   (b) 2   (c) -2 (d) -4 (e) None of these

   1—Answer: e

3. Use the Fundamental Theorem of Calculus to evaluate $\int_{1}^{2} \frac{1}{x^2} \, dx$.

   (a) $-\frac{1}{x} + C$ (b) $-\frac{3}{4}$ (c) $\frac{1}{2}$ (d) $-\frac{3}{2}$ (e) None of these

   1—Answer: c

4. Use the Fundamental Theorem of Calculus to evaluate $\int_{-2}^{1} (1 - 2x) \, dx$.

   (a) -6 (b) -2 (c) 2   (d) 6   (e) None of these

   1—Answer: d

5. Use the Fundamental Theorem of Calculus to evaluate $\int_{-1}^{1} \left(\sqrt[3]{t} - 2 \right) \, dt$.

   1—Answer: -4

6. Evaluate $\int_{0}^{2} |x - 1| \, dx$.

   (a) 0   (b) 1   (c) $\frac{1}{2}$ (d) 2   (e) None of these

   2—Answer: b

7. Use the Fundamental Theorem of Calculus to evaluate $\int_{-2}^{2} (x^2 - 4) \, dx$.

   1—Answer: $-\frac{32}{3}$

8. Use the Fundamental Theorem of Calculus to evaluate $\int_{0}^{1} \frac{x}{\sqrt{1 + x^2}} \, dx$.

   1—Answer: $\sqrt{2} - 1$

9. Use the Fundamental Theorem to evaluate $\displaystyle\int_{-3}^{0} (4x^4 - 5x^3 + 8)\, dx$.

1—**Answer:** $\frac{6393}{20} = 319.65$

10. Use the Fundamental Theorem of Calculus to evaluate $\displaystyle\int_{0}^{3} \frac{x}{(3 + 4x^2)^3}\, dx$.

1—**Answer:** $\frac{17}{1014} \approx 0.0069$

11. Evaluate $\displaystyle\int_{\sqrt{2}}^{\sqrt{3}} 20(x^5 - x^6)\, dx$.

1—T—**Answer:** $\dfrac{190}{3} + \dfrac{160\sqrt{2}}{7} - \dfrac{540\sqrt{3}}{7} \approx -37.957$

12. Use the Fundamental Theorem to evaluate $\displaystyle\int_{-2}^{1} (3x^3 - 4x^2 + 5)\, dx$.

(a) $\frac{155}{12}$ (b) $\frac{39}{4}$ (c) $-\frac{39}{4}$ (d) $\frac{79}{6}$ (e) None of these

1—**Answer:** e

13. Use the Fundamental Theorem to evaluate $\displaystyle\int_{-3}^{3} (4x^2 - x^4)\, dx$.

1—**Answer:** $-\frac{126}{5}$

14. Evaluate $\displaystyle\int_{0.1}^{0.4} 30(x^4 - x^5)\, dx$.

(a) 1.0495   (b) 2.3215   (c) 0.43208   (d) 0.040905   (e) None of these

1—T—**Answer:** d

15. Use the Fundamental Theorem to evaluate $\displaystyle\int_{-3}^{0} (2x^3 - 4x^2)\, dx$.

(a) $\frac{153}{2}$ (b) $-\frac{153}{2}$ (c) 198   (d) -198 (e) None of these

1—**Answer:** b

16. Evaluate $\displaystyle\int_{0}^{1} x\sqrt{1 - x^2}\, dx$.

1—**Answer:** $\frac{1}{3}$

17. Evaluate $\int_0^1 x\sqrt{x^2 + 1}\, dx$.

1—Answer: $\frac{1}{3}[2^{3/2} - 1]$

18. Use the Fundamental Theorem of Calculus to evaluate $\int_{-2}^0 (4t - 2)\, dt$.

(a) $2t^2 - 2t + C$ (b) -12 (c) 4

(d) 12 (e) None of these

1—Answer: b

19. Use the Fundamental Theorem of Calculus to evaluate $\int_1^2 x(1 - x^2)^2\, dx$.

(a) $\frac{1}{2}$ (b) $\frac{9}{2}$ (c) -27 (d) $-\frac{9}{2}$ (e) None of these

1—Answer: b

20. Use the Fundamental Theorem of Calculus to evaluate $\int_{-1}^1 (3t^2 + 2t - 5)\, dt$.

(a) 8 (b) 2 (c) $t^3 + t^2 - 5t + C$

(d) -8 (e) None of these

1—Answer: d

21. Use the Fundamental Theorem of Calculus to evaluate $\int_0^1 \frac{x}{(1 + 2x^2)^3}\, dx$.

(a) $-\frac{5}{36}$ (b) $\frac{1}{9}$ (c) $-\frac{1}{36}$ (d) $-\frac{1}{9}$ (e) None of these

1—Answer: b

22. Evaluate $\int_{-1}^1 |x|\, dx$.

(a) 1 (b) 0 (c) 2 (d) -1 (e) None of these

2—Answer: a

23. Evaluate $\int_0^3 |x - 2|\, dx$.

2—Answer: $\frac{5}{2}$

24. Evaluate the definite integral $\int_{1}^{\sqrt{e}} \frac{-4x}{x^2} dx$.

    (a) -1 (b) -6 (c) -4 (d) -2 (e) None of these

    1—Answer: d

25. Evaluate the definite integral $\int_{1}^{\sqrt{e}} \frac{2x}{x^2} dx$.

    (a) 1 (b) $\frac{1}{2}$ (c) 3 (d) 2 (e) None of these

    1—Answer: a

26. Evaluate the definite integral $\int_{1}^{\sqrt{e}} \frac{-7x}{x^2} dx$.

    (a) -7 (b) $-\frac{7}{4}$ (c) $-\frac{7}{2}$ (d) $-\frac{21}{2}$ (e) None of these

    1—Answer: c

27. Evaluate $\int_{e}^{4e} \frac{1}{x} dx$.

    (a) $\ln 3e$ (b) $\ln 4$ (c) $-\frac{3}{4e}$ (d) $\frac{15}{16e^2}$ (e) None of these

    1—Answer: b

28. Evaluate $\int_{1}^{5e} \frac{1}{x} dx$.

    (a) $\frac{1}{5e} - 1$ (b) 0 (c) ∞ (d) $1 + \ln 5$ (e) None of these

    1—Answer: d

29. Evaluate $\int_{1}^{e} \frac{5}{x} dx$.

    1—Answer: 5

30. Evaluate $\int_{2}^{e+1} \frac{1}{x-1} dx$.

    1—Answer: 1

31. What is the average value of $f(x) = 2x^3 + 1$ on the interval $[1, 4]$?

    (a) 109 (b) 42 (c) $\frac{104}{3}$ (d) $\frac{87}{2}$ (e) None of these

    2—Answer: d

32. What is the average value of $f(x) = 2x^2 + 3$ on the interval $[0, 2]$?

    (a) $\frac{22}{3}$ (b) $\frac{17}{3}$ (c) 4   (d) 27   (e) None of these

    1—Answer: b

33. What is the average value of $f(x) = 3x^2 - 2$ on the interval $[0, 2]$?

    (a) 1   (b) 5   (c) 6   (d) 2   (e) None of these

    1—Answer: d

34. What is the average value of $y = x^3$ over the interval $[0, 2]$?

    1—Answer: 2

35. What is the average value of $f(x) = 2x^3 + x$ on the interval $[-1, 2]$?

    (a) $\frac{3}{2}$ (b) 3   (c) 9   (d) 27   (e) None of these

    1—Answer: b

36. What is the average value of the function $f(x) = \dfrac{x^2}{x^3 + 1}$ on the interval $[2, 5]$?

    1—Answer: $\frac{1}{9} \ln(14)$

37. What is the average value of the function $f(x) = \dfrac{x}{x^2 + 1}$ on the interval $[1, 4]$?

    (a) $\frac{1}{2}(\ln 17 - \ln 2)$ (b) $\frac{1}{6} \ln\left(\frac{17}{2}\right)$ (c) $\frac{1}{3} \ln\left(\frac{17}{2}\right)$

    (d) $\frac{1}{6} \ln(17)$ (e) None of these

    1—Answer: b

38. Determine the area of the indicated region.

    (a) 16/3 sq. units   (b) 32/3 sq. units

    (c) 8/3 sq. units   (d) 16 sq. units

    (e) None of these

    1—Answer: b

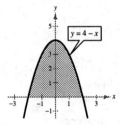

39. Determine the area of the indicated region.

    (a) 4 sq. units   (b) 12 sq. units

    (c) 32/3 sq. units   (d) 16/3 sq. units

    (e) None of these

    1—Answer: d

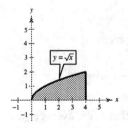

40. Determine the area of the indicated region.

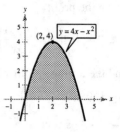

(a) 8 sq. units   (b) 128/3 sq. units

(c) 32/3 sq. units   (d) 16/3 sq. units

(e) None of these

1—Answer: c

41. Determine the area of the region bounded by the graphs of $y = -x^2 + 4$ and $y = 0$.

(a) 0   (b) $\frac{32}{3}$ (c) $\frac{16}{3}$ (d) $-\frac{32}{3}$ (e) None of these

1—Answer: b

42. Calculate the area of the region bounded by $y = e^{2x}, y = 0, x = 1, x = 4$.

1—Answer: $\frac{1}{2}e^2(e^6 - 1)$

43. Determine the area of the region bounded by the graphs of $y = -x^2 + 2x$ and $y = 0$.

(a) -4 (b) $\frac{2}{3}$ (c) $-\frac{4}{3}$ (d) $\frac{4}{3}$ (e) None of these

1—Answer: d

44. Determine the area bounded by the graphs of $y = -x^2 + 4x$ and $y = 0$.

(a) $\frac{16}{3}$ (b) $\frac{32}{3}$ (c) $\frac{8}{3}$ (d) $\frac{128}{3}$ (e) None of these

1—T—Answer: b

45. Determine the area bounded by the graphs of $y = \sqrt{4 - x}, x = 0$, and $y = 0$.

(a) $\frac{32}{3}$ (b) 8   (c) $\frac{8}{3}$ (d) $\frac{16}{3}$ (e) None of these

1—Answer: d

46. Determine the area bounded by the graphs of $y = e^x, x = 0$ and $y = 3$.

(a) $\ln 9 - 2$ (b) $3 \ln 3 - 4$ (c) $\ln 27$ (d) $3 \ln 3 - 2$ (e) None of these

1—Answer: d

47. Given the profit

$$P = 0.5\left(1 + \frac{1000}{x}\right),$$

find the average profit obtained when x varies from 4 to 7.

(a) $182.34   (b) $169.56   (c) $-$186.54   (d) $-$172.66   (e) None of these

2—T—Answer: e

48. Given the profit

$$P = 0.2\left(1 + \frac{1000}{3x}\right),$$

find the average profit when x varies from 12 to 18.

(a) $29.23   (b) $141.16   (c) $401.20   (d) $-$114.58   (e) None of these

2—T—Answer: a

49. Given the profit

$$P = 1.3\left(1 + \frac{1000}{x}\right),$$

find the average profit when x varies from 10 to 20.

2—T—Answer: $91.41

50. The marginal revenue for a certain product is given by

$$\frac{dR}{dx} = 20x + e^{-x}.$$

Find the change in revenue when sales increase from 100 to 101 units.

(a) $2010.00   (b) $1990.00   (c) $1874.34   (d) $2018.84   (e) None of these

2—T—Answer: a

51. The marginal revenue for a certain product is given by

$$\frac{dR}{dx} = 30x + e^{-2x}.$$

Find the change in revenue when sales increase from 100 to 101 units.

1—T—Answer: $3015

52. The marginal revenue for a certain product is given by

$$\frac{dR}{dx} = 20 - 0.2x.$$

Find the change in revenue when sales increase from 50 to 60 units.

1—Answer: $90

53. The marginal revenue for a certain product is given by

$$\frac{dR}{dx} = 0.2x - 50.$$

Find the change in revenue when sales increase from 400 to 500 units.

1—Answer: $4000

54. The marginal revenue for a certain product is given by

$$\frac{dR}{dx} = 0.4x - 25.$$

Find the change in revenue when sales increase from 70 to 80 units.

(a) $4   (b) $50   (c) $500   (d) $720   (e) None of these

1—Answer: b

55. The marginal profit for a certain product is given by

$$\frac{dP}{dx} = -4x + 72.$$

Find the change in profit when sales increase from 10 to 20 units.

(a) $1560   (b) $100   (c) $120   (d) $32   (e) None of these

1—Answer: c

56. The marginal revenue for a certain product is given by

$$\frac{dR}{dx} = 25 - 2x.$$

Find the change in revenue when sales increase from 7 to 10 units.

1—Answer: $24

57. The marginal revenue for a certain product is given by

$$\frac{dR}{dx} = 30 - 2x.$$

Find the change in revenue when sales increase from 5 to 10 units.

(a) $10   (b) $75   (c) $25   (d) −$25   (e) None of these

1—Answer: b

58. In a complete sentence, explain what the Fundamental Theorem of Calculus says about the evaluation of the definite integral

$$\int_a^b f(x)\, dx.$$

1—Answer: Answers will vary.

59. In a complete sentence, explain how to find the average value of a function $f(x)$ over an interval $[a, b]$.

1—Answer: Answers will vary.

Section 5.5   The Area of a Region Bounded by Two Graphs

1. Find the area of the region bounded by the graphs of $f(x) = x^3 - 2x$ and $g(x) = -x$.

(a) 2

(b) $\frac{1}{2}$

(c) 0

(d) $\frac{1}{4}$

(e) None of these

2—Answer: b

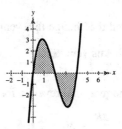

2. Find the area of the region bounded by the graphs of $f(x) = x^3 - 6x$ and $g(x) = -2x$.

(a) $\frac{1}{4}$

(b) 0

(c) 4

(d) 8

(e) None of these

2—Answer: d

3. Find the area of the region bounded by the graphs of $y = x^3 - 6x^2 + 8x$ and $y = 0$.

2—Answer: 8

4. Determine the area bounded by the graphs of $f(x) = e^{0.5x}$, $g(x) = e^x$ and $x = \ln 3$.

2—T—Answer: $4 - 2\sqrt{3}$

5. Determine the area of the region bounded by $y = x^2 - 4x$ and $y = x - 4$.

(a) $-\frac{9}{2}$ (b) $\frac{23}{6}$ (c) $\frac{9}{2}$ (d) $\frac{8}{3}$ (e) None of these

1—Answer: c

6. Determine the area of the region bounded by $y = -x^2 + 2x + 3$ and $y = 3$.

(a) $\frac{4}{3}$ (b) $\frac{9}{2}$ (c) $\frac{22}{3}$ (d) $-\frac{4}{3}$ (e) None of these

1—Answer: a

7. Find the area of the region bounded by the graphs of $f(x) = 6x - x^2$ and $g(x) = x^2 - 2x$.

(a) 32   (b) $\frac{20}{3}$ (c) $\frac{64}{3}$ (d) 128   (e) None of these

1—Answer: c

8. Find the area of the region bounded by the graphs of $f(x) = 5x - x^2$ and $g(x) = 3x^2 + x$.

(a) $\frac{2}{3}$ (b) 6   (c) $\frac{1}{6}$ (d) $\frac{13}{6}$ (e) None of these

1—Answer: a

9. Find the area of the region bounded by $y = 4 - 4x^2$ and $y = 0$.

1—Answer: $\frac{16}{3}$

10. Find the area of the region bounded by the graphs of $x = y^2 + 4y$ and $x = 0$.

1—Answer: $\frac{32}{3}$

11. Find the area of the region bounded by $y = \frac{1}{x}$ and $2x + 2y = 5$.

1—Answer: $\frac{15}{8} - 2 \ln 2$

12. Determine the area of the region bounded by the graphs of $f(x) = x^2 - 2x$ and $g(x) = x$.

1—Answer: $\frac{9}{2}$

13. Determine the area of the region bounded by the graphs of $y = 4x - x^2$ and $y = x - 4$.

1—T—Answer: $\frac{125}{6} \approx 20.83$

14. Determine the area of the region bounded by the graphs of $y = xe^{x^2}, y = 0, x = 0$, and $x = 2$.

(a) 38.165 sq. units   (b) 26.799 sq. units   (c) 53.598 sq. units

(d) 76.330 sq. units   (e) None of these

1—T—Answer: b

15. Determine the area of the region bounded by the graphs of $y = x - 4x^2$ and $y = -3$.

(a) $\frac{665}{96}$ sq. units   (b) $\frac{343}{96}$ sq. units   (c) $\frac{707}{96}$ sq. units

(d) $\frac{301}{96}$ sq. units   (e) None of these

1—T—Answer: b

16. Determine the area of the region bounded by the graphs of $y = e^{x/2}, y = e^{-x/2}, x = 0$ and $x = 1$.

(a) 0.51 sq. units   (b) 1.02 sq. units   (c) 0.26 sq. units

(d) 3.32 sq. units   (e) None of these

1—T—Answer: a

17. Determine the area of the region bounded by the graphs of $y = e^x, y = e$ and $x = 0$.

1—T—Answer: $4 - \ln(3)$

18. Find the producer surplus for the demand function $p_1(x) = 300 - \frac{1}{3}x$ and the supply function $p_2(x) = 100 + x$.

2—Answer: $11,250

19. Find the producer surplus for the demand function $p_1(x) = 200 - \frac{1}{3}x$ and the supply function $p_2(x) = 120 + x$.

2—Answer: $1800

20. Find the producer surplus for the demand function $p_1(x) = 200 - \frac{1}{2}x$ and the supply function $p_2(x) = 50 + x$.

   (a) $2500   (b) $5000   (c) $7500   (d) $9000   (e) None of these

2—Answer: b

Section 5.6   The Definite Integral as the Limit of a Sum

1. Use the Midpoint Rule with $n = 5$ to approximate the definite integral $\int_0^3 \sqrt{x^2 + 2}\, dx$.

(a) 6.22751   (b) 6.47154   (c) 6.52314   (d) 6.45797   (e) None of these

1—T—Answer: d

2. Use the Midpoint Rule with $n = 3$ to approximate the definite integral $\int_0^3 \sqrt{x^2 + 2}\, dx$.

(a) 6.43383   (b) 6.47154   (c) 6.52314   (d) 6.42227   (e) None of these

1—T—Answer: a

3. Use the Midpoint Rule with $n = 4$ to approximate the definite integral $\int_1^5 \sqrt{x^2 + 2}\, dx$.

(a) 13.4413   (b) 13.4774   (c) 13.4257   (d) 13.5797   (e) None of these

1—T—Answer: c

4. Approximate the definite integral by using the Midpoint Rule with $n = 4$. $\int_0^2 \sqrt{1 + x^2}\, dx$

1—Answer: 2.9486

5. Approximate the definite integral by using the Midpoint Rule with $n = 4$. $\int_0^4 \sqrt{1 + x^2}\, dx$

1—Answer: 9.2534

6. Approximate the definite integral by using the Midpoint Rule with $n = 4$. $\int_0^1 \sqrt{1 - x^2}\, dx$

1—Answer: 0.7960

7. Use the Trapezoidal Rule to approximate $\int_2^3 \frac{1}{(x - 1)^2}\, dx$ with $n = 4$.

(a) 0.5004   (b) 2.5000   (c) 0.5090   (d) 1.7396   (e) None of these

1—Answer: c

8. Use the Trapezoidal Rule to estimate the definite integral. [Use $n = 4$.] $\int_0^7 (x^2 - 7x)\, dx$.

(a) 57.17   (b) 53.59   (c) −57.17   (d) −53.59   (e) None of these

1—Answer: d

9. Use the Trapezoidal Rule to estimate the definite integral. [Use $n = 4$.] $\int_3^7 (x^2 - 10x + 21)\, dx$.

   (a) -10.67 (b) 10.67   (c) -10.00 (d) 10.00   (e) None of these

   1—Answer: c

10. Use the Midpoint Rule with $n = 4$ to approximate the area of the region bounded by $f(x) = x^3 - 4x^2 + 4x$ and the x-axis between $x = 0$ and $x = 2$.

    (a) 1.29   (b) 1.38   (c) 2.75   (d) 1.33   (e) None of these

    1—Answer: b

11. Use the Midpoint Rule with $n = 4$ to approximate the area of the region bounded by $f(x) = x^3 - 8x^2 + 16x$ and the x-axis between $x = 0$ and $x = 4$.

    (a) 22.00   (b) 23.00   (c) 20.67   (d) 21.33   (e) None of these

    1—Answer: a

12. Use the Midpoint Rule with $n = 4$ to approximate the area of the region bounded by $f(x) = x^3 - 6x^2 + 9x$ and the x-axis between $x = 0$ and $x = 3$.

    (a) 6.54   (b) 6.96   (c) 9.28   (d) 6.75   (e) None of these

    1—Answer: b

13. Use the Midpoint Rule with $n = 4$ to approximate the area of the region bounded by the graph of

    $$f(x) = \frac{1}{x^2 + 1}$$

    and the x-axis over the interval $[0, 1]$.

    (a) 0.785652   (b) 0.786700   (c) 0.785398   (d) 0.779820   (e) None of these

    1—T—Answer: b

14. Use the Midpoint Rule with $n = 4$ to approximate the area of the region bounded by the graph of

    $$f(x) = \frac{1}{x^2 + 1}$$

    and the x-axis over the interval $[1, 3]$.

    (a) 0.463647   (b) 0.459882   (c) 0.459067   (d) 0.461333   (e) None of these

    1—T—Answer: c

15. Use the Midpoint Rule with $n = 4$ to approximate the area of the region bounded by the graph of $f(x) = x^3 - 10x^2 + 25x$ and the x-axis between $x = 0$ and $x = 5$.

    (a) 52.08   (b) 42.97   (c) 53.71   (d) 50.46   (e) None of these

    1—T—Answer: c

16. Use the Midpoint Rule with $n = 4$ to approximate the area of the region bounded by $y = \sqrt{x}$ and the x-axis over the interval $[0, 2]$.

    1—T—Answer: $\frac{1}{4}\left(1\sqrt{3} + \sqrt{5} + \sqrt{7}\right) \approx 1.90$

17. Use the Midpoint Rule with $n = 4$ to approximate the area of the region bounded by $y = x^2$ and the x-axis over the interval $[1, 3]$.

    (a) $\frac{26}{3}$ (b) $\frac{33}{2}$ (c) $\frac{69}{8}$ (d) $\frac{69}{4}$ (e) None of these

    1—Answer: c

18. Use the Midpoint Rule with $n = 4$ to approximate the area of the region bounded by $y = x^2$ and the x-axis over the interval $[0, 2]$.

    (a) $\frac{21}{8}$ (b) $\frac{8}{3}$ (c) $\frac{15}{2}$ (d) $\frac{21}{4}$ (e) None of these

    2—Answer: a

19. Use the Midpoint Rule with $n = 3$ to approximate the area of the region bounded by the curve $y = x^2$ and the x-axis over the interval $[0, 3]$.

    (a) 5   (b) 9   (c) $\frac{35}{4}$ (d) 14   (e) None of these

    1—Answer: c

20. Use the Midpoint Rule with $n = 3$ to approximate the area of the region bounded by the curve $y = e^{x^2}$ and the x-axis over the interval $[0, 3]$.

    (a) 518.35   (b) 497.62   (c) 528.78   (d) 499.42   (e) None of these

    1—T—Answer: c

21. Use the Midpoint Rule with $n = 3$ to approximate the area of the region bounded by the curve $y = x^2 + x$ and the x-axis over the interval $[0, 3]$.

    (a) $\frac{53}{4}$ (b) $\frac{27}{2}$ (c) 8   (d) 20   (e) None of these

    1—T—Answer: a

22. Use the Midpoint Rule with $n = 3$ to approximate the area of the region bounded by the curve

    $$y = \frac{3}{x + 1}$$

    and the x-axis over the interval $[0, 3]$.

    1—Answer: $\frac{142}{35}$

Section 5.7   Volumes of Solids of Revolution

1. Find the volume of the solid formed by revolving the region bounded by the graphs of $y = -x^2 + 4$ and $y = 0$ about the x-axis.

   (a) $\dfrac{1472\pi}{15}$ (b) $\dfrac{736\pi}{15}$ (c) $\dfrac{2944\pi}{15}$ (d) $\dfrac{32\pi}{3}$ (e) None of these

   1—Answer: e

2. Find the volume of the solid formed by revolving the region bounded by the graphs of $y = -x^2 + 1$ and $y = 0$ about the x-axis.

   (a) $\dfrac{2\pi}{3}$ (b) $\dfrac{8\pi}{15}$ (c) $\dfrac{16\pi}{15}$ (d) $\dfrac{4\pi}{3}$ (e) None of these

   1—Answer: c

3. Find the volume of the solid formed by revolving the region bounded by the graphs of $y = 4x^2$ and $y = 16$ about the line $y = 16$.

   1—Answer: $\dfrac{8192\pi}{15}$

4. Find the volume of the solid of revolution formed by revolving the region bounded by $y = \sqrt{x - 2}$, $y = 0$, and $x = 6$ about the x-axis.

   1—Answer: 8π

5. Find the volume of the solid formed by revolving the region bounded by the graphs of $y = 2x^2$, $x = 0$, and $y = 2$ about the y-axis.

   (a) $\frac{1}{4}\pi$ (b) $\frac{2}{3}\pi$ (c) π (d) $\frac{16}{3}\pi$ (e) None of these

   1—Answer: c

6. Find the volume of the solid formed by revolving the region bounded by the graphs of $y = 4x - x^2$ and $y = 0$ about the x-axis.

   (a) $\frac{512}{15}\pi$ (b) $\frac{4352}{15}\pi$ (c) $\frac{2048}{15}\pi$ (d) $\frac{8192}{15}\pi$ (e) None of these

   2—Answer: a

7. Find the volume of the solid formed by revolving the region bounded by the graphs of $y = 3 - x^2$ and $y = 2$ about the line $y = 2$.

   (a) $\frac{8}{15}\pi$ (b) $\frac{16}{15}\pi$ (c) $\frac{32}{5}\pi$ (d) $\frac{48}{5}\pi$ (e) None of these

   1—Answer: b

8. Find the volume of the solid formed by revolving the region bounded by the graphs of $y = x^2 + 3$, $y = 3$, $x = 0$, and $x = 2$ about the line $y = 3$.

(a) $\frac{112}{5}\pi$ (b) $\frac{32}{5}\pi$ (c) $\frac{56}{5}\pi$ (d) $\frac{64}{5}\pi$ (e) None of these

1—Answer: b

9. Find the volume of the solid formed by revolving the region bounded by $y = x^3$, $y = 1$ and $x = 2$ about the x-axis.

(a) $\frac{127}{7}\pi$ (b) $\frac{120}{7}\pi$ (c) $\frac{240}{7}\pi$ (d) $\frac{1013}{10}\pi$ (e) None of these

1—Answer: b

10. Find the volume of the solid formed by revolving the region bounded by $y = x^3$, $x = 2$ and $y = 1$ about the y-axis.

(a) $\frac{93}{5}\pi$ (b) $\frac{120}{7}\pi$ (c) $\frac{47}{5}\pi$ (d) $\frac{62}{5}\pi$ (e) None of these

1—Answer: c

11. Set up the integral needed to find the volume of the solid generated by revolving the region bounded by the graph of $y = x^3$ and the line $y = x$, between $x = 0$ and $x = 1$, about the y-axis.

(a) $\pi \int_0^1 (x^2 - x^4)\, dx$ (b) $\pi \int_0^1 (y^{1/3} - y)^2\, dy$ (c) $\pi \int_0^1 (x^4 - x^2)\, dx$

(d) $\pi \int_0^1 (y^{2/3} - y^2)\, dy$ (e) None of these

2—Answer: d

12. Find the volume of the solid formed by revolving the region bounded by the graphs of $y = x^2 + 2$, $y = 2$, $x = 0$ and $x = 3$ about the x-axis.

1—Answer: $\frac{423}{5}\pi$

13. Find the volume of the solid formed by revolving the region bounded by $y = e^x$, $y = 0$, $x = 0$ and $x = 1$ about the x-axis.

1—Answer: $\frac{\pi}{2}(e^2 - 1)$

14. Find the volume of the solid formed by revolving the region bounded by $y = e^x$, $y = 0$, $x = 0$, and $x = 1$ about the y-axis.

(a) $\frac{e}{2}$ (b) 2π (c) $e\pi$ (d) π^2 (e) None of these

1—Answer: b

15. Find the volume of the solid formed by revolving the region bounded by $y = x^3$, $y = 0$, and $x = 1$ about the x-axis.

    1—**Answer:** $\dfrac{\pi}{7}$

16. Find the volume of the solid formed by revolving the region bounded by $y = \sqrt{x}$, $y = 1$, and $x = 4$ about the x-axis.

    (a) 4π (b) π (c) 3π (d) $\dfrac{9}{2}\pi$ (e) None of these

    1—**Answer:** d

17. Find the volume of the solid formed by revolving the region bounded by $y = x^2$, and $y = 4$ about the x-axis.

    (a) $\dfrac{256}{15}\pi$ (b) $\dfrac{256}{5}\pi$ (c) $\dfrac{512}{15}\pi$ (d) $\dfrac{256}{15}$ (e) None of these

    1—**Answer:** b

18. Find the volume of the solid formed by revolving the region bounded by $y = \sqrt{5 - x}$, $x = 4$, and $y = 1$ about the x-axis.

    (a) 6π (b) 4π (c) $\dfrac{7\pi}{2}$ (d) 10π (e) None of these

    1—**Answer:** e

19. Set up the integral needed to find the volume of the solid formed when the graph of the region bounded by $y = \sqrt{25 - x^2}$ and $y = 3$ is revolved about the x–axis.

    (a) $\pi \displaystyle\int_{-4}^{4} (16 - x^2)\, dx$ (b) $\pi \displaystyle\int_{0}^{4} (16 - x^2)\, dx$ (c) $\pi \displaystyle\int_{-4}^{4} (22 - x^2)\, dx$

    (d) $\pi \displaystyle\int_{-3}^{3} (16 - x^2)\, dx$ (e) None of these

    1—**Answer:** a

20. Find the volume of the solid formed when the graph of the region bounded by $y = \sqrt{9 - x^2}$ and $y = 1$ is revolved about the x-axis.

    1—**Answer:** $\dfrac{64\sqrt{2}\pi}{3}$

21. Find the volume of the solid formed when the graph of the region bounded by $y = e^x$, $y = 1$, and $x = 4$ is revolved about the x-axis.

    1—**Answer:** $\dfrac{\pi}{2}(e^8 - 9)$

22. Find the volume of the solid formed when the graph of the region bounded by $y = e^x$, $x = 0$, $x = 2$, and $y = 0$ is revolved about the x-axis.

(a) $\frac{\pi}{2}(e^4 - 1)$ (b) $\frac{\pi e^4}{2}$ (c) $\pi(e^2 - 1)$ (d) $\pi(e^2 - 1)$ (e) None of these

1—Answer: a

23. Use the washer method to find the volume of the solid of revolution formed by revolving the region bounded by $f(x) = 3x^2$ and $f(x) = 2x + 1$ about the x-axis.

(a) 3.4568   (b) 21.7197   (c) 10.8598   (d) 19.9967   (e) None of these

1—T—Answer: c

24. Use the washer method to find the volume of the solid of revolution formed by revolving the region bounded by $f(x) = 3x^2$ and $f(x) = 5x + 2$ about the x-axis.

(a) 180.924   (b) 57.589   (c) 96.314   (d) 67.667   (e) None of these

1—T—Answer: a

25. Use the washer method to find the volume of the solid of revolution formed by revolving the region bounded by $f(x) = -3x^2 + 8$ and $f(x) = 3x^2 + 2$ about the x-axis.

(a) 381.924   (b) 251.327   (c) 79.999   (d) 67.667   (e) None of these

1—T—Answer: b

CHAPTER 6
Techniques of Integration

Section 6.1 Integration by Substitution

1. Evaluate: $\int x\sqrt{1-x}\,dx$.

(a) $-\dfrac{x^2}{3}(1-x)^{3/2}+C$

(b) $\dfrac{2-3x}{2\sqrt{1-x}}+C$

(c) $\dfrac{x^2}{3}(1-x)^{3/2}+C$

(d) $-\dfrac{2}{15}(2+3x)(1-x)^{3/2}+C$

(e) None of these

1—Answer: d

2. Evaluate: $\int x\sqrt{x+1}\,dx$.

(a) $\dfrac{3x+2}{2\sqrt{x+1}}+C$

(b) $\dfrac{2}{15}(x+1)^{3/2}(3x-2)+C$

(c) $\dfrac{1}{4}(x+1)(x-1)+C$

(d) $\dfrac{1}{3}x^2(x+1)^{3/2}+C$

(e) None of these

1—Answer: b

3. Find the indefinite integral: $\int \dfrac{x}{\sqrt{x-1}}\,dx$.

1—Answer: $\frac{2}{3}\sqrt{x-1}(x+2)+C$

4. Evaluate: $\int \dfrac{x^3}{(x^4-2)^2}\,dx$.

1—Answer: $\dfrac{-1}{4(x^4-2)}+C$

5. Evaluate: $\int x^2\sqrt{1-x^3}\,dx$.

(a) $-\dfrac{2}{9}(1-x^3)^{3/2}+C$

(b) $2(1-x^3)^{3/2}+C$

(c) $\dfrac{-1}{6\sqrt{1-x^3}}+C$

(d) $\dfrac{2}{9\sqrt{1-x^3}}+C$

(e) None of these

1—Answer: a

6. Integrate: $\int \dfrac{2x}{\sqrt[3]{5 + 7x}} dx$.

(a) $\dfrac{3}{245}(7x + 5)^{2/3}(14x - 15) + C$

(b) $\dfrac{3}{7}(7x + 5)^{2/3} + C$

(c) $\dfrac{3}{686}(7x + 5)^{4/3}(28x - 15) + C$

(d) $\dfrac{(7x + 5)^4(28x - 5)}{490} + C$

(e) None of these

1—Answer: a

7. Integrate: $\int 3x\sqrt{4 - x} \, dx$.

(a) $-(4 - x)^{3/2} + C$

(b) $2(4 - x)^{3/2} + C$

(c) $-\dfrac{2}{5}(4 - x)^{3/2}(3x + 8) + C$

(d) $\dfrac{2(2 - x)}{\sqrt{4 - x}} + C$

(e) None of these

1—Answer: c

8. Integrate: $\int \dfrac{5x}{\sqrt[3]{5 + 2x}} dx$.

(a) $\dfrac{4}{5}(2x + 5^{2/3}(3x + 7) + C$

(b) $\dfrac{9}{5}(3x + 7)(2x + 5)^{2/3} + C$

(c) $\dfrac{3}{8}(2x + 5)^{2/3}(4x - 15) + C$

(d) $\dfrac{15}{112}(2x + 5)^{4/3}(8x - 15) + C$

(e) None of these

1—Answer: c

9. Integrate: $\int 3x\sqrt{5 - x} \, dx$.

1—Answer: $-\dfrac{2}{5}(5 - x)^{3/2}(3x + 10) + C$

10. Integrate: $\int 7x\sqrt{5 - 2x} \, dx$.

(a) $\dfrac{7}{15}(2x + 5)^{3/2}(3x - 5) + C$

(b) $-\dfrac{7}{15}(5 - 2x)^{3/2}(3x + 5) + C$

(c) $\dfrac{14}{15}(2x + 5)^{3/2}(3x - 10) + C$

(d) $-\dfrac{7}{3}(x + 5)\sqrt{5 - 2x} + C$

(e) None of these

1—Answer: b

11. Integrate: $\int x^2\sqrt{x + 1} \, dx$.

1—Answer: $\dfrac{2}{105}(x + 1)^{3/2}(15x^2 - 12x + 8) + C$

12. Integrate: $\int \dfrac{x^2}{\sqrt{x+1}}\,dx$.

   (a) $\frac{2}{105}(x+1)^{3/2}(15x^2 - 12x + 8) + C$ (b) $\frac{4}{15}\sqrt{x+1}(2x^2 - 3x + 7) + C$

   (c) $\frac{2}{15}\sqrt{x+1}(3x^2 - 4x + 8) + C$ (d) $-\frac{7}{105}\sqrt{x+1}(x+2)^2 + C$

   (e) None of these

   1—Answer: c

13. Find the indefinite integral using substitution: $\int \dfrac{x}{\sqrt{5x+1}}\,dx$.

   (a) $\frac{2}{75}\sqrt{5x+1}(5x-2) + C$ (b) $\frac{1}{5}x^2\sqrt{5x+1} + C$ (c) $\frac{1}{10}\left(5x - 2\ln\sqrt{5x+1}\right) + C$

   (d) $\frac{2x}{5}\sqrt{5x+1} + C$ (e) None of these

   1—Answer: a

14. Find the indefinite integral using substitution: $\int x\sqrt{2x+1}\,dx$.

   (a) $\frac{1}{6}x^2(2x+1)^{3/2} + C$ (b) $\frac{1}{15}(2x+1)^{3/2}(3x-1) + C$ (c) $\frac{2}{3}(2x^3 + x)^{3/2} + C$

   (d) $\dfrac{3x+1}{\sqrt{2x+1}} + C$ (e) None of these

   1—Answer: b

15. Evaluate using substitution: $\int \dfrac{x}{\sqrt[3]{2x+1}}\,dx$.

   (a) $\dfrac{3(2x+1)^{2/3}}{40}(4x-3) + C$ (b) $\dfrac{3(2x+1)^{2/3}}{20}(4x-3) + C$ (c) $\dfrac{(2x+1)^{2/3}}{4}(4x-3) + C$

   (d) $\dfrac{(2x+1)^{2/3}}{20}(4x+3) + C$ (e) None of these

   1—Answer: a

16. Evaluate using substitution: $\int \dfrac{x}{\sqrt[4]{x+1}}\,dx$.

   1—Answer: $\dfrac{4(3x-4)(x+1)^{3/4}}{21} + C$

17. Evaluate: $\int x\sqrt{2x+3}\,dx.$

1—Answer: $\dfrac{(x-1)(2x+3)^{3/2}}{5} + C$

18. Evaluate: $\int \dfrac{x}{\sqrt[3]{1-x^2}}\,dx.$

(a) $\frac{1}{3}(1-x^2)^{2/3} + C$ (b) $-\frac{3}{8}(1-x^2)^{4/3} + C$ (c) $-\frac{3}{4}(1-x^2)^{2/3} + C$

(d) $-\frac{2}{3}(1-x^2)^{4/3} + C$ (e) None of these

1—Answer: c

19. Evaluate: $\int \dfrac{e^{3x}}{7+e^{3x}}\,dx.$

1—Answer: $\frac{1}{3}\ln|7+e^{3x}| + C$

20. Evaluate: $\int \dfrac{3x-2}{3x^2-4x}\,dx.$

(a) $-\ln|x| + C$ (b) $\dfrac{-1}{4(3x^2-4x)^2} + C$ (c) $\dfrac{1}{(3x^2-4x)^2} + C$

(d) $\dfrac{1}{2}\ln|3x^2-4x| + C$ (e) None of these

1—Answer: d

21. Evaluate: $\displaystyle\int_{-1}^{0} x^2\sqrt{x+1}\,dx.$

2—Answer: $\frac{16}{105}$

22. Evaluate: $\displaystyle\int_{-1}^{0} x\sqrt[3]{1+x}\,dx.$

2—Answer: $-\frac{9}{28}$

23. Find the area bounded by $y = \dfrac{x}{(1+x)^2}$, $y = 0$, $x = 0$, and $x = 2$.

(a) $\frac{1}{2}\ln 5$ (b) $-\frac{3}{8}$

(c) $-\frac{2}{3} + \ln 3$ (d) $-\frac{1}{4} + \ln 2$

(e) None of these

2—Answer: c

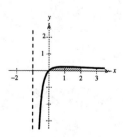

24. Find the area bounded by $y = x\sqrt[3]{1 - x}$, $y = 0$, $x = 0$, and $x = 1$.

(a) $-\frac{9}{28}$ (b) $\frac{9}{28}$

(c) 1 (d) $\frac{3}{7}$

(e) None of these

2—Answer: b

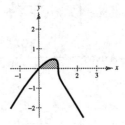

Section 6.2   Integration by Parts and Present Value

1. Evaluate: $\int xe^{2x}\,dx$.

   (a) $2e^{2x}(x - 2) + C$
       (b) $x^2 e^{x^2} + C$
       (c) $\dfrac{e^{2x}}{4}[2x - 1] + C$

   (d) $\dfrac{1}{2}x^2 e^{2x} + C$
       (e) None of these

   1—Answer: c

2. Evaluate: $\int \ln 3t\,dt$.

   (a) $t \ln 3t - t + C$
       (b) $\dfrac{1}{t} + C$
       (c) $\dfrac{1}{3t} + C$

   (d) $3t \ln 3t - 3t + C$
       (e) None of these

   2—Answer: a

3. Evaluate the indefinite integral: $\int (\ln x)^8\,dx$.

   (a) $x(\ln x)^8 - 8(\ln x)^7 + C$
       (b) $\dfrac{8}{x}(\ln x)^7 + C$
       (c) $\dfrac{1}{8}(\ln x)^9 + C$

   (d) $x(\ln x)^8 - 8\int (\ln x)^7\,dx$
       (e) None of these

   2—Answer: d

4. Evaluate the indefinite integral: $\int (\ln x)^3\,dx$.

   (a) $x(\ln x)^3 - 3(\ln x)^2 + C$
       (b) $x(\ln x)^3 - 3\int (\ln x)^2\,dx$
       (c) $\dfrac{1}{3}(\ln x)^4 + C$

   (d) $\dfrac{3}{x}(\ln x)^2 + C$
       (e) None of these

   2—Answer: b

5. Evaluate the indefinite integral: $\int (\ln x)^6\,dx$.

   (a) $\dfrac{1}{6}(\ln x)^7 + C$
       (b) $x(\ln x)^6 - 6\int (\ln x)^5\,dx$
       (c) $x(\ln x)^6 - 6(\ln x)^5 + C$

   (d) $\dfrac{6}{x}(\ln x)^5 + C$
       (e) None of these

   2—Answer: b

6. Evaluate: $\displaystyle\int \frac{e^{-1/x}}{x^3}\,dx.$

   1—Answer: $\displaystyle\frac{(x+1)e^{-1/x}}{x} + C$

7. Find the indefinite integral using integration by parts: $\displaystyle\int x \ln x\,dx.$

   (a) $\displaystyle\frac{x^2(\ln x)^2}{4} + C$ (b) $\displaystyle\frac{\ln x^4}{4}$ (c) $\displaystyle\frac{x^2}{6}(3\ln x - x) + C$

   (d) $\displaystyle\frac{x^2}{4}[2\ln x - 1] + C$ (e) None of these

   1—Answer: d

8. Find the indefinite integral using integration by parts: $\displaystyle\int x^2 e^x\,dx.$

   (a) $\displaystyle\frac{x^3 e^x}{3} + C$ (b) $\displaystyle\frac{x^3 e^{x+1}}{3(x+1)} + C$ (c) $e^x(x^2 - 2x + 2) + C$

   (d) $xe^x(x+2) + C$ (e) None of these

   1—Answer: c

9. Find the indefinite integral using integration by parts: $\displaystyle\int \sqrt{x}\,\ln x\,dx.$

   (a) $x^{3/2}(\ln x)^2 + C$ (b) $\ln x^{7/2} + C$ (c) $\displaystyle\frac{2}{9}x^{3/2}[\ln x - 2] + C$

   (d) $\displaystyle\frac{2 + \ln x}{2\sqrt{x}} + C$ (e) None of these

   1—Answer: c

10. Find the indefinite integral using integration by parts: $\displaystyle\int x^2 e^{-x}\,dx.$

   (a) $xe^{-x}(2 - x) + C$ (b) $\displaystyle\frac{-x^3 e^{-x}}{3} + C$ (c) $-xe^{-x}(x+2) + C$

   (d) $-e^{-x}(x^2 + 2x + 2) + C$ (e) None of these

   1—Answer: d

11. Evaluate using integration by parts: $\displaystyle\int \sqrt[3]{x} \ln x \, dx$.

(a) $\dfrac{3x^{4/3}}{4}(4 \ln x - 3) + C$

(b) $\dfrac{3x^{4/3}}{16}(\ln x + 3) + C$

(c) $\dfrac{3x^{4/3}}{16}(4 \ln x - 3) + C$

(d) $\dfrac{3x^{4/3}}{8}(4 \ln x - 3) + C$

(e) None of these

1—**Answer:** c

12. Evaluate: $\displaystyle\int \ln 2x \, dx$.

(a) $x(\ln 2x - 1) + C$

(b) $2x(2 \ln 2x - 1) + C$

(c) $\dfrac{1}{x} + C$

(d) $\dfrac{1}{2}\left[1 - \dfrac{1}{x}\right] + C$

(e) None of these

1—**Answer:** a

13. Find the indefinite integral using integration by parts: $\displaystyle\int x^2 e^{2x} \, dx$.

(a) $\dfrac{e^{2x}}{4}(x^2 - x + 1) + C$

(b) $\dfrac{e^{2x}}{2}(2x^2 - 2x + 1) + C$

(c) $\dfrac{e^{2x}}{4}(2x^2 + 2x + 1) + C$

(d) $\dfrac{e^{2x}}{4}(2x^2 - 2x + 1) + C$

(e) None of these

1—**Answer:** d

14. Evaluate: $\displaystyle\int x e^{2x^2} \, dx$.

1—**Answer:** $\frac{1}{4}e^{2x^2}$

15. Evaluate the indefinite integral: $\displaystyle\int (\ln x)^4 \, dx$.

(a) $x(\ln x)^4 - 4\displaystyle\int (\ln x)^3 \, dx$

(b) $x(\ln x)^4 - 4(\ln x)^3 + C$

(c) $\dfrac{4}{x}(\ln x)^4 + C$

(d) $\dfrac{1}{4}(\ln x)^5 + C$

(e) None of these

2—**Answer:** a

16. Evaluate: $\displaystyle\int x \ln x \, dx$.

1—**Answer:** $\frac{1}{4}x^2[2 \ln x - 1] + C$

17. Evaluate: $\int x^2 e^{3x}\, dx.$

    2—Answer: $\dfrac{e^{3x}}{3}\left(x^2 - \dfrac{2}{3}x + \dfrac{2}{9}\right) + C$

18. Evaluate: $\int x^3 \ln x\, dx.$

    1—Answer: $\frac{1}{4}x^4 \ln x - \frac{1}{16}x^4 + C$

19. Evaluate: $\int x^4 \ln x\, dx.$

  (a) $x^4 - \frac{4}{3}x^3 + C$ (b) $\frac{1}{25}x^5\left[\, 5 \ln x - 1\right] + C$ (c) $x^3 + \ln 4x^4 + C$

  (d) $x^3[1 + 4 \ln x] + C$ (e) None of these

  1—Answer: b

20. Evaluate: $\int x e^{5x}\, dx.$

  (a) $e^{5x}(5x + 1) + C$ (b) $\frac{1}{5}x e^{5x} + C$ (c) $\frac{1}{5}e^{5x}(x - 1) + C$

  (d) $\frac{1}{25}e^{5x}[5x - 1] + C$ (e) None of these

  1—Answer: d

21. Evaluate: $\int x e^{3x}\, dx.$

    1—Answer: $\dfrac{e^{3x}(3x - 1)}{9} + C$

22. Evaluate using integration by parts: $\int x^2 \ln x\, dx.$

  (a) $\dfrac{x^3}{9}(\ln x^3 - 1) + C$ (b) $\dfrac{x^3}{9}(\ln x^3 - 3) + C$ (c) $\dfrac{x^3}{3}(3 \ln x + 1) + C$

  (d) $\dfrac{x^3}{9}(3 \ln x + 1) + C$ (e) None of these

  1—Answer: a

23. Evaluate the definite integral: $\int_1^e \ln(2x)\, dx.$

    1—Answer: $e \ln 2 - \ln 2 + 1$

24. Evaluate the definite integral: $\int_1^e \ln x \, dx$.

1—Answer: 1

25. Evaluate using integration by parts: $\int_1^2 x \ln x \, dx$.

(a) $\ln 4 - \frac{5}{4}$ (b) $\ln 4 - 1$ (c) $2 \ln 2 + \frac{3}{4}$ (d) $\ln 4 - \frac{3}{4}$ (e) None of these

1—Answer: d

26. Find the present value of the income given by $c(t) = 1000 + 60e^{t/2}$ over 8 years at the annual interest rate of 10%.

2—T—Answer: $9036.59

27. Find the present value of the income given by $c(t) = 1000 + 60e^{t/2}$ over 6 years at the annual interest rate of 10%.

2—T—Answer: $6015.35

28. Find the present value of the income given by $c(t) = 1000 + 60e^{t/2}$ over 15 years at the annual interest rate of 10%.

2—T—Answer: $68,133.02

29. The annual income for a small company over the next ten years is given by the model $c(t) = 90,000t$, $0 \le t \le 10$. What is the present value of this income over the ten–year period if we assume an annual interest rate of 9%?

1—T—Answer: $2,527,973.85

30. Find the present value of the income given by $c(t) = 3000$, measured in dollars, over five years, at an annual interest rate of 4%.

(a) $75,000(1 - e^{-0.2})$ (b) $75,000(1 - e^{-0.4})$ (c) $75,000(e^{-0.2} - 1)$

(d) $15,000   (e) None of these

1—T—Answer: a

31. Find the present value of the income given by $c(t) = 5000$, measured in dollars, over four years, at an annual interest rate of 8%.

(a) $6600.00   (b) $5995.24   (c) $6885.64   (d) $4796.19   (e) None of these

1—T—Answer: b

32. Find the present value of the income given by $c(t) = 4000$, measured in dollars, over five years, at an annual interest rate of 8%.

(a) $5600.00   (b) $5967.30   (c) $4908.42   (d) $3926.74   (e) None of these

1—T—Answer: c

33. Find the present value of the income given by $c(t) = 1000e^{0.02t}$, measured in dollars, over four years, at an annual interest rate of 4%.

(a) $3814.25   (b) $50,000.00   (c) $3844.18   (d) $52,366.53   (e) None of these

1—T—Answer: c

34. Which of the following would be used to find the present value of the income given by $c(t) = 4000e^{0.06t}$, measured in dollars, over four years, at an annual interest rate of 5%.

(a) $\int_0^4 c(t)e^{0.06t} \, dt$ (b) $\int_0^4 4000e^{-0.01t} \, dt$ (c) $\int_0^4 4000e^{0.05t} \, dt$

(d) $\int_0^4 c(t)e^{-0.05t} \, dt$ (e) None of these

1—Answer: d

35. If the annual income of a small business is given by $c(t) = 100,000t$, $0 \le t \le 12$, and the inflation rate is 6%, find the present value of this income over a twelve–year period.

1—T—Answer: $4,521,836.67

36. For the income given by $c(t) = 3000$, the annual income over the next five years would be found by evaluating:

(a) $\int_0^5 3000e^{-0.04t} \, dt$ (b) $\int_0^5 3000e^{0.04t} \, dt$ (c) $\int_0^5 3000 \, dt$

(d) $\int_0^5 3000te^{-0.04t} \, dt$ (e) None of these

1—Answer: c

37. Find the actual income using $c(t) = 100,000t$, $0 \le t \le 12$ over the first six years of operation.

1—T—Answer: $7,200,000

Section 6.3   Partial Fractions and Logistics Growth

1. Find the partial fraction decomposition: $\dfrac{1-x}{2x^2+x}$.

1—Answer: $\dfrac{1}{x} - \dfrac{3}{2x+1}$

2. Find the partial fraction decomposition: $\dfrac{9x^2+x-1}{x^2(x+1)}$.

(a) $\dfrac{2}{x} - \dfrac{1}{x^2} + \dfrac{7}{x+1}$ (b) $\dfrac{20}{x} - \dfrac{1}{x^2} - \dfrac{11}{x+1}$ (c) $\dfrac{9}{x} + \dfrac{1}{x^2} - \dfrac{1}{x+1}$

(d) $\dfrac{-1}{x^2} + \dfrac{9}{x+1}$ (e) None of these

1—Answer: a

3. Find the partial fraction decomposition: $\dfrac{-9}{(1+1)^2(x-2)}$.

(a) $\dfrac{1}{x+1} + \dfrac{3}{(x+1)^2} - \dfrac{1}{x-2}$ (b) $\dfrac{10}{x+1} - \dfrac{4}{(x+1)^2} - \dfrac{15}{x-2}$ (c) $\dfrac{2}{x+1} - \dfrac{1}{(1+1)^2} - \dfrac{1}{x-2}$

(d) $\dfrac{1}{x+1} - \dfrac{3}{(x+1)^2} + \dfrac{5}{x-2}$ (e) None of these

2—Answer: a

4. Find the partial fraction decomposition: $\dfrac{-5x^2-19x-28}{x^3+4x^2+4x}$.

(a) $\dfrac{5x^2}{x^3} - \dfrac{19x}{4x^2} - \dfrac{28}{4x}$ (b) $-\dfrac{5x^2}{x} - \dfrac{19x}{x+2} - \dfrac{28}{(x+2)^2}$ (c) $\dfrac{2}{x} - \dfrac{5}{x+2} + \dfrac{16}{(x+2)^2}$

(d) $-\dfrac{7}{x} + \dfrac{2}{x+2} + \dfrac{5}{(x+2)^2}$ (e) None of these

1—Answer: d

5. Find the partial fraction decomposition: $\dfrac{12x^2-13x-3}{(x-1)^2(x+3)}$.

1—Answer: $\dfrac{3}{x-1} - \dfrac{1}{(x-1)^2} + \dfrac{9}{x+3}$

6. Find the partial fraction decomposition: $\dfrac{3x^2-7x+1}{(x-1)^3}$.

1—Answer: $\dfrac{3}{x-1} - \dfrac{1}{(x-1)^2} - \dfrac{3}{(x-1)^3}$

7. Find the partial fractions for: $\dfrac{3}{(x-2)^2(x+5)}$.

1—Answer: $\dfrac{3/49}{(x+5)} + \dfrac{3/7}{(x-2)^2} - \dfrac{3/49}{(x-2)}$

8. Find the partial fractions for: $\dfrac{1}{x^2(x+1)}$.

   (a) $\dfrac{1}{x^2} + \dfrac{1}{x+1}$ (b) $\dfrac{1}{x^2} - \dfrac{1}{x+1}$ (c) $-\dfrac{1}{x} + \dfrac{1}{x^2} + \dfrac{1}{x+1}$

   (d) $\dfrac{1/3}{x} + \dfrac{1/3}{x^2} + \dfrac{1/3}{x+1}$ (e) None of these

1—Answer: e

9. Find the partial fractions for: $\dfrac{1}{x^2(x-1)}$.

   (a) $-\dfrac{1}{x} - \dfrac{1}{x^2} + \dfrac{1}{x-1}$ (b) $-\dfrac{1}{x^2} + \dfrac{1}{x-1}$ (c) $\dfrac{1}{x} + \dfrac{1}{x^2} + \dfrac{1}{x-1}$

   (d) $\dfrac{1}{x^2} - \dfrac{1}{x-1}$ (e) None of these

1—Answer: a

10. Find the partial fraction decomposition for:

$$\frac{14x^2 - 9x + 10}{4x^3 - 3x^2 + 20x - 15}$$

by graphing the denominator on a graphing utility to find its zeros.

1—T—Answer: $\dfrac{2}{4x-3} + \dfrac{3x}{x^2+5}$

11. Find the partial fraction decomposition: $\dfrac{3x^2 - 31x - 25}{(x+1)(x^2 - 7x - 8)}$.

1—Answer: $\dfrac{4}{x+1} - \dfrac{1}{(x+1)^2} - \dfrac{1}{x-8}$

12. Let $\dfrac{2}{(x-1)^2(x-3)} = \dfrac{A}{x-1} + \dfrac{B}{(x-1)^2} + \dfrac{C}{x-3}$. Find A, B and C.

   (a) $A = -\frac{1}{2}, B = -1, C = \frac{1}{2}$ (b) $A = 1, B = 2, C = -1$ (c) $A = \frac{1}{2}, B = -1, C = \frac{1}{2}$

   (d) $A = 1, B = 2, C = 3$ (e) None of these

1—Answer: a

13. Find the partial fractions for $\dfrac{4x^2 + x - 9}{x^3 + 2x^2 - 3x}$.

1—Answer: $\dfrac{3}{x} - \dfrac{1}{x - 1} + \dfrac{2}{x + 3}$

14. Find the partial fraction decomposition for:

$$\frac{x^2 + 6x + 1}{2x^3 - x^2 + 8x - 4}$$

by graphing the denominator on a graphing utility to find its zeros.

(a) $\dfrac{1}{2x - 1} + \dfrac{3}{x^2 + 4}$

(b) $\dfrac{3}{2x - 1} + \dfrac{2}{x^2 + 4}$

(c) $\dfrac{2}{2x - 1} + \dfrac{3x - 4}{x^2 + 4}$

(d) $\dfrac{1}{2x + 1} + \dfrac{3}{x^2 - 4}$

(e) None of these

1—T—Answer: a

15. Find the partial fractions for $\dfrac{2}{(x - 1)^2(x - 3)}$.

1—Answer: $\dfrac{-1/2}{x - 1} - \dfrac{1}{(x - 1)^2} + \dfrac{1/2}{x - 3}$

16. Integrate: $\displaystyle\int \dfrac{1}{t^2 - 9}\, dt$.

1—Answer: $\dfrac{1}{6} \ln\left|\dfrac{t - 3}{t + 3}\right| + C$

17. Find the indefinite integral using partial fractions: $\displaystyle\int \dfrac{12}{9 - 4x^2}\, dx$.

(a) $12 \ln|9 - 4x^2| + C$

(b) $\dfrac{4x + 9}{3x} + C$

(c) $\ln\left|\dfrac{3 + 2x}{3 - 2x}\right| + C$

(d) $\dfrac{96x}{(9 - 4x^2)^2} + C$

(e) None of these

1—Answer: c

18. Evaluate using partial fractions: $\int \dfrac{6}{x^2 - 25} \, dx$.

(a) $\dfrac{18}{5} \ln \left| \dfrac{x + 5}{x - 5} \right| + C$ 　　　　 (b) $\dfrac{3}{5} \ln \left| \dfrac{x - 5}{x + 5} \right| + C$ 　　　　 (c) $\dfrac{6}{5} \ln \left| \dfrac{x - 5}{x + 5} \right| + C$

(d) $\dfrac{18}{5} \ln |x^2 - 25| + C$ 　　　　 (e) None of these

1—Answer: b

19. Evaluate using partial fractions: $\int \dfrac{10}{16 - 25x^2} \, dx$.

(a) $\dfrac{1}{8} \ln \left| \dfrac{4 + 5x}{4 - 5x} \right| + C$ 　　　　 (b) $\dfrac{1}{4} \ln \left| \dfrac{4 + 5x}{4 - 5x} \right| + C$ 　　　　 (c) $\dfrac{1}{4} \ln \left| \dfrac{4 - 5x}{4 + 5x} \right| + C$

(d) $\dfrac{5}{8} \ln \left| \dfrac{4 + 5x}{4 - 5x} \right| + C$ 　　　　 (e) None of these

1—Answer: b

20. Evaluate using partial fractions: $\int \dfrac{9}{x^2 - 81} \, dx$.

(a). $\ln \sqrt{\dfrac{x + 9}{x - 9}} + C$ 　　　　 (b) $\ln \left| \dfrac{x - 9}{x + 9} \right| + C$ 　　　　 (c) $\ln \sqrt{\dfrac{x - 9}{x + 9}} + C$

(d) $2 \ln \left| \dfrac{x - 9}{x + 9} \right| + C$ 　　　　 (e) None of these

1—Answer: c

21. Evaluate using partial fractions: $\int \dfrac{x + 1}{x^2 + 4x + 3} \, dx$.

1—Answer: $\ln |x + 3| + C$

22. Find the indefinite integral using partial fractions: $\int \dfrac{16}{x^2 - 16} \, dx$.

(a) $\dfrac{1 - x}{x} + C$ 　　　　 (b) $\dfrac{-32x}{(x^2 - 16)^2} + C$ 　　　　 (c) $2 \ln |x^2 - 16| + C$

(d) $\dfrac{1}{2} \ln \left| \dfrac{x - 4}{x + 4} \right| + C$ 　　　　 (e) None of these

1—Answer: e

23. Evaluate: $\int \dfrac{2}{(x+2)^2(2-x)} \, dx.$

(a) $\dfrac{1}{8} \ln|x+2| + \dfrac{1}{2} \ln(x+2)^2 - \dfrac{1}{8} \ln|2-x| + C$ (b) $\dfrac{1}{8} \ln\left|\dfrac{x+2}{2-x}\right| - \dfrac{1}{2(x+2)} + C$

(c) $-\dfrac{2}{(x+2)} + \ln|2-x| + C$ (d) $-\dfrac{1}{2(x+2)} - \dfrac{1}{8} \ln|2-x| + C$

(e) None of these

2—Answer: b

24. Use the method of partial fractions to evaluate the indefinite integral:

$$\int \dfrac{8 + 9(\ln x)^2}{x(\ln x)^3 + x \ln x} \, dx.$$

[Hint: Let $u = \ln x$.]

(a) $8 \ln|(\ln x)^3 + \ln x| + C$ (b) $8 \ln x + \dfrac{1}{2} \ln(x^2 + 1) + C$

(c) $8 \ln|\ln x| + \dfrac{1}{2} \ln|x^2 + 1| + C$ (d) $8 \ln|\ln x| + \dfrac{1}{2} \ln[(\ln x)^2 + 1] + C$

(e) None of these

2—Answer: d

25. Evaluate: $\int \dfrac{1}{x\sqrt{x+25}} \, dx.$ $\left[\text{Hint: Let } u = \sqrt{x+25}.\right]$

(a) $\dfrac{1}{5} \ln\left|\dfrac{\sqrt{x+25} - 5}{\sqrt{x+25} + 5}\right| + C$ (b) $\dfrac{1}{5} \ln\left|\dfrac{\sqrt{x+25} + 5}{\sqrt{x+25} - 5}\right| + C$

(c) $\ln|\sqrt{x+25} + 5| - \ln|\sqrt{x+25} - 5| + C$ (d) $\dfrac{2}{5} \ln\sqrt{x+25} + C$

(e) None of these

1—Answer: a

26. Use the method of partial fractions to evaluate the indefinite integral:

$$\int \dfrac{3 + 10(\ln x)^2}{x(\ln x)^3 + x \ln x} \, dx.$$

[Hint: Let $u = \ln x$.]

(a) $3 \ln|\ln x| + \dfrac{7}{2} \ln|x^2 + 1| + C$ (b) $3 \ln|(\ln x)^3 + \ln x| + C$

(c) $3 \ln x + \dfrac{7}{2} \ln(x^2 + 1) + C$ (d) $3 \ln|\ln x| + \dfrac{7}{2} \ln[(\ln x)^2 + 1] + C$

(e) None of these

2—Answer: d

27. Use the method of partial fractions to evaluate the indefinite integral:

$$\int \frac{7 + 11(\ln x)^2}{x(\ln x)^3 + x \ln x}\,dx.$$

[Hint: Let $u = \ln x$.]

(a) $7 \ln|\ln x| + 2 \ln|x^2 + 1| + C$

(b) $7 \ln x + 2 \ln(x^2 + 1) + C$

(c) $7 \ln|\ln x| + 2 \ln[(\ln x)^2 + 1] + C$

(d) $7 \ln|(\ln x)^3 + \ln x| + C$

(e) None of these

2—Answer: c

28. Evaluate: $\displaystyle\int \frac{1}{x\sqrt{x + 9}}\,dx.$ $\left[\text{Hint: Let } u = \sqrt{x + 9}.\right]$

(a) $\dfrac{1}{3} \ln\left|\dfrac{\sqrt{x + 9} - 3}{\sqrt{x + 9} + 3}\right| + C$

(b) $\ln|\sqrt{x + 9} - 3| - \ln|\sqrt{x + 9} + 3| + C$

(c) $\dfrac{1}{3} \ln\left|\dfrac{\sqrt{x + 9} + 3}{\sqrt{x + 9} - 3}\right| + C$

(d) $\dfrac{2}{3} \ln\sqrt{x + 9} + C$

(e) None of these

1—Answer: a

29. Evaluate: $\displaystyle\int \frac{1}{x\sqrt{x + 16}}\,dx.$ $\left[\text{Hint: Let } u = \sqrt{x + 16}.\right]$

(a) $\ln|\sqrt{x + 16} - 4| - \ln|\sqrt{x + 16} + 4| + C$

(b) $\dfrac{1}{4} \ln\left|\dfrac{\sqrt{x + 16} + 4}{\sqrt{x + 16} - 4}\right| + C$

(c) $\dfrac{1}{4} \ln\left|\dfrac{\sqrt{x + 16} - 4}{\sqrt{x + 16} + 4}\right| + C$

(d) $\dfrac{1}{2} \ln\sqrt{x + 16} + C$

(e) None of these

1—Answer: c

Section 6.4 Integration Tables and Completing the Square

1. Select the integral form that would be used to find the indefinite integral $\int \dfrac{x^3}{(4 + 2x^2)^2}\, dx$, by using tables.

(a) $\int \dfrac{u}{(a + bu)^2}\, du$ (b) $\int \dfrac{u^2}{(a + bu)^2}\, du$ (c) $\int \dfrac{u^3}{(a + bu)^2}\, du$

(d) $\int \dfrac{1}{u(a + bu)^2}\, du$ (e) None of these

1—Answer: a

2. Select the integral form that would be used to find the indefinite integral $\int \dfrac{x}{(4 + 2x)^2}\, dx$, by using tables.

(a) $\int \dfrac{u}{a + bu}\, du$ (b) $\int \dfrac{u}{(a + bu)^2}\, du$ (c) $\int \dfrac{1}{(a + bu)^2}\, du$

(d) $\int \dfrac{u}{a^2 + u^2}\, du$ (e) None of these

1—Answer: b

3. Select the integral form that would be used to find the indefinite integral $\int \dfrac{x^5}{\sqrt{x^4 - 4}}\, dx$, by using tables.

(a) $\int \dfrac{u^2}{\sqrt{a + bu}}\, du$ (b) $\int \dfrac{u}{\sqrt{a + bu}}\, du$ (c) $\int \dfrac{u}{\sqrt{u^2 \pm a^2}}\, du$

(d) $\int \dfrac{u^2}{\sqrt{u^2 \pm a^2}}\, du$ (e) None of these

1—Answer: d

4. Select the integral form that would be used to find the indefinite integral $\int \dfrac{x^2}{\sqrt{x^2 + 9}}\, dx$, by using tables.

(a) $\int \dfrac{u^2}{\sqrt{u^2 \pm a^2}}\, du$ (b) $\int \dfrac{u}{\sqrt{u^2 \pm a^2}}\, du$ (c) $\int \dfrac{u^2}{\sqrt{a + bu}}\, du$

(d) $\int \dfrac{u}{\sqrt{a + bu}}\, du$ (e) None of these

1—Answer: a

5. Select the integral form that would be used to find the indefinite integral $\int x^2\sqrt{x^2 + 9}\, dx$, by using tables.

(a) $\int u^n\sqrt{a + bu}\, du$

(b) $\int \sqrt{u^2 \pm a^2}\, du$

(c) $\int \dfrac{1}{u^2\sqrt{u^2 \pm a^2}}\, du$

(d) $\int u^2\sqrt{u^2 \pm a^2}\, du$

(e) None of these

1—Answer: d

6. Select the integral form that would be used to find the indefinite integral $\int \dfrac{3}{x\sqrt{3 - 5x^2}}\, dx$, by using tables.

(a) $\int \dfrac{1}{u^2 - a^2}\, du$

(b) $\int u\sqrt{a + bu}\, du$

(c) $\int \dfrac{1}{u\sqrt{a + bu}}\, du$

(d) $\int \dfrac{1}{u\sqrt{a^2 - u^2}}\, du$

(e) None of these

1—Answer: d

7. Use integration tables to evaluate the indefinite integral: $\int \dfrac{1}{x^2(9 + 3x)}\, dx$.

(a) $-\dfrac{1}{81}\left(\dfrac{9 + 6x}{x(9 + 3x)} + \dfrac{2}{3}\ln\left|\dfrac{x}{9 + 3x}\right|\right) + C$

(b) $\dfrac{1}{9}\left(\dfrac{1}{9 + 3x} + \dfrac{1}{9}\ln\left|\dfrac{x}{9 + 3x}\right|\right) + C$

(c) $-\dfrac{1}{9}\left(\dfrac{1}{x} + \dfrac{1}{3}\ln\left|\dfrac{x}{9 + 3x}\right|\right) + C$

(d) $\dfrac{1}{9}\ln\left|\dfrac{x}{9 + 3x}\right| + C$

(e) None of these

1—Answer: c

8. Use integration tables to evaluate the indefinite integral: $\int \dfrac{1}{x^2(4 + 6x)}\, dx$.

(a) $-\dfrac{1}{4}\left(\dfrac{1}{x} + \dfrac{3}{2}\ln\left|\dfrac{x}{4 + 6x}\right|\right) + C$

(b) $\dfrac{1}{4}\ln\left|\dfrac{x}{4 + 6x}\right| + C$

(c) $\dfrac{1}{4}\left(\dfrac{1}{4 + 6x} + \dfrac{1}{4}\ln\left|\dfrac{x}{4 + 6x}\right|\right) + C$

(d) $-\dfrac{1}{16}\left(\dfrac{4 + 12x}{x(4 + 6x)} + 3\ln\left|\dfrac{x}{4 + 6x}\right|\right) + C$

(e) None of these

1—Answer: a

9. Use integration tables to evaluate the indefinite integral: $\int \dfrac{1}{x^2(9 + 5x)}\, dx$.

(a) $\dfrac{1}{9}\left(\dfrac{1}{9 + 5x} + \dfrac{1}{9}\ln\left|\dfrac{x}{9 + 5x}\right|\right) + C$

(b) $-\dfrac{1}{9}\left(\dfrac{1}{x} + \dfrac{5}{9}\ln\left|\dfrac{x}{9 + 5x}\right|\right) + C$

(c) $\dfrac{1}{9}\ln\left|\dfrac{x}{9 + 5x}\right| + C$

(d) $-\dfrac{1}{81}\left(\dfrac{9 + 10x}{x(9 + 5x)} + \dfrac{10}{9}\ln\left|\dfrac{x}{9 + 5x}\right|\right) + C$

(e) None of these

1—Answer: b

10. Use integration tables to evaluate the indefinite integral: $\int \dfrac{1}{x^2(6 + 7x)}\, dx$.

(a) $\dfrac{1}{6}\ln\left|\dfrac{x}{6 + 7x}\right| + C$

(b) $-\dfrac{1}{36}\left(\dfrac{6 + 14x}{x(6 + 7x)} + \dfrac{7}{3}\ln\left|\dfrac{x}{6 + 7x}\right|\right) + C$

(c) $-\dfrac{1}{6}\left(\dfrac{1}{x} + \dfrac{7}{6}\ln\left|\dfrac{x}{6 + 7x}\right|\right) + C$

(d) $\dfrac{1}{6}\left(\dfrac{1}{6 + 7x} + \dfrac{1}{6}\ln\left|\dfrac{x}{6 + 7x}\right|\right) + C$

(e) None of these

1—Answer: c

11. Use integration tables to evaluate the indefinite integral: $\int \dfrac{1}{x^2(2 + 7x)}\, dx$.

(a) $\dfrac{1}{2}\ln\left|\dfrac{x}{2 + 7x}\right| + C$

(b) $-\dfrac{1}{4}\left(\dfrac{2 + 14x}{x(2 + 7x)} + 7\ln\left|\dfrac{x}{2 + 7x}\right|\right) + C$

(c) $-\dfrac{1}{2}\left(\dfrac{1}{x} + \dfrac{7}{2}\ln\left|\dfrac{x}{2 + 7x}\right|\right) + C$

(d) $\dfrac{1}{2}\left(\dfrac{1}{2 + 7x} + \dfrac{1}{2}\ln\left|\dfrac{x}{2 + 7x}\right|\right) + C$

(e) None of these

1—Answer: c

12. Use integration tables to evaluate the indefinite integral: $\int \dfrac{e^x}{(e^{2x} - 25)^2}\, dx$. [Hint: Let $u = e^x$.]

(a) $-\dfrac{1}{50}\left(\dfrac{x}{x^2 - 25} + \dfrac{1}{10}\ln\left|\dfrac{x - 5}{x + 5}\right|\right) + C$

(b) $-\dfrac{1}{50}\left(\dfrac{e^x}{e^{2x} - 25} + \dfrac{1}{10}\ln\left|\dfrac{e^x - 5}{e^x + 5}\right|\right) + C$

(c) $-\dfrac{1}{2x(x^2 - 25)} + C$

(d) $-\dfrac{1}{2e^x(e^{2x} - 25)} + C$

(e) None of these

1—Answer: b

13. Use integration tables to evaluate the indefinite integral: $\int \dfrac{e^x}{(e^{2x} - 4)^2}\, dx.$ [Hint: Let $u = e^x$.]

(a) $-\dfrac{1}{8}\left(\dfrac{e^x}{e^{2x}-4} + \dfrac{1}{4}\ln\left|\dfrac{e^x - 2}{e^x + 2}\right|\right) + C$

(b) $-\dfrac{1}{2e^x(e^{2x} - 4)} + C$

(c) $-\dfrac{1}{2x(x^2 - 4)} + C$

(d) $-\dfrac{1}{8}\left(\dfrac{x}{x^2-4} + \dfrac{1}{4}\ln\left|\dfrac{x - 2}{x + 2}\right|\right) + C$

(e) None of these

1—Answer: a

14. Use integration tables to evaluate the indefinite integral: $\int \dfrac{e^x}{(e^{2x} - 49)^2}\, dx.$ [Hint: Let $u = e^x$.]

(a) $-\dfrac{1}{2e^x(e^{2x} - 49)} + C$

(b) $-\dfrac{1}{98}\left(\dfrac{x}{x^2-49} + \dfrac{1}{14}\ln\left|\dfrac{x - 7}{x + 7}\right|\right) + C$

(c) $-\dfrac{1}{98}\left(\dfrac{e^x}{e^{2x}-49} + \dfrac{1}{14}\ln\left|\dfrac{e^x - 7}{e^x + 7}\right|\right) + C$

(d) $-\dfrac{1}{2x(x^2 - 49)} + C$

(e) None of these

1—Answer: c

15. Use integration tables to evaluate the indefinite integral: $\int \dfrac{e^x}{(e^{2x} - 1)^2}\, dx.$ [Hint: Let $u = e^x$.]

(a) $-\dfrac{1}{2x(x^2 - 1)} + C$

(b) $-\dfrac{1}{2}\left(\dfrac{e^x}{e^{2x}-1} + \dfrac{1}{2}\ln\left|\dfrac{e^x - 1}{e^x + 1}\right|\right) + C$

(c) $-\dfrac{1}{2e^x(e^{2x} - 1)} + C$

(d) $-\dfrac{1}{2}\left(\dfrac{x}{x^2-1} + \dfrac{1}{2}\ln\left|\dfrac{x - 1}{x + 1}\right|\right) + C$

(e) None of these

1—Answer: b

16. Use integration tables to evaluate the indefinite integral: $\int \dfrac{x}{1 + e^{6x^2}}\, dx.$

(a) $6x^2 - \ln(1 + e^{6x^2}) + C$

(b) $\dfrac{x^2}{2} - \dfrac{1}{12}\ln(1 + e^{6x^2}) + C$

(c) $x^2 - \ln(1 + e^{x^2}) + C$

(d) $x^2 - \dfrac{1}{6}\ln(1 + e^{6x^2}) + C$

(e) None of these

1—Answer: b

17. Use integration tables to evaluate the indefinite integral: $\int \dfrac{x}{1 + e^{2x^2}}\, dx$.

   (a) $\dfrac{x^2}{2} - \dfrac{1}{4} \ln(1 + e^{2x^2}) + C$ (b) $x^2 - \ln(1 + e^{x^2}) + C$

   (c) $x^2 - \dfrac{1}{2} \ln(1 + e^{2x^2}) + C$ (d) $2x^2 - \ln(1 + e^{2x^2}) + C$

   (e) None of these

   2—Answer: a

18. Use integration tables to evaluate the indefinite integral: $\int \dfrac{x}{1 + e^{7x^2}}\, dx$.

   (a) $7x^2 - \ln(1 + e^{7x^2}) + C$ (b) $x^2 - \dfrac{1}{7} \ln(1 + e^{7x^2}) + C$

   (c) $x^2 - \ln(1 + e^{x^2}) + C$ (d) $\dfrac{x^2}{2} - \dfrac{1}{14} \ln(1 + e^{7x^2}) + C$

   (e) None of these

   2—Answer: d

19. Use integration tables to evaluate the indefinite integral: $\int \dfrac{x}{1 + e^{9x^2}}\, dx$.

   (a) $x^2 - \dfrac{1}{9} \ln(1 + e^{9x^2}) + C$ (b) $9x^2 - \ln(1 + e^{9x^2}) + C$

   (c) $\dfrac{x^2}{2} - \dfrac{1}{18} \ln(1 + e^{9x^2}) + C$ (d) $x^2 - \ln(1 + e^{x^2}) + C$

   (e) None of these

   2—Answer: c

20. Complete the square, then use integration tables to evaluate the indefinite integral. $\int \sqrt{x^2 - 8x}\, dx$.

   1—Answer: $\dfrac{1}{2}\left[(x - 4)\sqrt{x^2 - 8x} - 16 \ln|(x - 4) + \sqrt{x^2 - 8x}|\right] + C$

21. Complete the square, then use integration tables to evaluate the indefinite integral. $\int \sqrt{x^2 + 10x}\, dx$.

(a) $\frac{1}{2}\left[x + 5\sqrt{x^2 + 10x} + 5\ln\left|x + 5 + \sqrt{x^2 + 10x}\right|\right] + C$

(b) $\frac{1}{2}\left[(x + 5)\sqrt{x^2 + 10x} - 25\ln\left|x + 5 + \sqrt{x^2 + 10x}\right|\right] + C$

(c) $\frac{1}{2}\left[x + 5\sqrt{x^2 + 10x} + 25\ln\left|x + 5 + \sqrt{x^2 + 10x}\right|\right] + C$

(d) $\frac{1}{2}\left[(x + 5)\sqrt{x^2 + 10x} - 5\ln\left|x + 5 + \sqrt{x^2 + 10x}\right|\right] + C$

(e) None of these

1—Answer: b

22. Complete the square, then use integration tables to evaluate the indefinite integral. $\int \dfrac{\sqrt{x^2 + 6x + 13}}{x + 3}\, dx$.

(a) $\sqrt{x^2 + 6x + 13} - 3\ln\left|\dfrac{3 + \sqrt{x^2 + 6x + 13}}{x + 3}\right| + C$

(b) $\sqrt{x^2 + 6x + 13} - \sqrt{13}\ln\left|\dfrac{\sqrt{13} + \sqrt{x^2 + 6x + 13}}{x + 3}\right| + C$

(c) $\sqrt{x^2 + 6x + 13} - 2\ln\left|\dfrac{2 + \sqrt{x^2 + 6x + 13}}{x + 3}\right| + C$

(d) $\sqrt{x^2 + 6x + 13} - 4\ln\left|\dfrac{4 + \sqrt{x^2 + 6x + 13}}{x + 3}\right| + C$

(e) None of these

1—Answer: c

23. Complete the square to express the polynomial, $2x^2 - 8x + 4$, as the sum or difference of squares.

(a) $(2x - 4)^2 - 12$ (b) $2(x - 2)^2 - 4$ (c) $2(x - 2)^2$

(d) $2(x - 2)^2 + 12$ (e) None of these

1—Answer: b

24. Complete the square to express the polynomial, $3x^2 - 6x + 7$, as the sum or difference of squares.

(a) $3(x - 1)^2 + 4$ (b) $(3x - 3)^2 - 2$ (c) $3(x - 1)^2 + 6$

(d) $3(x - 1)^2 + 10$ (e) None of these

1—Answer: a

25. Complete the square to express the polynomial, $2x^2 + 10x + 12$, as the sum or difference of squares.

(a) $2\left(x + \frac{5}{2}\right)^2 + \frac{1}{2}$

(b) $2\left(x + \frac{5}{2}\right)^2 - \frac{1}{2}$

(c) $(2x + 5)^2 - 13$

(d) $(2x + 5)^2 - \frac{1}{2}$

(e) None of these

1—Answer: b

26. Complete the square to express the polynomial, $3x^2 + 18x + 4$, as the sum or difference of squares.

(a) $3(x + 3)^2 - 23$

(b) $3(x - 3)^2 + 23$

(c) $(3x + 3)^2 - 12$

(d) $3(x + 3)^2 - 31$

(e) None of these

1—Answer: a

27. Complete the square to express the polynomial, $-2x^2 + 8x + 40$, as the sum or difference of squares.

1—Answer: $48 - 2(x - 2)^2 = 2[24 - (x - 2)^2]$

Section 6.5 Numerical Integration

1. Use the Trapezoidal Rule with $n = 4$ to approximate the definite integral: $\int_1^2 \frac{1}{x^2 + 1}\, dx$.

    (a) 0.323342   (b) 0.321747   (c) 0.321750   (d) 0.323522   (e) None of these

    1—T—Answer: d

2. Use the Trapezoidal Rule with $n = 4$ to approximate the definite integral: $\int_0^1 \frac{1}{x^2 + 1}\, dx$.

    (a) 0.784944   (b) 0.782794   (c) 0.785398   (d) 0.785392   (e) None of these

    1—T—Answer: b

3. Use the Trapezoidal Rule with $n = 4$ to approximate the definite integral: $\int_0^2 \frac{1}{x^2 + 1}\, dx$.

    (a) 1.10384   (b) 1.10512   (c) 1.10714   (d) 1.10924   (e) None of these

    1—T—Answer: a

4. Use the Trapezoidal Rule with $n = 4$ to approximate $\int_2^3 \frac{1}{(x-1)^2}\, dx$.

    (a) 0.5004   (b) 2.5000   (c) 0.5090   (d) 1.7396   (e) None of these

    1—Answer: c

5. Use the Trapezoidal Rule with $n = 4$ to estimate the definite integral: $\int_0^7 (x^2 - 7x)\, dx$.

    (a) 57.17   (b) 53.59   (c) -57.17 (d) -53.59 (e) None of these

    1—Answer: d

6. Use the Trapezoidal Rule with $n = 4$ to estimate the definite integral: $\int_3^7 (x^2 - 10x + 21)\, dx$.

    (a) -10.67 (b) 10.67   (c) -10.00 (d) 10.00   (e) None of these

    1—Answer: c

7. Use the Trapezoidal Rule with $n = 4$ to approximate $\int_1^3 \frac{4}{x}\, dx$.

    (a) $\frac{67}{30}$ (b) $\frac{134}{15}$ (c) $\frac{67}{60}$ (d) $\frac{67}{15}$ (e) None of these

    1—Answer: d

8. Use the Trapezoidal Rule with $n = 4$ to approximate $\int_{50}^{51} e^{-0.11(x-50)^2} \, dx$.

   (a) 0.9640   (b) 0.9645   (c) 0.9635   (d) 0.9630   (e) None of these

   1—T—**Answer:** c

9. Using the Trapezoidal Rule with $n = 4$, approximate $\int_{1}^{2} \frac{1}{x^2} \, dx$.

   (a) 1.7500   (b) 0.5090   (c) 0.5004   (d) 5.6319   (e) None of these

   1—T—**Answer:** b

10. Use the Trapezoidal Rule with $n = 4$ to approximate $\int_{60}^{61} e^{-0.11(x-60)^2} \, dx$.

    1—T—**Answer:** 0.9635

11. Using Simpson's Rule with $n = 4$, approximate $\int_{1}^{2} \frac{1}{x^2} \, dx$.

    (a) 1.9583   (b) 0.5090   (c) 0.5004   (d) 6.7176   (e) None of these

    1—T—**Answer:** c

12. Use Simpson's Rule with $n = 2$ to approximate the value of $\int_{2}^{4} \frac{3}{2x - 1} \, dx$.

    1—T—**Answer:** 1.27619

13. Use Simpson's Rule with $n = 2$ to approximate $\int_{1}^{2} \frac{1}{x} \, dx$.

    (a) $\frac{25}{12}$ (b) $\frac{25}{18}$ (c) $\frac{25}{36}$ (d) $\frac{25}{72}$ (e) None of these

    1—**Answer:** c

14. Use Simpson's Rule with $n = 4$ to approximate $\int_{2}^{3} \frac{1}{(x - 1)^2} \, dx$.

    (a) 0.5004   (b) 0.5090   (c) 2.5000   (d) 1.7396   (e) None of these

    1—**Answer:** a

15. Use Simpson's Rule with $n = 4$ to approximate $\int_{1}^{2} \frac{1}{(x + 1)^2} \, dx$.

    1—**Answer:** 0.1667

16. Use Simpson's Rule with $n = 4$ to approximate the definite integral: $\int_1^2 \dfrac{1}{x^2 + 1}\,dx$.

(a) 0.323342   (b) 0.321747   (c) 0.321750   (d) 0.323522   (e) None of these

1—T—**Answer:** b

17. Use Simpson's Rule with $n = 4$ to approximate the definite integral: $\int_0^1 \dfrac{1}{x^2 + 1}\,dx$.

(a) 0.784944   (b) 0.782794   (c) 0.785398   (d) 0.785392   (e) None of these

1—T—**Answer:** d

18. Use Simpson's Rule with $n = 4$ to approximate the definite integral: $\int_0^2 \dfrac{1}{x^2 + 1}\,dx$.

(a) 1.10384   (b) 1.10512   (c) 1.10714   (d) 1.10924   (e) None of these

1—T—**Answer:** b

19. A function f is given by the following table:

x	0	1	2	3	4
$f(x)$	9	8	7	9	2

Estimate the area between the x-axis and $y = f(x)$ from $x = 0$ to $x = 4$ using Simpson's Rule.

(a) $\dfrac{59}{2}$ (b) $\dfrac{124}{5}$ (c) 31   (d) None of these

2—**Answer:** c

20. A function f is given by the following table:

x	0	1	2	3	4
$f(x)$	1	4	8	5	3

Estimate the area between the x-axis and $y = f(x)$ from $x = 0$ to $x = 4$ using Simpson's Rule.

(a) None of these   (b) 19

(c) $\dfrac{224}{15}$ (d) $\dfrac{56}{3}$

2—**Answer:** d

21. A function f is given by the following table:

x	0	1	2	3	4
$f(x)$	9	2	2	8	5

Estimate the area between the x-axis and $y = f(x)$ from $x = 0$ to $x = 4$ using Simpson's Rule.

(a) None of these   (b) $\dfrac{58}{3}$

(c) $\dfrac{232}{15}$ (d) 19

2—**Answer:** b

22. Use Trapezoidal Rule with $n = 4$ to approximate the area of the region bounded by $f(x) = x^3 - 4x^2 + 4x$ and the x-axis between $x = 0$ and $x = 2$.

(a) 1.29   (b) 1.33   (c) 1.25   (d) 1.38   (e) None of these

1—T—Answer: c

23. Use Trapezoidal Rule with $n = 4$ to approximate the area of the region bounded by $f(x) = x^3 - 8x^2 + 16x$ and the x-axis between $x = 0$ and $x = 4$.

(a) 22.00   (b) 23.00   (c) 20.67   (d) 20.00   (e) None of these

1—Answer: d

24. Use the Midpoint Rule with $n = 4$ to approximate the area of the region bounded by $f(x) = x^3 - 6x^2 + 9x$ and the x-axis between $x = 0$ and $x = 3$.

(a) 6.54   (b) 6.96   (c) 9.28   (d) 6.75   (e) None of these

1—Answer: b

25. Use the Midpoint Rule with $n = 4$ to approximate the area of the region bounded by $f(x) = x^3 - 10x^2 + 25x$ and the x-axis between $x = 0$ and $x = 5$.

(a) 52.08   (b) 42.97   (c) 53.71   (d) 50.46   (e) None of these

1—Answer: c

26. Explain, in one complete sentence, the need for numerical integration techniques.

2—Answer: Answers will vary.

27. The integral $\int_0^4 2000te^{-0.07t}\, dt$ can be evaluated by:

(a) u substitution   (b) Partial fractions   (c) Parts

(d) Numeric approximation only   (e) None of these

1—Answer: c

28. The integral $\int \dfrac{1}{y(400 - y)}\, dy$ would be evaluated by:

(a) u substitution   (b) Partial fractions   (c) Parts

(d) Numeric approximation only   (e) None of these

1—Answer: b

Section 6.6 Improper Integrals

1. Evaluate the improper integral: $\displaystyle\int_0^\infty xe^{-x/2}\,dx$.

    (a) Diverges to $-\infty$ (b) Diverges to ∞ (c) Converges to -2

    (d) Converges to 4   (e) None of these

    2—Answer: d

2. Evaluate the improper integral: $\displaystyle\int_{-4}^0 \frac{1}{x+4}\,dx$.

    (a) Diverges to $-\infty$ (b) Diverges to ∞ (c) Converges to $\ln(4)$

    (d) Converges to 0   (e) None of these

    1—Answer: b

3. Evaluate the improper integral: $\displaystyle\int_0^\infty \ln(x)\,dx$.

    (a) Diverges to $-\infty$ (b) Diverges to ∞ (c) Converges to 0

    (d) Converges to 2   (e) None of these

    2—Answer: b

4. Evaluate the improper integral: $\displaystyle\int_0^\infty \frac{1}{e^{2x}}\,dx$.

    (a) Diverges to $-\infty$ (b) Diverges to ∞ (c) Converges to 0

    (d) Converges to $\frac{1}{2}$ (e) None of these

    1—Answer: d

5. Evaluate the improper integral: $\displaystyle\int_0^5 \frac{1}{(x-5)^2}\,dx$.

    (a) Diverges to $-\infty$ (b) Diverges to ∞ (c) Converges to 0

    (d) Converges to $-\frac{1}{5}$ (e) None of these

    1—Answer: a

6. Evaluate the improper integral: $\displaystyle\int_0^\infty \frac{(\ln x)^2}{x}\,dx$.

    (a) Diverges to $-\infty$ (b) Diverges to ∞ (c) Converges to $\frac{2}{3}$

    (d) Converges to -3 (e) None of these

    1—Answer: b

7. Evaluate the improper integral: $\int_0^\infty e^{-0.02t}\, dt$.

   (a) Diverges to $-\infty$ (b) Diverges to ∞ (c) Converges to 50

   (d) Converges to 0   (e) None of these

   1—Answer: c

8. Evaluate the improper integral: $\int_0^{10} e^{-0.02t}\, dt$.

   (a) Diverges to $-\infty$ (b) Diverges to ∞ (c) Converges to $50 - 50e^{-1/5}$

   (d) Converges to 0   (e) None of these

   1—Answer: c

9. Evaluate the improper integral: $\int_{10}^\infty e^{-0.02t}\, dt$.

   (a) Diverges to $-\infty$ (b) Diverges to ∞ (c) Converges to 50

   (d) Converges to $50e^{-1/5}$ (e) None of these

   1—Answer: d

10. Evaluate $\int_0^3 \dfrac{1}{x}\, dx$.

   (a) ∞ (b) $-\infty$ (c) 0   (d) $\ln 3$ (e) None of these

   1—Answer: a

11. Evaluate $\int_1^\infty e^{-x}\, dx$.

   (a) ∞ (b) $\dfrac{1}{e}$ (c) 0   (d) $-\dfrac{1}{e}$ (e) None of these

   1—Answer: b

12. Evaluate the improper integral: $\int_{-5}^{-3} \dfrac{dx}{(x + 4)^2}$.

   (a) -2 (b) The integral diverges.   (c) 2

   (d) 0   (e) None of these

   1—Answer: b

Techniques of Integration

13. Evaluate the improper integral: $\int_2^4 \dfrac{dx}{(x-3)^2}$.

   (a) The integral diverges.   (b) 2   (c) 0

   (d) -2 (e) None of these

   1—Answer: a

14. Evaluate the improper integral: $\int_{-9}^{-7} \dfrac{dx}{(x+8)^2}$.

   (a) 2   (b) 0   (c) -2

   (d) The integral diverges.   (e) None of these

   1—Answer: d

15. Evaluate the improper integral: $\int_0^\infty xe^{-x^2}\, dx$.

   1—Answer: $\frac{1}{2}$

16. Evaluate the improper integral: $\int_1^5 \dfrac{x}{\sqrt{5-x}}\, dx$. $\left[\text{Hint: Let } u = \sqrt{5-x}.\right]$

   2—Answer: $\frac{44}{3}$

17. Evaluate the improper integral: $\int_0^\infty \dfrac{1}{\sqrt{x+1}}\, dx$.

   1—Answer: The integral diverges.

18. Evaluate the improper integral: $\int_1^2 \dfrac{1}{(x-1)^{3/2}}\, dx$.

   1—Answer: The integral diverges.

19. Determine if the following improper integral converges or diverges. If it converges, find its value. $\int_2^\infty \dfrac{1}{x-1}\, dx$

   (a) Diverges   (b) Converges to 1   (c) Converges to -1

   (d) Converges to 0   (e) None of these

   1—Answer: a

20. Determine if the following improper integral converges or diverges. If it converges, find its value. $\int_2^\infty \dfrac{1}{(x-1)^2}\,dx$

   (a) Diverges   (b) Converges to 1   (c) Converges to -1

   (d) Converges to 0   (e) None of these

   1—Answer: b

21. Evaluate: $\int_0^\infty \dfrac{1}{10}e^{-t/10}\,dt$.

   (a) Diverges   (b) Converges to 0   (c) Converges to ln 2

   (d) Converges to 2   (e) None of these

   1—Answer: e

22. Determine the divergence or convergence of the improper integral $\int_0^\infty xe^{-x^2/2}\,dx$. If it converges, find its value.

   (a) Diverges   (b) Converges to 1   (c) Converges to -1

   (d) Converges to 0   (e) None of these

   1—Answer: b

23. Determine if the integral $\int_0^2 \dfrac{1}{x}\,dx$ converges or diverges. If it converges, find its value.

   (a) Diverges   (b) Converges to ln 2   (c) Converges to ln 2 $-$ 1

   (d) Converges to ln 3   (e) None of these

   1—Answer: a

24. Determine if the integral $\int_1^2 \dfrac{1}{\sqrt{x-1}}\,dx$ converges or diverges. If it converges, find its value.

   (a) Diverges   (b) Converges to 2   (c) Converges to $\sqrt{2}$

   (d) Converges to $2(\sqrt{2}-1)$ (e) None of these

   1—Answer: b

25. Determine the area between $f(x) = \dfrac{2x+1}{x^2}$, and the x-axis over the interval $[0, 4]$.

   (a) Infinite   (b) $2\ln 4 - \frac{1}{4}$ (c) $\frac{3}{8}$

   (d) $\frac{9}{64}$ (e) None of these

   1—Answer: a

26. Calculate the area under the curve $y = \dfrac{1}{x^2}$ above the x-axis on the interval $[1, \infty]$.

   (a) ∞ (b) 1   (c) 0   (d) 2   (e) None of these

   1—Answer: b

27. In a complete sentence, describe the two different types of improper integrals.

   1—Answer: Answers will vary.

CHAPTER 7

Functions of Several Variables

Section 7.1   The Three–Dimensional Coordinate System

1. Find the midpoint of the line segment connecting $(0, 5, -2)$ and $(1, 6, 3)$.

   (a) $\left(\frac{1}{2}, \frac{11}{2}, \frac{1}{2}\right)$ (b) $\left(-\frac{1}{2}, -\frac{1}{2}, -\frac{5}{2}\right)$ (c) $(1, 11, 1)$ (d) $\left(\frac{1}{2}, -\frac{1}{2}, \frac{1}{2}\right)$ (e) None of these

   1—Answer: a

2. Find the midpoint of the line segment connecting $(-1, 4, -2)$ and $(3, 7, -3)$.

   (a) $(2, 11, -5)$ (b) $\left(-2, -\frac{3}{2}, \frac{1}{2}\right)$ (c) $\left(1, \frac{11}{2}, \frac{1}{2}\right)$ (d) $\left(1, \frac{11}{2}, -\frac{5}{2}\right)$ (e) None of these

   1—Answer: d

3. Find the midpoint of the line segment connecting $(4, 0, -2)$ and $(3, -1, 6)$.

   (a) $\left(\frac{1}{2}, -\frac{1}{2}, 4\right)$ (b) $(7, -1, 4)$ (c) $\left(\frac{7}{2}, -\frac{1}{2}, 2\right)$ (d) $\left(\frac{1}{2}, \frac{1}{2}, -4\right)$ (e) None of these

   1—Answer: c

4. Find the midpoint of the line segment connecting $(2, 3, 5)$ and $(4, 7, -1)$.

   1—Answer: $(3, 5, 2)$

5. Find the midpoint of the line segment connecting $(-1, 3, 7)$ and $(3, 5, 3)$.

   1—Answer: $(1, 4, 5)$

6. Find the midpoint of the line segment joining $(-2, 3, 1)$ and $(4, 5, -1)$.

   1—Answer: $(1, 4, 0)$

7. Find the distance between the points $(3, 0, -5)$ and $(-1, 4, 2)$.

   (a) $\sqrt{29}$ (b) $\sqrt{41}$ (c) 9 (d) 1 (e) None of these

   1—Answer: c

8. Find the distance between the points $P(-1, 3, 5)$ and $Q(4, 5, -2)$.

   1—Answer: $\sqrt{78}$

9. Find the distance between the points $(1, -2, 3)$ and $(4, 1, -3)$.

   (a) $3\sqrt{6}$ (b) $3\sqrt{2}$ (c) $\sqrt{26}$ (d) $2\sqrt{3}$ (e) None of these

   1—Answer: a

Functions of Several Variables

10. Find the distance between the points $(4, 2, -1)$ and $(-2, 3, -2)$.

    (a) $2\sqrt{2}$ (b) $\sqrt{34}$ (c) $2\sqrt{10}$ (d) $\sqrt{38}$ (e) None of these

    1—Answer: d

11. Find the distance between the points $(-3, 6, 1)$ and $(4, -1, 1)$.

    (a) $7\sqrt{2}$ (b) $\sqrt{30}$ (c) $\sqrt{14}$ (d) 4   (e) None of these

    1—Answer: a

12. Find the distance between the points $(-1, 2, 5)$ and $(1, -1, 2)$.

    (a) $5\sqrt{2}$ (b) $\sqrt{22}$ (c) $2\sqrt{2}$ (d) 7   (e) None of these

    1—Answer: b

13. Find the distance between the points $(2, 1, 0)$ and $(-1, 2, 4)$.

    1—Answer: $\sqrt{26}$

14. Find the distance between the points $(-1, 4, 2)$ and $(3, 1, 4)$.

    1—Answer: $\sqrt{29}$

15. Find the distance between the points $(5, -3, 2)$ and $(-3, 4, 6)$. Approximate your answer to the nearest 0.01.

    (a) 9.00   (b) 13.30   (c) 11.36   (d) 8.31   (e) None of these

    1—T—Answer: b

16. Find the distance between the points $(4, 3, 5)$ and $(-3, -3, 6)$. Approximate your answer to the nearest 0.01.

    1—T—Answer: 9.27

17. Find the center and radius of the sphere whose equation is $x^2 + y^2 + z^2 - 4x - 6y + 4z + 3 = 0$.

    (a) Center $(2, 3, -2)$; radius $\sqrt{14}$ (b) Center $(-2, -3, 2)$; radius 14

    (c) Center $(4, 9, 4)$; radius $2\sqrt{5}$ (d) Center $(-4, -9, -4)$; radius 20

    (e) None of these

    1—Answer: a

18. Find the center and radius of the sphere whose equation is $x^2 + y^2 + z^2 - 3x - 2y + 6z = 4$.

    (a) Center $\left(-\frac{3}{2}, -1, 3\right)$; radius $\frac{\sqrt{65}}{2}$ (b) Center $\left(\frac{3}{2}, 1, 3\right)$; radius 2

    (c) Center $\left(-\frac{3}{2}, -1, 3\right)$; radius $\frac{\sqrt{55}}{2}$ (d) Center $\left(\frac{3}{2}, -1, -3\right)$; radius $\frac{\sqrt{65}}{2}$

    (e) None of these

    1—Answer: a

19. Find the center and radius of the sphere whose equation is $x^2 + y^2 + z^2 - 3x + 9y - 6z + 2 = 0$.

2—Answer: $\left(-\dfrac{3}{2}, -\dfrac{9}{2}, 3\right); r = \dfrac{\sqrt{118}}{2}$

20. Find the equation of the sphere whose center is $(1, -2, -4)$ and radius is $\sqrt{3}$.

    (a) $x^2 + y^2 + z^2 + 2x + 4y + 8z + 18 = 0$ (b) $x^2 + y^2 + z^2 - 2x - 4y - 8z + 18 = 0$

    (c) $x^2 + y^2 + z^2 + 2x - 4y - 8z + 18 = 0$ (d) $x^2 + y^2 + z^2 - 2x + 4y + 8z + 18 = 0$

    (e) None of these

2—Answer: d

21. Find the center and radius of the sphere given by the equation $x^2 + y^2 + z^2 - 4x - 2y + 2z = 10$.

    (a) Center: $(-2, -1, 1)$; radius: 4   (b) Center: $(2, 1, -1)$; radius: 4

    (c) Center: $(-2, -1, 1)$; radius: $\sqrt{10}$ (d) Center: $(2, 1, -1)$; radius: $\sqrt{10}$

    (e) None of these

1—Answer: b

22. Find the equation of the sphere whose center is $\left(-1, \dfrac{5}{2}, 2\right)$ and whose radius is $\dfrac{9}{2}$.

2—Answer: $x^2 + y^2 + z^2 + 10x - 5y - 8z + 9 = 0$

23. Determine which of the graphs is the xy-trace of the sphere $(x - 2)^2 + (y + 3)^2 + (z - 1)^2 = 17$.

    (a) 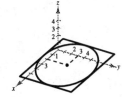   (b) 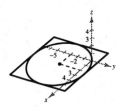

    (c) 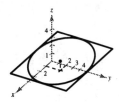   (d) 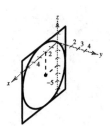

    (e) None of these

1—Answer: b

24. Determine which of the graphs is the xy-trace of the sphere $(x + 1)^2 + (y - 2)^2 + (z + 3)^2 = 25$.

(a)

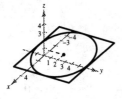

(b)

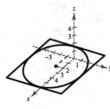

(c)

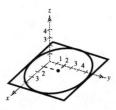

(d)

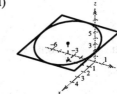

(e) None of these

1—Answer: a

25. Determine which of the graphs is the yz-trace of the sphere $(x - 2)^2 + (y - 1)^2 + (z - 3)^2 = 13$.

(a)

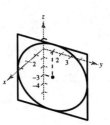

(b)

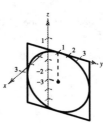

(c)

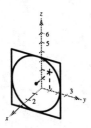

(d)

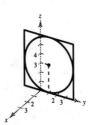

(e) None of these

1—Answer: d

26. Sketch the yz-trace of the sphere $(x - 1)^2 + (y - 2)^2 + (z - 1)^2 = 10$.

1—Answer:

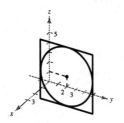

27. Determine which of the graphs is the trace of the intersection of the plane $x = 3$ and the sphere $x^2 + y^2 + z^2 = 25$.

(a)

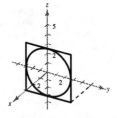

(b)

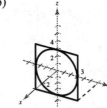

(c)

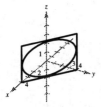

(d)

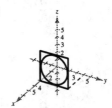

(e) None of these

1—Answer: d

Section 7.2 Surfaces in Space

1. Identify the quadric surface: $\dfrac{x^2}{1} + \dfrac{y^2}{4} - z = 0$.

(a) Elliptic cone   (b) Elliptic paraboloid   (c) Hyperbolic paraboloid

(d) Ellipsoid   (e) None of these

1—Answer: b

2. Identify the quadric surface: $z = \dfrac{x^2}{4} + \dfrac{y^2}{16}$.

(a) Elliptic cone   (b) Elliptic paraboloid   (c) Hyperbolic paraboloid

(d) Hyperboloid of one sheet   (e) Hyperboloid of two sheets

1—Answer: b

3. Identify the quadric surface: $z^2 = \dfrac{x^2}{4} + \dfrac{y^2}{16}$.

(a) Elliptic cone   (b) Elliptic paraboloid   (c) Hyperbolic paraboloid

(d) Hyperboloid of one sheet   (e) Hyperboloid of two sheets

1—Answer: a

4. Identify the quadric surface: $z = \dfrac{x^2}{25} + \dfrac{y^2}{16}$.

(a) Elliptic cone   (b) Hyperbolic paraboloid   (c) Elliptic paraboloid

(d) Hyperboloid of one sheet   (e) Hyperboloid of two sheets

1—Answer: c

5. Identify the quadric surface: $z = \dfrac{x^2}{9} + \dfrac{y^2}{25}$.

(a) Elliptic paraboloid   (b) Hyperbolic paraboloid   (c) Ellipsoid

(d) Elliptic cone   (e) None of these

1—Answer: a

6. Identify the quadric surface: $3x^2 + y^2 - z = 0$.

1—Answer: Elliptic paraboloid

7. Identify the quadric surface: $z^2 = \dfrac{x^2}{4} + \dfrac{y^2}{16}$.

(a) Elliptic cone   (b) Elliptic paraboloid   (c) Hyperbolic paraboloid

(d) Hyperboloid of one sheet   (e) Hyperboloid of two sheets

1—Answer: a

8. Identify the quadric surface sketched to the right.

    (a) Hyperboloid of two sheets   (b) Elliptic paraboloid

    (c) Hyperboloid of one sheet   (d) Elliptic cone

    (e) None of these

    1—Answer: e

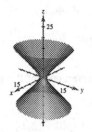

9. Identify the quadric surface sketched to the right.

    (a) Hyperboloid of two sheets   (b) Elliptic paraboloid

    (c) Hyperboloid of one sheet   (d) Elliptic cone

    (e) None of these

    1—Answer: c

10. Identify the quadric surface: $z = \dfrac{x^2}{9} - \dfrac{y^2}{25}$.

    (a) Elliptic paraboloid   (b) Hyperboloid paraboloid   (c) Ellipsoid

    (d) Elliptic cone   (e) None of these

    1—Answer: b

11. Determine whether the planes are parallel, perpendicular, or neither:

$$2x - 4y + 7z = 12, \; 3x - 6y + \left(\tfrac{21}{2}\right)z = 18.$$

    (a) Parallel   (b) Perpendicular   (c) Neither

    1—Answer: a

12. Determine whether the planes are parallel, perpendicular, or neither:

$$3x - 4y + 7z = 12, \; 3x + 4y - 7z = 12.$$

    (a) Parallel   (b) Perpendicular   (c) Neither

    1—Answer: c

13. Determine whether the planes are parallel, perpendicular, or neither:

$$x - 2y + 5z = 1, \; 5x + 10y + 3z = 1.$$

    (a) Parallel   (b) Perpendicular   (c) Neither

    1—Answer: b

14. Find all intercepts: $3x - 4y - 2z = 12$.

    (a) $(4, -3, -6)$ (b) $(4, -3), (0, -3, -6), (4, 0, -6)$

    (c) $(0, 0, -6), (0, -3, 0), (4, 0, 0)$ (d) $(3, 0, 0), (0, -4, 0), (0, 0, -2)$

    (e) None of these

    1—Answer: c

15. Find all intercepts: $2x + 4y - 5z = -20$.

1—Answer: $(0, 0, 4), (0, -5, 0), (-10, 0, 0)$

16. Find the intercepts of the plane $x + 2y - 3z = 6$.

(a) $(0, 0, 0)$

(b) $(6, 0, 0), (0, 3, 0), (0, 0, -2)$

(c) $(-6, 0, 0), (0, -3, 0), (0, 0, 2)$

(d) $(6, 3, 2)$

(e) None of these

1—Answer: b

17. Find the intercepts of the plane $2x - 3y + z = 6$.

(a) $(0, 0, 0)$

(b) $(-3, 0, 0), (0, 2, 0), (0, 0, -6)$

(c) $(3, 0, 0), (0, -2, 0), (0, 0, 6)$

(d) $(3, -2, 6)$

(e) None of these

1—Answer: c

18. Which of the following is a sketch of the plane $2x + y + 3z = 6$?

(a)

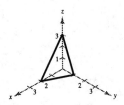

(b)

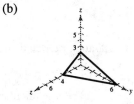

(c)

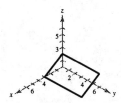

(d)

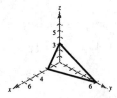

(e) None of these

1—Answer: b

19. Sketch the plane $3x + 4y + 2z = 12$.

2—Answer:

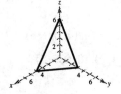

20. Sketch the graph of $5x + 2y + 3z = 30$.

1—Answer:

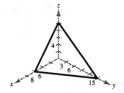

21. Sketch the graph of $z = 5$.

1—Answer:

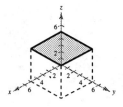

22. Which of the following is a sketch of the plane $4x + 3y + 2z = 12$?

(a)

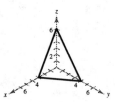

(b)

(c)

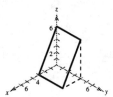

(d)

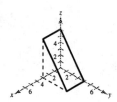

(e) None of these

1—Answer: a

23. Find the distance between the point $(1, -1, 3)$ and the plane $2x + 3y + z = 6$.

(a) $\dfrac{14}{\sqrt{14}}$
    (b) $\dfrac{14}{\sqrt{11}}$
    (c) $\dfrac{4}{\sqrt{14}}$
    (d) $\dfrac{8}{\sqrt{14}}$
    (e) None of these

1—Answer: c

24. Calculate the distance from the point $(1, -2, 3)$ to the plane $(x - 3) + 2(y + 1) - 4z = 0$.

(a) $\sqrt{14}$ (b) $\dfrac{14}{\sqrt{21}}$ (c) $\dfrac{12}{\sqrt{21}}$ (d) $\sqrt{65}$ (e) None of these

1—Answer: e

25. Find the distance between the point $(1, -2, 3)$ and the plane $3x - 4y + 2z - 1 = 0$.

1—Answer: $\dfrac{16}{\sqrt{29}}$

Section 7.3   Functions of Several Variables

1. Find $f(2, 3)$ for $f(x, y) = \dfrac{x^3 y}{x^2 + y^2}$.

    (a) $\frac{2}{3}$ (b) $\frac{9}{5}$ (c) $\frac{54}{13}$ (d) $\frac{24}{13}$ (e) None of these

    1—Answer: d

2. Find $f(-3, 0)$ for $f(x, y) = \sqrt{x^2 - xy}$.

    (a) 3   (b) 0   (c) -3 (d) 9   (e) None of these

    1—Answer: a

3. Find $f(-1, 3, 5)$ for the function $f(x, y, z) = \dfrac{xz - x^3}{y^2}$.

    (a) $-\frac{10}{3}$ (b) $\frac{2}{3}$ (c) $-\frac{4}{9}$ (d) 5   (e) None of these

    1—Answer: c

4. Find $f(1, 3, -1)$ when $f(x, y, z) = \dfrac{x^2 - yz}{x + y}$.

    (a) 1   (b) $-\frac{1}{4}$ (c) $\frac{1}{2}$ (d) $-\frac{3}{4}$ (e) None of these

    1—Answer: a

5. Find $f(-2, 3, 1)$ for $f(x, y, z) = \dfrac{xyz - x^2}{y}$.

    (a) $-\frac{10}{3}$ (b) $\frac{2}{3}$ (c) $-\frac{2}{3}$ (d) 5   (e) None of these

    1—Answer: a

6. Find $A(\$1000, 0.10, 5)$ when $A(P, r, t) = Pe^{rt}$.

    (a) \$693.15   (b) \$148,413.16   (c) \$1648.72   (d) \$1822.12   (e) None of these

    1—T—Answer: c

7. Find $A(1000, 0.06, 10)$ when $A(P, r, t) = Pe^{rt}$.

    (a) \$10,618.67   (b) \$1986.82   (c) \$1822.11   (d) \$114.97   (e) None of these

    1—T—Answer: c

8. Find $f(0, 2)$ if $f(x, y) = x^3 - y \ln(x + 3)$. Approximate your answer to the nearest 0.01.

    1—T—Answer: -2.20

9. Find the domain of the function $f(x, y) = \dfrac{3x^2 - 2y}{x - y}$.

(a) All (x, y) such that $x \neq y$

(b) All (x, y) such that $x \neq 1$

(c) All (x, y) such that $x \neq 1$ and $y \neq 0$

(d) All (x, y)

(e) None of these

1—Answer: a

10. Determine the domain of the function $f(x, y) = \sqrt{4 - x^2 - y^2}$.

1—Answer: $\{(x, y): x^2 + y^2 \leq 4\}$

11. Determine the domain of the function defined by $f(x, y) = \sqrt{1 - x^2 - y^2}$.

1—Answer: $\{(x, y): x^2 + y^2 \leq 1\}$

12. Describe the region R in the xy-coordinate plane that corresponds to the domain of the function

$$f(x, y) = \frac{xy}{x^2 - y^2}.$$

(a) Set of all points in the xy-plane

(b) $\{(x, y): x^2 = y^2\}$

(c) $\{(x, y): x \neq \pm y\}$

(d) $\{(x, y): y < x\}$

(e) None of these

1—Answer: c

13. Describe the region R in the xy-coordinate plane that corresponds to the domain of the function

$$f(x, y) = \sqrt{49 - x^2 + y^2}.$$

1—Answer: $\left\{(x, y): \dfrac{x^2}{49} - \dfrac{y^2}{49} \leq 1\right\}$

14. Describe the region R in the xy-coordinate plane that corresponds to the domain of the function

$$f(x, y) = \sqrt[3]{27 - x^2 - y^2}.$$

(a) Set of all points in the xy-plane

(b) $\{(x, y): x^2 + y^2 < 27\}$

(c) $\left\{(x, y): \sqrt[3]{x^2 + y^2} < 3\right\}$

(d) $\{(x, y): x \neq y\}$

(e) None of these

1—Answer: a

15. Find the domain of the function $f(x, y) = \sqrt{16 - 4x^2 - y^2}$.

(a) $\dfrac{x^2}{4} + \dfrac{y^2}{16} \geq 1$

(b) $\dfrac{x^2}{4} + \dfrac{y^2}{16} \leq 1$

(c) $4x^2 + y^2 \neq 0$

(d) $\dfrac{x^2}{2} + \dfrac{y^2}{4} \leq 16$

(e) None of these

1—Answer: b

16. Find the domain of the function $f(x, y) = \dfrac{2}{x - y^2}$.

    (a) All (x, y) such that $x = y^2$
    (b) All (x, y) such that $x \neq y$

    (c) All (x, y) such that $y \neq x^2$
    (d) All (x, y) such that $x \neq y^2$

    (e) None of these

    1—Answer: d

17. Identify the contour map for $f(x, y) = 16 - x^2 - y^2$, $c = 4, 8, 12$.

    (a)

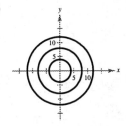

    (b)

    (c)

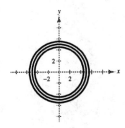

    (d)

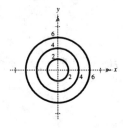

    (e) None of these

    1—Answer: b

18. Sketch the contour map for $f(x, y) = \sqrt{4 - x^2 - y^2}$ for $c = 0, 1,$ and 2.

    1—Answer:

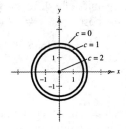

19. Identify the contour map for $f(x, y) = 25 - x^2 - y^2, c = 0, 10, 20$.

(a)

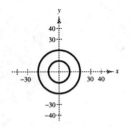

(b)

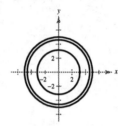

(c)

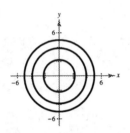

(d)

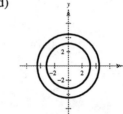

(e) None of these

1—Answer: c

20. Sketch the contour map for $f(x, y) = \ln(xy)$ for $c = -2, -1, 0, 1, 2$.

1—Answer:

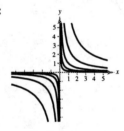

21. The cost function for producing x units of a certain model of a product and y units of a different model of the same product is given by $C(x, y) = 0.05(x + y)^2 + 4x + 10y + 15$. Find the cost when $x = 12$ and $y = 15$.

(a) $231.45   (b) $249.45   (c) $417.52   (d) $577.50   (e) None of these

1—T—Answer: b

22. The sum of $1500 is deposited in a savings account earning r percent interest compounded continuously. The amount $A(r, t)$ after t years is given by $A(r, t) = 1500e^{rt}$. Determine the amount earning 8% interest for 7 years.

(a) $2626   (b) $2714   (c) $2527   (d) $2172   (e) None of these

1—T—Answer: a

23. The sum of $2000 is deposited in a savings account earning r percent interest compounded continuously. The amount $A(r, t)$ after t years is given by $A(r, t) = 2000e^{rt}$. Determine the amount in an account earning 8% interest for 5 years.

1—T—Answer: $2983.65

Section 7.4 Partial Derivatives

1. Find $f_x(x, y)$ for $f(x, y) = \ln x + e^{xy}$.

   (a) $\ln x + xe^{xy}$ (b) $\dfrac{1}{x} + xe^{xy}$ (c) $\dfrac{1}{x} + ye^{xy}$ (d) $\dfrac{1}{x} + e^{xy}$ (e) None of these

   1—Answer: c

2. Find $f_y(x, y)$ for $f(x, y) = 2x^2y + xy^2 - y^3$.

   (a) $2x^2 + 2xy - 3y^3$ (b) $4xy + y^2$ (c) $2x^2 + 2xy - y^3$

   (d) $2x^2y + 2xy - 3y^2$ (e) None of these

   1—Answer: a

3. Find $f_x(x, y)$ for $f(x, y) = \dfrac{xy}{x^2 - y^2}$.

   (a) $\dfrac{-y}{x^2 - y^2}$ (b) $\dfrac{y}{2x}$ (c) $\dfrac{-y(y^2 + x^2)}{(y^2 - x^2)^2}$ (d) $\dfrac{x + y}{2x - 2y}$ (e) None of these

   1—Answer: c

4. Find $f_x(x, y)$ for $f(x, y) = e^{y/x}$.

   (a) $\dfrac{x - y}{x^2}e^{y/x}$ (b) $\dfrac{y}{x}e^{(y/x)-1}$ (c) $\dfrac{y}{x^2}e^{(y/x)-1}$ (d) $\dfrac{1}{x}e^{y/x}$ (e) None of these

   1—Answer: d

5. Find $f_x\left(\tfrac{1}{2}, 0\right)$ for $f(x, y) = \ln(x^2 + y)$.

   (a) 1   (b) 4   (c) 0   (d) $\tfrac{1}{4}$ (e) None of these

   1—Answer: b

6. Find $f_y(3, -1)$ for $f(x, y) = 3x^2 - xy + 7x^2$.

   (a) 19   (b) -17 (c) 11   (d) 17   (e) None of these

   1—Answer: b

7. Find $\dfrac{\partial w}{\partial x}$ if $w = x^2 + y\sqrt{z - x^2}$.

   1—Answer: $2x - \dfrac{xy}{\sqrt{z - x^2}}$

8. Find $f_x(3, 0)$ for $f(x, y) = e^{3xy}$.

   (a) e (b) 3   (c) 9   (d) 0   (e) None of these

   1—Answer: d

9. Find $f_y\left(\frac{1}{2}, 0\right)$ for $f(x, y) = \ln(x^2 + y^2)$.

(a) 4   (b) 0   (c) 1   (d) $\frac{1}{4}$ (e) None of these

1—Answer: b

10. Find $f_y(1, -1, 4)$ for $f(x, y, z) = 2x^2y - 2yx + xz$.

(a) 0   (b) 3   (c) -6 (d) -4 (e) None of these

1—Answer: c

11. Find $f_x(1, -1, 4)$ for $f(x, y, z) = 2x^2y - 2yz + xz$.

(a) 0   (b) 3   (c) -6 (d) -4 (e) None of these

1—Answer: a

12. Find $f_z(1, -1, 4)$ for $f(x, y, z) = 2x^2y - 2yz + xz$.

(a) 0   (b) 3   (c) -6 (d) -4 (e) None of these

1—Answer: b

13. Find $\dfrac{\partial f}{\partial x}$ for $f(x, y) = \dfrac{e^{y^2}}{xy}$.

(a) $\dfrac{e^{y^2}}{x^2y}$ (b) $-\dfrac{e^{y^2}}{x^2y}$ (c) $-\dfrac{2e^{y^2}}{y}$ (d) $\dfrac{e^{y^2}\ln x}{y}$ (e) None of these

1—Answer: b

14. Find $\dfrac{\partial f}{\partial y}$ for $f(x, y) = \dfrac{4x^2 - y^2}{xy}$.

(a) $\dfrac{4x^2 - y^2}{xy^2}$ (b) $\dfrac{4y^2 - x^2}{xy^2}$ (c) $\dfrac{4y^2 - x^2}{x^2y^2}$ (d) $-\dfrac{4x^2 + y^2}{xy^2}$ (e) None of these

1—Answer: d

15. Find $f_y(x, y)$ for $f(x, y) = \dfrac{xy}{x^2 - y^2}$.

(a) $\dfrac{-y}{x^2 - y^2}$ (b) $\dfrac{y}{2x}$ (c) $\dfrac{-y(y^2 - x^2)}{(y^2 - x^2)^2}$ (d) $\dfrac{x(x^2 + y^2)}{(x^2 - y^2)^2}$ (e) None of these

1—Answer: d

16. Find $f_x(x, y)$ for $f(x, y) = e^{y/x}$.

(a) $\dfrac{-ye^{y/x}}{x^2}$ (b) $\dfrac{ye^{(y/x)-1}}{x}$ (c) $\dfrac{ye^{(y/x)-1}}{x^2}$ (d) $\dfrac{1}{x}e^{y/x}$ (e) None of these

1—Answer: a

17. Find $\dfrac{\partial w}{\partial x}$ for the function given by $w = xye^{xyz}$.

  1—Answer: $y(xyz + 1)e^{xyz}$

18. Find $f_{xy}(x, y)$ for $f(x, y) = \dfrac{4x^2}{y} + \dfrac{y^2}{2x}$.

  (a) $-\dfrac{8x}{y^2} - \dfrac{y}{x^2}$ (b) $8x - y$ (c) $8x + y$

  (d) $\dfrac{16x^3y - 8x^4 + 2xy^3 - y^4}{2x^2y^2}$ (e) None of these

  1—Answer: a

19. Find $f_{xx}(x, y)$ for $f(x, y) = \dfrac{4x^2}{y} + \dfrac{y^2}{2x}$.

  (a) $4x + \dfrac{x}{2}$ (b) $\dfrac{8}{y} + \dfrac{y^2}{x^3}$ (c) $\dfrac{8}{y}$ (d) $\dfrac{8x}{y} + \dfrac{y^2}{2}$ (e) None of these

  1—Answer: b

20. Find $f_{xy}(x, y)$ for $f(x, y) = x^2y + 2y^2x^2 + 4x$.

  (a) $2x + 4yx$ (b) $4x^2$ (c) $4xy$ (d) $2x + 8yx + 4$ (e) None of these

  1—Answer: e

21. Find $f_{xx}(x, y)$ for $f(x, y) = e^{x^2y}$.

  (a) $(4x^2 + 2y)e^{x^2y}.$ (b) $4x^2y^2e^{x^2y}$ (c) $4x^2e^{x^2y}$

  (d) $(4x^2y^2 + 2y)e^{x^2y}$ (e) None of these

  1—Answer: d

22. Show that $f(x, y) = \ln(x^2 + y^2)$ satisfies Laplace's equation: $\dfrac{\partial^2 f}{\partial x^2} + \dfrac{\partial^2 f}{\partial y^2} = 0$.

  1—Answer: $\dfrac{\partial^2 f}{\partial x^2} = \dfrac{-2x^2 + 2y^2}{(x^2 + y^2)^2}, \quad \dfrac{\partial^2 f}{\partial y^2} = \dfrac{2x^2 - 2y^2}{(x^2 + y^2)^2}$

23. Let $f(x, y) = 520x^{0.2}y^{0.8}$ be a Cobb-Douglas production function. Find the marginal productivity of labor, $f_x(x, y)$, when $x = 1024$ and $y = 243$.

  (a) 65.81253 (b) 32.90625 (c) 1.21875 (d) 156 (e) None of these

  1—Answer: b

24. Find the slope in the y-direction of the surface $z = xy^2$ at the point $(3, -2, 12)$.

  (a) -12 (b) 4 (c) 12 (d) -4 (e) None of these

  1—Answer: a

25. Find the slope in the x-direction of the surface $z = xy^2 + x^2y$ at the point $(2, -3, 6)$.

    (a) -8 (b) -3 (c) 24   (d) 21   (e) None of these

    1—Answer: b

26. Find the slope in the y-direction of the surface $f(x, y) = \dfrac{xy^2}{1 + x^2}$ at the point $\left(1, 1, \dfrac{1}{2}\right)$.

    1—Answer: 1

27. Find the slope in the x-direction of the surface $f(x, y) = \dfrac{xy^2}{1 + x^2}$ at the point $\left(1, 1, \dfrac{1}{2}\right)$.

    (a) -1 (b) $\frac{2}{3}$ (c) 0   (d) 1   (e) None of these

    1—Answer: c

28. Find the slope in the x-direction of the surface $f(x, y) = xy^2$ at the point $(3, -2, 12)$.

    (a) -6 (b) 9   (c) 4   (d) -12 (e) None of these

    1—Answer: c

29. Find the slope in the y-direction of the surface $f(x, y) = xy^2 + x^2y$ at the point $(2, -3, 6)$.

    (a) -3 (b) -8 (c) -24 (d) 8   (e) None of these

    1—Answer: b

30. Find the slope in the x-direction of the surface

    $$z = \frac{1}{x^2} \ln(x + y^2)$$

    at the point $\left(2, 2, \frac{1}{4} \ln 6\right)$. Approximate your answer to the nearest 0.01.

    (a) -0.41 (b) -0.17 (c) 0.17   (d) 0.45   (e) None of these

    2—T—Answer: b

Section 7.5   Extrema of Functions of Two Variables

1. Find the minimum value of the function $f(x, y) = x^2 + y^2 - xy - 4$.

   (a) 0   (b) 2   (c) -12 (d) -4 (e) None of these

   1—Answer: d

2. Find the saddle point for $f(x, y) = x^2 - y^2 - 2x - 6y - 3$.

   (a) $(1, -3, 0)$ (b) $(-1, 3, 5)$ (c) $(-1, 3, 0)$

   (d) $(1, -3, 5)$ (e) None of these

   1—Answer: d

3. Determine the relative extrema of $f(x, y) = x^2 + x - 3xy + y^3 - 5$.

   1—Answer: $f(1, 1)$ is a relative minimum

4. Determine the relative extrema of $f(x, y) = x^2 + y^2 - 2x - 4y + 1$.

   (a) Minimum at $(1, 2)$ (b) Maximum at $(1, 2)$ (c) Saddle point at $(1, 2)$

   (d) Maximum at $(1, 1)$ (e) None of these

   1—Answer: a

5. Determine the relative extrema of $f(x, y) = y^3 - x^3$.

   (a) Minimum at $(0, 0)$ (b) Maximum at $(0, 0)$ (c) Saddle point at $(0, 0)$

   (d) Minimum at $(1, 1)$ (e) None of these

   1—Answer: c

6. Determine the relative extrema of $f(x, y) = x^3 + y^3 + 3xy - 2$.

   1—Answer: Saddle point: $(0, 0)$
   Relative maximum: $(-1, -1)$

7. Determine the relative extrema of $f(x, y) = y^5 + x^4 - 5y - 32x - 8$.

   1—Answer: Relative minimum: $(2, 1)$
   Saddle point: $(2, -1)$

8. Find the saddle point for $f(x, y) = x^2 - y^2 - 3x - 8y + 5$.

   (a) $\left(\frac{3}{2}, -4, \frac{33}{2}\right)$ (b) $\left(-4, \frac{3}{2}, \frac{33}{2}\right)$ (c) $(0, 0, 5)$ (d) $\left(\frac{3}{2}, 4, \frac{75}{4}\right)$ (e) None of these

   2—Answer: e

9. Determine the relative extrema of $f(x, y) = -6x + 2y - x^2 - y^2 - 4$.

    (a) Minimum at $(-3, 1)$ (b) Maximum at $(-3, 1)$ (c) Saddle point at $(-3, 1)$

    (d) Minimum at $(3, 1)$ (e) None of these

    1—Answer: b

10. Determine the relative extrema of $f(x, y) = x + y + \dfrac{1}{xy}$.

    (a) Minimum at $(1, 1)$ (b) Maximum at $(1, 1)$ (c) Minimum at $(-1, -1)$

    (d) Maximum at $(-1, -1)$ (e) None of these

    1—Answer: a

11. Determine the relative extrema of $f(x, y) = x + y - \dfrac{1}{xy}$.

    (a) Minimum at $(1, 1)$ (b) Maximum at $(1, 1)$ (c) Minimum at $(-1, -1)$

    (d) Maximum at $(-1, -1)$ (e) None of these

    1—Answer: d

12. Find the minimum value of the function $f(x, y) = x^2 + y^2 - xy - 4$.

    (a) 0   (b) 2   (c) -12 (d) -4 (e) None of these

    1—Answer: d

13. Find the saddle point for $f(x, y) = x^2 - y^2 - 2x - 6y - 3$.

    (a) $(1, -3, 0)$ (b) $(-1, 3, 5)$ (c) $(-1, 3, 0)$ (d) $(1, -3, 5)$ (e) None of these

    1—Answer: d

14. Find the minimum value of the function $f(x, y) = x^2 + y^2 + xy + 6x + 4$.

    (a) 40   (b) 0   (c) -4 (d) 8   (e) None of these

    2—Answer: e

15. Determine the relative extrema of the function $f(x, y) = x^2 - 4x + 6xy + 2y^3 - 6$.

    2—Answer: Relative minimum at $(-4, 2, -6)$
    Saddlepoint at $(-1, -1, 5)$

16. Find any critical points and classify them for the function $z = f(x, y) = x^3 + y^3 - 9xy + 10$.

    2—Answer: Relative minimum at $(3, 3, -17)$
    Saddlepoint at $(0, 0, 10)$

17. A corporation manufactures a product at two locations. The cost of producing x units at a location one and y units at location two are $C_1(x) = 0.01x^2 + 2x + 1000$ and $C_2(y) = 0.03\,y^2 + 2y + 300$, respectively. If the product sells for \$14 per unit, find the quantity that must be produced at each location to maximize the profit $P(x, y) = 14(x + y) - C_1 - C_2$.

(a) $x = 600, y = 200$ (b) $x = 14, y = 14$ (c) $x = 60, y = 20$

(d) $x = 100, y = 34$ (e) None of these

1—Answer: a

18. An open box has a volume of 64 cubic feet. Find the dimensions that minimize the surface area.

(a) $\sqrt{8} \times \sqrt{8} \times 8$ (b) $6 \times 6 \times \frac{16}{9}$ (c) $4\sqrt[3]{2} \times 4\sqrt[3]{2} \times 2\sqrt[3]{2}$

(d) $4 \times 4 \times 4$ (e) None of these

1—Answer: c

19. An open container is to be made at a cost of \$200. If material for the sides costs \$6 per square meter, and material for the bottom costs \$3 per square meter, find the dimensions of the container of greatest volume.

1—Answer: $\dfrac{10}{3}\sqrt{2} \times \dfrac{10}{3}\sqrt{2} \times \dfrac{5\sqrt{2}}{6}$

20. Find the maximum profit if the profit function is $P(x, y) = 30x + 90y - 0.5x^2 - 2y^2 - xy$.

(a) \$1050.00   (b) \$1020.00   (c) \$2010.00   (d) \$967.23   (e) None of these

1—T—Answer: a

21. Find three positive numbers x, y, z such that their product is 64 and their sum is a minimum.

(a) $x = y = z = 6$ (b) $x = y = 2, z = 16$ (c) $x = y = z = 4$

(d) $x = 2, y = 4, z = 8$ (e) None of these

1—Answer: c

22. Find the minimum distance from the point $(0, 0, 0)$ to the plane $x + 2y + z = 6$.

(a) 2 (b) $\sqrt{5}$ (c) $\sqrt{6}$ (d) $\sqrt{7}$ (e) None of these

1—Answer: c

23. Find the minimum distance from the point $(0, 0, 0)$ to the plane $-x + 3y + 2z = 5$.

(a) $\dfrac{\sqrt{105}}{9}$ (b) $\dfrac{\sqrt{95}}{7}$ (c) $\dfrac{105}{49}$ (d) $\dfrac{\sqrt{115}}{7}$ (e) None of these

1—Answer: e

24. A company manufactures two products. The total revenue from x_1 units of product 1 and x_2 units of product 2 is $R = -2x_1{}^2 - 3x_2{}^2 + 3x_1x_2 + 1000x_2 + 1600x_1$. Find x_1 and x_2 so as to maximize the revenue.

1—Answer: $x_1 = 840, x_2 = 586.67$

25. A corporation manufactures a product at two locations. The cost of producing x units at a location one and y units at location two are $C_1(x) = 0.01x^2 + 2x + 1000$ and $C_2(y) = 0.03\,y^2 + 2y + 300$, respectively. If the product sells for \$20 per unit, find the quantity that must be produced at each location to maximize the profit $P(x, y) = 20(x + y) - C_1 - C_2$.

   (a) $x = 100, y = 34$ (b) $x = 900, y = 300$ (c) $x = 20, y = 20$

   (d) $x = 600, y = 900$ (e) None of these

   1—Answer: b

26. Determine the maximum revenue obtained by a furniture store that sells two competitive products, the prices of which are p_1 and p_2.

   $$R = 300p_1 + 900p_2 + 1.8p_1 p_2 - 1.5p_1^2 - p_2^2.$$

   1—T—Answer: \$52,000

27. Describe, in a complete sentence, what must be true for the point $(a, b, f(a, b))$ to be a critical point for the function $f(x, y)$.

   1—Answer: Answers will vary.

28. Explain, in a complete sentence, what must be true about the first and second partial derivatives of a function $z = f(x, y)$ if the function has a saddle point at the point $P(a, b)$.

   1—Answer: Answers will vary.

Section 7.6   Lagrange Multipliers

1. Let $f(x, y, z) = 4x^2 + y^2 + 5z^2$. Use Lagrange Multipliers to find the point on the plane $2x + 3y + 4z = 12$ at which $f(x, y, z)$ has its least value.

   (a) $(1, 2, 1)$ (b) $\left(\frac{5}{11}, \frac{30}{11}, \frac{8}{11}\right)$ (c) $\frac{120}{11}$ (d) $\left(\frac{4}{7}, -\frac{2}{7}, \frac{82}{7}\right)$ (e) None of these

   1—Answer: b

2. Use Lagrange Multipliers to maximize $f(x, y, z) = 4x^2 + y^2 + z^2$ with the constraint that $2x - y + z = 4$.

   (a) $\frac{16}{3}$ (b) $\left(\frac{2}{3}, -\frac{4}{3}, \frac{4}{3}\right)$ (c) 36 (d) $\frac{16}{9}$ (e) None of these

   1—Answer: a

3. Use a Lagrange Multiplier to maximize the function $f(x, y) = x + 2xy + 2y$ with the constraint $x + 2y = 80$.

   2—Answer: $f(40, 20) = 1680$

4. Find the maximum of $f(x, y) = 2xy$ subject to the constraint $\dfrac{x^2}{4} + \dfrac{y^2}{2} = 1$.

   (a) $2\sqrt{2}$ (b) $\sqrt{2}$ (c) 2 (d) 4 (e) None of these

   1—Answer: a

5. Find the maximum of $f(x, y) = 4xy$ subject to the constraint $x^2 + (y + 1)^2 = 1$.

   (a) $\sqrt{3}$ (b) $3\sqrt{3}$ (c) $6\sqrt{3}$ (d) 0 (e) None of these

   1—Answer: b

6. Maximize $f(x, y, z) = 32xyz$ subject to the constraints $x + y + z = 4$ and $-x - y + z = 3$.

   (a) 3 (b) 8 (c) 4 (d) 7 (e) None of these

   1—Answer: d

7. Maximize $f(x, y, z) = 2yz + 2xy$ subject to $xy = 1$ and $y^2 + z^2 = 1$.

   (a) 1 (b) 2 (c) $\sqrt{2}$ (d) $2\sqrt{2}$ (e) None of these

   1—Answer: e

8. Use Lagrange Multipliers to maximize $f(x, y) = 3xy + x$ with the constraint $11x + 15y = 215$.

   (a) 256 (b) 220 (c) 200 (d) 185 (e) None of these

   1—Answer: b

9. Find the point on the line $y = 2x + 3$ that is closest to $(1, 1)$.

   (a) $(-1, 1)$ (b) $\left(-\frac{3}{2}, 0\right)$ (c) $\left(-\frac{1}{2}, 2\right)$ (d) $\left(-\frac{4}{5}, \frac{13}{5}\right)$ (e) None of these

   1—Answer: e

10. Find the point on the line $y = 2x + 3$ that is closest to $(1, 0)$.

(a) $(-2, -1)$ (b) $\left(-\frac{3}{2}, 0\right)$ (c) $(-1, 1)$ (d) $\left(-\frac{1}{2}, 2\right)$ (e) None of these

1—Answer: c

11. The temperature on the surface $x^2 + y^2 + 4z^2 = 12$ is given by $T(x, y, z) = x^2 + y^2$. Find the maximum temperature on this surface.

(a) 0   (b) 6   (c) 12   (d) 18   (e) None of these

1—Answer: c

12. The temperature on the surface $x^2 + y^2 + z^2 = 9$ is given by $T(x, y, z) = x + y + z$. Find the maximum temperature on this surface.

(a) $3\sqrt{3}$ (b) $\sqrt{3}$ (c) 3   (d) $\dfrac{\sqrt{3}}{2}$ (e) None of these

1—Answer: a

13. Use Lagrange Multipliers to find three positive numbers whose sum is 36 and whose product is a maximum.

(a) 10, 12, 14   (b) 8, 12, 16   (c) 12, 12, 12   (d) 9, 12, 15   (e) None of these

2—Answer: c

14. Use Lagrange Multipliers to find three positive numbers whose sum is 33 and whose product is a maximum.

1—Answer: 11, 11, 11

15. The Cobb-Douglas production function for a particular manufacturer is given by $f(x, y) = 200x^{1/4}y^{3/4}$ where x represents the units of labor (at \$100/unit) and y represents capital (at \$150/unit). Find the maximum production level if the total cost of labor and capital is limited to \$70,000. Also find λ, the marginal productivity of money.

1—Answer: $x = 400, y = 200, \lambda = 0.2973$

16. The Cobb-Douglas production function for a particular manufacturer is given by $f(x, y) = 120x^{1/3}y^{2/3}$ where x represents the units of labor (at \$60/unit) and y represents capital (at \$90/unit). Find the maximum production level if the total cost of labor and capital is limited to \$36,000. Also find λ, the marginal productivity of money.

1—Answer: $x = 200, y = \frac{800}{3}, \lambda = 0.8076$

17. The Cobb-Douglas production function for a certain manufacturer is given by $f(x, y) = 200x^{0.6}y^{0.4}$, where x represents the number of units of labor and y represents the number of units of capital. Suppose labor costs \$125 per unit and capital costs \$100 per unit. Find the maximum production level if the total cost of labor and capital is limited to \$100,000.

(a) 83,581 units   (b) 89,248 units   (c) 89,712 units   (d) 67,020 units   (e) None of these

2—T—Answer: b

18. A manufacturer has an order for 1500 units that can be produced at two locations. Let x_1 and x_2 be the number of units produced at the two plants. Find the minimum cost for producing this order if the cost function is

$$C = 0.125x_1{}^2 - 14x_1 + 0.25x_2{}^2 - 227x_2.$$

(a) $44,110   (b) $35,419   (c) $31,488   (d) $29,754   (e) None of these

2—T—Answer: d

19. A manufacturer has an order for 3500 units that can be produced at two locations. Let x_1 and x_2 be the number of units produced at the two plants. Find the number of units that should be produced at each plant to minimize the cost if the cost function is given by

$$C = 0.25x_1{}^2 + 16x_1 + 0.3x_2{}^2 + 160x_2.$$

(a) $x_1 = 2040, x_2 = 1460$ (b) $x_1 = 1862, x_2 = 1638$ (c) $x_1 = 1570, x_2 = 1980$

(d) $x_1 = 1250, x_2 = 2250$ (e) None of these

2—Answer: a

Section 7.7   Least Squares Regression Analysis

1. Find the least squares regression line for the points $(-2, 7)$, $(0, -5)$, $(1, -1)$ and $(2, -3)$.

(a) $y = -2.4617x + 1.1300$ (b) $y = 1.3182x^2 - 2.1545x - 2.9273$

(c) $y = 2.4619x^2 - 1.1320x + 3.0017$ (d) $y = -2.3429x + 0.0857$

(e) None of these

1—T—Answer: d

2. Find the least squares regression line for the points $(-2, 6)$, $(-1, 3)$, $(1, -4)$, $(2, 3)$ and $(4, -3)$.

(a) $y = -0.2975x^2 + 0.1835x + 2.2532$ (b) $y = -0.6818x + 2.0909$

(c) $y = -1.2719x + 2.0175$ (d) $y = -0.2186x^2 - 1.6861x + 1.2121$

(e) None of these

1—T—Answer: d

3. Find the least squares regression line for the points $(4, 1)$, $(-3, -1)$, $(2, -4)$ and $(-4, 7)$.

(a) $y = -0.7542x + 1.0615$ (b) $y = -0.3520x + 3.1620$

(c) $y = 0.5809x^2 - 0.6536x - 5.4482$ (d) $y = 0.0397x^2 - 0.3451x + 2.2715$

(e) None of these

1—T—Answer: a

4. Find the least squares regression line for the points $(1, 3)$, $(-5, -5)$, $(-3, -2)$ and $(5, 7)$.

1—T—Answer: $y = 1.1949x + 1.3475$

5. Find the least squares regression line for the points $(0, 1)$, $(1, 3)$, $(2, 2)$, $(3, 4)$, $(4, 5)$.

(a) $y = 1.2x + 0.8$ (b) $y = 0.8x + 0.9$ (c) $y = 0.9x + 1.2$

(d) $y = 1.2x + 0.9$ (e) None of these

2—Answer: c

6. Find the least squares regression line for the points $(0, 400)$, $(1, 200)$, $(2, 0)$, $(3, -100)$ and $(4, -300)$.

2—Answer: $y = -170x + 380$

7. Find the least squares regression line for the points $(0, 2)$, $(1, 4)$, $(2, 5)$, $(3, 7)$, $(4, 9)$.

(a) $y = 1.8x + 3$ (b) $y = 1.7x + 2$ (c) $y = 1.9x + 1.8$

(d) $y = 2.1x + 1$ (e) None of these

2—Answer: b

8. Find the least squares regression line for the points $(-9, 4)$, $(-3, 1,)$, $(-1, -2)$, $(5, -3)$ and $(8, -5)$.

2—Answer: $y = -\frac{23}{45}x - 1$

9. Find the least squares regression line for the points $(-2, -1), (-1, 1), (0, 1), (1, 2)$ and $(2, 2)$.

   1—Answer: $y = \frac{7}{10}x + 1$

10. Find the least squares regression line for the points $(0, 0), (1, 1)$ and $(2, 4)$.

   (a) $y = \frac{3}{2}x - \frac{1}{2}$

   (b) $y = 2x - \frac{1}{4}$

   (c) $y = \frac{7}{3}x - \frac{1}{3}$

   (d) $y = 2x - \frac{1}{3}$

   (e) None of these

   1—Answer: d

11. Find the least squares regression line for the points $(-2, 0), (-1, 1), (0, 1)$ and $(1, 2)$.

   (a) $y = 0.6x + 1.3$

   (b) $y = 1.3x + 0.6$

   (c) $y = 0.8x + 1.3$

   (d) $y = 0.6x + 1.2$

   (e) None of these

   1—Answer: a

12. Use the method of least squares to find an equation of the least squares regression line for the points:

   $(-2, 2), (-1, 3), (0, 1), (1, 1), (2, -1)$.

   (a) $y = -\frac{4}{5}x + \frac{7}{5}$

   (b) $y = -x + \frac{6}{5}$

   (c) $y = -\frac{4}{5}x + \frac{6}{5}$

   (d) $y = -x + \frac{7}{5}$

   (e) None of these

   1—Answer: c

13. Use the method of least squares to find an equation of the least squares regression line for the points:

   $(-2, -1), (-1, 1), (0, 1), (1, 2), (2, 2)$.

   (a) $y = \frac{4}{5}x + 1$

   (b) $y = \frac{7}{10}x + 1$

   (c) $y = \frac{7}{10}x + \frac{7}{5}$

   (d) $y = \frac{1}{2}x + 1$

   (e) None of these

   1—Answer: b

14. Find the least squares regression quadratic for the points $(-2, 7), (0, -5), (1, -1)$ and $(2, -3)$.

   (a) $y = 1.3182x^2 - 2.1545x - 2.9273$

   (b) $y = 0.9380x^2 - 1.1102x - 3.0017$

   (c) $y = -2.4617x + 1.1300$

   (d) $y = -2.3429x + 0.0857$

   (e) None of these

   1—T—Answer: a

15. Find the least squares regression quadratic for the points $(-2, 6), (-1, 3), (1, -4), (2, 3)$ and $(4, -3)$.

   (a) $y = -0.2975x^2 + 0.1835x + 2.2532$

   (b) $y = -0.6818x + 2.0909$

   (c) $y = -1.2719x + 2.0175$

   (d) $y = -0.2186x^2 - 1.6861x + 1.2121$

   (e) None of these

   1—T—Answer: d

16. Find the least squares regression quadratic for the points $(4, 1)$, $(-3, -1)$, $(2, -4)$ and $(-4, 7)$.

(a) $y = 0.5809x^2 - 0.6536x - 5.4482$

(b) $y = -0.7542x + 1.0615$

(c) $y = -0.3520x + 3.1620$

(d) $y = 0.0397x^2 - 0.3451x + 2.2715$

(e) None of these

1—T—Answer: a

17. Find the least squares regression quadratic for the points $(1, 4)$, $(3, 4)$, $(-1, -3)$, $(7, -1)$.

1—T—Answer: $y = 0.4205x^2 + 2.7x + 0.5568$

18. Find the least squares regression quadratic for the points $(-2, 0)$, $(-1, -6)$, $(1, 2)$ and $(2, 11)$.

(a) $\frac{5}{2}x^2 + 3x + \frac{9}{2}$

(b) $5x^2 + 3x - \frac{9}{2}$

(c) $3x^2 + 3x - 10$

(d) $\frac{5}{2}x^2 + 3x - \frac{9}{2}$

(e) None of these

1—Answer: d

19. Find the least squares regression quadratic for the points $(-2, 0)$, $(-1, 2)$, $(1, 0)$ and $(2, -6)$.

(a) $y = -\frac{2}{3}x^2 = \frac{7}{5}x + 1$

(b) $y = -\frac{4}{3}x^2 - \frac{7}{5}x + \frac{7}{3}$

(c) $y = \frac{4}{3}x^2 + \frac{7}{5}x - \frac{9}{2}$

(d) $y = -\frac{2}{3}x^2 + \frac{7}{5}x - \frac{2}{3}$

(e) None of these

1—Answer: b

20. Find the least squares regression quadratic for the points $(-2, 2)$, $(-1, 0)$, $(1, -2)$ and $(2, 1)$.

(a) $y = \frac{5}{6}x^2 - \frac{2}{5}x - \frac{11}{6}$

(b) $y = -\frac{6}{5}x^2 - \frac{2}{5}x + \frac{13}{2}$

(c) $y = -\frac{5}{6}x^2 + \frac{2}{5}x + \frac{11}{6}$

(d) $y = -\frac{5}{6}x^2 - \frac{2}{5}x + \frac{13}{6}$

(e) None of these

1—Answer: a

21. A retailer wants to know the demand for a certain product as a function of price. The daily sales for four different prices of the product are listed below.

Price, x	1.23	1.29	1.36	1.41
Demand, y	200	189	162	159

(a) Find the least squares regression line.

(b) Estimate the demand, if the price is $1.32.

2—T—Answer: (a) $y = -249.2637x + 507.1513$ (b) 178

22. A retailer wants to know the demand for a certain product as a function of price. The weekly sales for four different prices are listed below. Find the least squares regression line, then estimate the demand for a price of $499.

Price, x	471	450	480	475
Demand, y	93	102	90	92

  (a) 80   (b) 81   (c) 82   (d) 83   (e) None of these

  2—T—Answer: c

23. A company wishes to know the demand (y) for a certain product as a function of the price (x). The number of units sold for three different prices are (1, 35), (3, 26) and (4, 25). Find the least squares regression line for this data, then estimate the demand for a price of $2.00.

  (a) 29   (b) 30   (c) 31   (d) 32   (e) None of these

  2—Answer: c

24. A company wishes to know the demand (y) for a certain product as a function of the price (x). The number of units sold for three different prices are (1, 35), (3, 26) and (4, 25). Find the least squares regression line for this data, then estimate the demand for a price of $6.00.

  (a) 20   (b) 19   (c) 18   (d) 17   (e) None of these

  2—Answer: d

Section 7.8 Double Integrals and Area in the Plane

1. Evaluate the double integral: $\int_2^3 \int_1^x (4x^3 - e^{2y})\, dy\, dx$.

   (a) $\frac{1}{20}(-5e^6 + 5e^4 + 10e^2 + 2076)$ (b) $\frac{1}{20}(15e^6 - 5e^4 - 10e^2 + 2148)$

   (c) $\frac{1}{15}(5e^6 - 5e^4 + 2e^2 + 1002)$ (d) $\frac{1}{15}(3e^6 - 5e^4 + 12e^2 + 2078)$

   (e) None of these

   1—Answer: a

2. Evaluate $\int_0^a \int_0^{a-x} (x^2 + y^2)\, dy\, dx$.

   (a) $\dfrac{a^4}{12}$ (b) $\dfrac{a^4}{6} - 1$ (c) $\dfrac{a^3}{12}$ (d) $\dfrac{a^4}{6}$ (e) None of these

   1—Answer: d

3. Evaluate $\int_0^2 \int_0^{\sqrt{4-y^2}} (y + x)\, dx\, dy$.

   (a) $\dfrac{2\sqrt{2}}{3}$ (b) $\dfrac{16}{3}$ (c) $\dfrac{2}{3}$ (d) $\dfrac{8}{3}$ (e) None of these

   1—Answer: b

4. Evaluate $\int_0^3 \int_0^{\sqrt{9-y^2}} (y + x)\, dx\, dy$.

   1—Answer: 18

5. Evaluate $\int_{-2}^1 \int_0^{6-x^2} (4 + y)\, dy\, dx$.

   1—Answer: $\frac{993}{10}$

6. Evaluate the integral $\int_0^1 \int_{e^y}^e \ln x\, dx\, dy$.

   (a) e (b) $e + 1$ (c) $2 - e$ (d) $\dfrac{1}{e}$ (e) None of these

   1—Answer: e

7. Evaluate the integral $\int_0^y \sqrt{x+1} \, y \, dx$.

   (a) $\frac{2}{3}(y+1)^{3/2}$

   (b) $(y+1)^{3/2} - y$

   (c) $\frac{2y}{3}(y+1)^{3/2} - \frac{2}{3}y$

   (d) $\frac{2}{3}(x+1)^{3/2}y^2$

   (e) None of these

   1—Answer: c

8. Evaluate the integral $\int_0^{\ln 2} \int_{e^y}^2 x \, dx \, dy$.

   (a) $4 \ln 2 - \frac{3}{2}$ (b) $2 \ln 2 - 1$ (c) $2 \ln 2 - \frac{1}{4}e^2$ (d) $2 \ln 2 - \frac{5}{4}$ (e) None of these

   1—Answer: e

9. Evaluate $\int_1^2 \int_1^x \frac{x^2}{y^2} \, dy \, dx$.

   (a) $-\frac{1}{6}$ (b) $\frac{14}{3} - 2 \ln 2$ (c) 5 (d) $\frac{5}{6}$ (e) None of these

   1—Answer: d

10. Evaluate $\int_0^1 \int_{x^3}^{x^2} (x^2 - xy) \, dy \, dx$.

    (a) $-\frac{9}{80}$ (b) $\frac{1}{5}$ (c) $\frac{1}{80}$ (d) $-\frac{7}{40}$ (e) None of these

    1—Answer: c

11. Evaluate $\int_{-1}^2 \int_0^{1-x} (4 - y) \, dy \, dx$.

    1—Answer: $\frac{9}{2}$

12. Evaluate $\int_0^2 \int_{y/2}^1 e^{x^2} \, dx \, dy$ by reversing the order of integration.

    (a) $e - 1$ (b) $e + 1$ (c) e^2 (d) $e^4 - 1$ (e) None of these

    1—Answer: a

13. Evaluate $\int_0^1 \int_{2x}^2 e^{y^2} \, dy \, dx$ by reversing the order of integration.

    (a) 0 (b) $\frac{1}{4}(e^4 - 1)$ (c) $\frac{3e^4 + 1}{8}$ (d) $\frac{1}{4}e^4$ (e) None of these

    1—Answer: b

14. Reverse the order of integration of $\int_0^9 \int_0^{\sqrt{x}} f(x, y)\, dy\, dx$.

(a) $\int_0^3 \int_0^{y^2} f(x, y)\, dx\, dy$

(b) $\int_0^9 \int_0^y f(x, y)\, dx\, dy$

(c) $\int_0^3 \int_{y^2}^9 f(x, y)\, dx\, dy$

(d) $\int_0^3 \int_{y^2}^3 f(x, y)\, dx\, dy$

(e) None of these

1—**Answer:** c

15. Reverse the order of integration of $\int_{-2}^0 \int_0^{\sqrt{4-x^2}} f(x, y)\, dy\, dx$.

(a) $\int_0^2 \int_0^{\sqrt{4-y^2}} f(x, y)\, dx\, dy$

(b) $\int_2^0 \int_0^{\sqrt{4-y^2}} f(x, y)\, dx\, dy$

(c) $\int_2^0 \int_{\sqrt{4-y^2}}^0 f(x, y)\, dx\, dy$

(d) $\int_0^2 \int_{-\sqrt{4-y^2}}^0 f(x, y)\, dx\, dy$

(e) None of these

1—**Answer:** d

16. Sketch the region bounded by the graphs of $y = x^2$, $y = 4$, and $x = 0$, and use an iterated integral to find its area.

1—**Answer:** $\frac{16}{3}$

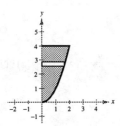

17. Evaluate the improper integral $\int_1^\infty \int_0^1 \frac{1}{x^2}\, dy\, dx$. Sketch the region represented by the integral.

1—**Answer:** 1

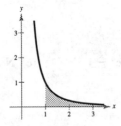

18. Which double integral would be used to find the area of the region bounded by the graphs of $y = \sqrt{16 - 6x^2}$ and $y = x^2$?

    (a) $\displaystyle \int_{-\sqrt{2}}^{\sqrt{2}} \int_{x^2}^{\sqrt{16-6x^2}} dx\, dy$

    (b) $\displaystyle \int_{-\sqrt{2}}^{\sqrt{2}} \int_{\sqrt{16-6x^2}}^{x^2} dy\, dx$

    (c) $\displaystyle \int_{-\sqrt{2}}^{\sqrt{2}} \int_{x^2}^{\sqrt{16-6x^2}} dy\, dx$

    (d) $\displaystyle \int_{-\sqrt{2}}^{\sqrt{2}} \int_{\sqrt{16-6x^2}}^{x^2} dx\, dy$

    (e) None of these

    1—Answer: c

19. Which double integral would be used to find the area of the region bounded by the graphs of $y = (x + 2)^2$ and $y = x + 8$?

    (a) $\displaystyle \int_{-4}^{1} \int_{x+8}^{x^2} dy\, dx$

    (b) $\displaystyle \int_{-4}^{1} \int_{x^2}^{x+8} dy\, dx$

    (c) $\displaystyle \int_{-1}^{4} \int_{x^2}^{x+8} dy\, dx$

    (d) $\displaystyle \int_{-1}^{4} \int_{x+8}^{x^2} dy\, dx$

    (e) None of these

    1—Answer: b

20. Set up a double integral to find the area of the region bounded by the graphs of $y = x^3 + 2$ and $y = x + 2$.

    1—Answer: $\displaystyle \int_{-1}^{0} \int_{x+2}^{x^3+2} dy\, dx + \int_{0}^{1} \int_{x^3+2}^{x+2} dy\, dx$

21. Set up a double integral to find the area of the region bounded by the graphs of $y = x^2$ and $y = 2 - x^2$.

    1—Answer: $\displaystyle \int_{-1}^{1} \int_{x^2}^{2-x^2} dy\, dx$

22. Set up a double integral to find the area of the region bounded by the graphs of $y = 2x^2$ and $y = x^3$.

    (a) $\displaystyle \int_{0}^{2} \int_{x^3}^{2x^2} dy\, dx$

    (b) $\displaystyle \int_{0}^{2} \int_{2x^2}^{x^3} dy\, dx$

    (c) $\displaystyle \int_{0}^{2} \int_{2x^2}^{x^3} dx\, dy$

    (d) $\displaystyle \int_{0}^{2} \int_{x^3}^{2x^2} dx\, dy$

    (e) None of these

    1—Answer: a

23. Set up a double integral to find the area of the region bounded by the graphs of $y = \sqrt{3 - x^2}$ and $y = x^2$.

    (a) $\displaystyle \int_{-\sqrt{2}}^{\sqrt{2}} \int_{x^2}^{\sqrt{3-x^2}} dy\, dx$

    (b) $\displaystyle \int_{-\sqrt{2}}^{\sqrt{2}} \int_{\sqrt{3-x^2}}^{x^2} dx\, dy$

    (c) $\displaystyle \int_{-1}^{1} \int_{\sqrt{3-x^2}}^{x^2} dx\, dy$

    (d) $\displaystyle \int_{-1}^{1} \int_{x^2}^{\sqrt{3-x^2}} dy\, dx$

    (e) None of these

    1—Answer: d

24. Set up a double integral to find the area of the region bounded by the graphs of $y = \sqrt{2 - x}$ and $y = x^2$.

(a) $\displaystyle\int_{-1.35321}^{1}\int_{\sqrt{2-x}}^{x^2} dx\, dy$

(b) $\displaystyle\int_{-1.35321}^{1}\int_{x^2}^{\sqrt{2-x}} dy\, dx$

(c) $\displaystyle\int_{-1.35321}^{1}\int_{x^2}^{\sqrt{2-x}} dx\, dy$

(d) $\displaystyle\int_{-1.35321}^{1}\int_{\sqrt{2-x}}^{x^2} dy\, dx$

(e) None of these

1—T—**Answer:** b

Section 7.9 Applications of Double Integrals

1. Evaluate $\displaystyle\int_0^1\int_{y^2}^1 ye^{x^2}\,dx\,dy$ by reversing the order of integration.

   1—Answer: $\frac{1}{4}(e-1)$

2. Evaluate $\displaystyle\int_0^2\int_{y/2}^1 e^{x^2}\,dx\,dy$ by reversing the order of integration.

   (a) $e-1$ (b) $e+1$ (c) e^2 (d) e^4-1 (e) None of these

   1—Answer: e

3. Evaluate $\displaystyle\int_0^1\int_{2x}^2 e^{y^2}\,dy\,dx$ by reversing the order of integration.

   (a) 0 (b) $\dfrac{e^4-1}{4}$ (c) $\dfrac{3e^4+1}{8}$ (d) $\dfrac{e^4+1}{8}$ (e) None of these

   1—Answer: b

4. Evaluate $\displaystyle\int_0^1\int_0^{\sqrt{1-x}} xy^2\,dy\,dx$ by reversing the order of integration.

   (a) $\frac{3}{32}$ (b) $\frac{4}{105}$ (c) $\frac{2}{15}$ (d) $\frac{7}{30}$ (e) None of these

   1—Answer: b

5. Sketch the region R and evaluate the double integral $\displaystyle\iint_R f(x,y)\,dA = \int_0^1\int_{\sqrt{x}}^1 x^2 y\,dy\,dx$.

   1—Answer: $\frac{1}{24}$

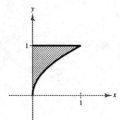

6. Sketch the region R and evaluate the double integral $\displaystyle\iint_R f(x,y)\,dA = \int_0^2\int_{x^2}^4 (x+y)\,dy\,dx$.

   1—Answer: $\frac{84}{5}$

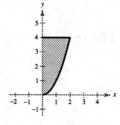

7. Evaluate $\displaystyle\iint_R (x^2 + 4y)\, dA$ where R is the region bounded by $y = 2x$ and $y = x^2$.

   (a) $\frac{77}{30}$ (b) $-\frac{152}{15}$ (c) $\frac{16}{3}$ (d) $\frac{152}{15}$ (e) None of these

   2—Answer: d

8. Evaluate $\displaystyle\iint_R \frac{x}{\sqrt{1 + y^2}}\, dA$ where R is the region in the first quadrant bounded by $y = x^2$, $y = 4$, and $x = 0$.

   (a) $\frac{1}{2}\sqrt{17} - 1$ (b) $4\sqrt{17} - \dfrac{10\sqrt{5}}{3} + 1$ (c) $68\sqrt{17}$

   (d) $34\sqrt{17}$ (e) None of these

   2—Answer: e

9. Integrate $\displaystyle\iint_R xy\, dA$ where R is the region bounded by $y = \sqrt{x}$, $y = \frac{1}{2}x$, $x = 2$, and $x = 4$.

   2—Answer: $\frac{11}{6}$

10. Reverse the order of integration and evaluate the double integral $\displaystyle\int_0^4 \int_{\sqrt{y}}^2 e^{x^3}\, dx\, dy$. Sketch the region R.

   1—Answer: $\displaystyle\int_0^2 \int_0^{x^2} e^{x^3}\, dy\, dx = \frac{1}{3}(e^8 - 1)$

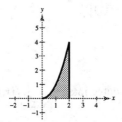

11. Sketch the solid region Q represented by the double integral $\displaystyle\int_{-2}^2 \int_{-\sqrt{4-x^2}}^{\sqrt{4-x^2}} (4 - x^2 - y^2)\, dy\, dx$.

   1—Answer:

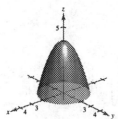

12. Use a double integral to find the volume in the first octant bounded by $f(x, y) = 1 - xy$, $x = y^2$, and $x = y$.

   (a) $\frac{1}{6}$ (b) $\frac{1}{8}$ (c) $\frac{1}{12}$ (d) $\frac{5}{12}$ (e) None of these

   1—Answer: b

13. Use a double integral to find the volume of the solid in the first octant bounded above by the plane $x + y + z = 4$ and below by the rectangle on the xy-plane: $\{(x, y) : 0 \leq x \leq 1, 0 \leq y \leq 2\}$.

(a) 2   (b) 4   (c) 8   (d) 5   (e) None of these

1—Answer: d

14. Use a double integral to find the volume of the solid in the first octant bounded above by the plane $z = 5 - 2y$ and below by the rectangle on the xy-plane: $\{(x, y) : 0 \leq x \leq 3, 0 \leq y \leq 2\}$.

(a) 12   (b) 6   (c) 18   (d) 9   (e) None of these

1—Answer: c

15. Find the volume inside the paraboloid $z = x^2 + y^2$ below the plane $z = 4$.

1—Answer: 8π

16. Use a double integral to find the volume of the given solid.

(a) $\frac{1}{2}$ (b) 1   (c) $\frac{2}{3}$

(d) $\frac{5}{2}$ (e) None of these

1—Answer: e

17. Use a double integral to find the volume of the solid bounded by the graph $z = 4 - 2x - 4y$ and the coordinate planes.

(a) $\frac{2}{3}$ (b) $\frac{4}{3}$ (c) 2   (d) $\frac{8}{3}$ (e) None of these

1—Answer: b

18. Use a double integral to find the volume of the solid in the first octant bounded by the plane $x = y$, the cylinder $z = 4 - y^2$, and the yz-plane.

(a) 2   (b) 3   (c) 4   (d) 6   (e) None of these

1—Answer: c

19. Find the average value of $f(x, y) = y$ over the rectangle with vertices $(0, 0)$, $(2, 0)$, $(2, 3)$, and $(0, 3)$.

(a) $\frac{1}{2}$ (b) $\frac{2}{3}$ (c) $\frac{4}{3}$ (d) $\frac{3}{2}$ (e) None of these

1—Answer: d

20. Find the average value of $f(x, y) = xy$ over the triangle with vertices $(0, 0)$, $(0, 2)$, and $(2, 2)$.

(a) $\frac{1}{2}$ (b) 1   (c) $\frac{3}{2}$ (d) 2   (e) None of these

1—Answer: b

21. A manufacturer determines that the profit for selling x units of one product and y units of a second product is $P = -x^2 + 340x - y^2 + 160y - 32,300$. The weekly sales for product 1 vary between 140 and 170 units and the weekly sales for product 2 vary between 50 and 80 units. Estimate the average weekly profit for the two products.

   2—T—Answer: $\dfrac{1}{900} \displaystyle\int_{140}^{170} \int_{50}^{80} (-x^2 + 340x - y^2 + 160y - 32,300)\, dy\, dx \approx \$2400.00$

22. A manufacturer determines that the profit for selling x units of one product and y units of a second product is $P = -x^2 + 300x - y^2 + 400y - 56,500$. The weekly sales for product 1 vary between 100 and 150 units and the weekly sales for product 2 vary between 160 and 200 units. Estimate the average weekly profit for the two products.

   2—T—Answer: $\dfrac{1}{2000} \displaystyle\int_{100}^{150} \int_{160}^{200} (-x^2 + 300x - y^2 + 400y - 56,500)\, dy\, dx \approx \$4633.33$

CHAPTER 8
Trigonometric Functions

Section 8.1   Radian Measure of Angles

1. Determine which of the following is coterminal to angle $\theta = 4.117$ radians.

   (a) -2.166 (b) 0.975   (c) 7.259   (d) -5.308 (e) None of these

   1—T—Answer: a

2. Determine which of the following is coterminal to $\theta = \dfrac{7\pi}{12}$.

   (a) $\dfrac{5\pi}{12}$ (b) $\dfrac{19\pi}{12}$ (c) $-\dfrac{17\pi}{12}$ (d) $-\dfrac{3\pi}{12}$ (e) None of these

   1—Answer: c

3. Determine which of the following is coterminal to $\theta = \dfrac{5\pi}{6}$.

   (a) $-\dfrac{7\pi}{6}$ (b) $\dfrac{11\pi}{6}$ (c) $-\dfrac{\pi}{6}$ (d) $\dfrac{7\pi}{6}$ (e) None of these

   1—Answer: a

4. Determine which of the following is coterminal to $\theta = \dfrac{2\pi}{15}$.

   (a) $\dfrac{4\pi}{15}$ (b) $\dfrac{17\pi}{15}$ (c) $\dfrac{32\pi}{15}$ (d) $-\dfrac{13\pi}{15}$ (e) None of these

   1—Answer: c

5. Determine which of the following is coterminal to $\theta = \dfrac{\pi}{8}$.

   (a) $\dfrac{3\pi}{8}$ (b) $-\dfrac{15\pi}{8}$ (c) $\dfrac{15\pi}{8}$ (d) $-\dfrac{\pi}{8}$ (e) None of these

   1—Answer: b

6. Convert $27.2°$ to radian measure.

   (a) 85.45   (b) 0.2374   (c) 0.4747   (d) 1558   (e) None of these

   1—T—Answer: c

7. Convert to radian measure: 300°.

(a) $\dfrac{54}{\pi}$ (b) $\dfrac{5\pi}{3}$ (c) $\dfrac{2\pi}{3}$ (d) $\dfrac{5\pi}{6}$ (e) None of these

1—Answer: b

8. Convert to radian measure: 135°.

(a) $\dfrac{\pi}{4}$ (b) $\dfrac{3\pi}{4}$ (c) $\dfrac{3\pi}{8}$ (d) $\dfrac{3\pi}{2}$ (e) None of these

1—Answer: b

9. Convert to radian measure: −210°.

(a) $-\dfrac{5\pi}{6}$ (b) $-\dfrac{3\pi}{4}$ (c) $-\dfrac{3\pi}{2}$ (d) $-\dfrac{7\pi}{6}$ (e) None of these

1—Answer: d

10. Convert to degree measure: $\dfrac{11\pi}{12}$.

(a) 105°   (b) 195°   (c) 165°   (d) 285°   (e) None of these

1—Answer: c

11. Convert to degree measure: $\dfrac{5\pi}{12}$.

(a) 75°   (b) 105°   (c) 165°   (d) 195°   (e) None of these

1—Answer: a

12. Convert to degree measure: $\dfrac{7\pi}{12}$.

(a) 75°   (b) 15°   (c) 105°   (d) 95°   (e) None of these

1—Answer: c

13. Find the area of the equilateral triangle, each of whose sides has a length of two inches.

(a) 2 in.^{2} (b) $\sqrt{3}$ in.^{2} (c) 1 in.^{2} (d) 6 in.^{2} (e) None of these

1—Answer: b

14. Find the area of the equilateral triangle, each of whose sides has a length of three centimeters.

(a) 4.5 cm^2 (b) $\dfrac{9}{4}$ cm^2 (c) $\dfrac{9\sqrt{3}}{4}$ cm^2 (d) 9 cm^2 (e) None of these

1—Answer: c

15. Find the area of an equilateral triangle with sides of length 12 units.

(a) $9\sqrt{3}$　　　　(b) $36\sqrt{3}$　　　　(c) $18\sqrt{2}$　　　　(d) 36　　　　(e) None of these

1—Answer: b

16. Find the area of an equilateral triangle with sides of length 7 units.

(a) $\dfrac{49}{2}$　　　　(b) $\dfrac{49\sqrt{3}}{4}$　　　　(c) $\dfrac{7\sqrt{3}}{2}$　　　　(d) 49　　　　(e) None of these

1—Answer: b

17. Find the area of an equilateral triangle with sides of length 6 units.

(a) $9\sqrt{3}$　　　　(b) $36\sqrt{2}$　　　　(c) $18\sqrt{3}$　　　　(d) 36　　　　(e) None of these

1—Answer: a

18. Find the area of the right triangle with a hypotenuse of 12 units and length of one of the legs 9 units.

(a) 72 units² 　(b) $\dfrac{7\sqrt{63}}{2}$ units²　(c) $\dfrac{135}{2}$ units²　(d) $\dfrac{9\sqrt{3}}{2}$ units²　(e) None of these

1—Answer: b

19. The minute hand on a clock is 3 inches long. Through what distance does the tip of the minute hand move in 16 minutes?

(a) 0.84 in.　　　(b) 5.33 in.　　　(c) 15.08 in.　　　(d) 5.03 in.　　　(e) None of these

2—T—Answer: d

20. Find s if $\theta = 60°$ and $r = 6$.

2—Answer: 2π

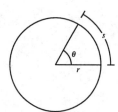

21. Find s if $\theta = 45°$ and $r = 12$.

2—Answer: 3π

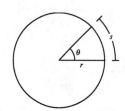

22. Find s if $\theta = 15°$ and $r = 30$.

  (a) π (b) 2π

  (c) 3π (d) 4π

  (e)   None of these

1—Answer: e

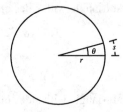

23. Solve the triangle for c.

  (a)   6   (b) $3\sqrt{2}$

  (c) $3\sqrt{3}$ (d) $\sqrt{6}$

  (e)   None of these

1—Answer: b

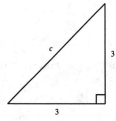

24. Solve the triangle for c.

  (a)   4   (b) $2\sqrt{3}$

  (c) $4\sqrt{2}$ (d) $2\sqrt{2}$

  (e)   None of these

1—Answer: d

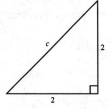

25. Solve the triangle for c.

  (a) $5\sqrt{10}$ (b) $10\sqrt{3}$

  (c) $25\sqrt{3}$ (d)   10

  (e)   None of these

1—Answer: d

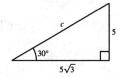

Section 8.2   The Trigonometric Functions

1. A right triangle has an acute angle θ such that $\cot\theta = 15$. Find $\cos\theta$.

(a) $\sqrt{226}$ (b) $\dfrac{\sqrt{226}}{226}$ (c) $\dfrac{15\sqrt{226}}{226}$ (d) $\dfrac{\sqrt{226}}{15}$ (e) None of these

1—Answer: c

2. A right triangle has an acute angle θ such that $\csc\theta = \frac{7}{3}$. Find $\tan\theta$.

(a) $\dfrac{2\sqrt{10}}{7}$ (b) $\dfrac{3\sqrt{10}}{20}$ (c) $\dfrac{2\sqrt{10}}{3}$ (d) $\dfrac{3}{7}$ (e) None of these

1—Answer: b

3. A right triangle has an acute angle θ such that $\sin\theta = \frac{7}{9}$. Find $\tan\theta$.

(a) $\dfrac{7\sqrt{2}}{8}$ (b) $\dfrac{4\sqrt{2}}{7}$ (c) $\dfrac{\sqrt{130}}{7}$ (d) $\dfrac{9\sqrt{130}}{130}$ (e) None of these

1—Answer: a

4. In the triangle shown at the right, use the fact that $\sin\theta = \frac{2}{5}$ to find $\tan\theta$.

1—Answer: $\dfrac{2\sqrt{21}}{21}$

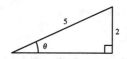

5. Evaluate: $\sec\left(\dfrac{\pi}{3}\right)$.

(a) $\dfrac{\sqrt{2}}{2}$ (b) $\dfrac{\sqrt{3}}{2}$ (c) $\dfrac{\sqrt{3}}{3}$ (d) 2   (e) None of these

1—Answer: d

6. Evaluate: $\cot\left(\dfrac{\pi}{3}\right)$.

1—Answer: $\dfrac{\sqrt{3}}{3}$

7. Evaluate: $\csc 14°$.

(a) 4.0960   (b) 4.1336   (c) 1.0306   (d) 0.9999   (e) None of these

1—T—Answer: b

8. Evaluate: $\cot 15°$.

(a) 3.7321   (b) 0.0012   (c) 86.1859   (d) 1.0353   (e) None of these

1—T—Answer: a

9. Evaluate: $\sec(4°\,15'42'')$.

    (a) 13.4569   (b) 0.9999   (c) 1.0028   (d) 13.8043   (e) None of these

    1—T—Answer: c

10. Evaluate: $\cot 49°$.

    1—T—Answer: 0.8693

11. Find θ such that $0 \le \theta < \dfrac{\pi}{2}$ and $\csc\theta = 1.4736$.

    1—T—Answer: 0.7459

12. Given $\tan\theta = 1.2617$, find θ.

    (a) 0.0220   (b) 0.9006   (c) 1.0145   (d) 0.3193   (e) None of these

    1—T—Answer: b

13. Given $\cos\theta = 0.9872$, find θ.

    (a) 80.8229°   (b) 0.9998°   (c) 9.1771°   (d) 1.0001°   (e) None of these

    1—Answer: c

14. Find $\cos\theta$ given that $\cot\theta = \dfrac{1}{\sqrt{15}}$ and $\sin\theta < 0$.

    1—Answer: $-\dfrac{1}{4}$

15. If $\sin\theta = \frac{1}{3}$ and $\cos\theta < 0$, find $\cot\theta$.

    1—Answer: $-2\sqrt{2}$

16. Find $\tan\theta$ given that $\csc\theta = \frac{3}{2}$ and $\cos\theta < 0$.

    (a) $\dfrac{2}{3}$ (b) $-\dfrac{\sqrt{5}}{3}$ (c) $-\dfrac{\sqrt{5}}{2}$ (d) $2\sqrt{5}$ (e) None of these

    1—Answer: e

17. Find $\sec\theta$ given that $\tan\theta = \dfrac{1}{\sqrt{14}}$ and $\sin\theta < 0$.

    (a) $\dfrac{1}{\sqrt{15}}$ (b) $-\dfrac{\sqrt{14}}{\sqrt{15}}$ (c) $\dfrac{\sqrt{14}}{\sqrt{15}}$ (d) $-\dfrac{1}{\sqrt{15}}$ (e) None of these

    1—Answer: b

18. Find $\tan\theta$ given that $\sec\theta = \frac{3}{2}$ and $\sin\theta < 0$.

(a) $\frac{\sqrt{5}}{2}$ (b) $-\frac{\sqrt{5}}{2}$ (c) $\frac{2}{\sqrt{5}}$ (d) $-\frac{2}{\sqrt{5}}$ (e) None of these

1—Answer: b

19. Find $\cos\theta$ given that $\tan\theta = \frac{1}{\sqrt{17}}$ and $\sin\theta < 0$.

(a) 0.9178   (b) 0.2357   (c) -0.2357 (d) -0.9178 (e) None of these

1—T—Answer: d

20. Find the $\sec\theta$ if the angle θ is in standard position and the terminal side of θ passes through the point $(-3, 4)$.

(a) $\frac{5}{4}$ (b) $-\frac{5}{3}$ (c) $-\frac{4}{3}$ (d) $-\frac{3}{4}$ (e) None of these

1—Answer: b

21. Find the $\csc\theta$ if the angle θ is in standard position and the terminal side of θ passes through the point $(-2, 3)$.

(a) 3   (b) $-\frac{\sqrt{13}}{2}$ (c) $\frac{\sqrt{13}}{3}$ (d) $\frac{1}{3}$ (e) None of these

1—Answer: c

22. Find the $\sec\theta$ if the angle is in the standard position and the terminal side of θ passes through the point $(-5, 6)$.

(a) $-\frac{6}{5}$ (b) $-\frac{5}{\sqrt{61}}$ (c) $-\frac{\sqrt{61}}{5}$ (d) $\frac{\sqrt{61}}{6}$ (e) None of these

1—Answer: c

23. Find the $\csc\theta$ if the angle θ is in the standard position and the terminal side of θ passes through $(-2, 5)$. Do not approximate your answer.

1—Answer: $\frac{\sqrt{29}}{5}$

24. Find the $\cos\theta$ if the angle θ is in the standard position and the terminal side of θ passes through $(-7, 3)$. Do not approximate your answer.

(a) $-\frac{7}{5}$ (b) $-\frac{7}{\sqrt{58}}$ (c) $-\frac{\sqrt{58}}{7}$ (d) $\frac{\sqrt{58}}{3}$ (e) None of these

1—Answer: b

25. A man that is 6 feet tall casts a shadow 14 feet long. Find the angle of elevation of the sun.

(a) 23.2°   (b) 66.8°   (c) 25.4°   (d) 64.6°   (e) None of these

1—Answer: a

26. Complete the following Pythagorean identity: $\tan^2\theta = $ _____.

    (a) $1 - \sec^2\theta$ (b) $1 - \csc^2\theta$ (c) $\csc^2\theta + 1$ (d) $\sec^2\theta - 1$ (e) None of these

    1—Answer: d

27. Solve for r:

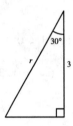

    (a) $\dfrac{6}{\sqrt{3}}$ (b) 6

    (c) $3\sqrt{2}$ (d) 3

    (e) None of these

    1—Answer: a

28. Solve for y:

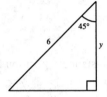

    (a) 3 (b) $6\sqrt{2}$

    (c) $3\sqrt{3}$ (d) $3\sqrt{2}$

    (e) None of these

    1—Answer: d

29. Solve for t:

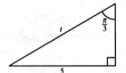

    1—Answer: $\dfrac{10}{\sqrt{3}}$

30. Find all angles in the interval $[0, \pi]$ that satisfy the equation $\sin^2\theta + \left(\dfrac{\sqrt{3}}{2} - 1\right)\sin\theta - \dfrac{\sqrt{3}}{2} = 0$.

    (a) $\theta = \dfrac{\pi}{2}, \dfrac{2\pi}{3}$ (b) $\theta = \dfrac{\pi}{2}$ (c) $\theta = \dfrac{\pi}{2}, \dfrac{5\pi}{6}$ (d) $\theta = \dfrac{2\pi}{3}$ (e) None of these

    1—Answer: b

31. Solve the given equation for θ, $(0 \le \theta < 2\pi)$: $2\sin^2\theta + \sin\theta = 1$.

    (a) $0, \dfrac{\pi}{2}, \pi$ (b) $\dfrac{\pi}{3}, \dfrac{2\pi}{3}, \dfrac{3\pi}{2}$ (c) $\dfrac{\pi}{6}, \dfrac{5\pi}{6}, \dfrac{3\pi}{2}$ (d) $\dfrac{\pi}{6}, \dfrac{3\pi}{2}$ (e) None of these

    2—Answer: c

32. Solve the given equation for θ, $(\theta \le \theta < 2\pi)$: $2\cos^2\theta - \cos\theta = 1$.

    (a) $0, \dfrac{\pi}{2}, \pi$ (b) $0, -\dfrac{4\pi}{3}$ (c) $0, \dfrac{\pi}{3}, \dfrac{5\pi}{3}$ (d) $\dfrac{\pi}{3}, \dfrac{\pi}{2}$ (e) None of these

    2—Answer: e

33. Solve for θ, $(0 \le \theta < 2\pi)$: $2 \cos \theta - 5 \cos \theta = 3$.

    2—Answer: $\dfrac{2\pi}{3}, \dfrac{4\pi}{3}$

34. Find all angles in the interval $[0, \pi]$ that satisfy the equation $1 + \cos 2\theta + \cos \theta = 0$.

    (a) 0.5236, 1.5708   (b) 1.5708, 2.0944   (c) 1.5708, 2.6180

    (d) 0.7854   (e) None of these

    1—T—Answer: b

35. Find all angles in the interval $[0, 2\pi)$ that satisfy the equation $2 \cos^2\theta - 3 \cos\theta + 1 = 0$.

    (a) $\theta = 0, \dfrac{2\pi}{3}, \dfrac{4\pi}{3}$ (b) $\theta = 0, \dfrac{\pi}{3}, \dfrac{5\pi}{3}$ (c) $\theta = 0, \dfrac{\pi}{6}, \dfrac{5\pi}{6}$

    (d) $\theta = 0, \dfrac{2\pi}{3}, \dfrac{5\pi}{3}$ (e) None of these

    1—Answer: b

36. Solve for θ, $(0 \le \theta < 2\pi)$: $2 \cos^2\theta - 5 \cos\theta = 3$.

    1—Answer: $\dfrac{2\pi}{3}, \dfrac{4\pi}{3}$

37. Find all angles in the interval $[0, 2\pi)$ that satisfy the equation $\cos 2\theta = 3 \sin\theta + 2$.

    (a) $\dfrac{3\pi}{2}$ (b) $\dfrac{\pi}{6}, \dfrac{3\pi}{2}$ (c) $\dfrac{3\pi}{2}, \dfrac{4\pi}{3}, \dfrac{5\pi}{3}$ (d) $\dfrac{3\pi}{2}, \dfrac{7\pi}{6}, \dfrac{11\pi}{6}$ (e) None of these

    1—Answer: d

38. Find all angles θ such that $2 \sin^2\theta - 5 \cos\theta - 3 = 0$, in the interval $[0, \pi]$.

    2—T—Answer: 1.79181

Section 8.3   Graphs of Trigonometric Functions

1. Using a graphing utility, find $\lim\limits_{x \to 0} \dfrac{\sin(10x)}{\sin(5x)}$.

   (a) 0   (b) 1   (c) 2

   (d) The limit does not exist   (e) None of these

   1—T—Answer: c

2. Using a graphing utility, find $\lim\limits_{x \to 0} \dfrac{\sin(3x)}{\sin(5x)}$.

   1—T—Answer: $\frac{3}{5}$

3. Using a graphing utility, find $\lim\limits_{x \to 0} \dfrac{1 - \cos(x)}{\sin(x)}$.

   (a) -1 (b) 0   (c) 1

   (d) The limit does not exist   (e) None of these

   1—T—Answer: b

4. Determine the period: $f(x) = 2 \sin \dfrac{x}{3}$.

   (a) $\dfrac{2\pi}{3}$ (b) 6π (c) 2π (d) 2   (e) None of these

   1—Answer: b

5. Determine the period: $f(x) = \tan 4x$.

   (a) 4   (b) π (c) $\dfrac{\pi}{4}$ (d) $\dfrac{\pi}{2}$ (e) None of these

   1—Answer: c

6. Determine the period and amplitude of the function: $f(x) = -7 \cos 3x$.

   1—Answer: Period: $\dfrac{2\pi}{3}$; Amplitude: 7

7. Determine the period and amplitude of the function: $f(x) = 5 \cos \dfrac{x}{2}$.

   1—Answer: Period: 4π; Amplitude: 5

8. Determine the period of the function: $y = 3 \tan 7x$.

   (a) $\dfrac{\pi}{3}$ (b) $\dfrac{\pi}{7}$ (c) $\dfrac{2\pi}{7}$ (d) 6π (e) None of these

   1—Answer: b

9. Sketch one period of the graph of $y = 2 \cos \dfrac{x}{3}$.

   1—Answer:

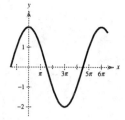

10. Sketch one period of the graph of the function $y = 2 \sin\left(\dfrac{x}{3}\right)$.

   1—Answer:

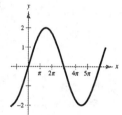

11. Sketch the graph: $y = -2 \sin x$.

   1—Answer:

12. Sketch the graph of $y = \tan(3x)$. $\left[-\dfrac{\pi}{2}, \dfrac{\pi}{2} \right]$

   1—Answer:

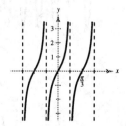

13. Sketch the graph of $y = \cot(3x)$. $[-\pi, \pi]$

1—Answer:

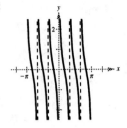

14. Sketch a graph of $y = \tan x$.

2—Answer:

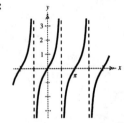

15. Match the graph with the correct function.

(a) $y = \dfrac{1}{2}\cos\left(\dfrac{2x}{3}\right)$ (b) $y = \dfrac{1}{2}\sin\left(\dfrac{2x}{3}\right)$

(c) $y = \dfrac{1}{2}\cos\left(\dfrac{3x}{2}\right)$ (d) $y = \dfrac{1}{2}\sin\left(\dfrac{3x}{2}\right)$

(e) None of these

1—Answer: a

16. Match the graph with the correct function.

(a) $y = 3\sin 4x$ (b) $y = 3\sin\left(\dfrac{x}{4}\right)$

(c) $y = 3\cos 4x$ (d) $y = 3\cos\left(\dfrac{x}{4}\right)$

(e) None of these

1—Answer: a

17. Match the graph with the correct function.

(a) $y = 2\sec 2\pi x$ (b) $y = -2\csc\left(\dfrac{\pi x}{2}\right)$

(c) $y = -2\cot\left(\dfrac{\pi x}{4}\right)$ (d) $y = -\sin\left(\dfrac{x}{2}\right)$

(e) None of these

1—Answer: b

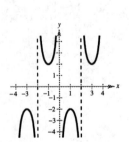

18. Suppose a seasonal business has its monthly revenue R, in thousands of dollars, given by

$$R = 150 + 120 \cos\left(\frac{\pi t}{6}\right) \text{ where } t = 0$$

on January 1. Determine the months when sales exceed $200,000.

(a) January, February, March, April, September, October, November, December

(b) January, February, March, October, November, December

(c) January, February, November, December

(d) January, December

(e) None of these

2—T—Answer: b

19. Suppose a seasonal business has its monthly revenue R, in thousands of dollars, given by

$$R = 150 + 120 \cos\left(\frac{\pi t}{6}\right) \text{ where } t = 0$$

on January 1. Determine the months when sales exceed $250,000.

(a) January, February, March, April, September, October, November, December

(b) January, February, March, October, November, December

(c) January, February, November, December

(d) January, December

(e) None of these

2—T—Answer: c

Section 8.4 Derivatives of Trigonometric Functions

1. Find $f'(x)$: $f(x) = x^2 + 3 \sin x$.

1—Answer: $2x + 3 \cos x$

2. Find $f'(x)$: $f(x) = x^2 + 2 \cos x$.

1—Answer: $2x - 2 \sin x$

3. Differentiate: $y = \dfrac{1 + \cos x}{1 - \cos x}$.

(a) -1 (b) $-2 \csc x$ (c) $2 \csc x$ (d) $\dfrac{-2 \sin x}{(1 - \cos x)^2}$ (e) None of these

1—Answer: d

4. Differentiate: $f(x) = x^2 + 2 \tan x$.

(a) $2x + 2 \tan x$ (b) $2x + \sec^2 x$ (c) $2 + \sec^2 x$

(d) $2x + 2 \sec^2 x$ (e) None of these

1—Answer: d

5. Differentiate: $f(x) = \tan^2(2x - \pi)$.

(a) $4 \tan(2x - \pi) \sec(2x - \pi)$ (b) $2 \tan(2x - \pi) \sec^2(2x - \pi)$

(c) $4 \tan(2x - \pi) \sec^2(2x - \pi)$ (d) $4 \sec^2(2x - \pi)$

(e) None of these

1—T—Answer: c

6. Differentiate: $f(x) = \sec(2x - \pi)$.

(a) $\sec(2x - \pi) \tan(2x - \pi)$ (b) $2 \tan^2(2x - \pi)$ (c) $2 \sec(2x - \pi) \tan(2x - \pi)$

(d) $2 \sec 2x \tan 2x + 1$ (e) None of these

1—Answer: c

7. Find $\dfrac{dy}{dx}$ for $y = \dfrac{\sin(x + 1)}{x + 1}$.

(a) $\dfrac{\cos(x + 1) - \sin(x + 1)}{x + 1}$

(b) $\dfrac{(x + 1) \cos(x + 1) - \sin(x + 1)}{(x + 1)^2}$

(c) $\cos(x + 1)$

(d) $\dfrac{\sin(x + 1) - (x + 1) \cos(x + 1)}{(x + 1)^2}$

(e) None of these

1—Answer: b

8. Find $\dfrac{dy}{dx}$ for the function $y = \dfrac{\sin x}{1 - \cos x}$.

1—Answer: $\dfrac{1}{\cos x - 1}$

9. Differentiate: $f(x) = \cot(\pi - 2x)$.

(a) $2 \csc^2(\pi - 2x)$ (b) $2 \csc^2 2x$ (c) $-\csc^2(\pi - 2x)$

(d) $2 \csc(\pi - 2x) \cot(\pi - 2x)$ (e) None of these

1—Answer: a

10. Find $\dfrac{dy}{dx}$ for the function $y = \dfrac{\cos(x^2 - 1)}{2x + 5}$.

(a) $\dfrac{2[2x + 5) \sin(x^2 - 1) + \cos(x^2 - 1)]}{(2x + 5)^2}$ (b) $\dfrac{-2[(2x^2 + 5x) \sin(x^2 - 1) + \cos(x^2 - 1)]}{(2x + 5)^2}$

(c) $\dfrac{2[(2x^2 + 5x) \cos(x^2 - 1) + \sin(x^2 - 1)]}{(2x + 5)^2}$ (d) $\dfrac{2[(2x^2 + 5x) \sin(x^2 - 1) - \cos(x^2 - 1)]}{(2x + 5)^2}$

(e) None of these

1—Answer: b

11. Differentiate: $y = \sec^2 x + \tan^2 x$.

(a) 0 (b) $\tan x + \sec^4 x$ (c) $\sec^2 x(\sec^2 x + \tan^2 x)$

(d) $4 \sec^2 x \tan x$ (e) None of these

1—Answer: d

12. Differentiate: $f(x) = 2 \tan 3x$.

1—Answer: $6 \sec^2 3x$

13. Find $\dfrac{dy}{dx}$ for $y = \dfrac{1 + \cos x}{1 - \cos x}$.

1—Answer: $\dfrac{-2 \sin x}{(1 - \cos x)^2}$

14. Find $\dfrac{dy}{dx}$ for $y = \dfrac{7 - \sin x}{x}$.

(a) $-\cos x$ (b) $\dfrac{7 + x \cos x - \sin x}{x^2}$ (c) $-\dfrac{7}{x^2}$

(d) $\dfrac{\sin x - x \cos x - 7}{x^2}$ (e) None of these

1—Answer: d

15. Find $\dfrac{dy}{dx}$ for the function $y = \dfrac{x^2 - \sin x}{x}$.

(a) $\dfrac{x^2 + x \cos x - \sin x}{x^2}$

(b) $\dfrac{x^2 - x \cos x + \sin x}{x^2}$

(c) $\dfrac{x^2 + x \cos x - \sin x}{x^2}$

(d) $\dfrac{x^2 - \cos x + \sin x}{x^2}$

(e) None of these

1—Answer: b

16. Find y' if $y = e^{\cot x^2}$.

(a) $e^{-2x \csc^2 x^2}$

(b) $-\csc^2 x^2\, e^{\cot x^2}$

(c) $-2x \csc^2 x^2\, e^{\cot x^2}$

(d) $(\cot x^2) e^{\cot x^2 - 1}$

(e) None of these

1—Answer: c

17. Find the derivative: $s(t) = \csc \dfrac{t}{2}$.

(a) $-\csc \dfrac{t}{2} \cot \dfrac{t}{2}$ (b) $-\dfrac{1}{2} \cot^2 \dfrac{t}{2}$ (c) $\dfrac{1}{2} \csc \dfrac{t}{2} \cot \dfrac{t}{2}$ (d) $\dfrac{1}{2} \cot^2 \dfrac{t}{2}$ (e) None of these

1—Answer: e

18. Find $f'(x)$ if $f(x) = \sin^3 4x$.

(a) $4 \cos^3 4x$

(b) $3 \sin^2 4x \cos 4x$

(c) $\cos^3 4x$

(d) $12 \sin^2 4x \cos 4x$

(e) None of these

1—Answer: d

19. Differentiate: $y = \csc^2 \theta + \cot^2 \theta$.

(a) $\cot \theta + \csc^4 \theta$

(b) 0

(c) $-4 \csc^2 \theta \cot \theta$

(d) $-\csc^2 \theta (\csc^2 \theta + \cot^2 \theta)$

(e) None of these

1—Answer: c

20. Find the derivative: $s(t) = \sec \sqrt{t}$.

(a) $\tan^2 \sqrt{t}$

(b) $\dfrac{\sec \sqrt{t} \tan \sqrt{t}}{2 \sqrt{t}}$

(c) $\sec \dfrac{1}{2\sqrt{t}} \tan \dfrac{1}{2\sqrt{t}}$

(d) $\sec \sqrt{t} \tan \sqrt{t}$

(e) None of these

1—Answer: b

21. Find the derivative: $f(\theta) = \sec \theta^2$.

1—Answer: $2\theta \sec \theta^2 \tan \theta^2$

22. Differentiate: $y = \sin^2 x - \cos^2 x$.

1—Answer: $2 \sin 2x$

23. Find the derivative of $y = \sin x^2$.

1—Answer: $2x \cos x^2$

24. Find the derivative of $y = \sin^2 x$.

1—Answer: $2 \sin x \cos x$

25. Find the derivative of $y = \tan\left(x^2 - \dfrac{\pi}{4}\right)$.

1—Answer: $2x \sec^2\left(x^2 - \dfrac{\pi}{4}\right)$

26. Find the derivative of $y = \sin^2 x + \cos^2 x$.

1—Answer: 0

27. Find $f'(x)$ if $f(x) = \cot^3 \sqrt{x}$.

1—Answer: $\dfrac{-3 \cot^2 \sqrt{x}\left(\csc^2 \sqrt{x}\right)}{2\sqrt{x}}$

28. Find $\dfrac{dy}{dx}$ if $y = \sin(x + y)$.

(a) 0

(b) $\dfrac{\cos(x + y)}{1 - \cos(x + y)}$

(c) $\cos(x + y)$

(d) 1

(e) None of these

1—Answer: b

29. Find $\dfrac{dy}{dx}$ if $x = \tan(x + y)$.

(a) $-\sin^2(x + y)$

(b) $\sec^2(x + y)$

(c) $-\tan^2(x + y)$

(d) $\dfrac{1 - \sec^2 x}{\sec^2 y}$

(e) None of these

1—Answer: a

30. Find $\dfrac{dy}{dx}$ if $x = \cos y$.

1—Answer: $-\csc y$

31. Find all extrema in the interval $[0, 2\pi]$ if $y = x + \sin x$.

(a) $\left(-1, -1 + \dfrac{3\pi}{2}\right)$ (b) (π, π) (c) $(-1, 0)$

(d) $\left(\dfrac{3\pi}{2}, 0\right)$ (e) None of these

1—Answer: b

32. Find all values of x in the interval $[0, 2\pi]$ that give extrema for the function $y = \sin x + \cos x$.

1—Answer: $\dfrac{\pi}{4}, \dfrac{5\pi}{4}$

33. Find the derivative of the given function and simplify the answer: $y = \ln(\sec x)$.

(a) $\sec x \tan x$ (b) $\tan x$ (c) $2 \tan x$ (d) $-\cot x$ (e) None of these

2—Answer: b

34. Find the derivative of the given function and simplify your answer by using trigonometric identities: $y = \ln(\sin x)$.

1—Answer: $\cot x$

35. Find the derivative of the given function and simplify the answer: $y = \ln(\sec^2 x)$.

(a) $2 \sec x \tan x$ (b) $\tan^2 x$ (c) $2 \tan x$ (d) $-2 \cot x$ (e) None of these

2—Answer: c

36. Find the derivative of the given function and simplify your answer by using trigonometric identities: $y = \ln(\cos x)$.

1—Answer: $-\tan x$

37. Find the derivative of the given function and simplify your answer by using trigonometric identities: $y = \ln(\sin^2 x)$.

(a) $2 \tan x$ (b) $2 \cos x \cot x$ (c) $2 \cot x$

(d) $-2 \cot x$ (e) None of these

1—Answer: c

38. Find $f'\left(\dfrac{\pi}{5}\right)$ for the function $f(x) = e^{\sin x}$.

(a) 1.3591 (b) 1.7800 (c) 1.4562 (d) 1 (e) None of these

2—T—Answer: c

39. Find $f'\left(\dfrac{\pi}{3}\right)$ for $f(x) = e^{\sec x}$.

  (a) $\dfrac{\pi}{3}e^2$ (b) πe^2 (c) $2\sqrt{3}e^2$ (d) $2e$ (e) None of these

  1—Answer: c

40. Find $f'\left(\dfrac{\pi}{4}\right)$ for $f(x) = e^{\tan x}$.

  (a) $2e$ (b) $\dfrac{\pi}{4}e^{\tan x}$ (c) $\sqrt{2}e$ (d) 1 (e) None of these

  1—Answer: a

41. Find $f'\left(\dfrac{\pi}{2}\right)$ for $f(x) = \csc\dfrac{t}{2}$.

  1—Answer: $-\dfrac{1}{\sqrt{2}}$

42. Find $f'\left(\dfrac{\pi}{8}\right)$ for the function $f(x) = e^{\cos x}$. Approximate your answer to 4 decimal places.

  1—T—Answer: -0.9640

43. Find all extrema in the interval $[0, 2\pi]$ if $y = \sin x + \cos x$.

  1—Answer: $\left(\dfrac{\pi}{4}, \sqrt{2}\right), \left(\dfrac{5\pi}{4}, -\sqrt{2}\right)$

44. Match the graph with the correct function.

  (a) $y = |x|\cos x$ (b) $y = 2^x \sin x$

  (c) $y = |x|\sin 2x$ (d) $y = x \sin x$

  (e) None of these

  1—T—Answer: c

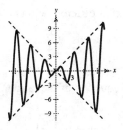

45. Match the graph with the correct function.

  (a) $y = 2x \cos x$ (b) $y = |2x|\sin|x|$

  (c) $y = 2x + \cos x$ (d) $y = 2x + \sin x$

  (e) None of these

  1—T—Answer: b

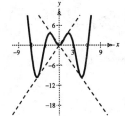

46. Match the graph with the correct function.

    (a) $y = x \sin x$ (b) $y = -x \sin x$

    (c) $y = -x + \sin x$ (d) $y = -x - \sin x$

    (e) None of these

    1—T—Answer: c

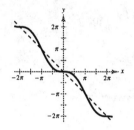

47. Use implicit differentiation to find $\dfrac{dy}{dx}$ for $x = \cos x + \cos y$.

    (a) $-\dfrac{1 + \sin x}{\sin y}$ (b) $\sec x \tan x - 1$ (c) $1 + \sin x$

    (d) $-\csc(x + y) - 1$ (e) None of these

    1—Answer: a

48. Use implicit differentiation to find $\dfrac{dy}{dx}$ for $x = \cos x + \sin y$.

    (a) $-\dfrac{1 + \sin x}{\sin y}$ (b) $\sec x \tan x - 1$ (c) $1 + \sin x$

    (d) $-\csc(x + y) - 1$ (e) None of these

    1—Answer: e

49. Use implicit differentiation to find $\dfrac{dy}{dx}$ for $x = \sin y$.

    1—Answer: $\sec y$

50. Use implicit differentiation to find $\dfrac{dy}{dx}$ for $x = \tan y$.

    1—Answer: $\cos^2 y$

51. Find an equation of the tangent line to the graph of the function $f(x) = \tan x$ at the point $\left(\dfrac{\pi}{4}, 1\right)$.

    (a) $y = 2x + 1 - \left(\dfrac{\pi}{2}\right)$ (b) $y = 2x - \left(\dfrac{\pi}{2}\right)$ (c) $y = 2x + 1$

    (d) $y = \sqrt{2}x + 1 - \left(\dfrac{\sqrt{2}\pi}{4}\right)$ (e) None of these

    1—Answer: a

52. Find an equation for the tangent line to the graph of $y = \csc(2x)$ at the point $\left(\dfrac{\pi}{6}, \dfrac{2\sqrt{3}}{3}\right)$.

(a) $y = -\dfrac{4}{\sqrt{3}}x + \dfrac{2\pi\sqrt{3}}{9} + \dfrac{2\sqrt{3}}{3}$ (b) $y = -\dfrac{4}{3}x + \dfrac{2\pi}{9} + \dfrac{2\sqrt{3}}{3}$ (c) $y = -\dfrac{1}{3}x + \dfrac{2\sqrt{3}}{3} + \dfrac{\pi}{18}$

(d) $y = \dfrac{4}{3}x + \dfrac{2\pi}{9} + \dfrac{2\sqrt{3}}{3}$ (e) None of these

2—Answer: b

53. Find an equation of the tangent line to the graph of $f(x) = \sec x$ at the point $\left(\dfrac{\pi}{3}, 2\right)$.

(a) $y = 2\sqrt{3}x + 2$ (b) $y = 2\sqrt{3}x + 2 - \dfrac{2\sqrt{3}\pi}{3}$ (c) $y = 2\sqrt{3}x - \dfrac{2\sqrt{3}\pi}{3}$

(d) $y = 2x + 2 - \dfrac{2\pi}{3}$ (e) None of these

2—Answer: b

54. Find an equation for the tangent line to the graph of $y = \sin^2 x$ at the point $\left(\dfrac{\pi}{6}, \dfrac{1}{4}\right)$.

(a) $y = \dfrac{\sqrt{3}}{2}x - \dfrac{1}{4} + \dfrac{\sqrt{3}\pi}{12}$ (b) $y = \dfrac{\sqrt{3}}{2}x + \dfrac{1}{4} - \dfrac{\sqrt{3}\pi}{12}$ (c) $y = \dfrac{\sqrt{3}}{4}x + \dfrac{1}{4} - \dfrac{\sqrt{3}\pi}{12}$

(d) $y = \dfrac{\sqrt{3}}{2}x + \dfrac{1}{4} + \dfrac{\sqrt{3}\pi}{12}$ (e) None of these

2—Answer: b

55. Find an equation of the tangent line to the graph of $f(x) = x \sin x$ when $x = 0$.

(a) $y = 0$ (b) $f'(x) = 0$ (c) $y = x \cos x + \sin x$

(d) $y = x$ (e) None of these

2—Answer: a

Section 8.5   Integrals of Trigonometric Functions

1. Evaluate $\int 5 \sec x \tan x \, dx$.

(a) $5 \sec^3 x \tan x + C$ (b) $5 \sec x + C$ (c) $\frac{1}{5} \sec^3 x \tan x + C$

(d) $5[\sec^3 x + \sec x \tan^2 x] + C$ (e) None of these

1—Answer: b

2. Evaluate $\int \frac{\sin^3 \theta}{1 - \cos^2 \theta} \, d\theta$.

(a) $-\cos \theta + C$ (b) $\cos \theta + C$ (c) $\frac{\cos \theta [3 - 3 \cos^2 \theta - 2 \sin^2 \theta]}{1 - \cos^2 \theta}$

(d) $\frac{1}{2} \sin^2 \theta + C$ (e) None of these

1—Answer: a

3. Evaluate $\int 3 \csc^2 x \, dx$.

(a) $\frac{1}{3} \csc^3 x + C$ (b) $6 \csc^2 x \cot x + C$ (c) $-3 \cot x + C$

(d) $-\frac{1}{3} \csc^3 x + C$ (e) None of these

1—Answer: c

4. Evaluate $\int \frac{\sec^3 \theta \tan \theta}{1 + \tan^2 \theta} \, d\theta$.

(a) $\frac{1}{4} \sec^4 \theta + C$ (b) $\frac{1}{2} \sec^2 \theta + C$ (c) $\frac{1}{4} \sec^2 \theta \tan^2 \theta + C$

(d) $\sec \theta + C$ (e) None of these

1—Answer: d

5. Evaluate $\int 3 \csc x \cot x \, dx$.

1—Answer: $-3 \csc x + C$

6. Evaluate $\int \frac{\cos^3 \theta}{2 - 2 \sin^2 \theta} \, d\theta$.

1—Answer: $\frac{1}{2} \sin \theta + C$

7. Evaluate $\int \dfrac{\cos 4x}{\sin 4x}\, dx.$

   1—Answer: $\frac{1}{4}\ln|\sin 4x| + C$

8. Evaluate $\int e^{\cot x}(\csc^2 x)\, dx.$

   1—Answer: $-e^{\cot x} + C$

9. Evaluate $\int \cos 3x\, dx.$

   (a) $\sin 3x + C$ (b) $-\sin 3x + C$ (c) $-\sin \frac{3}{2} x^2 + C$

   (d) $\frac{1}{3}\sin 3x + C$ (e) None of these

   1—Answer: d

10. Evaluate $\int \sin^3 3x \cos 3x\, dx.$

   (a) $\frac{1}{8}\sin^4 3x \cos^2 3x + C$ (b) $\frac{1}{4}\sin^4 3x + C$ (c) $3 \sin^2 3x(3 \cos^2 3x - \sin^2 3x) + C$

   (d) $\frac{1}{12}\sin^4 3x + C$ (e) None of these

   1—Answer: d

11. Evaluate $\int \sin \dfrac{x}{2}\, dx.$

   (a) $\cos \dfrac{x}{2} + C$ (b) $-2 \cos \dfrac{x}{2} + C$ (c) $\sin \dfrac{x^2}{4} + C$ (d) $2 \sin^2 \dfrac{x}{2} + C$ (e) None of these

   1—Answer: b

12. Evaluate $\int \dfrac{\sec^2 x}{\sqrt{\tan x}}\, dx.$

   1—Answer: $2\sqrt{\tan x} + C$

13. Evaluate $\int \sec 3x\, dx.$

   (a) $3 \sec 3x \tan 3x + C$ (b) $\frac{1}{3}\ln|\sec 3x + \tan 3x| + C$ (c) $\frac{1}{3}\csc 3x + C$

   (d) $\frac{1}{3}\tan^2 3x + C$ (e) None of these

   1—Answer: b

14. Evaluate $\int \tan^2 x \sec^2 x \, dx$.

(a) $\dfrac{\tan^3 x \sec^3 x}{9} + C$

(b) $\dfrac{(\tan x \sec x)^3}{3} + C$

(c) $\dfrac{\tan^3 x}{3} + C$

(d) $2 \sec^2 x \tan x (\tan^2 x + \sec^2 x) + C$

(e) None of these

1—Answer: c

15. Evaluate $\int \dfrac{\cos 2x}{1 - \sin 2x} \, dx$.

(a) $\dfrac{1}{2}[\sin 2x - \ln|\sin 2x|] + C$

(b) $-\dfrac{1}{2}\ln|1 - \sin 2x| + C$

(c) $\dfrac{\sin 2x}{2x + \cos 2x} + C$

(d) $\dfrac{1}{2}\sin 2x + C$

(e) None of these

1—Answer: b

16. Evaluate $\int \tan 3x \, dx$.

(a) $\frac{1}{3}\ln|\sec 3x| + C$

(b) $3 \sec^2 3x + C$

(c) $\frac{1}{3}\sec^2 3x$

(d) $\ln|\cos 3x| + C$

(e) None of these

1—Answer: a

17. Evaluate $\int \dfrac{\sin^2 x - \cos^2 x}{\sin x} \, dx$.

(a) $-2\cos x + \ln|\csc x + \cot x| + C$

(b) $-\ln|\csc x + \cot x| + C$

(c) $-\sec x + C$

(d) $\cos x + \ln|\csc x + \cot x| + C$

(e) None of these

1—Answer: a

18. Evaluate $\int x \cot x^2 \, dx$.

(a) $\dfrac{x^2}{2}\sec^2 x^2 + C$

(b) $\dfrac{x^2}{4}\ln|\sin x^2| + C$

(c) $x \cot x^2 \csc x^2 + C$

(d) $\dfrac{1}{2}\ln|\sin x^2| + C$

(e) None of these

1—Answer: d

19. Evaluate $\int \dfrac{\cos^3 x - \sin^2 x}{\cos^2 x}\, dx.$

(a) $\dfrac{\cos^2 x}{2} - \tan x + x + C$

(b) $\sin x - \sec x + C$

(c) $\sin x - \tan x + x + C$

(d) $\sin x - \dfrac{\tan^3 x}{3} + C$

(e) None of these

1—Answer: c

20. Evaluate $\int \sec 2x \tan 2x\, dx.$

1—Answer: $\frac{1}{2} \ln|\tan x| + C$

21. Evaluate $\int \cot^2 x \csc^2 x\, dx.$

(a) $\sin^3 x \cos x + C$

(b) $-\dfrac{\cot^3 x}{3} + C$

(c) $-\dfrac{\sin^3 x}{3} + C$

(d) $\dfrac{\sin^3 x \cos^2 x}{6} + C$

(e) None of these

1—Answer: b

22. Evaluate $\int \sin^2 x \cos x\, dx.$

(a) $\sin^3 x \cos x + C$

(b) $\dfrac{\sin^3 x}{3} + C$

(c) $-\dfrac{\sin^3 x}{3} + C$

(d) $\dfrac{\sin^3 x \cos^2 x}{6} + C$

(e) None of these

1—Answer: b

23. Evaluate $\int \csc \dfrac{x}{2}\, dx.$

(a) $-\dfrac{1}{2} \csc \dfrac{x}{2} \cos \dfrac{x}{2} + C$

(b) $\sin(\ln x^2) + C$

(c) $2 \sec \dfrac{x}{2} + C$

(d) $2 \ln\left|\csc \dfrac{x}{2} - \cot \dfrac{x}{2}\right| + C$

(e) None of these

1—Answer: d

24. Evaluate $\int \sin^3 x \cos x \, dx$.

(a) $\frac{1}{8} \sin^4 x \cos^2 x + C$ (b) $\frac{1}{4} \sin^4 x + C$ (c) $3 \sin^2 x \cos^2 x - \sin^4 x + C$

(d) $\frac{1}{4}(\sin x \cos x)^4 + C$ (e) None of these

1—Answer: b

25. Evaluate $\int \frac{\sec^2 x}{\tan x} \, dx$.

(a) $\ln|\tan x| + C$ (b) $\tan x + \ln|\tan x| + C$ (c) $\frac{\tan x}{\ln|\cos x|} + C$

(d) $x \tan x + C$ (e) None of these

1—Answer: a

26. Evaluate $\int \sqrt{\tan x} \sec^2 x \, dx$.

1—Answer: $\frac{2}{3}(\tan x)^{3/2} + C$

27. Evaluate $\int_{\pi/4}^{\pi/3} \sec^2 x \, dx$.

1—Answer: $\sqrt{3} - 1$

28. Evaluate $\int_0^{\pi} (x + \sin x) \, dx$.

(a) $\frac{\pi^2}{2}$ (b) $\frac{\pi^2}{2} - 2$ (c) $\frac{\pi^2}{2} + 1$ (d) $\frac{\pi^2}{2} + 2$ (e) None of these

1—Answer: d

29. Evaluate $\int_0^{\pi/8} \sec 2x \tan 2x \, dx$.

(a) 1.4142 (b) 1 (c) 0.2071 (d) 0 (e) None of these

1—T—Answer: c

30. Evaluate $\int_0^{\pi/6} \sec^2 (2x) \, dx$.

(a) $\frac{\pi^2}{2}$ (b) $\frac{\pi^2}{2} - 2$ (c) $\frac{\pi^2}{2} + 1$ (d) $\frac{\sqrt{3}}{2}$ (e) None of these

1—Answer: d

31. Evaluate $\displaystyle\int_{\pi/6}^{\pi/2} 3 \csc x \cot x \, dx.$

1—Answer: 3

32. Evaluate $\displaystyle\int_{\pi/2}^{\pi} (x + \cos x) \, dx.$

(a) $1 - \left(\dfrac{\pi}{2}\right)$ (b) 0   (c) π (d) $\dfrac{\pi}{2}$ (e) None of these

1—Answer: e

33. Determine the area of the region bounded by $y = -\cos\left(\dfrac{x}{2}\right)$ and $y = 0$ for $0 \le x \le \pi.$

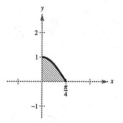

(a) $-\dfrac{1}{2}$ (b) $\dfrac{1}{2}$

(c) $2\sqrt{2}$ (d) 2

(e) None of these

1—Answer: d

34. Determine the area of the region bounded by $y = \cos 2x$ and $y = 0$ for $0 \le x \le \dfrac{\pi}{4}.$

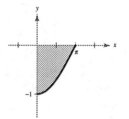

(a) -2 (b) $\dfrac{1}{2}$

(c) $2\sqrt{2}$ (d) 2

(e) None of these

1—Answer: b

35. Determine the area of the region bounded by the graphs of $y = \sin x$ and $y = 0$ in the interval $[0, \pi].$

1—Answer: 2

36. Find the area of the region bounded by the graphs of $f(x) = \sin x$ and $g(x) = \cos x$, for $\dfrac{\pi}{4} \le x \le \dfrac{5\pi}{4}.$

1—Answer: $2\sqrt{2}$

37. Find the volume of the solid formed by revolving the region bounded by $y = \sin x$ and $y = 0$ in the interval $[0, \pi]$ about the y-axis.

(a) π^3 (b) $\dfrac{1}{2}\pi^2$ (c) $2\pi^2$ (d) π (e) None of these

1—Answer: c

38. Find the average value of $f(x) = \sin x$ on the interval $\left[\dfrac{\pi}{4}, \dfrac{\pi}{2}\right]$. Approximate your answer to 4 decimal places.

1—Answer: 0.9003

39. Find the average value of the function $f(x) = \sin x$ on the interval $[0, \pi]$.

(a) 0.6366   (b) 0   (c) 0.3813   (d) 0.7283   (e) None of these

2—T—Answer: a

Section 8.6   L'Hôpital's Rule

1. Find the limit: $\lim\limits_{x \to 0} \dfrac{3 \sin(2x)}{\sin(4x)}$.

(a) $\frac{1}{2}$ (b) $\frac{3}{2}$ (c) 3   (d) 0   (e) None of these

1—Answer: b

2. Find the limit: $\lim\limits_{x \to \infty} \dfrac{3x^2 - 2x}{x^2 - 1}$.

(a) 3   (b) ∞ (c) 1   (d) 0   (e) None of these

1—Answer: a

3. Find the limit: $\lim\limits_{x \to 0} \dfrac{1 - \cos(2x)}{\sin(2x)}$.

(a) 1   (b) $\frac{1}{2}$ (c) ∞ (d) 0   (e) None of these

1—Answer: d

4. Find the limit: $\lim\limits_{x \to \infty} \dfrac{e^x}{x^2}$.

(a) 2   (b) ∞ (c) 1   (d) 0   (e) None of these

1—Answer: b

5. Find the limit: $\lim\limits_{x \to 5} \dfrac{\ln(x - 4)}{3x - 15}$.

(a) $-\frac{4}{15}$ (b) $\frac{1}{3}$ (c) ∞ (d) 0   (e) None of these

1—Answer: b

6. Find the limit: $\lim\limits_{x \to \infty} \dfrac{\ln(x + 1)}{e^{-x} - 1}$.

(a) 3   (b) ∞ (c) -1 (d) 0   (e) None of these

1—Answer: c

7. Find the limit: $\lim\limits_{x \to \infty} \dfrac{x^3 - 4x^2}{x + 1}$.

(a) 1   (b) -4 (c) ∞ (d) 0   (e) None of these

1—Answer: c

8. Find the limit: $\lim\limits_{x \to \infty} \dfrac{x}{\sqrt{4x^2 - 1}}$.

(a) $\frac{1}{2}$ (b) ∞ (c) 1   (d) 0   (e) None of these

1—Answer: a

9. Find the limit: $\lim\limits_{x \to \pi} \dfrac{\tan(x)}{\sin(x)}$.

(a) 1   (b) -1 (c) ∞ (d) 0   (e) None of these

1—Answer: b

10. Find the limit: $\lim\limits_{x \to 0} \dfrac{e^{-x} - e^x}{\sin(x)}$.

1—Answer: -2

11. Find the limit: $\lim\limits_{x \to \infty} \dfrac{2x}{\sqrt{4x^2 + 1}}$.

1—Answer: 1

12. Find the limit: $\lim\limits_{x \to \infty} \dfrac{4 - 2x}{7 + 6x^2}$.

(a) $\frac{4}{7}$ (b) $-\frac{1}{3}$ (c) ∞ (d) 0   (e) None of these

1—Answer: d

13. Find the limit: $\lim\limits_{x \to \infty} \dfrac{\ln(x - 4)}{x^2}$.

1—Answer: 0

14. Find the limit: $\lim\limits_{x \to \infty} \dfrac{x^2}{\ln(x + 2)}$.

1—Answer: ∞

15. Find the limit: $\lim\limits_{x \to 3} \dfrac{x - 3}{x^2 - 9}$.

1—Answer: $\frac{1}{6}$

16. Find the limit: $\lim\limits_{x \to \infty} \dfrac{2x^2 + x - 6}{x^2 + 4x + 12}$.

(a) $\frac{1}{2}$ (b) ∞ (c) 2   (d) 0   (e) None of these

1—Answer: c

17. Evaluate: $\lim\limits_{x \to \infty} \dfrac{e^{2x}}{3x}$.

(a) $\frac{2}{3}$ (b) $\frac{1}{3}$ (c) 0   (d) ∞ (e) None of these

1—Answer: d

CHAPTER 9

Probability and Calculus

Section 9.1 Discrete Probability

1. A coin is tossed four times. What is the event that at least three heads will occur?

   (a) {HHHT, HHTH, HTHH, THHH, HHHH}   (b) {HHHT, HHTH, HTHH, THHH}

   (c) {HHHT, HHHH}   (d) {HHHH}

   (e) None of these

   1—Answer: a

2. A coin is tossed four time. What is the event that no more than one head occurs?

   (a) {HTTT, TTTT}   (b) {HTTT, TTTH, THTT, TTHT}

   (c) {TTTT}   (d) {HTTT, THTT, TTHT, TTTH, TTTT}

   (e) None of these

   1—Answer: d

3. A die is tossed twice. What is the event that the sum of the tosses will be at least 10?

   (a) {(5, 5), (6, 6), (4, 6), (5, 6)}   (b) {(4, 6), (5, 6), (6, 6), (5, 5), (6, 4), (6, 5)}

   (c) (4, 6), (6, 4), (5, 5)}   (d) {(6, 4), (5, 5), (5, 6)}

   (e) None of these

   1—Answer: b

4. Two dice are cast. List the elements of the event A that the sum is 7.

   (a) {(1, 6), (2, 5), (3, 4)}

   (b) {(3, 4), (2, 5), (1, 6), (0, 7)}

   (c) {(1, 6), (2, 5), (3, 4), (4, 3), (5, 2), (6, 1)}

   (d) {(7, 0), (6, 1), (5, 2), (4, 3), (3, 4), (2, 5), (1, 6), (0, 7)}

   (e) None of these

   1—Answer: c

5. Three coins are tossed. Choose the event B that exactly two tails appear.

   (a) {(THT, TTT, TTH, HTT}   (b) {THT, TTH, HTT}

   (c) {THT, TTH, HTT, HTH, HHT, THH}   (d) {TTT}

   (e) None of these

   1—Answer: b

6. Two dice are cast. List the elements of the event A that the sum is 8.

(a) $\{(4, 4), (2, 6), (3, 5)\}$

(b) $\{(4, 4), (3, 5), (2, 6), (0, 8)\}$

(c) $\{(2, 6), (3, 5), (4, 4), (4, 4), (5, 3), (6, 2)\}$

(d) $\{(8, 0), (7, 1), (6, 2), (5, 3), (4, 4), (3, 5), (2, 6), (1, 7)\}$

(e) None of these

1—Answer: c

7. Three coins are tossed. List the event B that exactly two heads appear.

1—Answer: {HHT, HTH, THH}

8. Two dice are cast. List the elements of the event A that their sum is 4.

1—Answer: $\{(1, 3), (3, 1), (2, 2)\}$

9. A card is chosen at random from a standard 52-card deck of playing cards. What is the probability that the card will be a king?

(a) $\frac{1}{26}$ (b) $\frac{1}{13}$ (c) $\frac{1}{52}$ (d) $\frac{1}{4}$ (e) None of these

1—Answer: b

10. A card is chosen at random from a standard 52-card deck of playing cards. If aces are low, what is the probability that the face value of the card will be less than 5?

(a) $\frac{5}{52}$ (b) $\frac{4}{52}$ (c) $\frac{5}{13}$ (d) $\frac{1}{2}$ (e) None of these

1—Answer: e

11. A card is chosen at random from a standard 52-card deck of playing cards. What is the probability that the card will be red and an ace?

(a) $\frac{15}{26}$ (b) $\frac{1}{26}$ (c) $\frac{1}{13}$ (d) $\frac{1}{4}$ (e) None of these

1—Answer: b

12. A card is chosen at random from a standard 52-card deck of playing cards. If aces are low, what is the probability that the face value of the card will be less than 10?

(a) $\frac{5}{26}$ (b) $\frac{9}{13}$ (c) $\frac{10}{13}$ (d) $\frac{5}{13}$ (e) None of these

1—Answer: b

13. A card is chosen at random from a standard 52-card deck of playing cards. What is the probability that the card is red and a king?

1—Answer: $\frac{1}{26}$

14. A bag contains three red balls, two blue balls, and four green balls. If a ball is chosen at random, what is the probability that it will be blue?

    (a) $\frac{7}{9}$ (b) $\frac{2}{9}$ (c) $\frac{1}{2}$ (d) $\frac{1}{4}$ (e) None of these

    1—Answer: b

15. A bag containing three red balls, two blue balls, five green balls and a yellow ball, all the same size. If a ball is chosen at random, what is the probability that it will be green?

    (a) $\frac{5}{6}$ (b) $\frac{1}{5}$ (c) $\frac{1}{2}$ (d) 5   (e) None of these

    1—Answer: e

16. A card is chosen at random from a standard 52-card deck of playing cards. If aces are low, what is the probability that the card will be a 2 or a 3?

    (a) $\frac{1}{26}$ (b) $\frac{4}{13}$ (c) $\frac{1}{52}$ (d) $\frac{2}{13}$ (e) None of these

    1—Answer: d

17. An integer is chosen at random between the numbers 1 and 40 inclusive. What is the probability that the integer is divisible by 7?

    (a) $\frac{7}{39}$ (b) $\frac{7}{40}$ (c) $\frac{1}{8}$ (d) $\frac{1}{7}$ (e) None of these

    1—Answer: c

18. An integer is chosen at random between 10 and 29, inclusive. What is the probability that one of the digits of the integer will be a 1?

    1—Answer: $\frac{11}{20}$

19. An integer is chosen at random between the numbers 10 and 29, inclusive. What is the probability that one of the digits of the integer will be a 5?

    (a) $\frac{1}{20}$ (b) $\frac{2}{19}$ (c) $\frac{2}{29}$ (d) $\frac{1}{10}$ (e) None of these

    1—Answer: d

20. Find the variance, $V(x)$, for the given probability distribution.

x	0	1	2	3
$P(x)$	$\frac{1}{6}$	$\frac{1}{3}$	$\frac{1}{3}$	$\frac{1}{6}$

    (a) $\frac{3}{2}$ (b) $\frac{11}{12}$ (c) 0   (d) $\frac{5}{3}$ (e) None of these

    1—Answer: b

21. Find the variance, $V(x)$, for the given probability distribution.

x	-2	2	4	7
$P(x)$	$\frac{1}{5}$	$\frac{1}{5}$	$\frac{2}{5}$	$\frac{1}{5}$

   (a) 3   (b) $\frac{12}{5}$ (c) $\frac{44}{5}$ (d) 0   (e) None of these

   1—Answer: c

For problems 22 through 24, use the probability distribution for the discrete random variable x, given below.

x	0	1	2	3	4	5
$P(x)$	0.12	0.24	0.24	0.36	0.03	0.01

22. Find the expected value of x.

   (a) 1.87   (b) 2.02   (c) 1.97   (d) 1.79   (e) None of these

   1—T—Answer: c

23. Find the variance of x.

   (a) 1   (b) 1.4789   (c) 0.6789   (d) 1.2891   (e) None of these

   1—T—Answer: d

24. Find the standard derivation.

   (a) 1.1354   (b) 1.2161   (c) 0.8239   (d) 1   (e) None of these

   1—T—Answer: a

For problems 25 through 27, use the probability distribution for the discrete random variable x, given below.

x	0	1	2	3	4
$P(x)$	$\frac{1}{10}$	$\frac{4}{10}$	$\frac{3}{10}$	$\frac{1}{10}$	$\frac{1}{10}$

25. Find the expected value of x.

   (a) $\frac{3}{2}$ (b) $\frac{10}{17}$ (c) $\frac{17}{10}$ (d) $\frac{25}{16}$ (e) None of these

   1—T—Answer: c

26. Find the variance of x.

   (a) 1   (b) $\frac{3}{2}$ (c) $\frac{25}{16}$ (d) $\frac{5}{4}$ (e) None of these

   1—T—Answer: e

27. Find the standard derivation.

   (a) $\frac{11}{10}$ (b) $\frac{5}{4}$ (c) $\frac{\sqrt{6}}{2}$ (d) 1   (e) None of these

   1—T—Answer: a

For problems 28 through 30, use the probability distribution for the discrete random variable x, given below.

x	0	1	2	3	4	5
$P(x)$	0.12	0.20	0.28	0.34	0.05	0.01

28. Find the expected value of x.

    1—T—Answer: 2.03

29. Find the variance of x.

    1—T—Answer: 1.3091

30. Find the standard deviation.

    1—T—Answer: 1.144

For problems 31 through 33, use the probability distribution for the discrete random variable x, given below.

x	1	2	3	4
$P(x)$	$\frac{2}{10}$	$\frac{4}{10}$	$\frac{3}{10}$	$\frac{1}{10}$

31. Find the expected value of x.

    (a) 2   (b) 2.3   (c) $\frac{4}{10}$ (d) 3   (e) None of these

    1—Answer: b

32. Find the variance of x.

    (a) 0   (b) 5.16   (c) 8.1   (d) 0.81   (e) None of these

    1—T—Answer: d

33. Find the standard deviation of x.

    (a) 2.27   (b) 0   (c) 0.9   (d) 2.8   (e) None of these

    1—T—Answer: c

For problems 34 through 36, use the probability distribution for the discrete random variable x, given below.

x	0	1	2	3	4	5
$P(x)$	$\frac{1}{32}$	$\frac{5}{32}$	$\frac{10}{32}$	$\frac{10}{32}$	$\frac{5}{32}$	$\frac{1}{32}$

34. Find the expected value of x.

    (a) $\frac{3}{2}$ (b) $\frac{10}{32}$ (c) $\frac{5}{2}$ (d) $\frac{25}{16}$ (e) None of these

    1—T—Answer: c

35. Find the variance of x.

(a) 1 (b) $\frac{3}{2}$ (c) $\frac{25}{16}$ (d) $\frac{5}{4}$ (e) None of these

1—Answer: a

36. Find the standard derivation.

(a) $\frac{\sqrt{5}}{2}$ (b) $\frac{5}{4}$ (c) $\frac{\sqrt{6}}{2}$ (d) 1 (e) None of these

1—Answer: a

For problems 37 through 40, use the probability distribution for the discrete random variable x, given below.

x	1	2	3	4	5
$P(x)$	0.031	0.310	0.437	0.111	0.111

37. Find $P(x < 4)$.

1—T—Answer: 0.778

38. Find the expected value, $E(x)$.

1—T—Answer: 2.961

39. Find the variance, $V(x)$.

1—T—Answer: 0.987

40. Find the standard deviation, σ.

1—T—Answer: 0.994

For problems 41 through 43, use the probability distribution for the discrete random variable x, given below.

x	1	2	3	4	5
$P(x)$	$\frac{1}{10}$	$\frac{2}{10}$	$\frac{2}{10}$	$\frac{4}{10}$	$\frac{1}{10}$

41. Find the expected value of x.

(a) 4 (b) 3.2 (c) $\frac{4}{10}$ (d) 3 (e) None of these

1—Answer: b

42. Find the variance of x.

(a) $\frac{34}{25}$ (b) $\frac{1}{5}$ (c) $\frac{51}{5}$ (d) 10 (e) None of these

1—Answer: a

43. Find the standard deviation of x.

(a) $\dfrac{7}{25}$ (b) $\dfrac{17}{5}$ (c) $\sqrt{\dfrac{51}{5}}$ (d) $\dfrac{\sqrt{34}}{5}$ (e) None of these

1—Answer: d

For problems 44 through 46, use the probability distribution for the discrete random variable x, given below.

x	0	1	2	3	4
$P(x)$	$\frac{2}{10}$	$\frac{3}{10}$	$\frac{3}{10}$	$\frac{1}{10}$	$\frac{1}{10}$

44. Find the expected value of x.

    1—T—Answer: 1.6

45. Find the variance of x.

    1—T—Answer: 1.44

46. Find the standard deviation.

    1—T—Answer: 1.2

47. Find the variance, $V(x)$, for the given probability distribution.

x	-1	2	3	5
$P(x)$	$\frac{1}{6}$	$\frac{1}{3}$	$\frac{1}{3}$	$\frac{1}{6}$

(a) $\dfrac{29}{9}$ (b) $\dfrac{216}{56}$ (c) $\dfrac{7}{3}$ (d) 0   (e) None of these

1—Answer: a

48. A clearing house is giving away $20,000 to the person with the correct 6-digit number. If it costs $5.00 to enter the contest, what is the expected win?

x	-5	19995
$P(x)$	0.99999	0.00001

(a) Win $20,000   (b) Lose $5.00   (c) Lose $4.80   (d) Win $4.80   (e) None of these

1—Answer: c

49. One thousand dollars is to be given away in a raffle. The tickets are $5.00 per person and 4000 tickets are to be sold. What is the expected win?

x	-5	995
$P(x)$	$\frac{3999}{4000}$	$\frac{1}{4000}$

(a) Lose $4.75   (b) Win $4.75   (c) Lose $4.20   (d) Lose $5.00   (e) None of these

1—Answer: a

50. A $20.00 turkey is to be given away in a raffle. The tickets are $1.00 each and 50 tickets are to be sold. What is the expected win?

x	-1	19
$P(x)$	$\frac{49}{50}$	$\frac{1}{50}$

(a) Lose $1.00   (b) Lose $.50   (c) Lose $.60   (d) Lose $.80   (e) None of these

1—Answer: c

51. The 100 juniors at Tech High School take only one science course. If 53 juniors take chemistry, 37 juniors take biology, and 10 juniors take physics, find the probability that a junior chosen at random is taking biology.

1—Answer: $\frac{37}{100}$

52. Find $P(x \le 2)$ for the given probability distribution.

x	0	1	2	3
$P(x)$	0.051	0.459	0.367	0.123

(a) 0.367   (b) 0.510   (c) 0.123   (d) 0.877   (e) None of these

1—Answer: d

53. Find $P(x > 1)$ for the given probability distribution.

x	0	1	2	3
$P(x)$	0.051	0.459	0.367	0.123

(a) 0.949   (b) 0.367   (c) 0.490   (d) 0.0451   (e) None of these

1—Answer: c

54. Find $P(x \le 2)$ for the given probability distribution.

x	0	1	2	3
$P(x)$	0.023	0.312	0.367	0.298

1—Answer: 0.702

55. Find $P(x < 2)$ for the given probability distribution.

x	0	1	2	3
$P(x)$	0.151	0.359	0.167	0.323

(a) 0.677   (b) 0.359   (c) 0.510   (d) 0.323   (e) None of these

1—Answer: c

56. Find $P(x < 2)$ for the given probability distribution.

x	0	1	2	3
$P(x)$	0.151	0.359	0.267	0.223

1—**Answer:** 0.777

Section 9.2 Continuous Random Variables

1. Is the function $f(x) = \dfrac{3\sqrt{x}}{52}$ a continuous density function over the interval $[0, 9]$?

1—Answer: $\displaystyle\int_0^9 \dfrac{3\sqrt{x}}{52} = \dfrac{27}{26} \neq 1$

2. Is the function $f(x) = -\frac{3}{14}x(1 - x)$ a continuous density function over the interval $[1, 3]$?

1—Answer: Yes

3. Is the function $f(x) = 2x^{-2}$ a continuous density function over the interval $[1, 2]$?

1—Answer: Yes

4. Find $P(0 \le x \le 1)$, given the probability density function $f(x) = \dfrac{1}{(x + 1)^2}, x \ge 0$.

   (a) 1   (b) 0   (c) $\frac{7}{8}$ (d) $\frac{1}{2}$ (e) None of these

1—Answer: d

5. Show that the function $f(x) = \frac{3}{64}x^2$ is a probability density function over the interval $[0, 4]$.

1—Answer: $\displaystyle\int_0^4 \dfrac{3}{64}x^2\, dx = \dfrac{1}{64}x^3 \bigg]_0^4 = 1$

6. Find the constant k so that the function $f(x) = kx$ is a continuous density function over the interval $[1, 4]$.

   (a) $\frac{15}{2}$ (b) $\frac{2}{15}$ (c) $-\frac{1}{3}$ (d) 8   (e) None of these

1—Answer: b

7. Find the constant k so that the function $f(x) = kx^2$ is a continuous density function over the interval $[1, 4]$.

   (a) $\frac{1}{21}$ (b) 21   (c) $\frac{1}{3}$ (d) $-\frac{1}{3}$ (e) None of these

1—Answer: a

8. Find the constant k so that the function $f(x) = k(1 - x^2)$ is a continuous density function over the interval $[-1, 1]$.

   (a) $\frac{8}{3}$ (b) $-\frac{4}{3}$ (c) $\frac{1}{2}$ (d) $\frac{3}{4}$ (e) None of these

1—Answer: d

9. Find the constant k so that the function $f(x) = kx(6 - x)$ is a probability density function over the interval $[0, 6]$.

   (a) $\frac{1}{6}$ (b) $\frac{1}{36}$ (c) $\frac{1}{108}$ (d) $\frac{1}{12}$ (e) None of these

1—Answer: b

10. Find the constant k so that the function $f(x) = \dfrac{k}{x^2}$ is a probability density function over the interval $[1, 5]$.

    1—Answer: $\frac{5}{4}$

11. Find the constant k so that the function $f(x) = kx(8 - x)$ is a probability density function over the interval $[0, 8]$.

    1—Answer: $\frac{3}{256}$

12. Find the constant k so that the function $f(x) = k\sqrt{x}$ is a probability density function over the interval $[0, 9]$.

    (a) $\frac{1}{3}$ (b) $\frac{1}{18}$ (c) $\frac{1}{27}$ (d) 9   (e) None of these

    1—Answer: b

13. Find the constant k so that the function $f(x) = \dfrac{k}{x^2}$ is a probability density function over the interval $[1, 3]$.

    (a) 2   (b) $-\frac{9}{8}$ (c) $\frac{3}{2}$ (d) 3   (e) None of these

    1—Answer: c

14. Find $P(1 \le x \le 3)$ given the probability density function $f(x) = \dfrac{5}{4(x + 1)^2}, 0 \le x \le 4.$

    1—Answer: $\frac{5}{16}$

15. Find $P(0 \le x \le 2)$, for the probability density function, $f(x) = \dfrac{1}{(x + 1)^2}, x \ge 0.$

    (a) $\frac{2}{3}$ (b) $\frac{1}{9}$ (c) $\frac{8}{9}$ (d) 1   (e) None of these

    1—Answer: a

16. Find $P(0 \le x \le 2)$ given the probability density function $f(x) = \dfrac{8}{(x + 2)^3}, x \ge 0.$

    1—Answer: $\frac{3}{4}$

17. Find $P(0 \le x \le 2)$ given the probability density function $f(x) = \dfrac{8}{(x + 3)^3}, x \ge 0.$

    (a) $\frac{16}{25}$ (b) $\frac{8}{25}$ (c) $\frac{9}{50}$ (d) $\frac{18}{25}$ (e) None of these

    1—Answer: a

18. Find $P(2 \le x \le 4)$, given the probability density function $f(x) = \frac{1}{2}e^{-x/2}, x \ge 0.$

    (a) $\dfrac{1}{e}$ (b) $\dfrac{1}{e} - \dfrac{1}{e^2}$ (c) $\dfrac{1}{2e^2}$ (d) $\dfrac{1}{4}\left(\dfrac{1}{e} - \dfrac{1}{e^2}\right)$ (e) None of these

    1—Answer: b

19. Find $P(4 \le x \le 8)$, given the probability density function $f(x) = \frac{1}{2}e^{-x/2}, x \ge 0.$

    1—Answer: $\dfrac{1}{e^2} - \dfrac{1}{e^4}$

20. Find $P(0 \le x \le 2)$, given the probability density function $f(x) = \dfrac{5}{4(x+1)^2}, 0 \le x \le 4$.

(a) $\frac{5}{36}$ (b) $\frac{5}{6}$ (c) $\frac{5}{12}$ (d) $\frac{5}{2}$ (e) None of these

1—Answer: b

21. Find $P(0 \le x \le 2)$, given the probability density function $f(x) = \dfrac{8}{(x+2)^3}, x \ge 0$.

(a) $\frac{3}{16}$ (b) $\frac{3}{8}$ (c) $\frac{3}{4}$ (d) $\frac{1}{8}$ (e) None of these

1—Answer: c

22. Find $P(1 \le x \le 4)$ for the probability density function, $f(x) = \frac{1}{18}\sqrt{x}, [0, 9]$.

1—Answer: $\frac{7}{27}$

23. The daily demand, x, for a certain product is a random variable with the probability density function

$$f(x) = \frac{3x(4-x)}{32}, [0, 4].$$

Determine the probability that the demand will be less than three.

(a) $\frac{9}{32}$ (b) $\frac{27}{32}$ (c) $\frac{1}{2}$ (d) $\frac{3}{4}$ (e) None of these

1—Answer: b

24. The daily demand, x, for a certain product is a random variable with the probability density function

$$f(x) = \frac{6x(5-x)}{125}, [0, 5].$$

Determine the probability that the demand will be less than three.

(a) $\frac{81}{125}$ (b) $\frac{36}{125}$ (c) $\frac{96}{125}$ (d) $\frac{68}{125}$ (e) None of these

1—Answer: a

25. The daily demand, x, for a certain product is a random variable with the probability density function

$$f(x) = \frac{25}{12(x+1)^3}, [0, 4].$$

Determine the probability that the demand will be less than three.

1—Answer: $\frac{125}{128} \approx 0.976562$

26. The daily demand, x, for a certain product is a random variable with the probability density function

$$f(x) = \frac{x(6-x)}{36}, [0, 6].$$

Determine the probability that the demand will be greater than three.

1—Answer: 0.5

27. The daily demand, x, for a certain product is a random variable with the probability density function

$$f(x) = \frac{3x(4 - x)}{32}, [0, 4].$$

Determine the probability that the demand will be greater than three.

(a) $\frac{9}{32}$ (b) $\frac{27}{32}$ (c) $\frac{1}{2}$ (d) $\frac{3}{4}$ (e) None of these

1—Answer: e

28. The usable lifetime in years of a certain product is modeled by the probability density function $f(t) = 0.04e^{-0.04t}$, $t \geq 0$. Find the probability that a randomly selected unit will have a lifetime of more than four years.

1—T—Answer: $e^{-4/25} \approx 0.852143$

29. The usable lifetime in years of a certain product is modeled by the probability density function $f(t) = 0.05e^{-0.05t}$, $t \geq 0$. Find the probability that a randomly selected unit will have a lifetime of more than four years.

(a) 0.783   (b) 0.045   (c) 0.779   (d) 0.819   (e) None of these

1—T—Answer: d

Section 9.3   Expected Value and Variance

1. Use standard normal probability density function to find the probability of $x > 2.13$.

   (a) 0.0107   (b) 0.4834   (c) 0.0166   (d) 0.3258   (e) None of these

   1—T—Answer: c

2. Use standard normal probability density function to find the probability of $x \geq 1$.

   1—T—Answer: 0.1587

3. Use standard normal probability density function to find the probability of $x > 2.45$.

   (a) 0.4971   (b) 0.4929   (c) 0.5071   (d) 0.0071   (e) None of these

   1—T—Answer: d

4. Use standard normal probability density function to find the probability of $x < -1.23$.

   (a) 0.3907   (b) 0.6093   (c) 0.4906   (d) 0.1093   (e) None of these

   1—T—Answer: d

5. Use standard normal probability density function to find the probability of $x < -1.04$.

   (a) 0.3308   (b) 0.4192   (c) 0.0808   (d) 0.1492   (e) None of these

   1—T—Answer: d

6. Find $P(0.08 \leq x \leq 1.62)$ using the standard normal probability density function.

   (a) 0.4382   (b) 0.4155   (c) 0.0319   (d) 0.4474   (e) None of these

   1—T—Answer: b

7. Find $P(0.13 \leq x \leq 1.70)$ using the standard normal probability density function.

   (a) 0.4418   (b) 0.4554   (c) 0.0517   (d) 0.4037   (e) None of these

   1—T—Answer: d

8. Find $P(1.63 \leq x \leq 1.7)$ using the standard normal probability density function.

   (a) 0.4554   (b) 0.4484   (c) 0.007   (d) 0.0279   (e) None of these

   1—T—Answer: c

9. Use the standard normal probability density function to find the probability $x > 1.57$.

   1—T—Answer: 0.0582

10. Find $P(\mu - \sigma < x < \mu + \sigma)$ for the standard normal probability density function.

    1—T—Answer: 0.6826

11. Find the standard deviation of the special probability density function $f(x) = \dfrac{1}{3\sqrt{2\pi}} e^{-(x-100)^2/18}, (-\infty, \infty)$.

(a) 3   (b) 9   (c) 18   (d) $\frac{1}{3}$ (e) None of these

1—Answer: a

12. Find the standard deviation of the special probability density function $f(x) = \frac{1}{8}, [0, 8]$.

(a) $\dfrac{2\sqrt{3}}{3}$ (b) $8\sqrt{3}$ (c) $\sqrt{3}$ (d) $\dfrac{4\sqrt{3}}{3}$ (e) None of these

1—Answer: d

13. Find the standard deviation of the special probability density function $f(x) = \dfrac{1}{\sqrt{2\pi}} e^{-(x-50)^2/2}, (-\infty, \infty)$.

(a) 2   (b) $\sqrt{2}$ (c) 1   (d) $\dfrac{\sqrt{2}}{2}$ (e) None of these

1—Answer: c

14. Determine the standard deviation, σ, of the probability density function, $f(x) = \dfrac{3}{2x^2}, [1, 3]$.

(a) 0.084   (b) 1   (c) 0.533   (d) 0.825   (e) None of these

1—T—Answer: c

15. Determine the standard deviation, σ, of the probability density function, $f(x) = \frac{1}{18}\sqrt{x}, [0, 9]$.

(a) 5.89   (b) 5.85   (c) 0.70   (d) 2.36   (e) None of these

1—T—Answer: d

For problems 16 and 17, use the probability density function $f(x) = \dfrac{6x(5-x)}{125}, [0, 5]$.

16. Determine the mean of x.

1—Answer: $\frac{5}{2}$

17. Determine the standard deviation of x.

1—Answer: $\dfrac{\sqrt{5}}{2}$

18. Determine the median for the probability density function $f(x) = \frac{3}{2}e^{-2/3x}, [0, \infty]$.

1—Answer: $\frac{2}{3} \ln 2$

19. Find the expected value on the random variable x with probability density function, $f = \frac{x}{8}, 0 \le x \le 4$.

(a) $\frac{1}{8}$ (b) $\frac{8}{3}$ (c) $\frac{3}{16}$ (d) 2   (e) None of these

1—**Answer:** b

20. Determine the expected value of the probability density function, $f(x) = \frac{1}{18}\sqrt{x}, [0, 9]$.

(a) $\frac{1}{6}$ (b) $\frac{3}{2}$ (c) $\frac{27}{5}$ (d) $\frac{1}{12}$ (e) None of these

1—**Answer:** c

21. Determine the expected value of the probability density function, $f(x) = \frac{1}{12}\sqrt[3]{x}, [0, 8]$.

(a) $\frac{4}{7}$ (b) 1   (c) $\frac{32}{7}$ (d) $\frac{4}{3}$ (e) None of these

1—**Answer:** c

22. Determine the expected value for the probability density function, $f(x) = \frac{16}{15x^3}, [1, 4]$.

1—**Answer:** 2.4

23. Determine the expected value for the probability density function, $f(x) = \frac{4}{3x^2}, [1, 4]$.

(a) $\frac{4}{3}$ (b) 1   (c) $\frac{4}{3}\ln 4$ (d) $\frac{4}{3}\ln 3$ (e) None of these

1—**Answer:** c

24. Determine the expected value for the probability density function, $f(x) = \frac{3}{2x^2}, [1, 3]$.

(a) $\frac{7}{8}$ (b) $\frac{3}{2}\ln 3$ (c) $\frac{49}{72}$ (d) 2   (e) None of these

1—**Answer:** b

25. Find the expected value on the random variable x with probability density function, $f(x) = \frac{x}{18}, 0 \le x \le 6$.

1—**Answer:** 4

26. In the normal probability density function $f(x) = \frac{1}{\sigma\sqrt{2\pi}}e^{-(x-\mu^2)^2/2\sigma^2}$, the expected value is:

(a) σ (b) $\sqrt{\sigma}$ (c) μ (d) μ^2 (e) None of these

1—**Answer:** c

27. If z is a standard normal random variable, its expected value is:

(a) 1   (b) 0   (c) 0.5   (d) -1 (e) None of these

1—**Answer:** b

28. Find the variance of the special probability density function, $f(x) = \frac{1}{5}e^{-1/5x}, [0, \infty)$.

(a) 5   (b) $\frac{1}{5}$ (c) 25   (d) $\frac{1}{25}$ (e) None of these

1—Answer: c

29. Find the variance for the probability density function, $f(x) = \frac{1}{2}, 0 \le x \le 2$, if the expected value is 1.

(a) $\frac{1}{8}$ (b) $\frac{1}{4}$ (c) $\frac{1}{16}$ (d) $\frac{1}{6}$ (e) None of these

1—Answer: e

30. Find the variance for the probability density function, $f(x) = \frac{1}{3}, 0 \le x \le 3$, if the expected value is $\frac{3}{2}$.

(a) $\frac{1}{2}$ (b) $\frac{1}{4}$ (c) $\frac{3}{2}$ (d) $\frac{3}{4}$ (e) None of these

1—Answer: d

31. Find the variance for the probability density function, $f(x) = \frac{3}{4}, 0 \le x \le \frac{4}{3}$, if the expected value is $\frac{2}{3}$.

1—Answer: $\frac{4}{27}$

32. Find the variance of the special probability density function, $f(x) = \frac{2}{3}e^{-2x/3}, [0, \infty)$.

(a) $\frac{9}{4}$ (b) $\frac{4}{9}$ (c) $\frac{2}{3}$ (d) $\frac{3}{2}$ (e) None of these

1—Answer: a

33. Find the variance for the probability density function, $f(x) = \frac{1}{6}, 0 \le x \le 6$, if the expected value is 3.

1—Answer: 3

34. Determine the median for the probability density function, $f(x) = 2e^{-2x}, [0, \infty)$.

(a) $\dfrac{\ln 2}{2}$ (b) 0   (c) $\dfrac{1}{2}$ (d) $\dfrac{1}{4}$ (e) None of these

1—Answer: a

35. Determine the median for the probability density function, $f(x) = \frac{1}{3}e^{-x/3}, [0, \infty)$.

(a) $3 \ln 2$ (b) 0   (c) $\dfrac{1}{3}$ (d) $\dfrac{\ln 2}{3}$ (e) None of these

1—Answer: a

36. Determine the median for the probability density function $f(x) = 4e^{-4x}, [0, \infty)$.

(a) $\frac{1}{4} \ln 2$ (b) 0   (c) $\frac{1}{4}$ (d) $\frac{1}{16}$ (e) None of these

1—Answer: a

37. Find the median of the probability density function $f(x) = \frac{1}{8}x, [0, 4]$.

(a) $\frac{1}{2}$ (b) 1   (c) $2\sqrt{2}$ (d) 8   (e) None of these

1—Answer: c

38. Find the median of the probability density function $f(x) = \frac{1}{32}x$, $[0, 8]$.

   (a) $\frac{1}{4}$ (b) $4\sqrt{2}$ (c) 1   (d) $\frac{16}{3}$ (e) None of these

   1—Answer: b

39. Find the median of the probability density function $f(x) = \frac{1}{18}x$, $[0, 6]$.

   (a) $3\sqrt{2}$ (b) 1   (c) $\frac{1}{3}$ (d) 4   (e) None of these

   1—Answer: a

40. Find the median of the exponential probability density function $f(t) = \frac{1}{2}e^{-1/2t}$, $[0, \infty)$.

   (a) 2.7183   (b) 1.3863   (c) 1.6487   (d) 0.2500   (e) None of these

   1—T—Answer: b

41. Determine the median for the probability density function $f(x) = 3e^{-3x}$, $[0, \infty)$.

   (a) $\frac{1}{3}\ln 2$ (b) 0   (c) $\frac{1}{3}$ (d) $\frac{1}{9}$ (e) None of these

   1—Answer: a

42. Determine the median for the probability density function $f(x) = 4e^{-4x}$, $[0, \infty)$.

   (a) 0.173   (b) 0.982   (c) 0.327   (d) 0.137   (e) None of these

   1—T—Answer: a

43. Determine the median for the probability density function $f(x) = 0.2e^{-0.2x}$, $[0, \infty)$.

   1—Answer: 5 ln 2

44. Determine the median for the probability density function $f(x) = 4e^{-4x}$, $[0, \infty)$.

   1—Answer: $\frac{1}{4}\ln 2$

45. Explain, in a complete sentence, the difference between two normally distributed populations, where one population has a large standard deviation and the other has a very small standard deviation.

   1—Answer: Answers will vary.

46. Describe, in a complete sentence, the difference between a discrete and a continuous random variable.

   1—Answer: Answers will vary.

47. Let x be a continuous random variable that is normally distributed with a mean of 35 and a standard deviation of 5. Write the integral that could be solved to find the probability that $x \geq 40$.

(a) $\displaystyle\int_0^{45} \frac{1}{5\sqrt{2\pi}} e^{-(x-35)^2/50}$

(b) $\displaystyle\int_0^{45} \frac{1}{\sqrt{2\pi}} e^{-(x-35)^2/5}$

(c) $\displaystyle\int_{45}^{\infty} \frac{1}{\sqrt{2\pi}} e^{-(x-35)^2/25}$

(d) $\displaystyle\int_{45}^{\infty} \frac{1}{5\sqrt{2\pi}} e^{-(x-35)^2/50}$

(e) None of these

1—Answer: d

48. Let x be a continuous random variable that is normally distributed with a mean of 12 and a standard deviation of 3. Write the integral that could be solved to find the probability that $x \geq 14$.

(a) $\displaystyle\int_{14}^{\infty} \frac{1}{3\sqrt{2\pi}} e^{-(x-12)^2/18}$

(b) $\displaystyle\int_{14}^{\infty} \frac{1}{12\sqrt{2\pi}} e^{-(x-9)^2/24}$

(c) $\displaystyle\int_{14}^{\infty} \frac{1}{3\sqrt{2\pi}} e^{-(x-12)^2/144}$

(d) $\displaystyle\int_0^{\infty} \frac{1}{3\sqrt{2\pi}} e^{-(x-12)^2/18}$

(e) None of these

1—Answer: a

49. The standard normal probability density function is:

(a) $f(x) = \dfrac{1}{\sigma\sqrt{2\pi}} e^{-(x-\mu)^2/2\sigma^2}$

(b) $f(x) = ae^{-ax}$

(c) $f(x) = \dfrac{1}{\sqrt{2\pi}} e^{-x^2/2}$

(d) $f(x) = \dfrac{1}{b-a}$

(e) None of these

1—Answer: c

50. The normal probability density function is:

(a) $f(x) = \dfrac{1}{\sigma\sqrt{2\pi}} e^{-(x-\mu)^2/2\sigma^2}$

(b) $f(x) = ae^{-ax}$

(c) $f(x) = \dfrac{1}{\sqrt{2\pi}} e^{-x^2/2}$

(d) $f(x) = \dfrac{1}{b-a}$

(e) None of these

1—Answer: a

CHAPTER 10

Series and Taylor Polynomials

Section 10.1 Sequences

1. Find the first 5 terms of the sequence whose nth-term is $a_n = (-1)^n(2n + 9)$. (Assume that n begins with 1.)

   (a) $-11, -13, -15, -17, -19, \ldots$

   (b) $-11, 13, -15, 17, -19, \ldots$

   (c) $-11, 2, -13, 4, -15, \ldots$

   (d) $-11, -24, -39, -56, -75, \ldots$

   (e) None of these

   1—Answer: b

2. Find the first 5 terms of the sequence whose nth-term is $a_n = n!$. (Assume that n begins with 0.)

   (a) $0, 1, 2, 6, 24$

   (b) $0, 1, 2, 6, 12$

   (c) $1, 1, 2, 6, 12$

   (d) $1, 1, 2, 6, 24$

   (e) None of these

   1—Answer: d

3. Find the first 5 terms of the sequence whose nth-term is $a_n = 1 - \dfrac{1}{n}$. (Assume that n begins with 1.)

   (a) $\frac{1}{2}, \frac{1}{4}, \frac{1}{8}, \frac{1}{16}, \frac{1}{32}$

   (b) $0, \frac{1}{2}, \frac{2}{3}, \frac{3}{4}, \frac{4}{5}$

   (c) $0, \frac{1}{2}, \frac{1}{3}, \frac{1}{4}, \frac{1}{5}$

   (d) $1, \frac{1}{2}, \frac{2}{3}, \frac{3}{4}, \frac{4}{5}$

   (e) None of these

   1—Answer: b

4. Find the first 5 terms of the sequence whose nth-term is $a_n = \dfrac{n!}{(n + 2)!}$. (Assume that n begins with 0.)

   1—Answer: $\frac{1}{2}, \frac{1}{6}, \frac{1}{12}, \frac{1}{20}, \frac{1}{30}$

5. Find the first 5 terms of the sequence whose nth-term is $a_n = \dfrac{n - 2}{n^2 + 1}$. (Assume that n begins with 1.)

   1—Answer: $-\frac{1}{2}, 0, \frac{1}{10}, \frac{2}{17}, \frac{3}{26}$

6. Find the fifth term of the sequence: $\left\{ \dfrac{(-1)^{n-1}2^{n-1}}{n!} \right\}$.

   1—Answer: $\frac{2}{15}$

7. Find the third term of the sequence: $\left\{ \dfrac{(-2)^n(2^n + 1)}{\sqrt{n}} \right\}, n = 1, 2, 3, \cdots$.

   (a) 4.619

   (b) 5.196

   (c) -5.196

   (d) -4.619

   (e) None of these

   1—T—Answer: c

8. Find the fourth term of the sequence: $\left\{\dfrac{(-1)^{n+1}2^n}{3n-1}\right\}$, $n = 1, 2, 3, \cdots$.

(a) $\dfrac{16}{11}$ (b) $-\dfrac{16}{11}$ (c) $-\dfrac{8}{11}$ (d) $-\dfrac{16}{13}$ (e) None of these

1—Answer: b

9. Find the fourth term of the sequence: $\left\{\dfrac{(-1)^n(2^n+1)}{n!}\right\}$, $n = 1, 2, 3, \cdots$.

(a) $\dfrac{17}{4}$ (b) $\dfrac{-7}{4}$ (c) $\dfrac{9}{24}$ (d) $\dfrac{17}{24}$ (e) None of these

1—Answer: d

10. Find the fourth term of the sequence: $\left\{\dfrac{(-1)^{n+1}2^n}{3n-1}\right\}$, $n = 1, 2, 3, \cdots$.

1—Answer: $-\dfrac{16}{11}$

11. Find the 10th term of the sequence: $\dfrac{3^1}{2^0}, \dfrac{3^2}{2^1}, \dfrac{3^3}{2^2}, \dfrac{3^4}{2^3}, \dfrac{3^5}{2^4}, \cdots$.

(a) $\dfrac{3^{10}}{2^{10}}$ (b) $\dfrac{3^{11}}{2^{10}}$ (c) $\dfrac{3^{10}}{2^9}$ (d) $\dfrac{3^{11}}{2^{11}}$ (e) None of these

1—Answer: c

12. Find the 40th term of the sequence whose nth-term is $a_n = 500\left(1 + \dfrac{0.095}{12}\right)^n$. (Assume that n begins with 1.)

(a) 363.83   (b) 752.19   (c) 690.84   (d) 685.42   (e) None of these

1—T—Answer: d

13. Find a formula for the nth-term of the sequence. (Assume that n begins with 1.)

$\dfrac{3}{2}, \dfrac{6}{4}, \dfrac{9}{12}, \dfrac{12}{48}, \dfrac{15}{240}, \cdots$

(a) $\dfrac{3n}{2n!}$ (b) $\dfrac{3n}{n(n+1)}$ (c) $\dfrac{3n}{n!(n+1)!}$ (d) $\dfrac{3n}{2(n-1)!}$ (e) None of these

1—Answer: a

14. Find a formula for the nth-term of the sequence. (Assume that n begins with 1.)

$\dfrac{1}{4}, \dfrac{2}{9}, \dfrac{3}{16}, \dfrac{4}{25}, \cdots$

(a) $a_n = 1 - \dfrac{3n}{n^2}$ (b) $a_n = \dfrac{n}{(n+1)!}$ (c) $a_n = \dfrac{1}{2} + \dfrac{n}{(n+1)^3}$

(d) $a_n = \dfrac{n}{(n+1)^2}$ (e) None of these

1—Answer: d

Series and Taylor Polynomials

15. Find a formula for the *n*th-term of the sequence. (Assume that *n* begins with 1.)

$$\frac{2}{1}, \frac{3}{2}, \frac{4}{3}, \frac{5}{4}, \frac{6}{5}, \cdots$$

(a) $\dfrac{n+1}{n-1}$ (b) $2 - \dfrac{1}{n}$ (c) $1 + \dfrac{1}{n}$ (d) $\dfrac{2n-1}{n}$ (e) None of these

1—Answer: c

16. Write an expression for the *n*th-term of the sequence. (Start with *n* = 1.)

$$-2, 4, -\frac{8}{2}, \frac{16}{6}, \cdots$$

(a) $\dfrac{(-1)^{n+1}2^{n+1}}{n!}$ (b) $\dfrac{(-1)^{n+1}2^{n+1}}{(n+1)!}$ (c) $\dfrac{(-1)^n 2^n}{n!}$ (d) $\dfrac{(-1)^n 2^n}{(n-1)!}$ (e) None of these

2—Answer: d

17. Write an expression for the *n*th-term of the sequence. (Start with *n* = 1.)

$$-3, 9, -\frac{27}{2}, \frac{81}{6}, \cdots$$

(a) $\dfrac{(-1)^n 3^n}{(n-1)!}$ (b) $\dfrac{(-1)^{n+1}3^{n+1}}{n!}$ (c) $\dfrac{(-1)^{n+1}3^{n+1}}{(n+1)!}$ (d) $\dfrac{(-1)^n 3^n}{n!}$ (e) None of these

2—Answer: a

18. Write an expression for the *n*th-term of the sequence. (Start with *n* = 1.)

$$-4, 16, -\frac{64}{2}, \frac{256}{6}, \cdots$$

(a) $\dfrac{(-1)^n 4^n}{(n-1)!}$ (b) $\dfrac{(-1)^{n+1}4^{n+1}}{(n+1)!}$ (c) $\dfrac{(-1)^n 4^n}{n!}$ (d) $\dfrac{(-1)^{n+1}4^{n+1}}{n!}$ (e) None of these

2—Answer: a

19. Find a formula for the *n*th-term of the sequence. (Assume that *n* begins with 1.)

$$\frac{2}{1}, \frac{4}{1}, \frac{6}{2}, \frac{8}{6}, \frac{10}{24}, \cdots$$

(a) $\dfrac{2^n}{(n+1)!}$ (b) $\dfrac{3-2^2}{n(2^n)}$ (c) $\dfrac{2n}{2n-1}$ (d) $\dfrac{2n}{(n-1)!}$ (e) None of these

1—Answer: d

20. Write an expression for the *n*th-term of the sequence. (Start with *n* = 1.)

$$-6, 36, -\frac{216}{2}, \frac{1296}{6}, \cdots$$

(a) $\dfrac{(-1)^n 6^n}{n!}$ (b) $\dfrac{(-1)^{n+1}6^{n+1}}{(n+1)!}$ (c) $\dfrac{(-1)^{n+1}6^{n+1}}{n!}$ (d) $\dfrac{(-1)^n 6^n}{(n-1)!}$ (e) None of these

2—Answer: d

21. Determine if the following sequence converges or diverges:

$$\left\{\frac{2n-1}{3n^2+1}\right\}, n = 1, 2, 3, \cdots.$$

If the sequence converges, find its limit.

(a) Converges to $\frac{2}{3}$ (b) Converges to 0 (c) Converges to $-\frac{1}{3}$

(d) Diverges (e) None of these

2—Answer: b

22. Determine if the following sequence converges or diverges:

$$\left\{\frac{3n+1}{4n^2-3}\right\}, n = 1, 2, 3, \cdots.$$

(a) Converges to $\frac{3}{4}$ (b) Converges to 0 (c) Converges to $\frac{4}{3}$

(d) Diverges (e) None of these

1—Answer: b

23. Determine if the following sequence converges or diverges:

$$\left\{\frac{n!}{(n-2)!}\right\}, n = 2, 3, 4, \cdots.$$

If the sequence converges, find its limit.

(a) Converges to 2 (b) Converges to 0 (c) Converges to 4

(d) Diverges (e) None of these

1—Answer: d

24. Determine if the following sequence converges or diverges:

$$\left\{\frac{2n-1}{3n+1}\right\}, n = 1, 2, 3, \cdots.$$

If the sequence converges, find its limit.

(a) Converges to $\frac{2}{3}$ (b) Converges to 0 (c) Converges to $-\frac{1}{3}$

(d) Diverges (e) None of these

1—Answer: a

25. Determine if the following sequence converges or diverges:

$$\left\{\frac{5n^2+1}{4n^2+3n+2}\right\}, n = 0, 1, 2, \cdots.$$

If the sequence converges, find its limit.

1—Answer: Converges to $\frac{5}{4}$

26. Determine if the following sequence converges or diverges:

$$\left\{\frac{e^n}{e^n + 2}\right\}, n = 0, 1, 2, \cdots.$$

If the sequence converges, find its limit.

1—**Answer:** Converges to 1

27. Determine if the following sequence converges or diverges:

$$\left\{\frac{4n^2 + 1}{6n^2 - 3}\right\}, n = 1, 2, 3, \cdots.$$

(a) Converges to $-\frac{1}{3}$ (b) Converges to $\frac{2}{3}$ (c) Converges to 0

(d) Diverges   (e) None of these

1—**Answer:** b

28. Determine if the following sequence converges or diverges: $\{\ln(n^2 + 4) - \ln(n)\}, n = 2, 3, 4, \cdots.$

(a) Converges to ln 4   (b) Converges to ln 5   (c) Converges to ln 2

(d) Diverges   (e) None of these

1—**Answer:** d

29. Determine the behavior of the sequence: $\left\{\left(1 + \frac{2}{n}\right)^n\right\}, n = 1, 2, 3, \cdots.$

(a) Diverges   (b) Converges to 7.3891   (c) Converges to 2.7828

(d) Converges to 4.7891   (e) None of these

1—T—**Answer:** b

30. Determine the behavior of the sequence: $\left\{3\left(1 + \frac{4}{n}\right)^n\right\}, n = 0, 1, 2, \cdots.$

1—T—**Answer:** Converges to 163.8

31. Determine if the following sequence converges or diverges:

$$\left\{\frac{3n^2 + 1}{n}\right\}.$$

If the sequence converges, find its limit.

1—**Answer:** Diverges

32. Determine if the following sequence converges or diverges:

$$\left\{\frac{4n}{4^n - 1}\right\}.$$

If the sequence converges, find its limit.

1—**Answer:** Converges to 1

33. Determine if the following sequence converges or diverges:

$$\left\{\frac{2^n}{1+n}\right\}, n = 1, 2, 3, \cdots.$$

If the sequence converges, find its limit.

2—Answer: Diverges

34. Determine if the following sequence converges or diverges:

$$\left\{\left(\frac{n+1}{n}\right)^n\right\}, n = 1, 2, 3, \cdots.$$

If the sequence converges, find its limit.

2—Answer: Converges to e

35. Determine if the following sequence converges or diverges:

$$\left\{\frac{n!}{(n-2)!}\right\}, n = 2, 3, 4, \cdots.$$

If the sequence converges, find its limit.

(a) Converges to 1   (b) Converges to 0   (c) Converges to -2

(d) Diverges   (e) None of these

2—Answer: d

36. Determine if the following sequence converges or diverges:

$$\left\{\frac{n!}{(n-2)!}\right\}, n = 2, 3, 4, \cdots.$$

If the sequence converges, find its limit.

(a) Converges to 2   (b) Converges to 0   (c) Converges to 4

(d) Diverges   (e) None of these

2—Answer: d

37. Determine if the following sequence converges or diverges:

$$\left\{\frac{2n-1}{3n+1}\right\}, n = 1, 2, 3, \cdots.$$

If the sequence converges, find its limit.

(a) Converges to $\frac{2}{3}$ (b) Converges to 0   (c) Converges to $-\frac{1}{3}$

(d) Diverges   (e) None of these

2—Answer: a

38. Find the limit of the sequence: $\left\{ \dfrac{-9 + (-1)^n}{n!} \right\}$.

(a) -9 (b) 0   (c) 1

(d) The sequence diverges   (e) None of these

1—Answer: b

39. Find the limit of the sequence: $\left\{ \dfrac{-5 + (-1)^n}{n!} \right\}$.

(a) -5 (b) 1   (c) 0

(d) The sequence diverges   (e) None of these

1—Answer: c

40. Find the limit of the sequence: $\left\{ \dfrac{-2 + (-1)^n}{n!} \right\}$.

(a) -2 (b) 0   (c) The sequence diverges

(d) 1   (e) None of these

1—Answer: b

Section 10.2   Series and Convergence

1. Use sigma notation to write the sum: $\frac{2}{3} + \frac{4}{4} + \frac{6}{5} + \frac{8}{6} + \cdots + \frac{14}{9}$.

(a) $\displaystyle\sum_{n=1}^{7} \frac{2n}{n+2}$ (b) $\displaystyle\sum_{n=2}^{8} \frac{n+2}{n+1}$ (c) $\displaystyle\sum_{n=0}^{6} \frac{n+2}{n+3}$ (d) $\displaystyle\sum_{n=3}^{9} \frac{n-1}{n}$ (e) None of these

1—Answer: a

2. Use sigma notation to write the sum: $\frac{1}{2} + \frac{2}{6} + \frac{3}{24} + \frac{4}{120} + \frac{5}{720}$.

1—Answer: $\displaystyle\sum_{n=1}^{5} \frac{n}{(n+1)!}$

3. Find the sum: $\displaystyle\sum_{n=0}^{10} 2\left(\frac{3}{5}\right)^n$.

(a) 4.9698   (b) 5.0000   (c) 4.9819   (d) 55.0000   (e) None of these

1—T—Answer: c

4. Find the sum: $\displaystyle\sum_{n=3}^{6} \frac{3}{n-2}$.

(a) $\frac{12}{9}$ (b) $\frac{25}{4}$ (c) $\frac{3}{16}$ (d) $\frac{1}{2}$ (e) None of these

1—Answer: b

5. Find the sum: $\displaystyle\sum_{n=1}^{4} \frac{n+1}{n+2}$.

(a) $\frac{61}{20}$ (b) $\frac{31}{20}$ (c) $\frac{143}{60}$ (d) $\frac{131}{60}$ (e) None of these

1—Answer: a

6. Find the sum of the geometric series: $\displaystyle\sum_{n=0}^{\infty} 5\left(\frac{1}{10}\right)^n$.

(a) $\frac{1}{2}$ (b) $\frac{50}{9}$ (c) $\frac{5}{9}$ (d) 6   (e) None of these

1—Answer: b

7. Find the sum of the geometric series: $\displaystyle\sum_{n=0}^{\infty} 5\left(\frac{3}{4}\right)^n$.

(a) -10 (b) 5   (c) 20   (d) 15   (e) None of these

1—Answer: c

8. Find the sum of the geometric series: $\displaystyle\sum_{n=0}^{\infty} 5\left(\frac{1}{e^2}\right)^n$.

1—Answer: 5.783

9. Find the sum of the geometric series: $\displaystyle\sum_{n=0}^{\infty} 5\left(\frac{1}{e}\right)^n$.

(a) 2.910   (b) 1.839   (c) 7.910   (d) 5   (e) None of these

1—T—Answer: c

10. Find the sum of the geometric series: $\displaystyle\sum_{n=0}^{\infty} 3\left(\frac{4}{7}\right)^n$.

1—Answer: 7

11. Find the sum of the geometric series: $\displaystyle\sum_{n=0}^{\infty} 3(-0.02)^n = 3 - 0.06 + 0.12 - 0.24 + \cdots$.

(a) 0   (b) 3.06   (c) $\frac{50}{17}$ (d) 3   (e) None of these

1—Answer: c

12. Find the sum of the geometric series: $\displaystyle\sum_{n=0}^{\infty} 2\left(-\frac{1}{2}\right)^n = 2 - 1 + \frac{1}{2} - \frac{1}{4} + \cdots$.

(a) $\frac{4}{3}$ (b) -1 (c) 0   (d) 4   (e) None of these

1—Answer: a

13. Find the sum: $\displaystyle\sum_{n=0}^{\infty} 3\left(-\frac{1}{2}\right)^n$.

1—Answer: 2

14. Find the sum of the infinite geometric series with $a = 9$ and $r = 0.7$.

1—Answer: 30

15. Find the sum of the following infinite geometric series: $\displaystyle\sum_{n=1}^{\infty} 2(-0.9)^n$.

(a) 2   (b) 20   (c) -18 (d) $-\frac{18}{19}$ (e) None of these

1—Answer: d

16. Find the sum of the following infinite geometric series: $\displaystyle\sum_{n=1}^{\infty} 3(-0.6)^n$.

(a) $-\frac{9}{8}$ (b) $\frac{30}{7}$ (c) $\frac{15}{2}$ (d) $-\frac{9}{2}$ (e) None of these

1—Answer: a

17. Find the sum of the following infinite geometric series: $\displaystyle\sum_{n=1}^{\infty} 4(0.5)^n$.

(a) $\frac{4}{3}$ (b) $\frac{8}{3}$ (c) 4   (d) -10 (e) None of these

1—Answer: c

18. Find the sum of the following infinite geometric series: $\displaystyle\sum_{n=1}^{\infty} 6(0.5)^n$.

  (a) 6   (b) 2   (c) 4   (d) -15 (e) None of these

  1—Answer: a

19. Find the sum of the geometric series $\displaystyle\sum_{n=0}^{\infty} 3\left(\frac{1}{2}\right)^n$.

  (a) $\frac{3}{2}$ (b) 3   (c) 6   (d) $\frac{50}{9}$ (e) None of these

  1—Answer: c

20. Find the sum: $\displaystyle\sum_{j=0}^{40} 3(1.05)^j$.

  (a) 383.52   (b) 362.40   (c) 984.00   (d) 22.18   (e) None of these

  1—Answer: a

21. Find the sum: $\displaystyle\sum_{k=1}^{10} 4\left(\frac{3}{2}\right)^{k-1}$.

  1—T—Answer: 453.320

22. Find the sum of the first 30 terms in the sequence.

  $2, \frac{5}{2}, \frac{25}{8}, \frac{125}{32}, \frac{625}{128}, \cdots$

  (a) 791.25   (b) 5161.88   (c) 6454.35   (d) 7116.42   (e) None of these

  2—T—Answer: c

23. Find the sum of the infinite geometric series: $-7 - \frac{7}{3} - \frac{7}{9} - \frac{7}{27} - \cdots$.

  (a) -5 (b) $-\frac{21}{4}$ (c) $-\frac{5}{2}$ (d) $-\frac{21}{2}$ (e) None of these

  2—Answer: d

24. Find the sum of the infinite geometric series: $1 + 0.9 + 0.81 + 0.729 + \cdots$.

  (a) 23   (b) 90   (c) 10   (d) 57   (e) None of these

  2—Answer: c

25. Find the sum of the infinite geometric series: $1 + \frac{1}{3} + \frac{1}{9} + \frac{1}{27} + \cdots$.

  (a) $\frac{3}{2}$ (b) 3   (c) $\frac{5}{3}$ (d) $\frac{5}{2}$ (e) None of these

  2—Answer: a

26. Determine the convergence or divergence of the following series, and state the test used: $\displaystyle\sum_{n=0}^{\infty} \frac{1}{3^n}$.

  1—Answer: Converges, Geometric Series Test

27. Determine the convergence or divergence of the following series, and state the test used: $\displaystyle\sum_{n=1}^{\infty} \frac{1}{1 + e^{-n}}$.

1—Answer: Diverges, nth-Term Test

28. Choose the series that diverges by the nth-Term Test.

(a) $\displaystyle\sum_{n=0}^{\infty} \frac{14}{n}$
(b) $\displaystyle\sum_{n=0}^{\infty} \frac{n - 6}{n}$
(c) $\displaystyle\sum_{n=0}^{\infty} \frac{100n^{14}}{4^n}$
(d) $\displaystyle\sum_{n=0}^{\infty} \frac{n - 6}{n!}$
(e) None of these

2—Answer: b

29. Choose the series that diverges by the nth-Term Test.

(a) $\displaystyle\sum_{n=0}^{\infty} \frac{n - 9}{n!}$
(b) $\displaystyle\sum_{n=0}^{\infty} \frac{100n^{15}}{4^n}$
(c) $\displaystyle\sum_{n=0}^{\infty} \frac{n - 9}{n}$
(d) $\displaystyle\sum_{n=0}^{\infty} \frac{15}{n}$
(e) None of these

2—Answer: c

30. Choose the series that diverges by the nth-Term Test.

(a) $\displaystyle\sum_{n=0}^{\infty} \frac{n + 3}{n}$
(b) $\displaystyle\sum_{n=0}^{\infty} \frac{n + 3}{n!}$
(c) $\displaystyle\sum_{n=0}^{\infty} \frac{100n^8}{6^n}$
(d) $\displaystyle\sum_{n=0}^{\infty} \frac{8}{n}$
(e) None of these

2—Answer: a

31. Choose the series that diverges by the nth-Term Test.

(a) $\displaystyle\sum_{n=0}^{\infty} \frac{6}{n}$
(b) $\displaystyle\sum_{n=0}^{\infty} \frac{100n^6}{3n}$
(c) $\displaystyle\sum_{n=0}^{\infty} \frac{n - 1}{n}$
(d) $\displaystyle\sum_{n=0}^{\infty} \frac{n - 1}{n!}$
(e) None of these

2—Answer: c

32. Choose the series that diverges by the nth-Term Test.

(a) $\displaystyle\sum_{n=0}^{\infty} \frac{11}{n}$
(b) $\displaystyle\sum_{n=0}^{\infty} \frac{100n^{11}}{5n}$
(c) $\displaystyle\sum_{n=0}^{\infty} \frac{n + 6}{n}$
(d) $\displaystyle\sum_{n=0}^{\infty} \frac{n + 6}{n!}$
(e) None of these

2—Answer: c

33. A ball is dropped from a height of 24 feet. Each time it drops h feet, it rebounds $\frac{2}{3}h$ feet. Find the total distance traveled by the ball.

(a) 72 feet
(b) 144 feet
(c) 120 feet
(d) 84 feet
(e) None of these

1—Answer: c

34. A force is applied to a particle, which moves in a straight line, in such a way that after each second the particle moves only one-half the distance that it moved in the preceding second. If the particle moved 20 cm in the first second, how far will it move altogether?

(a) 30 cm
(b) 10 cm
(c) 40 cm
(d) 45 cm
(e) None of these

1—Answer: c

35. A ball is dropped from a height of 8 feet. Each time it drops h feet, it rebounds $\frac{4}{5}h$ feet. Find the total distance traveled by the ball.

   (a) 80 feet   (b) 40 feet   (c) 32 feet   (d) 72 feet   (e) None of these

   1—Answer: d

Section 10.3   *p*-Series and the Ratio Test

1. Which of the following converges?

(a) $\displaystyle\sum_{n=1}^{\infty} \frac{1}{n}$
(b) $\displaystyle\sum_{n=0}^{\infty} 3\left(\frac{4}{3}\right)^n$
(c) $\displaystyle\sum_{n=0}^{\infty} \frac{(n+1)!}{2^n}$
(d) $\displaystyle\sum_{n=1}^{\infty} \frac{1}{n^{3/2}}$
(e) None of these

1—Answer: d

2. Which of the following converges?

(a) $\displaystyle\sum_{n=1}^{\infty} (4 + (-1)^n)$
(b) $\displaystyle\sum_{n=1}^{\infty} \frac{2^n}{(n+1)!}$
(c) $\displaystyle\sum_{n=0}^{\infty} 5\left(\frac{3}{2}\right)^n$

(d) $\displaystyle\sum_{n=1}^{\infty} \frac{1}{\sqrt{n}}$
(e) None of these

1—Answer: b

3. Which of the following converges?

(a) $\displaystyle\sum_{n=1}^{\infty} \frac{2}{n^2}$
(b) $\displaystyle\sum_{n=0}^{\infty} 5\left(\frac{7}{3}\right)^n$
(c) $\displaystyle\sum_{n=0}^{\infty} \frac{(n+1)!}{2^n}$
(d) $\displaystyle\sum_{n=0}^{\infty} \frac{1}{n^{3/4}}$
(e) None of these

1—Answer: a

4. Which of the following converges?

(a) $\displaystyle\sum_{n=1}^{\infty} (4 + (-1^n))$
(b) $\displaystyle\sum_{n=1}^{\infty} \frac{1}{\sqrt[3]{n}}$
(c) $\displaystyle\sum_{n=0}^{\infty} 4\left(-\frac{5}{3}\right)^n$

(d) $\displaystyle\sum_{n=1}^{\infty} \frac{3^n}{(n+1)!}$
(e) None of these

1—Answer: d

5. Which of the following converges?

(a) $\displaystyle\sum_{n=0}^{\infty} (5 + (-2)^n)$
(b) $\displaystyle\sum_{n=1}^{\infty} \frac{5^n}{(2n+1)!}$
(c) $\displaystyle\sum_{n=0}^{\infty} 6\left(-\frac{7}{2}\right)^n$

(d) $\displaystyle\sum_{n=1}^{\infty} \frac{1}{\sqrt[4]{n}}$
(e) None of these

1—Answer: b

6. Which of the following diverges?

(a) $\displaystyle\sum_{n=0}^{\infty} \frac{n!}{5n! - 2}$
(b) $\displaystyle\sum_{n=1}^{\infty} \frac{1}{n^7}$
(c) $\displaystyle\sum_{n=0}^{\infty} 11\left(\frac{3}{8}\right)^n$
(d) $\displaystyle\sum_{n=1}^{\infty} \frac{n^2}{3^n}$
(e) None of these

1—Answer: a

7. Which of the following diverges?

(a) $\displaystyle\sum_{n=0}^{\infty}\frac{n!}{3n!-1}$ (b) $\displaystyle\sum_{n=1}^{\infty}\frac{1}{n^6}$ (c) $\displaystyle\sum_{n=0}^{\infty}5\left(\frac{1}{10}\right)^n$ (d) $\displaystyle\sum_{n=0}^{\infty}\frac{n}{2^n}$ (e) None of these

1—Answer: a

8. Which of the following diverges?

(a) $\displaystyle\sum_{n=0}^{\infty}\frac{1}{2^n}$ (b) $\displaystyle\sum_{n=1}^{\infty}(4+(-1)^n)$ (c) $\displaystyle\sum_{n=0}^{\infty}\frac{(-1)^n}{(n+1)!}$

(d) $\displaystyle\sum_{n=1}^{\infty}\frac{1}{n^2}$ (e) None of these

1—Answer: b

9. Which test would be used to prove the divergence of $\displaystyle\sum_{n=0}^{\infty}\left(\frac{1}{1+e^n}\right)$?

(a) *p*-Series Test   (b) Geometric Series Test   (c) *n*th-Term Test

(d) Ratio Test   (e) None of these

1—Answer: d

10. Which test would be used to prove the divergence of $\displaystyle\sum_{n=1}^{\infty}\frac{1}{\sqrt{n}}$?

(a) Geometric Series Test   (b) *p*-Series Test   (c) Ratio Test

(d) *n*th-Term Test   (e) None of these

1—Answer: b

11. Which test would be used to prove the divergence of $\displaystyle\sum_{n=0}^{\infty}\left(1+\frac{1}{e^n}\right)$?

(a) *p*-Series Test   (b) Geometric Series Test   (c) *n*th-Term Test

(d) Ratio Test   (e) None of these

1—Answer: c

12. Give a reason for the divergence of the series $\displaystyle\sum_{n=0}^{\infty}\frac{n!}{5n!-2}$.

1—Answer: Ratio Test; $L>1$

13. Apply any appropriate test to show that the series $\displaystyle\sum_{n=0}^{\infty}\left(\frac{1}{1+e^n}\right)$ diverges.

1—Answer: Ratio Test; $L=\dfrac{1}{e}<1$

14. Which test would be used to prove the divergence of $\displaystyle\sum_{n=1}^{\infty} \frac{n+1}{3n+1}$?

    (a) Geometric Series Test   (b) p-Series Test   (c) Ratio Test

    (d) nth-Term Test   (e) None of these

    2—Answer: d

15. Which test would be used to prove the convergence of $\displaystyle\sum_{n=1}^{\infty} \frac{1}{n^2}$?

    (a) p-Series Test   (b) Geometric Series Test   (c) nth-Term Test

    (d) Ratio Test   (e) None of these

    1—Answer: a

16. Give a reason for the convergence of the series $\displaystyle\sum_{n=1}^{\infty} \frac{5^n}{(2n+1)!}$.

    1—Answer: Ratio Test; $L = 0 < 1$

17. Which test would be appropriate to show that $\displaystyle\sum_{n=1}^{\infty} \frac{n!}{1 \cdot 3 \cdot 5 \cdots (2n-1)}$ converges?

    (a) Geometric Series Test   (b) p-Series Test   (c) Ratio Test

    (d) nth-Term Test   (e) None of these

    1—Answer: c

18. Which of the following tests could be used to show that $\displaystyle\sum_{n=1}^{\infty} \left(\frac{2n-1}{3n+5}\right)^n$ converges?

    (a) nth-Term Test   (b) Ratio Test   (c) Geometric Series Test

    (d) p-Series Test   (e) None of these

    1—Answer: a

19. Investigate $\displaystyle\sum_{n=1}^{\infty} \frac{1 \cdot 3 \cdot 5 \cdots (2n-1)}{n!}$ for convergence or divergence.

    (a) Diverges by Ratio Test   (b) Converges by nth-Term Test   (c) Diverges by nth-Term Test

    (d) Converges by Ratio Test   (e) None of these

    1—Answer: a

20. Investigate $\displaystyle\sum_{n=1}^{\infty} \left(\frac{n+1}{n}\right)^n$ for convergence or divergence.

    (a) Converges by Ratio Test   (b) Diverges by Root Test   (c) Converges by Ratio Test

    (d) Diverges by nth-Term Test   (e) None of these

    1—Answer: d

21. Determine the convergence or divergence of the series using the Ratio Test: $\displaystyle\sum_{n=1}^{\infty}\frac{n!}{(n+6)!}$.

    (a) Converges by the Ratio Test   (b) The Ratio Test does not apply   (c) The Ratio Test is inconclusive

    (d) Diverges by the Ratio Test   (e) None of these

    1—Answer: c

22. Investigate $\displaystyle\sum_{n=1}^{\infty}\frac{1}{1+e^{-n}}$ for convergence or divergence.

    (a) Converges by *p*-Series Test   (b) Converges by *n*th-Term Test

    (c) Converges by Ratio Test   (d) Diverges by Geometric Series Test

    (e) None of these

    1—Answer: e

23. Determine the convergence or divergence of the following series, and state the test used: $\displaystyle\sum_{n=1}^{\infty}\frac{2\cdot4\cdot6\cdots2n}{n!}$.

    1—Answer: Diverges, Ratio Test

24. Determine the convergence or divergence of the following series, and state the test used: $\displaystyle\sum_{n=1}^{\infty}\frac{1}{\sqrt[3]{n}}$.

    1—Answer: Diverges, *p*-Series

25. Determine the convergence or divergence of the following series, and state the test used: $\displaystyle\sum_{n=0}^{\infty}\frac{1}{3^n}$.

    1—Answer: Converges, Geometric Series Test

26. Determine the convergence or divergence of the following series, and state the test used: $\displaystyle\sum_{n=1}^{\infty}\frac{5n}{2n-1}$.

    1—Answer: Diverges, *n*th-Term Test

27. Determine the convergence or divergence of the following series, and state the test used: $\displaystyle\sum_{n=1}^{\infty}\frac{2\cdot4\cdot6\cdots2n}{n!}$.

    1—Answer: Diverges, Ratio Test

28. Determine the convergence or divergence of the following series, and state the test used: $\displaystyle\sum_{n=0}^{\infty}\frac{1}{e^n}$.

    1—Answer: Converges, Ratio Test

29. Determine the convergence or divergence of the following series, and state the test used:

$$\sum_{n=1}^{\infty}\frac{1\cdot3\cdot5\cdots(2n-1)}{n!}.$$

    1—Answer: Diverges, Ratio Test

30. Determine the convergence or divergence of the series using the Ratio Test: $\displaystyle\sum_{n=0}^{\infty} \frac{3^n}{(n+1)!}$.

(a) The Ratio Test does not apply

(b) The Ratio Test is inconclusive

(c) Diverges by the Ratio Test

(d) Converges by the Ratio Test

(e) None of these

1—Answer: d

31. Determine the convergence or divergence of the series using the Ratio Test: $\displaystyle\sum_{n=1}^{\infty} \frac{n!}{(n+5)!}$.

(a) The Ratio Test does not apply

(b) Converges by the Ratio Test

(c) Diverges by the Ratio Test

(d) The Ratio Test is inconclusive

(e) None of these

1—Answer: d

32. Determine the convergence or divergence of the series using the Ratio Test: $\displaystyle\sum_{n=1}^{\infty} \frac{n!}{(n-1)!}$.

(a) The Ratio Test is inconclusive

(b) Diverges by the Ratio Test

(c) Converges by the Ratio Test

(d) The Ratio Test does not apply

(e) None of these

1—Answer: a

33. Determine the convergence or divergence of the series using the Ratio Test: $\displaystyle\sum_{n=1}^{\infty} \frac{n!}{(n-8)!}$.

(a) Diverges by the Ratio Test

(b) The Ratio Test is inconclusive

(c) Converges by the Ratio Test

(d) The Ratio Test does not apply

(e) None of these

1—Answer: b

34. Determine the convergence or divergence of the series using the Ratio Test: $\displaystyle\sum_{n=1}^{\infty} \frac{n!}{(n-4)!}$.

(a) The Ratio does not apply

(b) The Ratio Test is inconclusive

(c) Converges by the Ratio Test

(d) Diverges by the Ratio Test

(e) None of these

1—Answer: b

35. Find N so that $R_N < 0.001$ for the convergent series $\displaystyle\sum_{n=1}^{\infty} \frac{1}{n^2}$.

2—Answer: 1000

36. Find N so that $R_N < 0.001$ for the convergent series $\sum\limits_{n=1}^{\infty} \dfrac{1}{n^{3/2}}$.

(a) $10\sqrt{2}$ (b) 4,000,000   (c) 1000   (d) 4000   (e) None of these

2—Answer: b

37. Choose the best answer. (Use the fourth partial sum.) $S = \sum\limits_{n=1}^{\infty} \dfrac{8}{n^2}$

(a) $\dfrac{437}{36} < S < \dfrac{455}{36}$ (b) $\dfrac{401}{36} < S < \dfrac{419}{36}$ (c) $\dfrac{383}{36} < S < \dfrac{401}{36}$

(d) $\dfrac{419}{36} < S < \dfrac{437}{36}$ (e) None of these

1—Answer: b

38. Choose the best answer. (Use the fourth partial sum.) $S = \sum\limits_{n=1}^{\infty} \dfrac{6}{n^2}$

(a) $\dfrac{199}{24} < S < \dfrac{211}{24}$ (b) $\dfrac{223}{24} < S < \dfrac{235}{24}$ (c) $\dfrac{187}{24} < S < \dfrac{199}{24}$

(d) $\dfrac{211}{24} < S < \dfrac{224}{24}$ (e) None of these

1—Answer: a

39. Choose the best answer. (Use the fourth partial sum.) $S = \sum\limits_{n=1}^{\infty} \dfrac{4}{n^2}$

(a) $\dfrac{89}{18} < S < \dfrac{49}{9}$ (b) $\dfrac{107}{18} < S < \dfrac{58}{9}$ (c) $\dfrac{49}{9} < S < \dfrac{107}{18}$

(d) $\dfrac{59}{8} < S < \dfrac{125}{18}$ (e) None of these

1—Answer: c

40. In a complete sentence, state what must be true about the series

$$\sum_{n=0}^{\infty} a_n$$

if the ratio test is used to show that it converges.

1—Answer: Answers will vary.

41. Explain, in a complete sentence, how a convergent series converges by explaining what must happen to the corresponding sequence of partial sums.

1—Answer: Answers will vary.

Section 10.4 Power Series and Taylor's Theorem

1. Find the radius of convergence for the power series $\sum_{n=1}^{\infty} \frac{(2x)^n}{n}$.

   (a) $\frac{1}{2}$ (b) 2   (c) ∞ (d) 0   (e) None of these

   1—Answer: a

2. Find the radius of convergence for the power series $\sum_{n=0}^{\infty} \left(\frac{x}{2}\right)^n$.

   (a) $\frac{1}{2}$ (b) 2   (c) ∞ (d) 0   (e) None of these

   1—Answer: b

3. Find the radius of convergence: $\sum_{n=1}^{\infty} \frac{2 \cdot 5 \cdot 8 \cdots (3n-1)}{3 \cdot 7 \cdot 11 \cdots (4n-1)} x^n$.

   2—Answer: $\frac{4}{3}$

4. Find the radius of convergence for the power series $\sum_{n=1}^{\infty} \frac{(3x)^n}{n}$.

   (a) $\frac{1}{3}$ (b) 3   (c) ∞ (d) 0   (e) None of these

   1—Answer: a

5. Find the radius of convergence for the power series $\sum_{n=0}^{\infty} \left(\frac{x}{2}\right)^n$.

   (a) $\frac{1}{2}$ (b) 2   (c) ∞ (d) 0   (e) None of these

   1—Answer: b

6. Find the radius of convergence for the power series $\sum_{n=0}^{\infty} \frac{(3x)^n}{n+1}$.

   (a) 3   (b) ∞ (c) $\frac{1}{3}$ (d) 0   (e) None of these

   1—Answer: c

7. Find the radius of convergence for the power series $\sum_{n=0}^{\infty} \frac{x^n}{4(n^2+3)}$.

   (a) 3   (b) $\frac{1}{4}$ (c) 1   (d) 4   (e) None of these

   1—Answer: c

8. Find the radius of convergence for the power series $\sum_{n=0}^{\infty} \frac{x^n}{3(n^2+4)}$.

   (a) 3   (b) $\frac{1}{3}$ (c) 1   (d) 4   (e) None of these

   1—Answer: c

9. Find the radius of convergence for the power series $\displaystyle\sum_{n=0}^{\infty}\left(\frac{2x}{3}\right)^n$.

1—Answer: $\frac{3}{2}$

10. Find the Maclaurin Series for $f(x) = e^{2x}$.

(a) $1 + 4x + \dfrac{16x^2}{2!} + \dfrac{64x^3}{3!} + \dfrac{256x^4}{4!} + \cdots$

(b) $1 + 2x + \dfrac{4x^2}{2!} + \dfrac{8x^3}{3!} + \dfrac{16x^4}{4!} + \cdots$

(c) $2\left(1 + x + \dfrac{x^2}{2!} + \dfrac{x^3}{3!} + \dfrac{x^4}{4!} + \cdots\right)$

(d) $2\left(1 - x + \dfrac{x^2}{2!} - \dfrac{x^3}{3!} + \dfrac{x^4}{4!} - \cdots\right)$

(e) None of these

1—Answer: b

11. Find the Maclaurin Series for $f(x) = e^{-2x}$.

(a) $1 - 2x + \dfrac{4x^2}{2!} - \dfrac{8x^3}{3!} + \dfrac{16x^4}{4!} - \cdots$

(b) $1 + 2x + \dfrac{4x^3}{2!} + \dfrac{8x^3}{3!} + \dfrac{16x^4}{4!} + \cdots$

(c) $-2\left(1 + x + \dfrac{x^2}{2!} + \dfrac{x^3}{3!} + \dfrac{x^4}{4!} + \cdots\right)$

(d) $-2 + x + \dfrac{x^2}{2!} + \dfrac{x^3}{3!} + \dfrac{x^4}{4!} + \cdots$

(e) None of these

1—Answer: a

12. Find the Maclaurin Series for $f(x) = xe^x$.

(a) $x + \dfrac{x^3}{3!} + \dfrac{x^5}{5!} + \dfrac{x^7}{7!} + \cdots$

(b) $1 + x + \dfrac{x^2}{2!} + \dfrac{x^3}{3!} + \dfrac{x^4}{4!} + \cdots$

(c) $1 + \dfrac{x^2}{2!} + \dfrac{x^4}{4!} + \dfrac{x^6}{6!} + \cdots$

(d) $x + x^2 + \dfrac{x^3}{2!} + \dfrac{x^4}{3!} + \dfrac{x^5}{4!} + \cdots$

(e) None of these

1—Answer: d

13. Find the Maclaurin Series for $f(x) = \ln(x + 1)$.

(a) $x - \dfrac{x^2}{2!} + \dfrac{x^3}{3!} + \dfrac{x^4}{4!} + \cdots$

(b) $x + \dfrac{x^2}{2} + \dfrac{x^3}{3} + \dfrac{x^4}{4} + \cdots$

(c) $x - x^2 + x^3 - x^4 + \cdots$

(d) $x - \dfrac{x^2}{2} + \dfrac{x^3}{3} + \dfrac{x^4}{4} + \cdots$

(e) None of these

1—Answer: d

14. Find the first three nonzero terms in the Maclaurin Series for the function $f(x) = \ln(x + 2)$.

1—Answer: $\ln(x + 2) = \ln 2 + \dfrac{x}{2} - \dfrac{x^2}{8} + \cdots$

15. Find the first three nonzero terms in a Maclaurin Series for the function $f(x) = \dfrac{2}{x+3}$.

(a) $\dfrac{2}{3} + \dfrac{2}{9}x + \dfrac{2}{27}x^2$ (b) $\dfrac{2}{3} - \dfrac{2}{9}x + \dfrac{4}{27}x^2$ (c) $\dfrac{2}{3} - \dfrac{2}{9}x + \dfrac{2}{27}x^2$

(d) $\dfrac{2}{3} - 2x + 2x^2$ (e) None of these

1—Answer: c

16. Find the first three nonzero terms in a Taylor Series for the function $y = \ln x$ centered at 3.

1—Answer: $\ln 3 + \dfrac{1}{3}(x-3) - \dfrac{1}{18}(x-3)^2$

17. Find the first three nonzero terms in a Taylor Series for the function $y = \ln x$ centered at 2.

(a) $\ln 2 + \dfrac{x-2}{2} - \dfrac{(x-2)^2}{8}$ (b) $\ln 2 - \dfrac{x-2}{2} - \dfrac{(x-2)^2}{8}$ (c) $\ln 2 + \dfrac{x-2}{2} - \dfrac{(x-2)^2}{4}$

(d) $\ln 2 + \dfrac{x-2}{2} + \dfrac{(x-2)^2}{8}$ (e) None of these

1—Answer: a

18. Find the fourth term of the Taylor Series for $f(x) = \ln x$ centered at $x = 1$.

2—Answer: $-\dfrac{1}{4}(x-1)^4$

19. Find the first four terms in the Taylor Series centered at 2 for the function $f(x) = \dfrac{1}{x}$.

1—Answer: $\dfrac{1}{2} - \dfrac{1}{4}(x-2) + \dfrac{1}{8}(x-2)^2 - \dfrac{1}{16}(x-2)^3$

20. Find a power series centered at $x = 0$ for $f(x) = \dfrac{1}{x+4}$.

(a) $\displaystyle\sum_{n=0}^{\infty} \dfrac{(-1)^n}{4^{n+1}}x^n$ (b) $\displaystyle\sum_{n=0}^{\infty} \dfrac{(-1)^n n!}{4^{n+1}}x^n$ (c) $\displaystyle\sum_{n=0}^{\infty} \dfrac{(-1)^n n!}{(x+4)^n}$

(d) $\displaystyle\sum_{n=0}^{\infty} \dfrac{(-1)^n}{4^{n+1}}(x+4)^n$ (e) None of these

2—Answer: a

21. Find a power series centered at $x = 0$ for $f(x) = \dfrac{1}{x+9}$.

(a) $\displaystyle\sum_{n=0}^{\infty} \dfrac{(-1)^n n!}{9^{n+1}}x^n$ (b) $\displaystyle\sum_{n=0}^{\infty} \dfrac{(-1)^n n!}{(x+9)^n}$ (c) $\displaystyle\sum_{n=0}^{\infty} \dfrac{(-1)^n}{9^{n+1}}x^n$

(d) $\displaystyle\sum_{n=0}^{\infty} \dfrac{(-1)^n}{9^{n+1}}(x+9)^n$ (e) None of these

2—Answer: c

22. Given $f(x) = \sum_{n=0}^{\infty} \dfrac{3x^n}{n!}$, find a power series for $f'(x)$.

1—Answer: $f'(x) = \sum_{n=0}^{\infty} \dfrac{3x^n}{n!}$

23. Given $f(x) = \sum_{n=0}^{\infty} \dfrac{(-1)^n x^{2n}}{(2n)!}$, find a power series for $f'(x)$.

1—Answer: $f'(x) = \sum_{n=1}^{\infty} \dfrac{(-1)^n x^{2n-1}}{(2n-1)!}$

24. Given $f(x) = \sum_{n=0}^{\infty} \dfrac{(-1)^n x^{2n+1}}{(2n+1)!}$, find a power series for $f'(x)$.

1—Answer: $f'(x) = \sum_{n=0}^{\infty} \dfrac{(-1)^n x^{2n}}{(2n)!}$

25. If $\dfrac{1}{1-x} = \sum_{n=0}^{\infty} x^n = 1 + x + x^2 + x^3 + \cdots$, which of the following is a power series expansion for the function

$f(x) = \dfrac{1}{1-x^2}$?

(a) $1 + x^2 + x^3 + x^4 + \cdots$ (b) $x + x^2 + x^3 + x^4 + \cdots$ (c) $1 + x^2 + x^4 + x^6 + \cdots$

(d) $x^2 + x^3 + x^4 + x^5 + \cdots$ (e) None of these

1—Answer: c

26. If $\dfrac{1}{1-x} = 1 + x + x^2 + x^3 + \cdots$, which of the following is a power series expansion for the function

$f(x) = \ln|1 - x|$?

(a) $x + \dfrac{x^2}{2} + \dfrac{x^3}{3} + \dfrac{x^4}{4} + \cdots$ (b) $\ln|1 + x + x^2 + x^3 + \cdots|$ (c) $1 + 2x + 3x^2 + \cdots$

(d) $-x - \dfrac{x^2}{2} - \dfrac{x^3}{3} - \dfrac{x^4}{4} - \cdots$ (e) None of these

1—Answer: d

27. Find a power series centered at $x = 0$ for $f(x) = \dfrac{1}{x+8}$.

(a) $\sum_{n=0}^{\infty} \dfrac{(-1)^n n!}{(x+8)^n}$ (b) $\sum_{n=0}^{\infty} \dfrac{(-1)^n}{8^{n+1}} x^n$ (c) $\sum_{n=0}^{\infty} \dfrac{(-1)^n n!}{8^{n+1}} x^n$

(d) $\sum_{n=0}^{\infty} \dfrac{(-1)^n}{8^{n+1}} (x+8)^n$ (e) None of these

2—Answer: b

28. Find a power series centered at $x = 0$ for $f(x) = \dfrac{1}{x + 6}$.

(a) $\displaystyle\sum_{n=0}^{\infty} \frac{(-1)^n}{6^{n+1}}(x + 6)^n$

(b) $\displaystyle\sum_{n=0}^{\infty} \frac{(-1)^n n!}{(x + 6)^n}$

(c) $\displaystyle\sum_{n=0}^{\infty} \frac{(-1)^n}{6^{n+1}} x^n$

(d) $\displaystyle\sum_{n=0}^{\infty} \frac{(-1)^n n!}{6^{n+1}} x^n$

(e) None of these

2—Answer: c

Section 10.5 Taylor Polynomials

1. Find the third-degree Taylor polynomial centered at $c = 1$ for the function $f(x) = e^{3x}$.

(a) $e^3 + 3e^3x + \dfrac{9e^3x^2}{2} + \dfrac{9e^3x^3}{2}$

(b) $e^3x + \dfrac{3e^3x^2}{2} + \dfrac{3e^3x^3}{2} + \dfrac{9e^3x^4}{8}$

(c) $e^3(x + 1) + \dfrac{3e^3(x + 1)^2}{2} + \dfrac{3e^3(x + 1)^3}{2} + \dfrac{9e^3(x + 1)^4}{8}$

(d) $e^3 + 3e^3(x - 1) + \dfrac{9e^3(x - 1)^2}{2} + \dfrac{9e^3(x - 1)^3}{2}$

(e) None of these

1—Answer: d

2. Find the third-degree Taylor polynomial centered at $c = 0$ for the function $f(x) = e^{3x}$.

(a) $1 + 3x + 9x^2 + 27x^3$ 　　　　(b) $e + 3ex + 9ex^2 + 27ex^3$ 　　　　(c) $1 + 3x + \dfrac{9}{2}x^2 + \dfrac{9}{2}x^3$

(d) $1 + x + \dfrac{x^2}{2} + \dfrac{x^3}{3}$ 　　　　(e) None of these

1—Answer: c

3. Find the third-degree Taylor polynomial centered at $c = 0$ for the function $f(x) = \sqrt{x + 4}$.

(a) $2 + \dfrac{1}{4}x - \dfrac{1}{64}x^2 + \dfrac{1}{512}x^3$ 　　　　　　　　(b) $4 + \dfrac{1}{2}x - \dfrac{1}{32}x^2 + \dfrac{3}{256}x^3$

(c) $2 + (x + 4) + \dfrac{(x + 4)^2}{32} + \dfrac{(x + 4)^3}{512}$ 　　　　(d) $2 - \dfrac{x + 4}{4} - \dfrac{(x + 4)^2}{32} + \dfrac{3(x + 4)^3}{256}$

(e) None of these

1—Answer: a

4. Find the fourth-degree Taylor polynomial centered at $c = 3$ for the function $f(x) = \ln(x - 2)$.

(a) $1 + x - \dfrac{x^2}{2} + \dfrac{x^3}{3} + \dfrac{x^4}{4}$ 　　　　　　　　(b) $(x + 3) - \dfrac{(x + 3)^2}{2!} + \dfrac{(x + 3)^3}{3!} - \dfrac{(x + 3)^4}{4!}$

(c) $(x - 3) - \dfrac{(x - 3)^2}{2!} + \dfrac{(x - 3)^3}{3!} + \dfrac{(x - 3)^4}{4!}$ 　　(d) $(x - 3) - \dfrac{(x - 3)^2}{2} + \dfrac{(x - 3)^3}{3} - \dfrac{(x - 3)^4}{4}$

(e) None of these

1—Answer: d

5. Find the third-degree Taylor polynomial centered at 0 for the function $f(x) = e^{2x} + 3x$.

   (a) $4 + 5x + 2x^2 + \frac{4}{3}x^3$ (b) $1 + 5x + 4x^2 + 8x^3$ (c) $1 + 5x + 2x^2 + 8x^3$

   (d) $1 + 5x + 2x^2 + \frac{4}{3}x^3$ (e) None of these

   1—Answer: d

6. Find the third-degree Taylor polynomial centered at 1 for the function $f(x) = \dfrac{x + 3}{x}$.

   (a) $13 - 18 + 12x^2 - 3x^3$ (b) $4 + 3x + 3x^2 + 3x^3$ (c) $4 - 3x + 6x^2 - 18x^3$

   (d) $4 + 3x + 6x^2 + 18x^3$ (e) None of these

   1—Answer: a

7. Find the Taylor polynomial of degree two for the function $f(x) = \ln(x^2 + 4)$ centered at 0.

   (a) $\ln 4 + \dfrac{5}{32}x^2$ (b) $\ln 4 + \dfrac{x}{2} + \dfrac{x^2}{4}$ (c) $\ln 4 + \dfrac{x^2}{2}$ (d) $\ln 4 + \dfrac{x^2}{4}$ (e) None of these

   1—Answer: d

8. Find the third-degree Taylor polynomial centered at 0 for $f(x) = e^x$.

   1—Answer: $P_3(x) = 1 + x + \dfrac{x^2}{2} + \dfrac{x^3}{3!}$

9. Find the fourth-degree Taylor polynomial for $f(x) = \ln x$, centered at $x = 1$.

   1—Answer: $P_4(x) = (x - 1) - \dfrac{(x - 1)^2}{2} + \dfrac{(x - 1)^3}{3} - \dfrac{(x - 1)^4}{4}$

10. Find the third term of the Taylor polynomial centered at 0 for $f(x) = e^{x/2}$.

    (a) $\dfrac{x^2}{8}$ (b) $\dfrac{x^2}{2}$ (c) $\dfrac{x^3}{48}$ (d) $\dfrac{x^3}{6}$ (e) None of these

    1—Answer: a

11. Find the third term of the Taylor polynomial centered at 0 for $f(x) = e^{-x^2}$.

    (a) $\dfrac{x^2}{2}$ (b) $\dfrac{x^4}{2}$ (c) $\dfrac{-x^6}{6}$ (d) $\dfrac{x^6}{12}$ (e) None of these

    1—Answer: b

12. Use a power series centered at 0 to get a degree two approximation for $\sqrt[4]{1.5}$ using the function $f(x) = \sqrt[4]{x + 1}$.

    1—Answer: 1.1015625

13. Use a fourth-degree Taylor polynomial, centered at 2, for the function $f(x) = \ln(x - 2)$ to approximate $\ln(1.5)$.

   (a) 0.416   (b) 0.401   (c) 0.427   (d) 0.399   (e) None of these

   1—T—Answer: b

14. Use a third-degree Taylor polynomial, centered at $c = 4$, for the function $f(x) = \sqrt{x}$ to approximate $\sqrt{6}$.

   (a) $\frac{149}{64}$ (b) $\frac{151}{64}$ (c) $\frac{157}{64}$ (d) $\frac{163}{64}$ (e) None of these

   1—Answer: c

15. Use a fourth-degree Taylor polynomial (centered at 1) to approximate $\ln 1.1$.

   (a) 0.095310   (b) 0.095308   (c) 3.004160   (d) 0.105355   (e) None of these

   1—Answer: b

16. Use a fourth-degree Taylor polynomial to approximate e^2.

   1—Answer: 7

17. Use a third-degree Taylor polynomial to approximate the number e.

   1—T—Answer: $\frac{8}{3}$

18. Find an approximation for

$$f(3) \text{ where } f(x) = \frac{1}{x}$$

   by using the first four terms of a Taylor polynomial centered at 2.

   1—Answer: $\frac{5}{16}$

19. Use a power series, centered at 0, to get a degree two approximation for $\sqrt[3]{1.5}$ using the function $f(x) = \sqrt[3]{x + 1}$.

   (a) 1.139   (b) 1.743   (c) 1.043   (d) 1.424   (e) None of these

   1—T—Answer: a

20. Find the error in using a degree two Taylor polynomial (centered at 0) to approximate $\ln 2$ by using the function $f(x) = \ln(x + 1)$.

   1—T—Answer: 0.193

Section 10.6 Newton's Method

1. Complete two iterations of Newton's Method to approximate a zero of $f(x) = x^3 + 2x - 1$ using $x_1 = 0.5$ as an initial estimate. Round to four decimal places.

   (a) $x_3 = 0.4545$ (b) $x_3 = 0.4562$ (c) $x_3 = 0.4534$ (d) $x_3 = 0.4529$ (e) None of these

   1—T—Answer: c

2. Complete two iterations of Newton's Method to approximate a zero of $f(x) = x^5 + 2x - 1$ using $x_1 = 0.5$ as an initial estimate. Round to four decimal places.

   (a) $x_3 = 0.4865$ (b) $x_3 = 0.4864$ (c) $x_3 = 0.4863$ (d) $x_3 = 0.4866$ (e) None of these

   1—T—Answer: b

3. Complete two iterations of Newton's Method to approximate a zero in the interval $(0, 0.9)$ of $f(x) = 2x^5 - 3x^2 + 1$ using $x_1 = 0.8$ as an initial estimate. Round to four decimal places.

   (a) $x_3 = 0.6651$ (b) $x_3 = 0.6437$ (c) $x_3 = 0.6502$ (d) $x_3 = 0.6614$ (e) None of these

   1—T—Answer: b

4. Complete two iterations of Newton's Method to approximate a zero of $f(x) = 3x^3 - 7$ using $x_1 = 1.2$ as an initial estimate. Round to four decimal places.

   (a) $x_3 = 1.3431$ (b) $x_3 = 1.3392$ (c) $x_3 = 1.3265$ (d) $x_3 = 1.3252$ (e) None of these

   1—T—Answer: c

5. Complete two iterations of Newton's Method to approximate a zero of $f(x) = -3x^3 - 2x + 2$ using $x_1 = 0.5$ as an initial estimate. Round to four decimal places.

   (a) $x_3 = 0.6471$ (b) $x_3 = 0.6285$ (c) $x_3 = 0.6282$ (d) $x_3 = 0.6281$ (e) None of these

   1—T—Answer: b

6. Complete two iterations of Newton's Method to approximate a zero of $f(x) = x^3 - 10$ using $x_1 = 3$ as an initial estimate. Round to four decimal places.

   (a) $x_3 = 2.14$ (b) $x_3 = 2.28$ (c) $x_3 = 2.17$ (d) $x_3 = 2.71$ (e) None of these

   1—T—Answer: c

7. Complete one iteration of Newton's Method for $f(x) = 2x^2 - 3$ using $x_1 = 1.3$ as an initial estimate. What is the value of x_2? Use four decimal places.

   (a) 0.3800 (b) 1.2247 (c) 12.3842 (d) 1.2269 (e) None of these

   1—Answer: d

8. Complete one iteration of Newton's Method for $f(x) = 2x^2 - 3$ using $x_1 = 1.5$ as an initial estimate. What is the value of x_2? Use four decimal places.

   (a) 1.5000 (b) 1.2247 (c) 2.5000 (d) 1.2500 (e) None of these

   1—Answer: d

9. Calculate three iterations of Newton's Method to approximate a zero of $f(x) = -x^3 + x + 1$. Use $x_1 = 1.0000$ as the initial guess and round to four decimal places after each iteration.

   (a) 1.5432   (b) 1.1056   (c) 1.3252   (d) 1.3198   (e) None of these

   1—Answer: c

10. Calculate three iterations of Newton's Method to approximate a zero of $f(x) = x^3 - 2x - 2$. Use $x_1 = 1.5000$ as the initial guess and round to four decimal places after each iteration.

    (a) 1.7693   (b) 1.9867   (c) 2.0003   (d) 1.8196   (e) None of these

    1—Answer: a

11. Calculate three iterations of Newton's Method to approximate a zero of $f(x) = x^3 - x + 1$. Use $x_1 = -1.5000$ as the initial guess and round to four decimal places after each iteration.

    1—Answer: -1.3247

12. Use Newton's Method to approximate the real zero of the function in the interval $[-1, 0]$: $f(x) = x^3 + x + 1$.

    (a) -0.83 (b) -0.68 (c) -0.48 (d) -0.23 (e) None of these

    2—Answer: b

13. Use Newton's Method to approximate the real zero of the function in the interval $[0, 1]$: $f(x) = 3x^3 + x^2 - 16x + 10$.

    (a) 0.58   (b) 0.65   (c) 0.73   (d) 0.94   (e) None of these

    2—Answer: c

14. Use Newton's Method to approximate the real zero of the function in the interval $[0, 1]$: $f(x) = x^3 + 2x - 1$.

    (a) 0.450   (b) 0.453   (c) 0.456   (d) 0.459   (e) None of these

    2—Answer: b

15. Use Newton's Method to approximate the zero of $f(x) = x^3 + 4x + 2$ in the interval $[-1, 0]$. (Use an accuracy of ± 0.001.)

    2—Answer: 0.473

16. Use Newton's Method to approximate the zero of $f(x) = x^3 + x - 3$ in the interval $[-2, -1]$. (Use an accuracy of ± 0.001.)

    2—Answer: -1.213

MID-CHAPTER QUIZZES

Mid-Chapter Quiz Name _____ Date _____

Chapter 0 Class _____ Section _____

1. Solve for x: $\frac{5}{8}x - 4 \geq x - 1$

   (a) $[8, \infty)$ (b) $x \geq \frac{24}{5}$ (c) $(-\infty, -8]$ (d) $[-8, \infty)$ (e) $x \leq -\frac{24}{5}$

2. Find the directed distance from a to b. $b = -4$, $a = 5$

   (a) 9 (b) -9 (c) 1 (d) -1 (e) None of these

3. Solve for x: $|2x - 6| < 10$.

   (a) $(2, 8)$ (b) $(-\infty, -2) \cup (8, \infty)$ (c) $(8, \infty)$

   (d) $(-2, \infty)$ (e) $(-\infty, -2] \cup [8, \infty)$

4. Simplify: $\left(\frac{3x^2y^3}{xw^{-2}}\right)^3$

   (a) $9w^6x^3y^9$ (b) $9w^{-8}x^8y^{27}$ (c) $27w^6x^3y^9$

   (d) $3w^6x^3y^9$ (e) None of these

5. Evaluate the following expression when $x = 2$, $y = -1$, $a = 1$, $b = -2$: $-\frac{2(xy)^3}{a^2b^3}$

   (a) 2 (b) -2 (c) $\frac{1}{2}$

   (d) $-\frac{1}{2}$ (e) None of these

6. Simplify: $(2x^3)^4(3x^2)^3$.

   (a) $432x^{18}$ (b) $279{,}936x^{42}$ (c) $6x^{18}$ (d) $6x^{32}$ (e) None of these

7. Determine which of the following values for x satisfies the inequality $3 \leq \dfrac{4 - x}{2} < 5$.

   (a) $x = 4$ (b) $x = -2$ (c) $x = -1$

   (d) All of these (e) None of these

8. The revenue for selling x units of a product is $R = 79.99x$, and the cost of producing x units of the product is $C = 61x + 1050$. To obtain a profit, the revenue must be greater than the cost. For what values of x will this product return a profit?

   (a) $x \geq 52$ (b) $x \geq 8$ (c) $x \geq 18$ (d) $x \geq 53$ (e) None of these

9. Graph the solution: $|2 - x| \le 5$.

(a)

(b)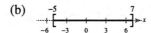

(c)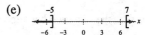

(d)

(e)

10. A 20-year mortgage for $P = \$56,000$ at an annual percentage rate of $r = .07$ requires a monthly payment of $M = \$424.17$. Payments have been made on the loan for 3 years ($N = 36$ monthly payments). Determine the balance B due on the loan if the balance is given by $B = \left(1 + \dfrac{r}{12}\right)^N \left(P - \dfrac{12M}{r}\right) + \dfrac{12M}{r}$.

(a) $53,207.02   (b) $47,492.18   (c) $52,106.68   (d) $40,729.88   (e) None of these

Mid-Chapter Quiz

Name _____   Date _____

Chapter 1

Class _____   Section _____

1. Find x so that the distance between $(x, -4)$ and $(5, -8)$ is 5.

    (a) $x = 1, 9$ (b) $x = 2, 8$ (c) $x = 0, 10$ (d) $x = -1, 1$ (e) None of these

2. Find the center of the circle: $4x^2 + 4y^2 - 2x + 8y - 1 = 0$.

    (a) $(1, -4)$ (b) $(-1, 4)$ (c) $\left(\frac{1}{2}, -2\right)$ (d) $(1, 1)$ (e) None of these

3. Find the x-intercept(s): $y = x^3(x + 2)(3x - 1)$.

    (a) $0, -2, \frac{1}{3}$ (b) 0 (c) $0, 2, -1$ (d) $-2, \frac{1}{3}$ (e) There are no x-intercepts.

4. Find the equation of the line that has a slope of $-\frac{3}{4}$ and passes through $(1, 2)$.

    (a) $3x - 4y - 7 = 0$ (b) $3x - 4y - 11 = 0$ (c) $3x + 4y - 11 = 0$

    (d) $3x + 4y + 11 = 0$ (e) None of these

5. Find the equation of the line that passes through $(1, 3)$ and is perpendicular to the line $2x + 3y + 5 = 0$.

    (a) $3x - 2y + 3 = 0$ (b) $2x + 3y - 11 = 0$ (c) $2x + 3y - 9 = 0$

    (d) $3x - 2y - 7 = 0$ (e) None of these

6. Identify the graph of the equation: $y = \sqrt{2 - x}$.

    (a)

    (b)

    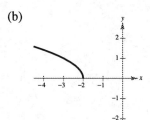

    (c)

    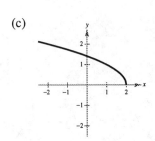

    (d)

    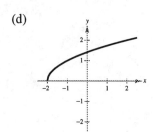

    (e) None of these

7. Find the midpoint of the line segment joining $(-2, 1)$ and $(16, 3)$.

    (a) $(7, 2)$ (b) $(9, 1)$ (c) $(14, 4)$ (d) $(-9, -1)$ (e) None of these

8. A triangle with the vertices $(2, 8)$, $(4, 1)$, and $(7, 5)$ is translated to a new position in the plane. The vertex $(2, 8)$ is translated to the position $(-4, -1)$. Determine the new vertex corresponding to the point $(4, 1)$.

    (a) $(-5, -5)$ (b) $(-2, -8)$

    (c) $(1, -4)$ (d) $(-1, -2)$ (e) None of these

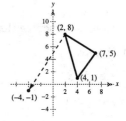

9. Find all points of intersection of the graphs of $x^2 + 3x - y = 3$ and $x + y = 2$.

    (a) $(5, -3), (1, 1)$ (b) $(0, -3), (0, 2)$ (c) $(-5, -3), (1, 1)$

    (d) $(-5, 7), (1, 1)$ (e) None of these

10. A local worker earns a base pay of \$11.15 per hour plus an additional piecework rate of \$0.19 per unit produced. Write a linear equation giving the weekly 40-hour wage W in terms of x, the number of units produced.

    (a) $W = 11.34x$ (b) $W = 446 + 0.19x$ (c) $W = 11.15 + 7.6x$

    (d) $W = 11.15 + 0.19x$ (e) None of these

Mid-Chapter Quiz

Chapter 2

Name _____ Date _____

Class _____ Section _____

1. Determine whether the slope at the indicated point is positive, negative, or zero.

   (a) Positive   (b) Zero

   (c) Negative   (d) No Slope

   (e) None of these

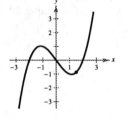

2. Determine where the function is not differentiable.

   (a) $(-\infty, 0)(0, \infty)$

   (b) $y = 0$

   (c) $(-\infty, 1)(1, \infty)$

   (d) $x = 1$

   (e) None of these

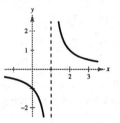

3. Find an equation of the line tangent to $f(x) = 3x^2 + 1$ at the point $(2, 13)$.

   (a) $y = 12x - 11$ (b) $y = 12x - 154$ (c) $y = 3x + 7$

   (d) $y = 3x + 37$ (e) None of these

4. Find $\dfrac{dy}{dx}$ for $y = \sqrt{x}(3x - 1)$.

   (a) $\dfrac{9x - 1}{2\sqrt{x}}$ (b) $\dfrac{9}{2}\sqrt{x} - 1$ (c) $3\sqrt{x}$ (d) $\dfrac{3}{2\sqrt{x}}$ (e) None of these

5. Let $g(x) = 3f(x) + 5$ and let $f'(4) = 2$. Use the Constant and Constant Multiple Rules to find $g'(4)$.

   (a) 11   (b) 7   (c) 6   (d) 17   (e) None of these

6. Differentiate: $y = \dfrac{x^2}{3x^2 - 1}$.

   (a) $\dfrac{2x}{(3x^2 - 1)^2}$ (b) $\dfrac{2x(6x^2 + 1)}{(3x^2 - 1)^2}$ (c) $\dfrac{-2x}{(3x^2 - 1)^2}$ (d) $\dfrac{2x(6x^2 - 1)}{(3x^2 - 1)^2}$ (e) None of these

7. Find an equation of the tangent line to the graph of $f(x) = \dfrac{(x - 1)}{(x + 1)}$ when $x = 1$.

   (a) $y = \dfrac{2}{(x + 1)^2}(x - 1)$ (b) $x - 2y = 1$ (c) $y - 1 = \dfrac{1}{2}x$

   (d) $y = 2(x - 1)$ (e) None of these

8. The demand function and cost function for x units of a product are $p = \dfrac{40}{\sqrt{x}}$ and $C = 0.5x + 400$. Find the revenue as a function of x.

(a) $R = 40\sqrt{x}$

(b) $R = \dfrac{40}{\sqrt{x}} - 0.5x - 400$

(c) $R = \dfrac{40}{\sqrt{x}} + 0.5x + 400$

(d) $R = \dfrac{40}{\sqrt{x}}(0.5x + 400)$

(e) None of these

9. Find the derivative of y with respect to x if $y = 4x(2x + 3)$.

(a) $16x + 12$ (b) $20x$ (c) $8x + 12$ (d) $4x + 6$ (e) None of these

10. Find the derivative of $9x^2 f(x)$.

(a) $9x^2 f'(x)$

(b) $9x[xf(x) + 2f'(x)]$

(c) $18xf'(x)$

(d) $9x[xf'(x) + 2f(x)]$

(e) None of these

Mid-Chapter Quiz   Name _____   Date _____

Chapter 3   Class _____   Section _____

1. Find all open intervals on which the function is increasing: $f(x) = (3x + 1)\sqrt[3]{x + 2}$.

    (a) $\left(-2, \frac{1}{3}\right)$ (b) $(-2.8, -1.58)$ (c) $(-1.58, \infty)$ (d) $(-2.8, \infty)$ (e) None of these

2. Find all critical numbers: $f(x) = (9 - x^2)^{3/5}$.

    (a) 0   (b) 3   (c) $-3, 3$ (d) $-3, 0, 3$ (e) None of these

3. Find the absolute maximum and absolute minimum of f on $(-1, 2]$. $f(x) = \dfrac{x^3 - x^2 - 3x - 1}{x + 1}$.

    (a) Maximum: $(-1, 2)$; Minimum: $(2, -1)$ (b) Maximum: None; Minimum: $(1, -2)$

    (c) Maximum: $(-1, 2)$; Minimum: $(1, -2)$ (d) Maximum: None; Minimum: $(2, -1)$

    (e) None of these

4. Which of the following statements is true of $f(x) = -x^3 + 18x^2 - 105x + 198$?

    (a) f is decreasing on $(6, \infty)$ (b) f is decreasing on $(5, 7)$

    (c) f is increasing on $(-\infty, 5)$ (d) f is increasing on $(5, 7)$

    (e) None of these

5. Given that $f(x) = -x^2 + 18x - 78$ has an absolute maximum at $x = 9$, choose the correct statement.

    (a) f' is negative on the interval $(-\infty, 9)$

    (b) f' is negative on the interval $(9, \infty)$

    (c) f' is positive on the interval $(-\infty, \infty)$

    (d) f' is positive on the interval $(9, \infty)$

    (e) None of these

6. Find all points of inflection of the function $f(x) = x^4 - x^3$.

    (a) $(0, 0)$ and $\left(\frac{3}{4}, -\frac{27}{256}\right)$ (b) $(0, 0)$ (c) $(0, 0)$ and $\left(\frac{1}{2}, -\frac{1}{16}\right)$
    (d) $\left(\frac{1}{2}, -\frac{1}{16}\right)$ (e) None of these

7. Find all intervals on which the function is concave upward: $f(x) = \dfrac{x^2 + 1}{x^2}$.

    (a) $(-\infty, \infty)$ (b) $(-\infty, -1)$ and $(1, \infty)$ (c) $(-\infty, 0)$ and $(0, \infty)$

    (d) $(1, \infty)$ (e) None of these

8. Find two positive integers whose sum is a minimum of all sets of two numbers whose product is 36.

    (a) 3 and 12   (b) 4 and 9   (c) 2 and 18   (d) 6 and 6   (e) None of these

9. A farmer has 160 ft of fencing to enclose two adjacent rectangular pig pens. What dimensions should be used for each pig pen so that the enclosed area will be a maximum?

    (a) $4\sqrt{15}$ ft by $\frac{8}{5}\sqrt{15}$ ft   (b) 40 ft by $\frac{80}{3}$ ft   (c) 20 ft by $\frac{80}{3}$ ft

    (d) 40 ft by 40 ft   (e) None of these

10. Give the sign of the second derivative of f at the indicated point.

    (a) Zero   (b) Negative

    (c) Positive   (d) The sign cannot be determined

    (e) None of these

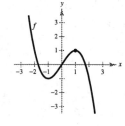

Mid-Chapter Quiz
Chapter 4

Name _____ Date _____

Class _____ Section _____

1. Evaluate: $\left(\frac{1}{16}\right)^{3/4}$.

   (a) $\frac{3}{64}$　　　　(b) $\frac{1}{8}$　　　　(c) 12　　　　(d) $\frac{1}{12}$　　　　(e) None of these

2. Solve for x: $\left(\frac{1}{2}\right)^{x-1} = 32$.

   (a) 4　　　　(b) 6　　　　(c) 7　　　　(d) -4　　　　(e) None of these

3. Find the derivative: $y = e^{3-x}$.

   (a) $(3-x)e^{2-x}$　(b) e^{x-3}　　　(c) $-e^{3-x}$　　　(d) $\frac{1}{e}$　　　　(e) None of these

4. Find $\frac{dy}{dx}$ if $y = \frac{10}{1 + e^{-(1/x)}}$.

   (a) $\dfrac{dy}{dx} = \dfrac{-10e^{-(1/x)}}{x^2(1 + e^{-(1/x)})^2}$　　　　(b) $\dfrac{dy}{dx} = \dfrac{-10}{(1 + e^{-(1/x)})^2}$　　　　(c) $\dfrac{dy}{dx} = \dfrac{-10e^{-(1/x)}}{x^2(1 + e^{-(1/x)})^2}$

   (d) $\dfrac{dy}{dx} = \dfrac{10e^{-(1/x)}}{(1 + e^{-(1/x)})^2}$　　　　(e) None of these

5. Find $f'(x)$ for $f(x) = \dfrac{2}{2x + e^{2x}}$.

   (a) 0　　　(b) $\dfrac{1}{1 + e^{2x}}$　　　(c) $\dfrac{-4(1 + e^{2x})}{(2x + e^{2x})^2}$　　(d) $\dfrac{1 + xe^{2x-1}}{(2x + e^{2x})^2}$　　(e) None of these

6. Find an expression that is equivalent to $\dfrac{3^x + 3^{x+y}}{2^x}$.

   (a) $\left(\dfrac{3}{2}\right)^x + \left(\dfrac{3^y}{2}\right)^x$　　　　　(b) $\dfrac{2(3^x) + 3^y}{2^x}$　　　　　(c) $3(2^{-x}) + 3^y$

   (d) $3^x 2^{-x}(1 + 3^y)$　　　　　(e) None of these

7. Find the second derivative of the function: $f(x) = e^{2x-x^2}$.

   (a) $2(1-x)e^{2x-x^2}$　　　　(b) $(2x - x^2)e^{2x-x^2-2}$　　　　(c) $2(2x^2 - 4x + 1)e^{2x-x^2}$

   (d) $(2 - 2x)e^x$　　　　(e) None of these

8. Determine where the graph of $f(x) = \dfrac{e^x}{x^2}$ is increasing.

   (a) $(-\infty, 0), (2, \infty)$　　　　(b) $(0, 2)$　　　　(c) $(-\infty, 2)$

   (d) $(2, \infty)$　　　　(e) None of these

9. Match the graph shown with the correct function.

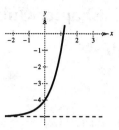

   (a) $f(x) = 4^x - 5$ (b) $f(x) = 4^x + 5$

   (c) $f(x) = 4^{-x} + 5$ (d) $f(x) = 4^{-x} - 5$

   (e) None of these

10. Match the graph shown with the correct function.

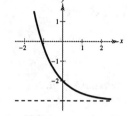

   (a) $f(x) = e^{(x+3)}$ (b) $f(x) = e^{-x} - 3$

   (c) $f(x) = e^x - 3$ (d) $f(x) = e^{-(x+3)}$

   (e) None of these

Mid-Chapter Quiz

Chapter 5

Name _____ Date _____

Class _____ Section _____

1. Evaluate $\int (2x^4 + 3x^2 - 2x)\, dx$.

   (a) $\frac{3}{8}x^8 + C$

   (b) $8x^3 + 6x - 2 + C$

   (c) $\frac{2}{5}x^5 + x^3 - x^2 + C$

   (d) $2x^5 + 5x^3 - 5x^2 + C$

   (e) None of these

2. Evaluate $\int \frac{1}{t^6}\, dt$.

   (a) $-\frac{1}{5t^5} + C$

   (b) $-\frac{6}{t^7} + C$

   (c) $\frac{7}{t^7} + C$

   (d) $\frac{1}{6t^7} + C$

   (e) None of these

3. Evaluate: $\int \frac{1}{\sqrt{1+x}}\, dx$.

   (a) $\frac{-1}{2(1+x)^{3/2}}$

   (b) $\ln|1+x| + C$

   (c) $-\frac{1}{2}\sqrt{1+x} + C$

   (d) $2\sqrt{x+1} + C$

   (e) None of these

4. Evaluate: $\int 5y(2y^2 - 3)^6\, dy$.

   (a) $\frac{5}{28}(2y^2 - 3)^7 + C$

   (b) $\frac{5}{14}y^2(2y^2 - 3)^7 + C$

   (c) $\frac{5}{7}(2y^2 - 3)^7 + C$

   (d) $-\frac{5(2y^2 - 3)^7}{28} + C$

   (e) None of these

5. Evaluate $\int xe^{5x^2}\, dx$.

   (a) $\frac{1}{10}e^{5x^2} + C$

   (b) $\frac{x^2 e^{5x^2 + 1}}{2(5x^2 + 1)} + C$

   (c) $10e^{5x^2} + C$

   (d) $e^{5x^2}(10x^2 + 1) + C$

   (e) None of these

6. Evaluate the integral: $\int \frac{8x^2 + 9x + 8}{x^2 + 1}\, dx$.

   (a) $8 + \frac{9}{2}\ln(x^2 + 1) + C$

   (b) $8x + 9\ln(x^2 + 1) + C$

   (c) $8 + 9\ln(x^2 + 1) + C$

   (d) $8x + \frac{9}{2}\ln(x^2 + 1) + C$

   (e) None of these

7. Evaluate $\displaystyle\int \frac{x+2}{x+1}\,dx$.

(a) $\dfrac{x^2 + 4x}{x^2 + 2x} + C$

(b) $2x + C$

(c) $x + C$

(d) $x + \ln|x+1| + C$

(e) None of these

8. Use the general power rule to evaluate the integral: $\displaystyle\int x\sqrt{9 - 5x^2}\,dx$.

(a) $-\frac{1}{10}(9 - 5x^2)^{3/2} + C$

(b) $-\frac{1}{15}(9 - 5x^2)^{3/2} + C$

(c) $\frac{2}{3}(9 - 5x^2)^{3/2} + C$

(d) $-\frac{4}{15}(9 - 5x^2)^{3/2} + C$

(e) None of these

9. Evaluate $\displaystyle\int \frac{x^3 + x}{x}\,dx$.

(a) $x^3 + 3x + C$

(b) $2x + C$

(c) $\dfrac{x^3}{3} + x + C$

(d) $\dfrac{2x^3 + x - 1}{x^2}$

(e) None of these

10. Find the cost function if the marginal cost function is $\dfrac{dC}{dx} = 0.03x^2 + 0.6x$ and fixed costs are \$3000.

(a) $C = 0.06x + 0.6 + \dfrac{3000}{x}$

(b) $C = 0.01x^3 + 0.3x^2 - 3000$

(c) $C = 0.03x + 0.6 - \dfrac{3000}{x}$

(d) $C = 0.01x^3 + 0.3x^2 + 3000$

(e) None of these

Mid-Chapter Quiz

Chapter 6

Name _____   Date _____

Class _____   Section _____

1. Evaluate: $\int x\sqrt{1-x}\,dx$.

   (a) $-\dfrac{x^2}{3}(1-x)^{3/2} + C$

   (b) $\dfrac{2-3x}{2\sqrt{1-x}} + C$

   (c) $\dfrac{x^2}{3}(1-x)^{3/2} + C$

   (d) $-\dfrac{2}{15}(2+3x)(1-x)^{3/2} + C$

   (e) None of these

2. Evaluate: $\int x^2\sqrt{1-x^3}\,dx$.

   (a) $-\dfrac{2}{9}(1-x^3)^{3/2} + C$

   (b) $2(1-x^3)^{3/2} + C$

   (c) $\dfrac{-1}{6\sqrt{1-x^3}} + C$

   (d) $\dfrac{2}{9\sqrt{1-x^3}} + C$

   (e) None of these

3. Find the partial fraction decomposition: $\dfrac{-9}{(1+1)^2(x-2)}$.

   (a) $\dfrac{1}{x+1} + \dfrac{3}{(x+1)^2} - \dfrac{1}{x-2}$

   (b) $\dfrac{10}{x+1} - \dfrac{4}{(x+1)^2} - \dfrac{15}{x-2}$

   (c) $\dfrac{2}{x+1} - \dfrac{1}{(1+1)^2} - \dfrac{1}{x-2}$

   (d) $\dfrac{1}{x+1} - \dfrac{3}{(x+1)^2} + \dfrac{5}{x-2}$

   (e) None of these

4. Evaluate using integration by parts: $\int \sqrt[3]{x}\ln x\,dx$.

   (a) $\dfrac{3x^{4/3}}{4}(4\ln x - 3) + C$

   (b) $\dfrac{3x^{4/3}}{16}(\ln x + 3) + C$

   (c) $\dfrac{3x^{4/3}}{16}(4\ln x - 3) + C$

   (d) $\dfrac{3x^{4/3}}{8}(4\ln x - 3) + C$

   (e) None of these

5. Evaluate: $\int xe^{2x}\,dx$.

   (a) $2e^{2x}(x-2) + C$

   (b) $x^2e^{x^2} + C$

   (c) $\dfrac{e^{2x}}{4}[2x-1] + C$

   (d) $\dfrac{1}{2}x^2e^{2x} + C$

   (e) None of these

6. Let $\dfrac{2}{(x-1)^2(x-3)} = \dfrac{A}{x-1} + \dfrac{B}{(x-1)^2} + \dfrac{C}{x-3}$. Find A, B and C.

   (a) $A = -\dfrac{1}{2}, B = -1, C = \dfrac{1}{2}$
   (b) $A = 1, B = 2, C = -1$
   (c) $A = \dfrac{1}{2}, B = -1, C = \dfrac{1}{2}$

   (d) $A = 1, B = 2, C = 3$
   (e) None of these

7. Find the area bounded by $y = \dfrac{x}{(1+x)^2}$, $y = 0$, $x = 0$, and $x = 2$.

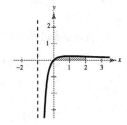

   (a) $\dfrac{1}{2}\ln 5$
   (b) $-\dfrac{3}{8}$

   (c) $-\dfrac{2}{3} + \ln 3$
   (d) $-\dfrac{1}{4} + \ln 2$

   (e) None of these

8. Find the indefinite integral using partial fractions: $\displaystyle\int \dfrac{16}{x^2 - 16}\, dx$.

   (a) $\dfrac{1-x}{x} + C$
   (b) $\dfrac{-32x}{(x^2-16)^2} + C$
   (c) $2\ln|x^2 - 16| + C$

   (d) $\dfrac{1}{2}\ln\left|\dfrac{x-4}{x+4}\right| + C$
   (e) None of these

9. Evaluate: $\displaystyle\int \dfrac{2}{(x+2)^2(2-x)}\, dx$.

   (a) $\dfrac{1}{8}\ln|x+2| + \dfrac{1}{2}\ln(x+2)^2 - \dfrac{1}{8}\ln|2-x| + C$
   (b) $\dfrac{1}{8}\ln\left|\dfrac{x+2}{2-x}\right| - \dfrac{1}{2(x+2)} + C$

   (c) $-\dfrac{2}{(x+2)} + \ln|2-x| + C$
   (d) $-\dfrac{1}{2(x+2)} - \dfrac{1}{8}\ln|2-x| + C$

   (e) None of these

10. Find the present value of the income given by $c(t) = 5000$, measured in dollars, over four years, at an annual interest rate of 8%.

   (a) \$6600.00
   (b) \$5995.24
   (c) \$6885.64
   (d) \$4796.19
   (e) None of these

Mid-Chapter Quiz   Name _____ Date _____

Chapter 7   Class _____ Section _____

1. Find the distance between the points $(3, 0, -5)$ and $(-1, 4, 2)$.

    (a) $\sqrt{29}$ (b) $\sqrt{41}$ (c) 9   (d) 1   (e) None of these

2. Find the center and radius of the sphere given by the equation $x^2 + y^2 + z^2 - 4x - 2y + 2z = 10$.

    (a) Center: $(-2, -1, 1)$; radius: 4   (b) Center: $(2, 1, -1)$; radius: 4

    (c) Center: $(-2, -1, 1)$; radius: $\sqrt{10}$ (d) Center: $(2, 1, -1)$; radius: $\sqrt{10}$

    (e) None of these

3. Find all intercepts: $3x - 4y - 2z = 12$.

    (a) $(4, -3, -6)$ (b) $(4, -3), (0, -3, -6), (4, 0, -6)$

    (c) $(0, 0, -6), (0, -3, 0), (4, 0, 0)$ (d) $(3, 0, 0), (0, -4, 0), (0, 0, -2)$

    (e) None of these

4. Calculate the distance from the point $(1, -2, 3)$ to the plane $(x - 3) + 2(y + 1) - 4z = 0$.

    (a) $\sqrt{14}$ (b) $\dfrac{14}{\sqrt{21}}$ (c) $\dfrac{12}{\sqrt{21}}$ (d) $\sqrt{65}$ (e) None of these

5. Find $f_x(x, y)$ for $f(x, y) = e^{y/x}$.

    (a) $\dfrac{x - y}{x^2} e^{y/x}$ (b) $\dfrac{y}{x} e^{(y/x)-1}$ (c) $\dfrac{y}{x^2} e^{(y/x)-1}$ (d) $\dfrac{1}{x} e^{y/x}$ (e) None of these

6. Find $f_y(1, -1, 4)$ for $f(x, y, z) = 2x^2y - 2yx + xz$.

    (a) 0   (b) 3   (c) -6 (d) -4 (e) None of these

7. Find $f_{xx}(x, y)$ for $f(x, y) = e^{x^2y}$.

    (a) $(4x^2 + 2y)e^{x^2y}$.   (b) $4x^2y^2e^{x^2y}$ (c) $4x^2e^{x^2y}$

    (d) $(4x^2y^2 + 2y)e^{x^2y}$ (e) None of these

8. Determine the relative extrema of $f(x, y) = -6x + 2y - x^2 - y^2 - 4$.

    (a) Minimum at $(-3, 1)$ (b) Maximum at $(-3, 1)$ (c) Saddle point at $(-3, 1)$

    (d) Minimum at $(3, 1)$ (e) None of these

9. Find the slope in the x-direction of the surface $f(x, y) = xy^2$ at the point $(3, -2, 12)$.

    (a) -6 (b) 9   (c) 4   (d) -12 (e) None of these

10. Find the distance between the point $(1, -1, 3)$ and the plane $2x + 3y + z = 6$.

    (a) $\dfrac{14}{\sqrt{14}}$ (b) $\dfrac{14}{\sqrt{11}}$ (c) $\dfrac{4}{\sqrt{14}}$ (d) $\dfrac{8}{\sqrt{14}}$ (e) None of these

11. The sum of $1500 is deposited in a savings account earning r percent interest compounded continuously. The amount $A(r, t)$ after t years is given by $A(r, t) = 1500e^{rt}$. Determine the amount earning 8% interest for 7 years.

    (a) $2626   (b) $2714   (c) $2527   (d) $2172   (e) None of these

12. Which of the following is a sketch of the plane $2x + y + 3z = 6$?

    (a)

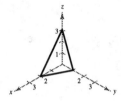

    (b)

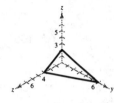

    (c)

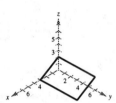

    (d)

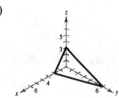

    (e) None of these

Mid-Chapter Quiz

Chapter 8

Name _____ Date _____

Class _____ Section _____

1. Convert to radian measure: $135°$.

   (a) $\dfrac{\pi}{4}$ (b) $\dfrac{3\pi}{4}$ (c) $\dfrac{3\pi}{8}$ (d) $\dfrac{3\pi}{2}$ (e) None of these

2. Find the area of an equilateral triangle with sides of length 6 units.

   (a) $9\sqrt{3}$ (b) $36\sqrt{2}$ (c) $18\sqrt{3}$ (d) 36 (e) None of these

3. Convert to degree measure: $\dfrac{7\pi}{12}$.

   (a) $75°$ (b) $15°$ (c) $105°$ (d) $95°$ (e) None of these

4. Solve the triangle for c.

   (a) $5\sqrt{10}$ (b) $10\sqrt{3}$

   (c) $25\sqrt{3}$ (d) 10

   (e) None of these

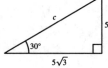

5. A right triangle has an acute angle θ such that $\csc\theta = \frac{7}{3}$. Find $\tan\theta$.

   (a) $\dfrac{2\sqrt{10}}{7}$ (b) $\dfrac{3\sqrt{10}}{20}$ (c) $\dfrac{2\sqrt{10}}{3}$ (d) $\dfrac{3}{7}$ (e) None of these

6. Solve the given equation for θ, $(\theta \le \theta < 2\pi)$: $2\cos^2\theta - \cos\theta = 1$.

   (a) $0, \dfrac{\pi}{2}, \pi$ (b) $0, -\dfrac{4\pi}{3}$ (c) $0, \dfrac{\pi}{3}, \dfrac{5\pi}{3}$ (d) $\dfrac{\pi}{3}, \dfrac{\pi}{2}$ (e) None of these

7. Solve for y:

   (a) 3 (b) $6\sqrt{2}$

   (c) $3\sqrt{3}$ (d) $3\sqrt{2}$

   (e) None of these

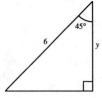

8. Complete the following Pythagorean identity: $\tan^2\theta = $ _____.

   (a) $1 - \sec^2\theta$ (b) $1 - \csc^2\theta$ (c) $\csc^2\theta + 1$ (d) $\sec^2\theta - 1$ (e) None of these

9. Find the $\cos\theta$ if the angle θ is in the standard position and the terminal side of θ passes through $(-7, 3)$. Do not approximate your answer.

(a) $-\dfrac{7}{5}$ (b) $-\dfrac{7}{\sqrt{58}}$ (c) $-\dfrac{\sqrt{58}}{7}$ (d) $\dfrac{\sqrt{58}}{3}$ (e) None of these

10. Match the graph with the correct function.

(a) $y = \dfrac{1}{2}\cos\left(\dfrac{2x}{3}\right)$ (b) $y = \dfrac{1}{2}\sin\left(\dfrac{2x}{3}\right)$

(c) $y = \dfrac{1}{2}\cos\left(\dfrac{3x}{2}\right)$ (d) $y = \dfrac{1}{2}\sin\left(\dfrac{3x}{2}\right)$

(e) None of these

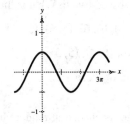

11. Determine the period: $f(x) = \tan 4x$.

(a) 4 (b) π (c) $\dfrac{\pi}{4}$ (d) $\dfrac{\pi}{2}$ (e) None of these

12. Determine which of the following is coterminal to $\theta = \dfrac{2\pi}{15}$.

(a) $\dfrac{4\pi}{15}$ (b) $\dfrac{17\pi}{15}$ (c) $\dfrac{32\pi}{15}$ (d) $-\dfrac{13\pi}{15}$ (e) None of these

Mid-Chapter Quiz   Name _____ Date _____

Chapter 9   Class _____ Section _____

1. A die is tossed twice. What is the event that the sum of the tosses will be at least 10?

   (a) $\{(5, 5), (6, 6), (4, 6), (5, 6)\}$ (b) $\{(4, 6), (5, 6), (6, 6), (5, 5), (6, 4), (6, 5)\}$

   (c) $(4, 6), (6, 4), (5, 5)\}$ (d) $\{(6, 4), (5, 5), (5, 6)\}$

   (e) None of these

2. An integer is chosen at random between the numbers 10 and 29, inclusive. What is the probability that one of the digits of the integer will be a 5?

   (a) $\frac{1}{20}$ (b) $\frac{2}{19}$ (c) $\frac{2}{29}$ (d) $\frac{1}{10}$ (e) None of these

For problems 3 through 5, use the probability distribution for the discrete random variable x, given below.

x	1	2	3	4	5
$P(x)$	$\frac{1}{10}$	$\frac{2}{10}$	$\frac{2}{10}$	$\frac{4}{10}$	$\frac{1}{10}$

3. Find the expected value of x.

   (a) 4   (b) 3.2   (c) $\frac{4}{10}$ (d) 3   (e) None of these

4. Find the variance of x.

   (a) $\frac{34}{25}$ (b) $\frac{1}{5}$ (c) $\frac{51}{5}$ (d) 10   (e) None of these

5. Find the standard deviation of x.

   (a) $\frac{7}{25}$ (b) $\frac{17}{5}$ (c) $\sqrt{\frac{51}{5}}$ (d) $\frac{\sqrt{34}}{5}$ (e) None of these

6. A $20.00 turkey is to be given away in a raffle. The tickets are $1.00 each and 50 tickets are to be sold. What is the expected win?

x	-1	19
$P(x)$	$\frac{49}{50}$	$\frac{1}{50}$

   (a) Lose $1.00   (b) Lose $.50   (c) Lose $.60   (d) Lose $.80   (e) None of these

7. Find $P(0 \le x \le 1)$, given the probability density function $f(x) = \dfrac{1}{(x + 1)^2}, x \ge 0$.

   (a) 1   (b) 0   (c) $\frac{7}{8}$ (d) $\frac{1}{2}$ (e) None of these

8. Find the constant k so that the function $f(x) = kx^2$ is a continuous density function over the interval $[1, 4]$.

   (a) $\frac{1}{21}$ (b) 21   (c) $\frac{1}{3}$ (d) $-\frac{1}{3}$ (e) None of these

9. Find $P(0 \leq x \leq 2)$, for the probability density function, $f(x) = \dfrac{1}{(x+1)^2}, x \geq 0$.

   (a) $\frac{2}{3}$ (b) $\frac{1}{9}$ (c) $\frac{8}{9}$ (d) 1   (e) None of these

10. A bag containing three red balls, two blue balls, five green balls and a yellow ball, all the same size. If a ball is chosen at random, what is the probability that it will be green?

   (a) $\frac{5}{6}$ (b) $\frac{1}{5}$ (c) $\frac{1}{2}$ (d) 5   (e) None of these

Mid-Chapter Quiz   Name _____   Date _____

Chapter 10   Class _____   Section _____

1. Find the first 5 terms of the sequence whose nth-term is $a_n = n!$. (Assume that n begins with 0.)

   (a) 0, 1, 2, 6, 24   (b) 0, 1, 2, 6, 12   (c) 1, 1, 2, 6, 12

   (d) 1, 1, 2, 6, 24   (e) None of these

2. Find a formula for the nth-term of the sequence. (Assume that n begins with 1.)

   $$\frac{2}{1}, \frac{3}{2}, \frac{4}{3}, \frac{5}{4}, \frac{6}{5}, \cdots$$

   (a) $\dfrac{n+1}{n-1}$ (b) $2 - \dfrac{1}{n}$ (c) $1 + \dfrac{1}{n}$ (d) $\dfrac{2n-1}{n}$ (e) None of these

3. Determine if the following sequence converges or diverges:

   $$\left\{\frac{2n-1}{3n+1}\right\}, n = 1, 2, 3, \cdots.$$

   If the sequence converges, find its limit.

   (a) Converges to $\frac{2}{3}$ (b) Converges to 0   (c) Converges to $-\frac{1}{3}$

   (d) Diverges   (e) None of these

4. Determine if the following sequence converges or diverges:

   $$\left\{\frac{n!}{(n-2)!}\right\}, n = 2, 3, 4, \cdots.$$

   If the sequence converges, find its limit.

   (a) Converges to 2   (b) Converges to 0   (c) Converges to 4

   (d) Diverges   (e) None of these

5. Find the sum: $\displaystyle\sum_{n=1}^{4} \frac{n+1}{n+2}$.

   (a) $\frac{61}{20}$ (b) $\frac{31}{20}$ (c) $\frac{143}{60}$ (d) $\frac{131}{60}$ (e) None of these

6. Find the sum of the geometric series $\displaystyle\sum_{n=0}^{\infty} 3\left(\frac{1}{2}\right)^n$.

   (a) $\frac{3}{2}$ (b) 3   (c) 6   (d) $\frac{50}{9}$ (e) None of these

7. Find the sum of the infinite geometric series: $1 + \frac{1}{3} + \frac{1}{9} + \frac{1}{27} + \cdots$.

   (a) $\frac{3}{2}$ (b) 3   (c) $\frac{5}{3}$ (d) $\frac{5}{2}$ (e) None of these

8. Which of the following converges?

(a) $\displaystyle\sum_{n=1}^{\infty} (4 + (-1)^n)$

(b) $\displaystyle\sum_{n=1}^{\infty} \frac{2^n}{(n+1)!}$

(c) $\displaystyle\sum_{n=0}^{\infty} 5\left(\frac{3}{2}\right)^n$

(d) $\displaystyle\sum_{n=1}^{\infty} \frac{1}{\sqrt{n}}$

(e) None of these

9. Determine the convergence or divergence of the series using the Ratio Test: $\displaystyle\sum_{n=1}^{\infty} \frac{n!}{(n+6)!}$.

(a) Converges by the Ratio Test   (b) The Ratio Test does not apply   (c) The Ratio Test is inconclusive

(d) Diverges by the Ratio Test   (e) None of these

10. Choose the best answer. (Use the fourth partial sum.) $S = \displaystyle\sum_{n=1}^{\infty} \frac{6}{n^2}$

(a) $\frac{199}{24} < S < \frac{211}{24}$

(b) $\frac{223}{24} < S < \frac{235}{24}$

(c) $\frac{187}{24} < S < \frac{199}{24}$

(d) $\frac{211}{24} < S < \frac{224}{24}$

(e) None of these

CUMULATIVE TESTS

Cumulative Test A   Name _____ Date _____

Chapters 0–3   Class _____ Section _____

1. Write the general equation of the circle with center at $(2, -3)$ and radius of 7.

   (a) $x^2 + y^2 - 4x + 6y + 6 = 0$ (b) $x^2 + y^2 + 4x - 6y + 6 = 0$ (c) $x^2 + y^2 - 4x + 6y - 36 = 0$

   (d) $x^2 + y^2 + 4x - 6y - 36 = 0$ (e) None of these

2. Add, then simplify: $\dfrac{2}{x^2 - 9} + \dfrac{5}{x^2 - x - 12}$.

   (a) $\dfrac{7}{(x^2 - 9)(x^2 - x - 12)}$ (b) $\dfrac{7x^2 - x - 21}{(x^2 - 9)(x^2 - x - 12)}$ (c) $\dfrac{7x - 7}{(x - 3)(x - 4)(x + 3)}$

   (d) $\dfrac{7x - 23}{(x - 3)(x + 3)(x - 4)}$ (e) None of these

3. Find the intervals in which the function is continuous: $f(x) = \dfrac{x - 4}{(x - 2)(x + 1)}$.

   (a) $(-\infty, 4)(4, \infty)$ (b) $(-\infty, -1)(-1, 2)(2, 4)(4, \infty)$

   (c) $(-\infty, -1)(-1, 2)(2, \infty)$ (d) $(-\infty, -2)(-2, -1)(-1, 2)(2, \infty)$

   (e) None of these

4. Find $\lim\limits_{x \to 0} \left(2 + \dfrac{5}{x^2} \right)$.

   (a) 7   (b) 2   (c) ∞ (d) $-\infty$ (e) None of these

5. Evaluate: $\lim\limits_{x \to 0} \dfrac{x}{\sqrt{x + 4} - 2}$.

   (a) 2   (b) 8   (c) 0   (d) Does not exist   (e) None of these

6. Differentiate: $\sqrt[3]{x^3 + 12x^2 - 3}$.

   (a) $\dfrac{-9x(x + 8)}{(x^3 + 12x^2 - 3)^4}$ (b) $\dfrac{x(x - 8)}{(x^3 + 12x^2 - 3)^{2/3}}$ (c) $1 + \dfrac{8}{\sqrt[3]{x}}$

   (d) $\dfrac{1}{3(3x^2 + 2x)^{2/3}}$ (e) None of these

7. Differentiate: $y = \dfrac{3x}{x^2 + 1}$.

   (a) $\dfrac{3}{1 + x^2}$ (b) $\dfrac{3}{2x}$ (c) $\dfrac{3x^2 - 3}{(1 + x^2)^3}$ (d) $\dfrac{3(1 - x^2)}{(1 + x^2)^2}$ (e) None of these

8. Find the slope of the line tangent to the graph of $y^3 - 2xy^2 = x^2$ at the point $(-1, -1)$.

   (a) $\frac{3}{28}$ (b) $\frac{4}{71}$ (c) undefined   (d) 0   (e) None of these

9. Find $f''(x) : f(x) = \dfrac{4}{\sqrt[3]{2 - 3x^2}}$.

   (a) $\dfrac{8(5x^2 + 2)}{(2 - 3x^2)^{7/3}}$ (b) $\dfrac{-8x}{(2 - 3x^2)^{2/3}}$ (c) $\dfrac{-8(x^2 + 2)}{(2 - 3x^2)^{5/3}}$ (d) 0   (e) None of these

10. Find the derivative of $9x^2 f(x)$.

    (a) $9x^2 f'(x)$ (b) $9x[xf(x) + 2f'(x)]$ (c) $18xf'(x)$

    (d) $9x[xf'(x) + 2f(x)]$ (e) None of these

11. Calculate the differential dy for the function $y = x^4 - x^2$.

    (a) $dy = 4x^3 - 2x$ (b) $dy = (2x^2 - 1)\,dx$ (c) $dy = (4x^3 - 2x)\,dx$

    (d) $y' = (4x^3 - 2x)\,dx$ (e) None of these

12. Let $f''(x) = 4x^3 - 2x$ and let $f(x)$ have critical numbers $-1, 0$, and 1. Use the Second-Derivative Test to determine which critical numbers, if any, give a relative maximum.

    (a) -1 (b) 0   (c) 1   (d) -1 and 1   (e) None of these

13. Find the horizontal asymptote, if any, for the function $y = \dfrac{x^2 + 1}{x - 2}$.

    (a) $x = 2$ (b) $y = 1$ (c) $y = -\frac{1}{2}$ (d) $x = 1$ (e) None of these

14. The management of a large store wishes to add a fenced-in rectangular storage yard of 20,000 ft², using the building as one side of the yard. Find the minimum amount of fencing that must be used to enclose the remaining three sides of the yard.

    (a) 400 ft   (b) 200 ft   (c) 20,000 ft   (d) 500 ft   (e) None of these

15. Two boats leave the same port at the same time with one boat traveling north at 35 knots per hour and the other traveling east at 40 knots per hour. How fast is the distance between the two boats changing after 2 hours?

    (a) 106.4 knots/hr   (b) 429.4 knots/hr   (c) 53.2 knots/hr

    (d) 57.9 knots/hr   (e) None of these

Cumulative Test B   **Name** _____ **Date** _____

Chapters 0–7   **Class** _____ **Section** _____

1. Find all points of inflection: $f(x) = \frac{1}{12}x^4 - 2x^2 + 15$.

   (a) $(2, 0)$ (b) $(2, 0), (-2, 0)$ (c) $(0, 15)$

   (d) $\left(2, \frac{25}{3}\right), \left(-2, \frac{25}{3}\right)$ (e) None of these

2. Find the slope of the line tangent to the graph of $4y^2 - xy = 3$ at the point $\left(-1, \frac{3}{4}\right)$.

   (a) $\frac{3}{28}$ (b) $\frac{1}{7}$ (c) $\frac{4}{71}$ (d) undefined   (e) None of these

3. Find the derivative $\dfrac{dy}{dx}$ if $y = e^{-x^3}$.

   (a) $-x^3 e^{-x^3-1}$ (b) $-3x^2 e^{-x^3}$ (c) $\dfrac{1}{x^3 e^{-x^3-1}}$ (d) e^{-3x^2} (e) None of these

4. Find the domain of the function: $f(x) = 3 + \ln(x - 1)$.

   (a) $(-\infty, \infty)$ (b) $(0, \infty)$ (c) $(1, \infty)$ (d) $(3, \infty)$ (e) None of these

5. Evaluate $\displaystyle\int (x - 1)x^2\, dx$.

   (a) $3x^4 - 4x^3 + C$ (b) $\frac{1}{4}x^4 - \frac{1}{3}x^3 + C$ (c) $\frac{1}{6}x^3(x - 1)^2 + C$

   (d) $3x^2 - 2x + C$ (e) None of these

6. Evaluate: $\displaystyle\int (2t^2 + 1)^2\, dt$.

   (a) $\frac{4}{5}t^5 + \frac{4}{3}t^3 + t + C$ (b) $\dfrac{(2t^3 + 1)^3}{3} + C$ (c) $4t^5 + 4t^3 + t + C$

   (d) $12t^5 - 20t^3 + 15t + C$ (e) None of these

7. Evaluate the definite integral $\displaystyle\int_1^{\sqrt{e}} \frac{-4x}{x^2}\, dx$.

   (a) -1 (b) -6 (c) -4 (d) -2 (e) None of these

8. Find the volume of the solid formed by revolving the region bounded by the graphs of $y = x^2 + 3$, $y = 3$, $x = 0$, and $x = 2$ about the line $y = 3$.

   (a) $\frac{112}{5}\pi$ (b) $\frac{32}{5}\pi$ (c) $\frac{56}{5}\pi$ (d) $\frac{64}{5}\pi$ (e) None of these

9. Find the partial fraction decomposition: $\dfrac{-5x^2 - 19x - 28}{x^3 + 4x^2 + 4x}$.

(a) $\dfrac{5x^2}{x^3} - \dfrac{19x}{4x^2} - \dfrac{28}{4x}$

(b) $-\dfrac{5x^2}{x} - \dfrac{19x}{x + 2} - \dfrac{28}{(x + 2)^2}$

(c) $\dfrac{2}{x} - \dfrac{5}{x + 2} + \dfrac{16}{(x + 2)^2}$

(d) $-\dfrac{7}{x} + \dfrac{2}{x + 2} + \dfrac{5}{(x + 2)^2}$

(e) None of these

10. Evaluate the indefinite integral: $\displaystyle\int (\ln x)^3 \, dx$.

(a) $x(\ln x)^3 - 3(\ln x)^2 + C$

(b) $x(\ln x)^3 - 3\displaystyle\int (\ln x)^2 \, dx$

(c) $\dfrac{1}{3}(\ln x)^4 + C$

(d) $\dfrac{3}{x}(\ln x)^2 + C$

(e) None of these

11. Use Trapezoidal Rule with $n = 4$ to approximate the area of the region bounded by $f(x) = x^3 - 8x^2 + 16x$ and the x-axis between $x = 0$ and $x = 4$.

(a) 22.00 (b) 23.00 (c) 20.67 (d) 20.00 (e) None of these

12. Determine the area between $f(x) = \dfrac{2x + 1}{x^2}$, and the x-axis over the interval $[0, 4]$.

(a) Infinite

(b) $2 \ln 4 - \dfrac{1}{4}$

(c) $\dfrac{3}{8}$

(d) $\dfrac{9}{64}$

(e) None of these

13. Find the slope in the x-direction of the surface $f(x, y) = xy^2$ at the point $(3, -2, 12)$.

(a) -6 (b) 9 (c) 4 (d) -12 (e) None of these

14. Use a double integral to find the volume of the given solid.

(a) $\dfrac{1}{2}$

(b) 1

(c) $\dfrac{2}{3}$

(d) $\dfrac{5}{2}$

(e) None of these

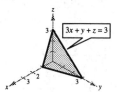

15. A radioactive isotope has a half-life of 30 years. At $t = 0$, there are 100 grams of this substance. Find the amount of this isotope present at time t using an exponential model of decay.

(a) $y = 100e^{(\ln 2)t/30}$

(b) $y = 100e^{-[\ln (1/2)]t/30}$

(c) $y = 30e^{-(\ln 2)t/100}$

(d) $y = 100e^{-(\ln 2)t/30}$

(e) None of these

Cumulative Test C

Chapters 0–10

Name _____ Date _____

Class _____ Section _____

1. Find $\lim_{x \to -1} \dfrac{x^2 + 2x + 3}{x^2 + 1}$.

    (a) 0   (b) 1   (c) ∞ (d) Does not exist   (e) None of these

2. Find all vertical asymptotes of $f(x) = \dfrac{2x - 1}{x + 3}$.

    (a) $x = 2$ (b) $x = \frac{1}{2}, x = -3$ (c) $x = -3$

    (d) $x = \frac{1}{2}$ (e) None of these

3. Find the limit: $\lim_{x \to 5} \dfrac{\ln(x - 4)}{3x - 15}$.

    (a) $-\frac{4}{15}$ (b) $\frac{1}{3}$ (c) ∞ (d) 0   (e) None of these

4. Assume x and y are both differentiable functions of t. Find $\dfrac{dx}{dt}$ given $x = 2$ and $\dfrac{dy}{dt} = 60 : y = 3x^3 - 6x + 4$.

    (a) 2   (b) 4   (c) 30   (d) $\frac{1}{2}$ (e) None of these

5. Write the equation of the tangent line to the curve $y = \ln\left(\dfrac{2}{e^{2x}}\right)$ at the point $(0, \ln 2)$.

    (a) $2x + y + \ln 2 = 0$ (b) $2x - y + \ln 2 = 0$ (c) $2x + y - \ln 2 = 0$

    (d) $2x - y - \ln 2 + 0$ (e) None of these

6. Evaluate $\displaystyle\int \dfrac{2x}{3x^2 + 4}\, dx$.

    (a) $\dfrac{2(4 - 9x^2)}{(3x^2 + 4)^2} + C$ (b) $\dfrac{x}{x^2 + 4} + C$ (c) $\dfrac{1}{3}\ln(3x^2 + 4) + C$

    (d) $\dfrac{1}{6}(3x^2 + 4)^2 + C$ (e) None of these

7. Evaluate $\displaystyle\int x(x^2 - 1)^4\, dx$.

    (a) $\frac{1}{10}(x^2)(x^2 - 1)^5$ (b) $\frac{1}{10}(x^2 - 1)^5 + C$ (c) $\frac{1}{5}(x^3 - x)^5 + C$

    (d) $\frac{1}{5}(x^2 - 1)^5 + C$ (e) None of these

8. Differentiate: $y = \dfrac{3x}{x^2 + 1}$.

(a) $\dfrac{3}{1 + x^2}$ (b) $\dfrac{3}{2x}$ (c) $\dfrac{3x^2 - 3}{(1 + x^2)^3}$ (d) $\dfrac{3(1 - x^2)}{(1 + x^2)^2}$ (e) None of these

9. Evaluate the indefinite integral: $\displaystyle\int (\ln x)^6 \, dx$.

(a) $\dfrac{1}{6}(\ln x)^7 + C$ (b) $x(\ln x)^6 - 6\displaystyle\int (\ln x)^5 \, dx$ (c) $x(\ln x)^6 - 6(\ln x)^5 + C$

(d) $\dfrac{6}{x}(\ln x)^5 + C$ (e) None of these

10. Evaluate the improper integral: $\displaystyle\int_{-9}^{-7} \dfrac{dx}{(x + 8)^2}$.

(a) 2   (b) 0   (c) -2

(d) The integral diverges.   (e) None of these

11. Find the point on the line $y = 2x + 3$ that is closest to $(1, 1)$.

(a) $(-1, 1)$ (b) $\left(-\frac{3}{2}, 0\right)$ (c) $\left(-\frac{1}{2}, 2\right)$ (d) $\left(-\frac{4}{5}, \frac{13}{5}\right)$ (e) None of these

12. Find $f_x(x, y)$ for $f(x, y) = \ln x + e^{xy}$.

(a) $\ln x + xe^{xy}$ (b) $\dfrac{1}{x} + xe^{xy}$ (c) $\dfrac{1}{x} + ye^{xy}$ (d) $\dfrac{1}{x} + e^{xy}$ (e) None of these

13. Find an equation of the tangent line to the graph of $f(x) = \sec x$ at the point $\left(\dfrac{\pi}{3}, 2\right)$.

(a) $y = 2\sqrt{3}x + 2$ (b) $y = 2\sqrt{3}x + 2 - \dfrac{2\sqrt{3}\pi}{3}$ (c) $y = 2\sqrt{3}x - \dfrac{2\sqrt{3}\pi}{3}$

(d) $y = 2x + 2 - \dfrac{2\pi}{3}$ (e) None of these

14. Find the median of the probability density function $f(x) = \frac{1}{8}x$, $[0, 4]$.

(a) $\frac{1}{2}$ (b) 1   (c) $2\sqrt{2}$ (d) 8   (e) None of these

15. Find the radius of convergence for the power series $\displaystyle\sum_{n=1}^{\infty} \dfrac{(3x)^n}{n}$.

(a) $\frac{1}{3}$ (b) 3   (c) ∞ (d) 0   (e) None of these

FINAL EXAMS

Final Exam A

Name _____ Date _____

Class _____ Section _____

1. Let $f(x) = \dfrac{1}{\sqrt{x}}$ and $g(x) = x - 1$. Find the intervals on which $f(g(x))$ is continuous.

  (a) $(-\infty, 0)(0, \infty)$ (b) $(-\infty, 1)(1, \infty)$ (c) $(-\infty, 0)(0, 1)(1, \infty)$

  (d) $(-\infty, -1)(-1, 1)(1, \infty)$ (e) None of these

2. Find $f'(x)$: $f(x) = \dfrac{1}{x^2}$.

  (a) $f'(x) = -\dfrac{1}{x^3}$ (b) $f'(x) = \dfrac{1}{x}$ (c) $f'(x) = -\dfrac{2}{x^3}$ (d) $f'(x) = \dfrac{2}{x}$ (e) None of these

3. Find an equation for the tangent line to the graph of $f(x) = 2x^2 - 2x + 3$ at the point where $x = 1$.

  (a) $y = 2x - 2$ (b) $y = 4x^2 - 6x + 5$ (c) $y = 2x + 1$

  (d) $y = 4x^2 - 6x + 2$ (e) None of these

4. Suppose the position equation for a moving object is given by $s(t) = 4t^2 + 2t + 8$ where s is measured in meters and t is measured in seconds. Find the velocity of the object when $t = 3$.

  (a) 50 m/sec.   (b) 36 m/sec.   (c) 32 m/sec.   (d) 26 m/sec.   (e) None of these

5. Differentiate: $y = \dfrac{x^2}{3x - 1}$.

  (a) $\dfrac{2x}{3}$ (b) $-2x$ (c) $\dfrac{x(3x - 2)}{(3x - 1)^2}$ (d) $\dfrac{2x - 3x^2}{(3x - 1)^2}$ (e) None of these

6. Differentiate: $\dfrac{2x}{\sqrt{4 + 3x}}$.

  (a) $\dfrac{3x + 8}{(3x + 4)^{3/2}}$ (b) $\dfrac{5x + 8}{3x + 4}$ (c) $\dfrac{-2(6x^2 + 12x - 1)}{\sqrt{3x + 4}}$

  (d) $\frac{4}{3}\sqrt{4 + 3x}$ (e) None of these

7. Find $f''(x)$: $f(x) = 4\sqrt[3]{2 - 3x^2}$.

  (a) 0   (b) $\dfrac{-8(x^2 + 2)}{(2 - 3x^2)^{5/3}}$ (c) $\dfrac{8x}{(2 - 3x^2)^{4/3}}$ (d) $\dfrac{8(5x^2 + 2)}{(2 - 3x^2)^{7/3}}$ (e) None of these

8. Assume x and y are both differentiable functions of t. Find $\dfrac{dy}{dt}$ given $x = 2$ and $\dfrac{dx}{dt} = 6 : 2x^2 - y^3 = 16$.

  (a) -4 (b) $\frac{2}{3}$ (c) $\frac{1}{9}$ (d) 4   (e) None of these

9. Find $\dfrac{dy}{dx}$ for $7x^2 + 6xy + 9y^2 = 0$.

(a) $-\dfrac{14x + 6y}{18y}$

(b) $-\dfrac{14x + 6y}{6x + 18y}$

(c) $\dfrac{14x + 18y}{-6x}$

(d) $14x + 6y + 18y$

(e) None of these

10. Find the horizontal asymptote: $f(x) = \dfrac{3x^2 + 2x - 16}{x^2 - 7}$.

(a) $x = \pm\sqrt{7}$ (b) $y = 3$ (c) $y = 3x + 7$ (d) $y = 0$ (e) None of these

11. The cost of producing x units of a certain product is given by $C = 10{,}000 + 5x + \frac{1}{9}x^2$. Find the value of x that gives the minimum average cost.

(a) $30{,}000$ (b) 300 (c) 3000 (d) 30 (e) None of these

12. Find all open intervals on which the function is increasing: $f(x) = (3x + 1)\sqrt[3]{x + 2}$.

(a) $\left(-2, \frac{1}{3}\right)$ (b) $(-2.8, -1.58)$ (c) $(-1.58, \infty)$ (d) $(-2.8, \infty)$ (e) None of these

13. Find all points of inflection: $f(x) = \frac{1}{12}x^4 - 2x^2 + 15$.

(a) $(2, 0)$

(b) $(2, 0), (-2, 0)$

(c) $(0, 15)$

(d) $\left(2, \frac{25}{3}\right), \left(-2, \frac{25}{3}\right)$

(e) None of these

14. Use implicit differentiation to find $\dfrac{dy}{dx}$: $\ln y = y + e^2$.

(a) $\dfrac{ye^x}{1 - y}$ (b) $\dfrac{1}{y} - e^x$ (c) $y(1 + e^x)$ (d) $\dfrac{1}{y} - xe^{x-1}$ (e) None of these

15. The number of fruit flies increases according to the law of exponential growth. If initially there are 10 fruit flies and after 6 hours there are 24, find the number of fruit flies after t hours.

(a) $y = 10e^{[\ln(12/5)](t/6)}$

(b) $y = 10e^{[\ln(12/5)]t}$

(c) $y = 10e^{[-\ln(12/5)](t/6)}$

(d) $y = 10e^{(\ln 12)(t/6)}$

(e) None of these

16. Find the second derivative of the function: $f(x) = e^{-7x^3}$.

(a) $21x(21x^3 - 2)e^{-7x^3}$

(b) $-21x^2e^{-7x^3}$

(c) $7x^3(7x^3 + 1)e^{-7x^3-2}$

(d) $-7x^3e^{-7x^3-1}$

(e) None of these

17. Evaluate $\displaystyle\int \dfrac{x^4 - x^3}{x^2}\,dx$.

(a) $2x^3 - 3x^2 + C$

(b) $\dfrac{x^3}{3} - \dfrac{x^2}{2} + C$

(c) $2x - 1 + C$

(d) $\dfrac{3}{20}(4x^2 - 5x) + C$

(e) None of these

18. Find the cost function if the marginal cost function is $\dfrac{dC}{dx} = 2x + 50$ and fixed costs are \$150.

(a) $C = 2x^2 + 50x + 150$

(b) $C = x^2 + 50x + 150$

(c) $C = 2x^2 + 50x - 150$

(d) $x^2 + 50x - 150$

(e) None of these

19. Evaluate: $\displaystyle\int \dfrac{1}{\sqrt{2x + 1}}\, dx.$

(a) $\sqrt{x^2 + x} + C$

(b) $\dfrac{1}{\sqrt{x^2 + x}} + C$

(c) $\sqrt{2x + 1} + C$

(d) $\dfrac{1}{2}\sqrt{2x + 1} + C$

(e) None of these

20. Evaluate $\displaystyle\int \dfrac{e^{1/(x+1)}}{(x + 1)^2}\, dx.$

(a) $\dfrac{e^{1/(x+1)}}{2(x + 1)} + C$

(b) $\dfrac{e^{-x/(x+1)}}{(x + 1)^2} + C$

(c) $-e^{1/(x+1)} + C$

(d) $\dfrac{e^{-x/(x+1)}}{(x + 1)^2}$

(e) None of these

21. Find the volume of the solid formed by revolving the region bounded by the graphs of $y = -x^2 + 4$ and $y = 0$ about the x-axis.

(a) $\dfrac{1472\pi}{15}$

(b) $\dfrac{736\pi}{15}$

(c) $\dfrac{2944\pi}{15}$

(d) $\dfrac{32\pi}{3}$

(e) None of these

22. Integrate: $\displaystyle\int 7x\sqrt{5 - 2x}\, dx.$

(a) $\frac{7}{15}(2x + 5)^{3/2}(3x - 5) + C$

(b) $-\frac{7}{15}(5 - 2x)^{3/2}(3x + 5) + C$

(c) $\frac{14}{15}(2x + 5)^{3/2}(3x - 10) + C$

(d) $-\frac{7}{3}(x + 5)\sqrt{5 - 2x} + C$

(e) None of these

23. Find the partial fraction decomposition: $\dfrac{9x^2 + x - 1}{x^2(x + 1)}.$

(a) $\dfrac{2}{x} - \dfrac{1}{x^2} + \dfrac{7}{x + 1}$

(b) $\dfrac{20}{x} - \dfrac{1}{x^2} - \dfrac{11}{x + 1}$

(c) $\dfrac{9}{x} + \dfrac{1}{x^2} - \dfrac{1}{x + 1}$

(d) $\dfrac{-1}{x^2} + \dfrac{9}{x + 1}$

(e) None of these

24. Evaluate: $\displaystyle\int \ln 3t\, dt.$

(a) $t \ln 3t - t + C$

(b) $\dfrac{1}{t} + C$

(c) $\dfrac{1}{3t} + C$

(d) $3t \ln 3t - 3t + C$

(e) None of these

25. Evaluate the improper integral: $\int_2^4 \dfrac{dx}{(x-3)^2}$.

    (a) The integral diverges.   (b) 2   (c) 0

    (d) -2 (e) None of these

26. Find $f_x(x, y)$ for $f(x, y) = \dfrac{xy}{x^2 - y^2}$.

    (a) $\dfrac{-y}{x^2 - y^2}$ (b) $\dfrac{y}{2x}$ (c) $\dfrac{-y(y^2 + x^2)}{(y^2 - x^2)^2}$ (d) $\dfrac{x + y}{2x - 2y}$ (e) None of these

27. Find the saddle point for $f(x, y) = x^2 - y^2 - 2x - 6y - 3$.

    (a) $(1, -3, 0)$ (b) $(-1, 3, 5)$ (c) $(-1, 3, 0)$

    (d) $(1, -3, 5)$ (e) None of these

28. Set up a double integral to find the area of the region bounded by the graphs of $y = 2x^2$ and $y = x^3$.

    (a) $\int_0^2 \int_{x^3}^{2x^2} dy\, dx$ (b) $\int_0^2 \int_{2x^2}^{x^3} dy\, dx$ (c) $\int_0^2 \int_{2x^2}^{x^3} dx\, dy$

    (d) $\int_0^2 \int_{x^3}^{2x^2} dx\, dy$ (e) None of these

29. Evaluate $\int_1^2 \int_1^x \dfrac{x^2}{y^2}\, dy\, dx$.

    (a) $-\dfrac{1}{6}$ (b) $\dfrac{14}{3} - 2\ln 2$ (c) 5   (d) $\dfrac{5}{6}$ (e) None of these

30. Find the derivative: $s(t) = \csc \dfrac{t}{2}$.

    (a) $-\csc \dfrac{t}{2} \cot \dfrac{t}{2}$ (b) $-\dfrac{1}{2} \cot^2 \dfrac{t}{2}$ (c) $\dfrac{1}{2} \csc \dfrac{t}{2} \cot \dfrac{t}{2}$

    (d) $\dfrac{1}{2} \cot^2 \dfrac{t}{2}$ (e) None of these

31. Evaluate $\int \dfrac{\cos^3 x - \sin^2 x}{\cos^2 x}\, dx$.

    (a) $\dfrac{\cos^2 x}{2} - \tan x + x + C$ (b) $\sin x - \sec x + C$ (c) $\sin x - \tan x + x + C$

    (d) $\sin x - \dfrac{\tan^3 x}{3} + C$ (e) None of these

Final Exam A

32. Find the limit: $\lim\limits_{x\to\infty} \dfrac{\ln(x+1)}{e^{-x}-1}$.

(a) 3   (b) ∞ (c) -1 (d) 0   (e) None of these

33. Find $P(2 \le x \le 4)$, given the probability density function $f(x) = \frac{1}{2}e^{-x/2}, x \ge 0$.

(a) $\dfrac{1}{e}$ (b) $\dfrac{1}{e} - \dfrac{1}{e^2}$ (c) $\dfrac{1}{2e^2}$ (d) $\dfrac{1}{4}\left(\dfrac{1}{e} - \dfrac{1}{e^2}\right)$ (e) None of these

34. Determine the expected value for the probability density function, $f(x) = \dfrac{3}{2x^2}, [1, 3]$.

(a) $\frac{7}{8}$ (b) $\frac{3}{2}\ln 3$ (c) $\frac{49}{72}$ (d) 2   (e) None of these

35. Choose the series that diverges by the nth-Term Test.

(a) $\sum\limits_{n=0}^{\infty} \dfrac{n+3}{n}$ (b) $\sum\limits_{n=0}^{\infty} \dfrac{n+3}{n!}$ (c) $\sum\limits_{n=0}^{\infty} \dfrac{100n^8}{6^n}$ (d) $\sum\limits_{n=0}^{\infty} \dfrac{8}{n}$ (e) None of these

36. Find the third term of the Taylor polynomial centered at 0 for $f(x) = e^{-x^2}$.

(a) $\dfrac{x^2}{2}$ (b) $\dfrac{x^4}{2}$ (c) $\dfrac{-x^6}{6}$ (d) $\dfrac{x^6}{12}$ (e) None of these

37. Find the sum of the following infinite geometric series: $\sum\limits_{n=1}^{\infty} 2(-0.9)^n$.

(a) 2   (b) 20   (c) -18 (d) $-\frac{18}{19}$ (e) None of these

38. The radius of a sphere is measured to be 3.0 inches. If the measurement is correct to within 0.01 inch, use differentials to estimate the propagated error in the volume of the sphere.

(a) ± 0.000001 in.^{3} (b) $\pm 0.36\pi$ in.^{3} (c) $\pm 0.036\pi$ in.^{3}

(d) ± 0.06 in.^{3} (e) None of these

39. A spherical balloon is inflated at the rate of 16 cubic feet per minute. How fast is the radius of the balloon changing at the instant the radius is 2 feet?

(a) 4π ft/min   (b) $\dfrac{32}{3}\pi$ ft/min   (c) $\dfrac{1}{\pi}$ ft/min   (d) 2π ft/min   (e) None of these

40. Evaluate $\displaystyle\int_0^2 \int_{y/2}^1 e^{x^2}\, dx\, dy$ by reversing the order of integration.

(a) $e - 1$ (b) $e + 1$ (c) e^2 (d) $e^4 - 1$ (e) None of these

Final Exam B

Name _____   **Date** _____

Class _____   **Section** _____

1. Let $f(x) = \dfrac{5}{x - 1}$ and $g(x) = x^4$.

   (a) Find $f(g(x))$.

   (b) Find the intervals on which $f(g(x))$ is continuous.

2. Find the first derivative of $f(x) = \dfrac{7}{x^3}$.

3. Find an equation of the tangent line to the graph of $f(x) = 3x^3 + 4x^2 - 1$ at the $x = 2$.

4. If the movement of a particle is given by the position equation

$$s(t) = 2t^2 + \frac{1}{t}$$

   where s is measured in meters and t is measured in seconds, find the velocity at $t = 2$.

5. Differentiate: $y = \dfrac{2x}{1 - 3x^2}$.

6. Differentiate: $\dfrac{3}{(1 - 4x^3)^2}$.

7. Find $f''(x) : f(x) = (1 + x^2)^3$.

8. Assume x and y are both differentiable functions of t. Find $\dfrac{dx}{dt}$ given $y = -1$ and $\dfrac{dy}{dt} = 12 : 2x^3 + y^2 = 3$.

9. Use implicit differentiation to get $\dfrac{dy}{dx}$ for $x^2 + xy + y^2 = 5$.

10. Find the horizontal asymptote for $f(x) = \dfrac{2x^2 + x - 7}{x^2 - 1}$.

11. Find the critical numbers of $f(x) = x^3 - 12x^2$.

12. Find all open intervals on which the function is increasing: $f(x) = 2x\sqrt{4 - x}$.

13. Find all points of inflection: $f(x) = 2x(x - 4)^3$.

14. Find $\dfrac{dy}{dx}$ using implicit differentiation: $y^3 + \dfrac{1}{e^y} = \ln\sqrt{x} + 4x$.

15. The number of fruit flies increases according to the law of exponential growth. If initially there are 10 fruit flies and after 8 hours there are 30, find the number of fruit flies after t hours.

16. Find the second derivative of the function: $f(x) = e^{1/x}$.

17. Evaluate $\int \dfrac{x^3 - x^2}{x^2}\, dx$.

18. A company produces a product for which the marginal cost of producing x units is

$$\frac{dC}{dx} = 0.12x + 8$$

and fixed costs are \$1500. Find the average cost of producing 50 units.

19. Evaluate: $\int \dfrac{3x^2}{(x^3 - 1)^4}\, dx$.

20. Evaluate $\int (2x^4 + 3x^2 - 2x)\, dx$.

(a) $\frac{3}{8}x^8 + C$ (b) $8x^3 + 6x - 2 + C$ (c) $\frac{2}{5}x^5 + x^3 - x^2 + C$

(d) $2x^5 + 5x^3 - 5x^2 + C$ (e) None of these

21. Find the volume of the solid formed by revolving the region bounded by the graphs of $y = 4x^2$ and $y = 16$ about the line $y = 16$.

22. Integrate: $\int 3x\sqrt{5 - x}\, dx$.

23. Find the partial fraction decomposition: $\dfrac{12x^2 - 13x - 3}{(x - 1)^2(x + 3)}$.

24. Evaluate: $\int x^2 e^{3x}\, dx$.

25. Evaluate the improper integral: $\displaystyle\int_0^\infty \dfrac{1}{\sqrt{x + 1}}\, dx$.

26. Find $f_y(x, y)$ for $f(x, y) = 2x^2y + xy^2 - y^3$.

27. Determine the relative extrema of $f(x, y) = x^2 + x - 3xy + y^3 - 5$.

28. Set up a double integral to find the area of the region bounded by the graphs of $y = x^2$ and $y = 2 - x^2$.

29. Evaluate $\displaystyle\int_{-1}^{2}\int_{0}^{1-x}(4 - y)\,dy\,dx$.

30. Find the derivative: $f(\theta) = \sec\theta^2$.

31. Evaluate $\displaystyle\int\frac{\sin^2 x - \cos^2 x}{\sin x}\,dx$.

32. Find the limit: $\displaystyle\lim_{x\to\infty}\frac{\ln(x - 4)}{x^2}$.

33. Find $P(4 \le x \le 8)$, given the probability density function $f(x) = \frac{1}{2}e^{-x/2}$, $x \ge 0$.

34. Find the expected value on the random variable x with probability density function, $f(x) = \dfrac{x}{18}$, $0 \le x \le 6$.

35. Determine the convergence or divergence of the following series, and state the test used: $\displaystyle\sum_{n=1}^{\infty}\frac{1}{1 + e^{-n}}$.

36. Find the third-degree Taylor polynomial centered at 0 for $f(x) = e^x$.

37. Find the sum: $\displaystyle\sum_{n=0}^{\infty}3\left(-\frac{1}{2}\right)^n$.

38. The volume of a cube is claimed to be 27 in.^{3}, correct to within 0.027 in.^{3}. Use differentials to estimate the propagated error in the measurement of the side of the cube.

39. As a balloon in the shape of a sphere is being blown up, the volume is increasing at the rate of 4 in^3/sec. At what rate is the radius increasing when the radius is 1 in.?

40. Evaluate $\displaystyle\int_{0}^{1}\int_{y^2}^{1}ye^{x^2}\,dx\,dy$ by reversing the order of integration.

Final Exam C

Name _____ Date _____

Class _____ Section _____

1. Determine the value of c so that $f(x)$ is continuous on the entire real line if $f(x) = \begin{cases} x^2, & x \le 3 \\ \dfrac{c}{x} & x > 3 \end{cases}$.

2. Find the derivative of y with respect to x if $y = 4\sqrt[3]{x}(2x + 3)$.

3. Find all points at which the graph of $f(x) = x^3 - 3x$ has horizontal tangent lines.

4. Use a graphing utility to find the point(s) on the graph of the function $P(x) = -0.3x^2 + 5.6x + 9$ where the marginal profit is zero.

5. Differentiate: $f(x) = \dfrac{x^2 - 2}{x^2 + 2}$.

6. Find the slope of the curve $y^4 - xy^2 = x$ at the point $\left(\frac{1}{2}, 1\right)$.

7. The position equation for the movement of a particle is given by $s = (t^3 + 1)^2$ where s is measured in feet and t is measured in seconds. Find the acceleration of this particle at 1 second.

8. Differentiate: $\dfrac{2x + 1}{(1 - x^2)^3}$.

9. Find all open intervals on which the function is increasing: $f(x) = 3x\sqrt{x + 2}$.

10. A metal cube contracts when it is cooled. If the edge of the cube is decreasing at a rate of 0.2 cm/hr, how fast is the volume changing when the edge is 60 cm?

11. Find the absolute minimum and absolute maximum for $f(x) = \dfrac{10}{(x^2 + 1)}$ on the interval $[-1, 2]$.

12. Find all intervals on which $y = \dfrac{4x^2 - x}{x^4}$ is concave up.

13. An open box is to be constructed from cardboard by cutting out squares of equal size in the corners and then folding up the sides. If the cardboard is 6 in. by 11 in., determine the volume of the largest box which can be so constructed.

14. Find the differential dy if $y = \dfrac{x - 2}{x + 3}$.

15. Find $\lim\limits_{x \to \infty} \left(\dfrac{2x}{x + 2} + \dfrac{x}{x - 1} \right)$.

16. Find the limit: $\lim\limits_{x \to 3} \dfrac{x - 3}{x^2 - 9}$.

17. Use a graphing utility to find the number of units which maximizes the profit for a product whose demand function is

$$p = \dfrac{1000}{1 + e^{-x}}$$

and cost function is $C = e^x + 100$.

18. The demand function for a certain product is given by $p = 750 - 0.5e^{0.002x}$. Find the price of the product if the quantity demanded is 2500.

19. Find $\dfrac{dy}{dx}$ if $y = \ln \dfrac{\sqrt{x}}{5 - x}$.

20. A deposit of \$2000 is made into a fund with an annual interest rate of 10%. Find the time (in years) necessary for the investment to amount to \$10,000 if the interest is compounded continuously. Round your answer to two decimal places.

21. Write an equation for the amount Q of a radioactive substance with a half-life of 30 days, if 10 grams are present when $t = 0$.

22. Evaluate $\displaystyle\int \dfrac{x - 3}{x + 1}\, dx$.

23. Evaluate: $\displaystyle\int 5y(2y^2 + 1)^3\, dy$.

24. Find the function, $y = f(x)$, if $y' = 2x - 1$ and $f(1) = 3$.

25. Evaluate $\displaystyle\int_1^e \dfrac{5}{x}\, dx$.

26. Use the Midpoint Rule with $n = 4$ to approximate the area of the region bounded by $f(x) = x^3 - 6x^2 + 9x$ and the x-axis between $x = 0$ and $x = 3$.

(a) 6.54   (b) 6.96   (c) 9.28   (d) 6.75   (e) None of these

27. Evaluate: $\displaystyle\int_{-1}^0 x^2\sqrt{x + 1}\, dx$.

28. Find the partial fraction decomposition: $\dfrac{3x^2 - 31x - 25}{(x + 1)(x^2 - 7x - 8)}$.

29. The annual income for a small company over the next ten years is given by the model $c(t) = 90{,}000t$, $0 \le t \le 10$. What is the present value of this income over the ten–year period if we assume an annual interest rate of 9%?

30. Use the Trapezoidal Rule with $n = 4$ to approximate $\displaystyle\int_{60}^{61} e^{-0.11(x - 60)^2}\, dx$.

31. Find the distance between the point $(1, -2, 3)$ and the plane $3x - 4y + 2z - 1 = 0$.

32. The sum of $2000 is deposited in a savings account earning r percent interest compounded continuously. The amount $A(r, t)$ after t years is given by $A(r, t) = 2000e^{rt}$. Determine the amount in an account earning 8% interest for 5 years.

33. Find $f_z(1, -1, 4)$ for $f(x, y, z) = 2x^2y - 2yz + xz$.

34. Determine the maximum revenue obtained by a furniture store that sells two competitive products, the prices of which are p_1 and p_2.

$$R = 300p_1 + 900p_2 + 1.8p_1p_2 - 1.5p_1^2 - p_2^2.$$

35. Find the least squares regression quadratic for the points $(1, 4)$, $(3, 4)$, $(-1, -3)$, $(7, -1)$.

36. Evaluate $\displaystyle\int_{-2}^{1}\int_{0}^{6-x^2} (4 + y)\, dy\, dx$.

37. Find the derivative of $y = \tan\!\left(x^2 - \dfrac{\pi}{4}\right)$.

38. Find the expected value on the random variable x with probability density function, $f(x) = \dfrac{x}{18}, 0 \le x \le 6$.

39. Complete two iterations of Newton's Method to approximate a zero of $f(x) = x^5 + 2x - 1$ using $x_1 = 0.5$ as an initial estimate. Round to four decimal places.

40. Use a power series centered at 0 to get a degree two approximation for $\sqrt[4]{1.5}$ using the function $f(x) = \sqrt[4]{x + 1}$.

41. Determine the convergence or divergence of the following series, and state the test used: $\displaystyle\sum_{n=1}^{\infty} \dfrac{2 \cdot 4 \cdot 6 \cdots 2n}{n!}$.

42. A force is applied to a particle, which moves in a straight line, in such a way that after each second the particle moves only one-half the distance that it moved in the preceding second. If the particle moved 20 cm in the first second, how far will it move altogether?

CHAPTER TESTS

Test Form A

Chapter 0

Name _____ Date _____

Class _____ Section _____

1. Solve for x: $-x^2 + 4x - 3 > 0$.

   (a) $(0, 3)$ 　　　　　　 (b) $[1, 3)$ 　　　　　　 (c) 2

   (d) $(1, 3)$ 　　　　　　 (e) $(-\infty, 1)$ or $(3, \infty)$

2. Solve for x: $-\frac{2}{3}x > x + 2$.

   (a) $\left(-\frac{6}{5}, \infty\right)$ 　　　　 (b) $\left(\frac{6}{5}, \infty\right)$ 　　　　 (c) $\left(\frac{2}{5}, \infty\right)$

   (d) $\left(-\infty, -\frac{6}{5}\right)$ 　　　　 (e) None of these

3. Graph the solution: $|2 - x| \le 5$.

   (a)

   (b)

   (c)

   (d)

   (e)

4. Use absolute value to describe the following set: x is less than 4 units from y.

   (a) $|y - 4| < x$ 　　　　 (b) $|x - 4| < y$ 　　　　 (c) $|x - y| < 4$

   (d) $|x + 4| < y$ 　　　　 (e) None of these

5. Evaluate the following expression when $x = 2, y = -1, a = 1, b = -2$:

   $$-\frac{2(xy)^3}{a^2 b^3}.$$

   (a) 2 　　 (b) -2 　　 (c) $\frac{1}{2}$ 　　 (d) $-\frac{1}{2}$ 　　 (e) None of these

6. Simplify: $\dfrac{4x^{-2}y^2 z^3 w^{-1}}{64x^2 \sqrt{y} z^{-2} w^3}$.

   (a) $\dfrac{y^{5/2} z^3}{16x^4 w^4}$ 　 (b) $\dfrac{y^{3/2} z^5}{16x^4 w^4}$ 　 (c) $\dfrac{y^{3/2} z^3}{16x^2 w}$ 　 (d) $\dfrac{y^{5/2} z}{16x^4 w^4}$ 　 (e) $\dfrac{y^{3/2} z}{16x^4 w^2}$

7. Find the domain: $\dfrac{1}{\sqrt{x - 1}}$.

   (a) $(-\infty, \infty)$ 　　 (b) 1 　　 (c) $(1, \infty)$ 　　 (d) $(-\infty, 1)$ 　　 (e) None of these

8. Completely factor: $(x + 2)^{1/2} + x(x + 2)^{-1/2}$.

   (a) $\dfrac{1 + x}{\sqrt{x + 2}}$ (b) $\dfrac{2(1 + x)}{\sqrt{x + 2}}$ (c) $x\sqrt{x + 2}$ (d) $x^2 + 2x$ (e) $\sqrt{x + 2}(1 + x)$

9. Completely factor: $3x^4 - 375x$.

   (a) $3x(x + 5)(x^2 - 5x + 25)$ (b) $3x(x - 5)(x^2 - 5x + 25)$ (c) $3x(x - 5)(x^2 + 5x + 25)$

   (d) $3(x - 5)(x^2 + 5x + 25)$ (e) $3x(x - 5)(x^2 + 10x + 25)$

10. Use the quadratic formula to find any real roots: $3x^2 + x - 3 = 0$.

   (a) $\dfrac{-1 \pm \sqrt{37}}{6}$ (b) $\dfrac{1 \pm \sqrt{37}}{6}$ (c) $-\dfrac{7}{6}, \dfrac{5}{6}$ (d) $\dfrac{-1 \pm \sqrt{37}}{3}$ (e) $\dfrac{-1 \pm \sqrt{37}}{2}$

11. Use the rational zero theorem as an aid to find all real zeros of $x^4 - 3x^3 + 4x$.

   (a) $\{-1, 0, 2\}$ (b) $\{-2, -1, 0\}$ (c) $\left\{-\frac{1}{2}, 0, 1, 3\right\}$

   (d) $\{-1, -1, 0, 2\}$ (e) None of these

12. Perform the indicated operation: $x - 2 + \dfrac{3}{x + 1}$.

   (a) $\dfrac{x^2 + x + 1}{x + 1}$ (b) $\dfrac{x^2 + x - 1}{x + 1}$ (c) $\dfrac{x^2 - x + 1}{x + 1}$

   (d) $\dfrac{x^2 - x - 1}{x + 1}$ (e) $x + 2$

13. Rationalize the denominator and simplify: $\dfrac{2}{\sqrt{x + 1} + \sqrt{x}}$.

   (a) $\dfrac{2}{2x + 1}$ (b) $\dfrac{1}{x + 1}$ (c) $2\sqrt{2x}$

   (d) $2\left(\sqrt{x + 1} + \sqrt{x}\right)$ (e) $2\left(\sqrt{x + 1} - \sqrt{x}\right)$

14. Simplify: $\dfrac{\dfrac{2}{x + \Delta x} - \dfrac{2}{x}}{\Delta x}$.

   (a) $\dfrac{2}{x(x + \Delta x)}$ (b) $-\dfrac{2}{x + \Delta x}$ (c) 1 (d) $-\dfrac{2}{x(x + \Delta x)}$ (e) $-\dfrac{2}{x^2}$

15. Add and simplify: $-\dfrac{\sqrt{x + 1}}{x} + \dfrac{1}{\sqrt{x + 1}}$.

   (a) $-\dfrac{1}{x\sqrt{x + 1}}$ (b) $\dfrac{x - 1}{x}$ (c) $\dfrac{1}{x\sqrt{x + 1}}$ (d) $-\dfrac{1}{x}$ (e) None of these

Test Form B

Chapter 0

Name _____ Date _____

Class _____ Section _____

1. Solve for x: $-x^2 - 3x > 0$.

   (a) $(-3, \infty)$

   (b) $(-3, 0)$

   (c) $(0, 3)$

   (d) $(-\infty, -3)$ or $(0, \infty)$

   (e) None of these

2. Solve for x: $-\frac{4}{5}x < 4x - 8$.

   (a) $\left(-\frac{6}{5}, \infty\right)$

   (b) $\left(\frac{5}{3}, \infty\right)$

   (c) $\left(\frac{2}{5}, \infty\right)$

   (d) $\left(-\infty, -\frac{2}{5}\right)$

   (e) None of these

3. Graph the solution: $|2x - 1| \geq 3$.

   (a)

   (b)

   (c)

   (d)

   (e) None of these

4. Use absolute value to describe the following set: x is less than 5 units from y.

   (a) $|y - 5| < x$

   (b) $|x - 5| < y$

   (c) $|x - y| < 5$

   (d) $|x + 5| < y$

   (e) None of these

5. Evaluate the following expression when $x = 2$, $y = -1$, $a = 1$, $b = -2$:

   $$-\frac{2xy^3}{a^2b^3}.$$

   (a) 2

   (b) -2

   (c) $\frac{1}{2}$

   (d) $-\frac{1}{2}$

   (e) None of these

6. Simplify: $\dfrac{100x^{-2}y^3z^{3/2}w^{-1}}{5x^2\sqrt{y}z^{-2}w^{-3}}$.

   (a) $\dfrac{20y^{5/2}z^{7/2}w^2}{x^4}$

   (b) $\dfrac{20y^{3/2}z^5}{x^4w^4}$

   (c) $\dfrac{20y^{3/2}z^3}{x^2w}$

   (d) $\dfrac{20y^{5/2}z}{x^4w^4}$

   (e) $\dfrac{20y^{3/2}z}{x^4w^2}$

7. Find the domain: $\sqrt[3]{1 + x}$.

   (a) $(-\infty, \infty)$

   (b) $[-1, \infty)$

   (c) -1

   (d) $(-\infty, -1]$

   (e) None of these

8. Completely factor: $(x - 1)^{-2/3}(x + 2) + (x - 1)^{1/3}$.

(a) $\dfrac{1 + x}{\sqrt[3]{x + 2}}$ (b) $\dfrac{2(1 + x)}{\sqrt[3]{x + 2}}$ (c) $x\sqrt[3]{x + 2}$ (d) $x^2 + 2x$ (e) None of these

9. Completely factor: $3x^4 - 24x$.

(a) $3x(x + 2)(x^2 - 2x + 4)$ (b) $3x(x - 2)(x^2 - 2x + 4)$ (c) $3x(x - 2)(x^2 + 2x + 4)$

(d) $3(x - 2)(x^2 + 2x + 4)$ (e) None of these

10. Use the quadratic formula to find any real roots: $2x^2 + 4x - 1 = 0$.

(a) $\dfrac{-1 \pm \sqrt{37}}{6}$ (b) $\dfrac{1 \pm \sqrt{37}}{6}$ (c) $-\dfrac{7}{6}, \dfrac{5}{6}$ (d) $\dfrac{-1 \pm \sqrt{37}}{3}$ (e) None of these

11. Use the rational zero theorem as an aid to find all real zeros of $2x^3 + 3x^2 - 8x - 12$.

(a) $-1, 0, 2$ (b) $-\dfrac{3}{2}$ (c) $-1, 0, 4$ (d) $-2, -\dfrac{3}{2}, 2$ (e) None of these

12. Perform the indicated operation: $3x - 4 - \dfrac{1}{3x - 2}$.

(a) $-3(3x - 2)$ (b) $\dfrac{9x^2 - 18x + 8}{3x - 2}$ (c) $\dfrac{9x^2 - 18x - 9}{3x - 2}$

(d) $\dfrac{9x^2 - 18x + 7}{3x - 2}$ (e) None of these

13. Rationalize the denominator and simplify: $\dfrac{\Delta x}{\sqrt{x + \Delta x} - \sqrt{x}}$.

(a) 1 (b) $\sqrt{x + \Delta x} + \sqrt{x}$ (c) $\sqrt{2x + \Delta x}$

(d) Δx (e) None of these

14. Simplify: $\dfrac{\dfrac{5}{3 + x} - \dfrac{5}{x}}{3x}$.

(a) $\dfrac{10x - 15}{3x^2(3 + x)}$ (b) $\dfrac{5}{3x^2(3 + x)}$ (c) -5 (d) $\dfrac{-5}{x^2(3 + x)}$ (e) None of these

15. Add and simplify: $-\dfrac{\sqrt{x}}{x - 5} + \dfrac{1}{\sqrt{x}}$.

(a) $\dfrac{5}{\sqrt{x}(5 - x)}$ (b) $2x - 5$ (c) $\dfrac{1 - \sqrt{x}}{x - 5 + \sqrt{x}}$ (d) $\dfrac{-2\sqrt{x} + 1}{\sqrt{x}(x - 5)}$ (e) None of these

Test Form C

Chapter 0

Name _____ Date _____

Class _____ Section _____

1. Solve for x: $3 - 2x \geq 0$.

2. Solve for x: $-\frac{3}{2}x < 6x + 12$.

3. Evaluate: $-\dfrac{x^2}{y^3 z}$ if $x = 2$, $y = 1$, and $z = 3$.

4. Simplify: $\dfrac{7x^{-1/2}y^3 z^{-2}}{3x^3 y^{-1} z^2}$.

5. Factor and simplify: $x(x + 1)^{-1/2} + 2(x + 1)^{1/2}$.

6. Factor completely: $x^5 - 9x^3 + 8x^2 - 72$.

7. Solve for x: $x^2 - 2x = 8$.

8. Find all of the real zeros of the function: $f(x) = 2x^3 + 14x^2 + 24x$.

9. Perform the indicated operations and simplify: $\dfrac{A}{x} + \dfrac{B}{x^2} + \dfrac{C}{x + 2}$.

10. Simplify: $\dfrac{3(x + \Delta x)^2 - 4(x + \Delta x) + 5 - (3x^2 - 4x + 5)}{\Delta x}$.

11. Rationalize the denominator and simplify: $\dfrac{4 - x}{2 + \sqrt{x}}$.

12. Perform the indicated operation and simplify: $\dfrac{-3}{\sqrt{x - 1}} + 4\sqrt{x - 1}$.

13. The weekly cost of operating a certain manufacturing plant is $C = 0.2x^2 + 11x + 3000$, where x represents the number of units produced. Management wants to produce at least 100 units, but also wants to keep operating costs at less than 10,000 per week. At what values of x can both goals be met?

14. In a complete sentence, write the meaning of the statement $|x - 2| < 4$, as it refers to two points on a real number line.

Test Form D

Chapter 0

Name _____ Date _____

Class _____ Section _____

1. Solve for x: $-x^2 - 3x > 0$.

   (a) $(-3, \infty)$ (b) $(-3, 0)$ (c) $(0, 3)$

   (d) $(-\infty, -3)$ or $(0, \infty)$ (e) None of these

2. Solve for x: $-\frac{5}{4}x < 5x - 10$.

   (a) $\left(-\infty, \frac{8}{5}\right)$ (b) $x > \frac{8}{5}$ (c) $x < \frac{8}{5}$

   (d) $\left[\frac{8}{5}, \infty\right)$ (e) None of these

3. Solve for x: $|-3x + 6| \geq 12$.

   (a) $(-\infty, -2] \cup [6, \infty)$ (b) $[-2, 6]$ (c) $x \geq 6$

   (d) $x \leq -2$ (e) None of these

4. Find the domain of the algebraic expression $\sqrt{x^2 + 4}$.

   (a) $(-2, 2)$ (b) $x > 2$ (c) $x < -2$

   (d) $x < -2$ or $x > 2$ (e) None of these

5. Use a calculator to find the *interest accrued* (rounded to the nearest penny) on a principal P of \$5000 after two years if the interest rate is $r = 5\%$ per annum and the interest is compounded monthly (i.e., $n = 12$). The formula for the amount A of money in the bank is $A = P\left(1 + \frac{r}{n}\right)^N$, where N is the number of compoundings.

   (a) \$5524.71   (b) \$7083.33   (c) \$524.70   (d) \$2083.33   (e) None of these

6. The daily cost of producing x units of a certain product is given by $C = \sqrt{700 + 0.05x + .002x^2}$. Use a calculator to find the cost, to the nearest penny, of producing 400 units for 7 days.

   (a) \$225.74   (b) \$32.25   (c) \$19.36   (d) \$135.55   (e) None of these

7. Evaluate the following expression when $x = 2, y = -1, a = -5, b = -2$:

$$-\frac{3x^2y^4}{a^3b^{-3}}.$$

   (a) -0.768 (b) 0.769 (c) -0.769 (d) 0.768 (e) None of these

8. Simplify: $\dfrac{125x^{-2}y^4z^{-5/2}w^{-1}}{5x^3\sqrt{yz^{-2}w^{-3}}}$.

(a) $\dfrac{25y^{7/2}x^4w^2}{z^{1/2}}$ (b) $\dfrac{25z^{1/2}w^2}{x^5y^{7/2}}$ (c) $\dfrac{25y^{7/2}w^2}{x^5z^{1/2}}$ (d) $\dfrac{25x^5z^{1/2}}{y^{7/2}w^2}$ (e) None of these

9. Completely factor: $(2x-5)^{-3/4}(x+2)-(2x-5)^{1/4}$.

(a) $\dfrac{-x-3}{(2x-5)^{3/4}}$ (b) $\dfrac{(7-x)}{(2x-5)^{3/4}}$ (c) $\dfrac{3x-3}{(2x-5)^{3/4}}$ (d) $\dfrac{-x-3}{(2x-5)^{5/4}}$ (e) None of these

10. The cost C of manufacturing x radios is given by $C = 400 + 100x + 0.1x^2$. How many radios can be produced for less than \$2000?

(a) $x < 15$ (b) $x > 16$ (c) $x < 14$ (d) $x < 16$ (e) None of these

11. Determine the domain of the algebraic expression $\sqrt{x-4} + \dfrac{1}{\sqrt{x+4}}$.

(a) $(-4, \infty)$ (b) $(-4, 4)$ (c) $(4, \infty)$ (d) $[4, \infty)$ (e) None of these

12. Use the quadratic formula and a calculator to estimate the roots of $2x^2 + 5x - 1 = 0$ to the nearest 0.1.

(a) $-0.2, -2.3$ (b) $-0.4, 5.2$ (c) $-2.7, 0.2$ (d) $0.2, 2.3$ (e) None of these

13. Find all of the real zeros of the function: $f(x) = 6x^4 + 32x^3 - 70x^2$.

(a) $0, -1, 5$ (b) $0, -7, \frac{5}{3}$ (c) $\frac{7}{3}, 5$ (d) $0, -1, -7, \frac{5}{3}$ (e) None of these

14. Perform the indicated operation: $x - 4 - \dfrac{1}{x-2}$.

(a) $x - 3$ (b) $\dfrac{x^2 - 6x + 8}{x - 2}$ (c) $\dfrac{x^2 - 6x - 8}{x - 2}$ (d) $\dfrac{x^2 + 6x + 8}{x - 2}$ (e) None of these

15. Rationalize the denominator and simplify: $\dfrac{3x}{\sqrt{x}-5}$.

(a) $3x\sqrt{x}$ (b) $\dfrac{3x\sqrt{x}+15x}{x-25}$ (c) $\dfrac{3x\sqrt{x}+15}{x-25}$ (d) $\dfrac{3x\sqrt{x}+15x}{x-5}$ (e) None of these

16. Simplify: $\dfrac{\dfrac{2}{1+x} - \dfrac{2}{x}}{4x}$.

(a) $\dfrac{-1}{2x^2(1+x)}$ (b) $\dfrac{x-1}{2x^2(1+x)}$ (c) -2 (d) $\dfrac{-1}{4x^2(1+x)}$ (e) None of these

17. Use synthetic division to perform the indicated division:

$\dfrac{x^3 - x^2 + 4x - 3}{x + 3}$.

(a) $x^2 - 4x + 16 + \dfrac{45}{x+3}$

(b) $x^2 - 4x + 16 + \dfrac{51}{x+3}$

(c) $x^2 - 4x - 16 - \dfrac{51}{x+3}$

(d) $x^2 - 4x + 16 - \dfrac{51}{x+3}$

(e) None of these

Test Form E

Chapter 0

Name _____ Date _____

Class _____ Section _____

1. Solve for x: $-x^2 + 5x + 6 < 0$.

2. Solve for x (accurate to the nearest 0.1): $-x^2 + 5x < -7$.

3. Solve for x: $|-4x + 8| \geq 12$.

4. Find the domain: $\sqrt{3x + 2}$.

5. A 20-year mortgage for $P = \$56,000$ at an annual percentage rate of $r = .07$ requires a monthly payment of $M = \$424.17$. Payments have been made on the loan for 2 years ($N = 24$ monthly payments). Determine the balance B due on the loan if the balance is given by $B = \left(1 + \dfrac{r}{12}\right)^N \left(P - \dfrac{12M}{r}\right) + \dfrac{12M}{r}$.

6. The daily cost of producing x units of a certain product is given by $C = \sqrt{700 + 0.05x + .002x^2}$. Use a calculator to find the cost, to the nearest penny, of producing 300 units for 14 days.

7. Evaluate the following expression when $x = 3, y = -1, a = -6, b = -3$:

   $-\dfrac{3x^2y^4}{a^3b^{-3}}$.

8. Simplify: $\dfrac{130x^{-3}y^5z^{-7/2}w^{-1}}{5x^4\sqrt{y}z^{-3}w^{-4}}$.

9. The cost C of manufacturing x compact disks is given by $C = 2000 + 10x + 0.2x^2$, where x is a positive integer or 0. How many compact disks can be produced for less than \$3000?

10. Determine the domain of the algebraic expression $\sqrt{x + 3} + \dfrac{1}{\sqrt{x - 3}}$.

11. Completely factor: $(x - 5)^{-2/3}(3x + 4) - (x - 5)^{1/3}$.

12. Use the quadratic formula and a calculator to estimate the roots of $3x^2 + 5x - 4 = 0$ to the nearest 0.1.

13. Use the rational zero theorem as an aid to find the one rational zero of $3x^3 - 4x^2 - 9x + 12$.

14. Perform the indicated operation: $x - 5 - \dfrac{1}{x - 3}$.

15. Rationalize the numerator and simplify: $\dfrac{\sqrt{x} - 3}{2x}$.

16. Simplify: $\dfrac{\dfrac{2}{3 - x} - \dfrac{2}{x}}{3x^2}$.

17. Use synthetic division to perform the indicated division:

$$\dfrac{x^3 - x^2 - 4x - 5}{x + 2}.$$

18. In a complete sentence, give a definition of a rational number.

Test Form A Name _____ Date _____

Chapter 1 Class _____ Section _____

1. Find y such that the distance from $(3, y)$ to $(-1, 2)$ is $\sqrt{65}$ units.

   (a) 5, -9 (b) $\pm 3\sqrt{5}$ (c) 9, -5 (d) 15, -3 (e) None of these

2. Use the vertical line test to determine which of the following represent the graphs of functions.

   (1) 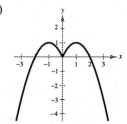   (2 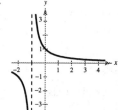   (3)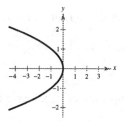

   (4) 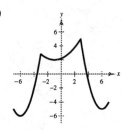   (5)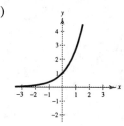

   (a) 1, 2, 3, 4, 5   (b) 1, 2, 3, 5   (c) 1, 2, 4, 5   (d) 1, 3, 4, 5   (e) None of these

3. Find all intercepts: $y = \dfrac{x + 2}{x - 3}$.

   (a) $(-2, 0)$ (b) $(-2, 0), (3, 0)$ (c) $\left(0, \frac{2}{3}\right), (3, 0)$

   (d) $(-2, 0), \left(0, -\frac{2}{3}\right)$ (e) None of these

4. Find the center of the circle: $2x^2 + 2y^2 - 4x + 12y + 15 = 0$.

   (a) $(1, -3)$ (b) $(-1, 3)$ (c) $(-1, -3)$ (d) $(1, 3)$ (e) None of these

5. Find an equation for the straight line passing through the points $(2, -1)$ and $(-3, 1)$.

   (a) $2x + 5y + 1 = 0$ (b) $2x - 5y - 9 = 0$ (c) $2x + 5y + 9 = 0$

   (d) $2x - 5y - 1 = 0$ (e) None of these

6. Find an equation of the line passing through the point $(2, 3)$ and perpendicular to the line whose equation is $2x - 4y + 1 = 0$.

(a) $2x - y + 3 = 0$ (b) $2x + y - 3 = 0$ (c) $x - 2y - 4 = 0$

(d) $2x + y - 7 = 0$ (e) None of these

7. Find $f(-2)$ if $f(x) = \dfrac{-4x}{x^2 + 1}$.

(a) $-\dfrac{8}{5}$ (b) $-\dfrac{8}{3}$ (c) $\dfrac{8}{5}$ (d) $\dfrac{8}{3}$ (e) None of these

8. Find the points of intersection of the graphs of the equations $y = 4x - 2$ and $y = x^2 + 1$.

(a) $(1, 10), (3, 2)$ (b) $(-1, 2), (-3, 10)$ (c) $(1, 2), (3, 9)$

(d) $(1, 2), (3, 10)$ (e) None of these

9. If the total cost of running a business is given by the equation $C = 450x + 1000$ and the revenue is given by the equation $R = 500x$, find the sales necessary to break even.

(a) 220   (b) 11   (c) 20   (d) 2000   (e) None of these

10. What is the domain of the function $y = f(x) = \dfrac{x^2 - 3x + 5}{x^2 - 4}$?

(a) $x < 2$ (b) $(-\infty, -2) \cup (-2, 2) \cup (2, \infty)$ (c) $x \neq 2$

(d) All real numbers   (e) None of these

11. Find $f(-1)$ if $f(x) = -x^2 + 3x - 5$.

(a) -7 (b) -1 (c) -9 (d) -3 (e) None of these

12. Find $f(x + \Delta x)$ if $f(x) = 2x^3 + 4$.

(a) $2x^3 + 6x^2(\Delta x) + 6x(\Delta x)^2 + 2(\Delta x)^3 + 4$ (b) $2x^3 + 2(\Delta x)^3 + 4$

(c) $6x^2(\Delta x) + 6x(\Delta x)^2 + 2(\Delta x)^3$ (d) $2x^3 + 6x^2(\Delta x) + 6x(\Delta x)^2 + 2(\Delta x)^3$

(e) None of these

13. Find $f(g(1))$ for $f(x) = x - 2$ and $g(x) = x^2 + 5$.

(a) $x^2 - 4x + 9$ (b) 6   (c) 4   (d) $x^2 + 3$ (e) None of these

14. Find $f^{-1}(x)$ for the function $f(x) = 2x + 4$.

(a) $\dfrac{x - 4}{2}$ (b) $\dfrac{1}{2}x - 4$ (c) $\dfrac{1}{2x + 4}$ (d) $\dfrac{1}{2}x + 4$ (e) None of these

15. Find $\lim\limits_{x \to -3} \dfrac{x^2 + 2x - 3}{x - 3}$.

(a) -2 (b) 4   (c) 0   (d) Does not exist   (e) None of these

16. Find $\lim\limits_{x \to 0} \dfrac{\sqrt{x + 3} - \sqrt{3}}{x}$.

(a) $\dfrac{1}{2\sqrt{3}}$ (b) $\dfrac{1}{3\sqrt{3}}$ (c) $\dfrac{1}{3}$ (d) Does not exist   (e) None of these

17. Find $\lim\limits_{\Delta x \to 0} \dfrac{2(x + \Delta x) - 3 - (2x - 3)}{\Delta x}$.

(a) 0   (b) ∞ (c) 2   (d) Does not exist   (e) None of these

18. Find $\lim\limits_{x \to 4^-} \dfrac{|x - 4|}{x - 4}$.

(a) Does not exist   (b) -1 (c) 0

(d) ∞ (e) None of these

19. Find all values of x for which $f(x) = \dfrac{x^3 - 2x^2 - 3x}{x^2 + x}$ has removable discontinuities.

(a) $-1, 0$ (b) 0   (c) $-1, 0, 3$

(d) $-3, -1, 0$ (e) None of these

20. Find the value(s) of x for which the function $f(x) = \dfrac{x - 3}{x^2 - 5x + 6}$ has a removable discontinuity.

(a) 2, 3   (b) 2   (c) -3 (d) 0   (e) None of these

Test Form B   Name _____ Date _____

Chapter 1   Class _____ Section _____

1. Find x such that the distance from $(x, -5)$ to $(-1, 2)$ is $\sqrt{65}$ units.

    (a) $5, -3$ (b) $\pm\sqrt{15}$ (c) $15, -1$ (d) $-5, 3$ (e) None of these

2. Use the vertical line test to determine which of the following represent the graphs of functions.

    (1) 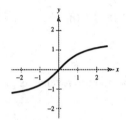   (2) 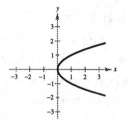   (3)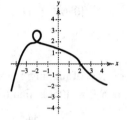

    (4) 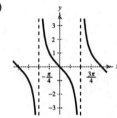   (5)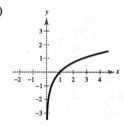

    (a) $1, 2, 3$ (b) $1, 4, 5$ (c) $2, 3$ (d) $4, 5$ (e) None of these

3. Find all intercepts: $y = \dfrac{x - 1}{x + 3}$.

    (a) $(1, 0), \left(0, -\frac{1}{3}\right)$ (b) $(1, 0)$ (c) $(-3, 0), (1, 0)$

    (d) $(-3, 0), \left(0, -\frac{1}{3}\right)$ (e) None of these

4. Find the center of the circle: $2x^2 + 2y^2 + 4x - 12y + 24 = 0$.

    (a) $(1, -3)$ (b) $(-1, 3)$ (c) $(-3, 1)$ (d) $(0, 0)$ (e) None of these

5. Find an equation for the straight line passing through the points $(2, -1)$ and $(-6, -1)$.

    (a) $x - 2y - 4 = 0$ (b) $y + 1 = 0$ (c) $x - 4y - 6 = 0$

    (d) $x + 4y = 0$ (e) None of these

6. Find an equation of the line passing through the point $(-2, 1)$ and perpendicular to the line whose equation is $3x - 4y + 2 = 0$.

   (a) $-4x + 3y + 5 = 0$ (b) $3x - 4y + 10 = 0$ (c) $4x + 3y - 5 = 0$

   (d) $3x + 4y - 10 = 0$ (e) None of these

7. Find $f(-1)$ if $f(x) = -x^2 + 3x - 5$.

   (a) -7 (b) -1 (c) -9 (d) -3 (e) None of these

8. Find the points of intersection of the graphs of the equations $y = x$ and $y = x^3$.

   (a) $(-1, -1), (0, 0), (1, 1)$ (b) $(-1, 1), (0, 0), (1, -1)$ (c) $(-1, 1), (0, 0)$

   (d) $(-1, -1), (1, 1)$ (e) None of these

9. If the total cost of running a business is given by the equation $C = 1000x + 75,000$ and the revenue is given by the equation $R = 1250x$, find the sales necessary to break even.

   (a) 3000   (b) 34   (c) 300   (d) 30   (e) None of these

10. What is the domain of the function $y = f(x) = \dfrac{x^2 + 3x - 6}{x^2 - 9}$?

    (a) $(-\infty, -3) \cup (-3, 3) \cup (3, \infty)$ (b) $x > 3$ (c) $x \neq 3$

    (d) $(-3, 3)$ (e) None of these

11. Find $f(-1)$ for $f(x) = -x^3 - 3x^2 - 2x - 1$.

    (a) 11   (b) 7   (c) 1   (d) -1 (e) None of these

12. Find $f(x + \Delta x)$ if $f(x) = 2x^3 + 3x + 1$.

    (a) $6x^2(\Delta x) + 6x(\Delta x)^2 + 2(\Delta x)^3 + 3\Delta x$

    (b) $6x^2 + 3$

    (c) $x^3 + 3x^2(\Delta x) + 3x(\Delta x)^2 + 3(\Delta x)^3 + 3x + 3\Delta x + 1$

    (d) $2x^3 + 6x^2(\Delta x) + 6x(\Delta x)^2 + 2(\Delta x)^3 + 3x + 3\Delta x + 1$

    (e) None of these

13. Find $f(g(1))$ for $f(x) = x^2 + 5$ and $g(x) = x - 2$.

    (a) 6   (b) 4   (c) $x^2 - 4x + 4$ (d) $x^2 + 3$ (e) None of these

14. Find $f^{-1}(x)$ for the function $f(x) = \dfrac{3}{4}x + 6$.

    (a) $\dfrac{4}{3}x - 8$ (b) $\dfrac{1}{\frac{3}{4}x + 6}$ (c) $\dfrac{3}{4x + 24}$ (d) $3x + 24$ (e) None of these

15. Find $\lim\limits_{x \to -1} \dfrac{x^2 - 3x - 4}{x - 1}$.

    (a) -5 (b) -3 (c) Does not exist   (d) 0   (e) None of these

16. Evaluate: $\lim\limits_{x \to 0} \dfrac{x}{\sqrt{x + 4} - 2}$.

    (a) 2   (b) 8   (c) 0   (d) Does not exist   (e) None of these

17. Find $\lim\limits_{\Delta x \to 0} \dfrac{2(x + \Delta x)^2 + 1 - (2x^2 + 1)}{\Delta x}$.

    (a) 0   (b) $4x$ (c) ∞ (d) $4x + 1$ (e) None of these

18. Find $\lim\limits_{x \to 3^-} \dfrac{|x - 3|}{x - 3}$.

    (a) ∞ (b) 0   (c) -1 (d) Does not exist   (e) None of these

19. At which value(s) of x is the function $f(x) = \dfrac{x - 1}{x^2 + x - 2}$ discontinuous? Further classify each discontinuity as removable or nonremovable.

    (a) $x = -2$ removable, $x = 1$ nonremovable   (b) $x = -2$ nonremovable, $x = 1$ removable

    (c) $x = -2$ nonremovable   (d) $x = 1$ nonremovable

    (e) None of these

20. Find any value(s) of x for which $f(x) = \dfrac{x - 1}{x^2 + x - 2}$ has removable discontinuities.

    (a) $1, -2$ (b) $-1, 2$ (c) 0   (d) 1   (e) None of these

Test Form C Name _____ Date _____

Chapter 0 Class _____ Section _____

1. Calculate the distance between the points $(-1, 5)$ and $(-3, -1)$.

2. Given $f(x) = |3x - 6|$, find $f(0) - f(3)$.

3. Find all intercepts: $y = \dfrac{2x - 1}{3 - x}$.

4. Write the equation of the circle with center $(3, -4)$ and radius $r = 5$ in general form.

5. Find an equation for the straight line passing through the points $(-2, -4)$ and $(2, -1)$.

6. Write an equation for the line perpendicular to the line $2x + 5y - 6 = 0$, which passes through the point $(2, 0)$. Put the answer in general form.

7. Find the sales necessary to break even if the cost function for a business is $C = 70x + 500$ and the revenue function is $R = 90x$.

8. Sketch the graph of $f(x) = x^2 - 5x + 4$. Be sure to include all intercepts.

9. Find the points of intersection of the graphs of the equations $y = x$ and $y = -x^2 + 4x$.

10. What is the domain of the function $y = \sqrt{4 - 3x}$? Use interval notation.

11. Find $f(2)$ if $f(x) = \dfrac{-4x}{x^2 + 1}$.

12. Find $f(x + \Delta x)$ if $f(x) = -x^2 + 4x + 5$.

13. Find $g(f(x))$ if $f(x) = x^2$ and $g(x) = \dfrac{x + 1}{x}$.

14. If $f(x) = \dfrac{2}{\sqrt{2 - x}}$, find $f^{-1}(x)$.

15. Find $\lim\limits_{x \to 2} \dfrac{x-2}{x^2-x-2}$.

16. Find $\lim\limits_{x \to 3} \dfrac{x^2-9}{x^2}$.

17. Evaluate $\lim\limits_{\Delta x \to 0} \dfrac{2(x+\Delta x)+5-(2x+5)}{\Delta x}$.

18. Find the limit: $\lim\limits_{x \to 6^-} \dfrac{|3x-18|}{6-x}$.

19. Find any points of discontinuity of $f(x) = \dfrac{x^2-6x+5}{x-6}$. Are they removable or nonremovable?

20. Find all values of x that make the function $f(x) = \begin{cases} x^2+1, & x \ge 3 \\ 4x+2, & x < 3 \end{cases}$ discontinuous.

Test Form D   **Name** _____ **Date** _____

Chapter 1   **Class** _____ **Section** _____

1. Find x so that the point $(x, 4)$ is the midpoint between the points $(2, -6)$ and $(3, 14)$.

   (a) 3   (b) $\frac{5}{2}$ (c) 4   (d) -3 (e) None of these

2. Which of the following determine y as a function of x?

   (1) $y = x^2$ (2) $x = y^2$ (3) $x^2 + y^2 = 1$ (4) $y^3 = x$

   (a) 2, 3   (b) 2, 3, 4   (c) 1, 4   (d) 1, 2, 3   (e) None of these

3. Find all x–intercepts of the graph of the function $f(x) = 2x^3 + x^2 - 10x - 5$, accurate to the nearest 0.1.

   (a) $-2.2, -0.5, 2.2$ (b) $-0.5, 1.7, 2.2$ (c) $-2.2, 0.5, 2.3$

   (d) -0.5 (e) None of these

4. Write the equation of the circle with center $(-3, 4)$ and radius $r = \sqrt{3}$ *in general form.*

   (a) $x^2 + y^2 - 6x + 8y + 22 = 0$ (b) $(x + 3)^2 + (y - 4)^2 = 3$ (c) $(x - 3)^2 + (y + 4)^2 = 3$

   (d) $x^2 + y^2 + 6x - 8y + 22 = 0$ (e) None of these

5. Determine the points of intersection of the circle $x^2 + y^2 + 16y = 0$ and the line $x + y + 3 = 0$ (accurate to the nearest 0.1).

   (a) $(-1.2, -4.2)(-3.8, -6.8)$ (b) $(-6.8, -3.8)(-4.2, -1.2)$ (c) $(-2.6, -0.5), (7.6, -10.6)$

   (d) $(-0.5, -2.6)(-10.6, 7.6)$ (e) None of these

6. Write an equation for the line perpendicular to the line $3x + 6y - 10 = 0$, which passes through the point $(2, 0)$. Put the answer in general form.

   (a) $2x + y - 4 = 0$ (b) $2x + y + 4 = 0$ (c) $-2x + y + 4 = 0$

   (d) $2x - y - 4 = 0$ (e) None of these

7. Use a graphing utility to find the sales necessary to break even if the cost function for a business is $C = 1000x - 5000$ and the revenue function is $R(x) = -80x^2 + 5000x$.

   (a) 1.2   (b) 20.5   (c) 42.8   (d) 51.2   (e) None of these

8. Find the equation of the line that passes through $(2, -1)$ and is parallel to the line $2x + 7y = 5$.

   (a) $2x - 7y - 11 = 0$ (b) $2x + 7y + 3 = 0$ (c) $2x + 7y - 12 = 0$

   (d) $7x - 2y - 16 = 0$ (e) None of these

9. Find the points of intersection of the graphs of $y = x$ and $y = -x^2 + 6x$.

    (a) $(0, 0), (5, 5)$ (b) $(-1, -1), (6, 6)$ (c) $(1, 1), (-6, -6)$

    (d) $(-1, -1), (5, 5)$ (e) None of these

10. What is the domain of the function $y = \dfrac{3}{\sqrt{4 - 2x}}$? Use interval notation.

    (a) $(2, \infty)$ (b) $[2, \infty)$ (c) $(-\infty, 2)$ (d) $(-\infty, 2]$ (e) None of these

11. Find $f(-2)$ if $f(x) = \dfrac{-4x}{x^2 + 1}$.

    (a) $-\dfrac{8}{5}$ (b) $-\dfrac{8}{3}$ (c) $\dfrac{8}{5}$ (d) $\dfrac{8}{3}$ (e) None of these

12. Find $f(x + \Delta x)$ if $f(x) = -x^2 + 4x - 3$.

    (a) $-x^2 - 2x\Delta x - (\Delta x)^2 + 4x + 4\Delta x - 3$ (b) $2x\Delta x - (\Delta x)^2 + 4\Delta x$

    (c) $-x^2 + 2x\Delta x + (\Delta x)^2 + 4x + 4\Delta x - 3$ (d) $-x^2 + 2x\Delta x - (\Delta x)^2 - 4x + 4\Delta x - 3$

    (e) None of these

13. Find $g(f(x))$ if $f(x) = x^2$ and $g(x) = \dfrac{2x}{x + 1}$.

    (a) $\dfrac{4x^2}{(x + 1)^2}$ (b) $\dfrac{2x^2}{x^2 + 1}$ (c) $\dfrac{2x^2}{x + 1}$ (d) $\dfrac{4x^2}{x^4 + 2x^2 + 1}$ (e) None of these

14. If $f(x) = \dfrac{3}{\sqrt{4 + x}}$, find $f^{-1}(x)$.

    (a) $f^{-1}(x) = \dfrac{9 - 4x^2}{x^2}$ (b) $f^{-1}(x) = \dfrac{9 - 4x}{x}$ (c) $f^{-1}(x) = \dfrac{\sqrt{4 + 3x}}{3}$

    (d) $f^{-1}(x) = \dfrac{3 - 4x^2}{x^2}$ (e) None of these

15. Evaluate the limit: $\displaystyle\lim_{x \to 3} \dfrac{x + 3}{x^2 - 9}$.

    (a) Limit does not exist   (b) 0 (c) $\dfrac{1}{6}$

    (d) $-\dfrac{1}{6}$ (e) None of these

16. Evaluate $\displaystyle\lim_{\Delta x \to 0} \dfrac{f(x + \Delta x) - f(x)}{\Delta x}$ if $f(x) = x^2 - 3$.

    (a) $2x$ (b) $2x - 3$ (c) $2x + \Delta x$

    (d) Limit does not exist   (e) None of these

17. At which value(s) of x is the function $f(x) = \dfrac{x - 1}{x^2 + x - 2}$ discontinuous? Further classify each discontinuity as removable or nonremovable.

 (a) $x = -2$ removable, $x = 1$ nonremovable   (b) $x = -2$ nonremovable, $x = 1$ removable

 (c) $x = -2$ nonremovable   (d) $x = 1$ nonremovable

 (e) None of these

18. Find all values of x that make the function $f(x) = \begin{cases} x^2 + 3, & x \geq 1 \\ 2x + 2, & x < 1 \end{cases}$ discontinuous.

 (a) $x = 1$ (b) $x = 0$ and $x = 1$ (c) $x = 3$

 (d) $x = -1$ (e) None of these

19. Determine which of the following functions have nonremovable discontinuities at $x = 2$.

 (a) $f(x) = \dfrac{x - 2}{x^2 - 3x + 2}$ (b) $f(x) = \begin{cases} 3x + 1, & x < 2 \\ 2x^2 - 1, & x > 2 \end{cases}$ (c) $f(x) = \dfrac{1}{x - 2}$

 (d) All of these   (e) None of these

20. Using a graphing utility, find the domain of the function $f(x) = \sqrt{10 - x - x^3}$.

 (a) $(-\infty, 10.0]$ (b) $(-\infty, -2.1]$ (c) $(-\infty, -0.4]$ (d) $(-\infty, 2.0]$ (e) None of these

Test Form E

Chapter 1

Name _____ Date _____

Class _____ Section _____

1. Calculate the distance between the points $(-1, -6)$ and $(3, -1)$.

2. Determine if y is a function of x in the equation $y = \dfrac{2x^2}{2 + |x|}$.

3. Find all intercepts of the graph of the equation $y = \dfrac{x^3}{3} - \dfrac{x^2}{2} - 2x + 5$, accurate to the nearest 0.1.

4. Write the equation for the circle with center $(-1, 3)$ and radius $r = 3$. Give your answer in general form.

5. Determine the points of intersection of the circle $x^2 + y^2 - 4y = 0$ and the line $x + y - 1 = 0$ (accurate to the nearest 0.1).

6. Find an equation in general form for the straight line that passes through the point $(-1, 4)$ and is perpendicular to the line $2x + 3y = 6$.

7. Use a graphing utility to find the sales necessary to break even if the cost function for a business is $C = 700x - 500$ and the revenue function is $R(x) = -90x^2 + 5000x$.

8. Sketch the graph of $f(x) = x^2 - 5x + 4$. Be sure to include all intercepts.

10. Find all points of intersection: $y = -x^2 + 4x$ and $y = x^2$.

11. What is the domain of $f(x) = \sqrt{2 - 3x}$?

12. Find $f(-1)$ if $f(x) = \dfrac{-4x}{x^2 + 1}$.

13. Find $f(x + \Delta x)$ if $f(x) = -x^2 + 4x + 5$.

14. If $f(x) = \dfrac{1}{\sqrt{x}}$ and $g(x) = x^2 - 5$, find $g(f(x))$.

15. If $f(x) = \dfrac{3}{\sqrt{2 + x}}$, find $f^{-1}(x)$.

15. Find $\lim\limits_{x \to 3} \dfrac{x^2 - 9}{x^2}$.

16. Evaluate $\lim\limits_{\Delta x \to 0} \dfrac{2(x + \Delta x) + 5 - (2x + 5)}{\Delta x}$.

17. At which value(s) of x is the function $f(x) = \dfrac{x + 3}{x^2 + x - 6}$ discontinuous? Label each discontinuity removable or nonremovable.

18. Find all values of x that make the function $f(x) = \begin{cases} x^2 + 1, & x \geq 3 \\ 4x + 2, & x < 3 \end{cases}$ discontinuous.

19. Sketch the graph of the function. Then use the graph to describe the intervals on which the function is continuous:

$$f(x) = \frac{x^2 - 9}{x + 3}.$$

20. State in at least one complete sentence the difference between a removable discontinuity and a nonremovable discontinuity.

Test Form A

Chapter 2

Name _____ Date _____

Class _____ Section _____

1. Differentiate: $(3x - 4)(x^2 - 2x + 1)$.

   (a) $3x^2 - 8x + 5$ (b) $6x - 6$ (c) $3x^2 - 20x + 11$

   (d) $9x^2 - 20x + 11$ (e) None of these

2. Differentiate: $y = \dfrac{x^2}{3x - 1}$.

   (a) $\dfrac{2x}{3}$ (b) $-2x$ (c) $\dfrac{x(3x - 2)}{(3x - 1)^2}$ (d) $\dfrac{2x - 3x^2}{(3x - 1)^2}$ (e) None of these

3. Differentiate: $2(4 - 2x^4)^5$.

   (a) $10(-8x^3)^4$ (b) $(4 - 2x^4)(-80x^3 + 1)$ (c) $-80x^3(4 - 2x^4)^4$

   (d) $-80x^{12}$ (e) None of these

4. Find the second derivative of y with respect to x if $y = \dfrac{x + 3}{x - 4}$.

   (a) $\dfrac{-14}{(x - 4)^3}$ (b) $\dfrac{-7}{(x - 4)^2}$ (c) $\dfrac{14}{(x - 4)^3}$ (d) 0 (e) None of these

5. Find y' for $x^2y + y^2 = x$.

   (a) $\dfrac{1}{2x + 2y}$ (b) $\dfrac{1 - 2xy - 2y}{x^2}$ (c) $\dfrac{1 - 2xy}{x^2 + 2y}$ (d) $\dfrac{1}{x}$ (e) None of these

6. Write the equation of the tangent line, in slope–intercept form, to the graph of $y = -3x^4 + 4x - 3$ at the point $(1, -2)$.

   (a) $y = -8x + 10$ (b) $y = 8x - 6$ (c) $y = -8x - 10$

   (d) $y = -8x + 6$ (e) None of these

7. Find the instantaneous rate of change of w with respect to z for the function $w = \dfrac{1}{z} + \dfrac{z}{2}$.

   (a) $2\dfrac{1}{2}$ (b) -2 (c) $\dfrac{z^2 - 2}{2z^2}$ (d) $\dfrac{-1}{z^2}$

   (e) None of these

8. Find the instantaneous rate of change of y with respect to x when $x = 36$ for the function $y = 3 - 2x$.

   (a) 36 (b) -69 (c) -2 (d) 3 (e) None of these

9. Find the derivative: $f(x) = \sqrt{x^2 - 2x + 5}$.

(a) $\sqrt{2x - 2}$

(b) $\dfrac{1}{2\sqrt{x^2 - 2x + 5}}$

(c) $\dfrac{1}{2\sqrt{2x - 2}}$

(d) $\dfrac{x - 1}{\sqrt{x^2 - 2x + 5}}$

(e) None of these

10. The area of a circle is decreasing at a rate of 2 square centimeters/minute. Find the rate of change of the radius with respect to time when the radius is 4 cm.

(a) $\dfrac{1}{4\pi}$ cm/min (b) $-\dfrac{1}{8\pi}$ cm/min (c) $-\dfrac{1}{2\pi}$ cm/min (d) $-\dfrac{1}{4\pi}$ cm/min (e) None of these

11. Find the point on the graph of the function $f(x) = 2x^2 - 2x - 9$ where the slope is 10.

(a) $(3, 10)$ (b) $(1, -9)$ (c) $(10, 171)$ (d) $(3, 3)$ (e) None of these

12. The position equation for the movement of a particle is given by $s = (t^2 - 1)^3$ when s is measured in feet and t is measured in seconds. Find the acceleration at two seconds.

(a) 342 units/sec^2

(b) 18 units/sec^2

(c) 288 units/sec^2

(d) 90 units/sec^2

(e) None of these

13. If $f(x) = 2x^2 + 4$, which of the following will calculate the derivative of $f(x)$?

(a) $\dfrac{[2(x + \Delta x)^2 + 4] - (2x^2 + 4)}{\Delta x}$

(b) $\lim\limits_{\Delta x \to 0} \dfrac{(2x^2 + 4 + \Delta x) - (2x^2 + 4)}{\Delta x}$

(c) $\lim\limits_{\Delta x \to 0} \dfrac{[2(x + \Delta x)^2 + 4] - (2x^2 + 4)}{\Delta x}$

(d) $\dfrac{(2x^2 + 4 + \Delta x) - (2x^2 + 4)}{\Delta x}$

(e) None of these

Test Form B   Name _____ Date _____

Chapter 2   Class _____ Section _____

1. Differentiate: $(2x + 5)(x^2 - 3x + 1)$.

 (a) $4x - 6$ (b) $2x^2 + 10x - 17$ (c) $6x^2 - 2x - 13$

 (d) $2x^2 - 2x - 13$ (e) None of these

2. Differentiate: $y = \dfrac{x^2}{3x^2 - 1}$.

 (a) $\dfrac{2x}{(3x^2 - 1)^2}$ (b) $\dfrac{2x(6x^2 + 1)}{(3x^2 - 1)^2}$ (c) $\dfrac{-2x}{(3x^2 - 1)^2}$ (d) $\dfrac{2x(6x^2 - 1)}{(3x^2 - 1)^2}$ (e) None of these

3. Find $f'(x)$ for $f(x) = (4 - x^2)^5$.

 (a) $80x^4$ (b) $-10x(4 - x^2)^4$ (c) $10x(x^2 - 4)^4$

 (d) $5(4 - x^2)^4$ (e) None of these

4. Find the second derivative of y with respect to x if $y = \dfrac{x - 5}{x + 3}$.

 (a) $\dfrac{16}{(x + 3)^3}$ (b) $\dfrac{8}{(x + 3)^2}$ (c) $\dfrac{-16}{(x + 3)^4}$ (d) 0 (e) None of these

5. Find y' for $xy^2 + y = x^2$.

 (a) $\dfrac{2x - y^2}{2xy + 1}$ (b) $\dfrac{2x}{2y + 1}$ (c) $2x - y^2$ (d) y (e) None of these

6. Write the equation of the tangent line, in slope–intercept form, to the the graph of $f(x) = -3x^3 + 5x^2 - 3$ at the point $(2, -7)$.

 (a) $y = 16x + 39$ (b) $y = -16x + 39$ (c) $8x + y + 10 = 0$

 (d) $y = -16x + 25$ (e) None of these

7. Find the instantaneous rate of change of w with respect to z for the function $w = \dfrac{7}{3z^2}$.

 (a) $\dfrac{7}{6z}$ (b) $\dfrac{14}{3}z$ (c) $-\dfrac{14}{3z}$ (d) $-\dfrac{14}{3z^3}$ (e) None of these

8. Find the instantaneous rate of change of y with respect to x when $x = 20$ for the function $y = x - x^2$.

 (a) -380 (b) -39 (c) -19 (d) -20 (e) None of these

9. Find the derivative: $f(x) = \sqrt{4 - 3x + x^2}$.

(a) $\sqrt{2x - 3}$

(b) $\dfrac{1}{2\sqrt{4 - 3x + x^2}}$

(c) $\dfrac{2x - 3}{2\sqrt{4 - 3x + x^2}}$

(d) $\dfrac{1}{2\sqrt{2x - 3}}$

(e) None of these

10. The radius of a circle is increasing at the rate of 2 ft/min. Find the rate at which the area is increasing when the radius is 7 feet.

(a) 28 ft²/min   (b) 49π ft²/min   (c) 14π ft²/min   (d) 28π ft²/min   (e) None of these

11. Find the point(s) on the graph of the function $f(x) = x^3 - 2$ where the slope is 3.

(a) $(1, 3), (-1, 3)$

(b) $(1, -1), (-1, -3)$

(c) $\left(\sqrt[3]{2}, 0\right)$

(d) $(1, 3)$

(e) None of these

12. A particle moves along the curve given by $y = \sqrt{x^3 + 1}$. Find the acceleration at 2 seconds.

(a) 3 units/sec²

(b) $\frac{2}{3}$ units/sec²

(c) $-\frac{1}{108}$ units/sec²

(d) $-\frac{1}{9}$ units/sec²

(e) None of these

13. If $f(x) = -x^2 + x$, which of the following will calculate the derivative of $f(x)$?

(a) $\displaystyle\lim_{\Delta x \to 0} \frac{(-x^2 + x + \Delta x) - (-x^2 + x)}{\Delta x}$

(b) $\displaystyle\lim_{\Delta x \to 0} \frac{[-(x + \Delta x)^2 + (x + \Delta x)] - (-x^2 + x)}{\Delta x}$

(c) $\dfrac{[-(x + \Delta x)^2 + (x + \Delta x)] - (-x^2 + x)}{\Delta x}$

(d) $\dfrac{(-x^2 + x + \Delta x) - (-x^2 + x)}{\Delta x}$

(e) None of these

Test Form C　　Name _____ Date _____

Chapter 2　　Class _____ Section _____

1. Let $y = (x^2 + 1)(2 - x)$. Use the product rule to find $\dfrac{dy}{dx}$ and simplify.

2. Let $y = \dfrac{x^2}{x^2 + 2}$. Use the quotient rule to find y' and simplify.

3. Differentiate: $y = 5(x^4 - 3x)^{-2}$.

4. Find $\dfrac{d^2y}{dx^2}$ if $y = \sqrt{x^2 + 1}$.

5. Find $\dfrac{dy}{dx}$ for the equation $x^3 - 2x^2y + 3xy^2 = 38$.

6. Find an equation for the tangent line, in slope–intercept form, to the curve $y = f(x) = 4 - 3x + x^3$ at the point $(1, 2)$.

7. For the function $y = f(x) = -x^2 + 4x$, find the average rate of change on $[2, 3]$ and the instantaneous rate of change at $x = 2$.

8. A certain particle moves so that its position as a function of time is given by $s(t) = \dfrac{3t^2 + 4}{t}$, where s is measured in meters and t in seconds. Find the velocity when $t = 4$ seconds.

9. Find $\dfrac{dy}{dx}$ for $y = x^3\sqrt{x + 1}$.

10. The profit for a product is increasing at a rate of \$4000 per month. Find the rate of change of sales with respect to time when the monthly sales are $x = 300$ units, if profit is given by $P = 178x - 0.01x^2 - 200$.

11. Find the values of x for all points on the graph of $f(x) = x^3 - 2x^2 + 5x - 16$ at which the slope of the tangent line is 4.

12. The position equation for the movement of a particle is given by $s = (t^3 + 1)^2$ where s is measured in feet and t is measured in seconds. Find the acceleration of this particle at 1 second.

13. In at least one complete sentence, describe the difference between the average velocity of a particle and the instantaneous velocity of a particle.

Test Form D   Name _____ Date _____

Chapter 2   Class _____ Section _____

1. Differentiate: $(x + 2)(x^2 - 5x + 1)$.

   (a) $3x^2 - 6x - 9$ (b) $x^2 + 4x - 11$ (c) $x^2 - 6x - 9$

   (d) $2x - 5$ (e) None of these

2. Differentiate: $y = \dfrac{x^2}{3x^2 - 1}$.

   (a) $\dfrac{2x}{(3x^2 - 1)^2}$ (b) $\dfrac{2x(6x^2 + 1)}{(3x^2 - 1)^2}$ (c) $\dfrac{-2x}{(3x^2 - 1)^2}$ (d) $\dfrac{2x(6x^2 - 1)}{(3x^2 - 1)^2}$ (e) None of these

3. Differentiate: $x^2(3 - 2x^2)^3$.

   (a) $-36x^3(3 - 2x^3)$ (b) $3x^2(3 - 2x^2)^2$ (c) $2x(3 - 4x^2)$

   (d) $2x(3 - 2x^2)^2(3 - 8x^2)$ (e) None of these

4. If $f''(x) = 3x^2 + 6x + 4$, find $f^{(4)}(x)$.

   (a) 0 (b) 6 (c) $6x + 6$ (d) None of these

5. Find $\dfrac{dy}{dx}$ if $x^2y + y^2 = x$.

   (a) $\dfrac{1}{2x + 2y}$ (b) $\dfrac{1 - 2xy - 2y}{x^2}$ (c) $\dfrac{1 - 2xy}{x^2 + 2y}$ (d) $\dfrac{1}{x}$ (e) None of these

6. Use a graphing utility to find all points at which the graph of $f(x) = x^4 - 4x + 5$ has horizontal tangent lines.

   (a) $(2, 0)$ (b) $(1, 0)$ (c) $(1, 2)$

   (d) $(1, 2), (-1, 10)$ (e) None of these

7. Use the marginal Cost function to estimate the additional cost if the production level is increased from 50 to 51 units: $C(x) = 2.4\sqrt{x} + 400$.

   (a) $0.15   (b) $0.17   (c) $0.20   (d) $0.23   (e) None of these

8. The demand function and cost function for x units of a product are $p = \dfrac{60}{\sqrt{x}}$ and $C = .65x + 400$. Find the marginal profit when $x = 100$.

   (a) $193.50   (b) $4.58   (c) $2.35   (d) $87.35   (e) None of these

9. Find $\dfrac{dy}{dx}$ for $y = \sqrt{x}(3x - 1)$.

   (a) $\dfrac{9x - 1}{2\sqrt{x}}$ (b) $\dfrac{9}{2}\sqrt{x} - 1$ (c) $3\sqrt{x}$ (d) $\dfrac{3}{2\sqrt{x}}$ (e) None of these

10. Two boats leave the same port at the same time with one boat traveling north at 15 knots per hour and the other traveling west at 12 knots per hour. How fast is the distance between the two boats changing after 2 hours?

(a) 19.2 knots/hr   (b) 26.8 knots/hr   (c) 17.7 knots/hr

(d) 38.4 knots/hr   (e) None of these

11. Use a graphing utility to find the point on the graph of the function $C(x) = \dfrac{2x^2 - 2x + 9}{\sqrt{x}}, x \geq 0$ where the marginal cost is 0.

(a) 0.8   (b) 1.4   (c) 3.5   (d) 5.3   (e) None of these

12. A particle moves along the curve given by $y = \sqrt{x^3 + 1}$. Find the acceleration at 2 seconds.

(a) 3 units/sec^2 (b) $\frac{2}{3}$ units/sec^2 (c) $-\frac{1}{108}$ units/sec^2

(d) $-\frac{1}{9}$ units/sec^2 (e) None of these

13. If $f(x) = 2x^2 + 4$, which of the following will calculate the derivative of $f(x)$?

(a) $\dfrac{[2(x + \Delta x)^2 + 4] - (2x^2 + 4)}{\Delta x}$ (b) $\displaystyle\lim_{\Delta x \to 0} \dfrac{(2x^2 + 4 + \Delta x) - (2x^2 + 4)}{\Delta x}$

(c) $\displaystyle\lim_{\Delta x \to 0} \dfrac{[2(x + \Delta x)^2 + 4] - (2x^2 + 4)}{\Delta x}$ (d) $\dfrac{(2x^2 + 4 + \Delta x) - (2x^2 + 4)}{\Delta x}$

(e) None of these

Test Form E

Chapter 2

Name _____ Date _____

Class _____ Section _____

1. Let $y = (x^3 + 4x)(4 - 3x)$. Use the product rule to find $\dfrac{dy}{dx}$ and simplify.

2. Find $\dfrac{dy}{dx}$ if $y = \dfrac{4x}{1/x + 3}$.

3. Differentiate: $y = 3(x^3 - 1)^4$.

4. Find the second derivative of y with respect to x if $y = \dfrac{x^2 - 3}{x}$.

5. Find $\dfrac{dy}{dx}$ if $x\sqrt{y} + y^2 = x$.

6. Use a graphing utility to find all points at which the graph of $f(x) = x^4 - 4x + 5$ has horizontal tangent lines.

   (a) $(2, 0)$ (b) $(1, 0)$ (c) $(1, 2)$

   (d) $(1, 2), (-1, 10)$ (e) None of these

7. Use the marginal Cost function to estimate the additional cost if the production level is increased from 50 to 51 units: $C(x) = 3.7\sqrt{x} + 400$.

8. The demand function and cost function for x units of a product are $p = \dfrac{60}{\sqrt{x}}$ and $C = .65x + 400$. Find the marginal profit when $x = 81$.

9. Find $\dfrac{dy}{dx}$ for $y = \sqrt{2x + 1}\,(x^3)$.

10. A metal cube contracts when it is cooled. If the edge of the cube is decreasing at a rate of 0.2 cm/hr, how fast is the volume changing when the edge is 60 cm?

11. Use a graphing utility to find all points on the graph of $C(x) = x^5 - 6x^2 + 10$ where the marginal cost function is zero.

12. The position equation for the movement of a particle is given by $s = (t^3 + 1)^2$ where s is measured in feet and t is measured in seconds. Find the acceleration of this particle at 1 second.

13. In a complete sentence, explain the difference between an explicit function and an implicit function.

Test Form A

Chapter 3

Name _____ Date _____

Class _____ Section _____

1. Find all open intervals on which $f(x) = \dfrac{x}{x^2 + x - 2}$ is decreasing.

   (a) $(-\infty, \infty)$

   (b) $(-\infty, 0)$

   (c) $(-\infty, -2)$ and $(1, \infty)$

   (d) $(-\infty, -2), (-2, 1)$ and $(1, \infty)$

   (e) None of these

2. Find all critical numbers for $f(x) = 5\sqrt[3]{4 - x^2}$.

   (a) 0 (b) $-2, 2$ (c) $-2, 0, 2$ (d) 2 (e) None of these

3. Find the values of x that give relative extrema for the function $f(x) = (x + 1)^2(x - 2)$.

   (a) Relative maximum: $x = -1$; Relative minimum: $x = 1$

   (b) Relative maxima: $x = 1$, $x = 3$; Relative minimum: $x = -1$

   (c) Relative minimum: $x = 2$

   (d) Relative maximum: $x = -1$; Relative minimum: $x = 2$

   (e) None of these

4. Find all intervals on which $y = \dfrac{x - 3}{x + 4}$ is concave down.

   (a) $(-\infty, -4)$ (b) $(-4, \infty)$ (c) $(0, \infty)$ (d) $(-\infty, \infty)$ (e) None of these

5. Let $f''(x) = 3x^2 - 4$ and let $f(x)$ have critical numbers $-2, 0,$ and 2. Use the Second-Derivative Test to determine which critical numbers, if any, gives a relative maximum.

   (a) -2 (b) 2 (c) 0 (d) -2 and 2 (e) None of these

6. Determine the vertical asymptote(s) for the graph of $f(x) = \dfrac{x^2 + 2x}{x^2 - 4x}$.

   (a) $x = -4$ (b) $x = 0, x = 4$ (c) $x = -2, x = 0$

   (d) $x = 4$ (e) None of these

7. Find $\displaystyle\lim_{x \to \infty} \dfrac{2x^2 + 6x + 5}{3 + x^3}$.

   (a) $\frac{2}{3}$ (b) ∞ (c) 1 (d) 2 (e) None of these

8. Evaluate: $\lim\limits_{x \to \infty} \dfrac{6 + x^2}{x^2 + 2x + 3}$.

   (a) 6   (b) 1   (c) 0   (d) ∞ (e) None of these

9. Find the horizontal asymptote, if any, for the function $y = \dfrac{x^2 + 1}{x - 2}$.

   (a) $x = 2$ (b) $y = 1$ (c) $y = -\frac{1}{2}$ (d) $x = 1$ (e) None of these

10. The graph of the function $y = x^3 - 3x + 4$ has:

   (a) One relative extremum and one inflection point.   (b) Two relative extrema and one inflection point.

   (c) One relative extremum and two inflection points.   (d) No extrema and two inflection points.

   (e) None of these

11. Which of the following is the correct sketch of the graph of the function $f(x) = \dfrac{x - 1}{x + 2}$?

   (a)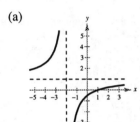   (b)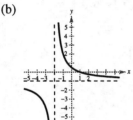   (c)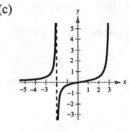   (d)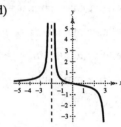   (e) None of these

12. Find two positive numbers whose product is a maximum if the sum of the numbers is 10.

   (a) 1, 9   (b) 2, 8   (c) 3, 7   (d) 5, 5   (e) None of these

13. Find the number of units, x, that will minimize the average cost function if the total cost function is $C = \frac{1}{4}x^2 - 3x + 400$.

   (a) 6   (b) 40   (c) 400   (d) 1612   (e) None of these

14. If the cost function is $C = 100 + 40x$ and the demand function is $p = 200 - 10x$, find the price p that maximizes the profit.

   (a) \$8   (b) \$120   (c) \$20   (d) \$540   (e) None of these

15. Calculate the differential dy for the function $y = x^4 - x^2$.

   (a) $dy = 4x^3 - 2x$ (b) $dy = (2x^2 - 1)\,dx$ (c) $dy = (4x^3 - 2x)\,dx$

   (d) $y' = (4x^3 - 2x)\,dx$ (e) None of these

Test Form B   Name _____ Date _____

Chapter 3   Class _____ Section _____

1. Find all open intervals on which $f(x) = \dfrac{x^2}{x^2 + 4}$ is decreasing.

   (a) $(0, \infty)$ (b) $(-2, 2)$ (c) $(-\infty, 0)$ (d) $(-\infty, \infty)$ (e) None of these

2. Find all critical numbers for $f(x) = \dfrac{x^2 - 1}{x^3}$.

   (a) 0 (b) $-\sqrt{3}, 0, \sqrt{3}$ (c) $-\sqrt{3}, \sqrt{3}$ (d) $-1, 1$ (e) None of these

3. Find the values of x that give relative extrema for the function $f(x) = 3x^5 - 5x^3$.

   (a) Relative maximum: $x = 0$; Relative minimum: $x = \sqrt{5/3}$

   (b) Relative maximum: $x = -1$; Relative minimum: $x = 1$

   (c) Relative maxima: $x = \pm 1$; Relative minimum: $x = 0$

   (d) Relative maximum: $x = 0$; Relative minima: $x = \pm 1$

   (e) None of these

4. Find all intervals on which $y = \dfrac{x^2 - 1}{x^3}$ is concave up.

   (a) $\left(-\sqrt{6}, 0\right)$ and $\left(\sqrt{6}, \infty\right)$ (b) $\left(-\sqrt{3}, \sqrt{3}\right)$ (c) $\left(-\infty, -\sqrt{6}\right)$ and $\left(\sqrt{6}, \infty\right)$

   (d) $\left(-\sqrt{6}, 0\right)$ and $\left(0, \sqrt{6}\right)$ (e) None of these

5. Let $f''(x) = 4x^3 - 2x$ and let $f(x)$ have critical numbers $-1, 0,$ and 1. Use the Second-Derivative Test to determine which critical numbers, if any, give a relative maximum.

   (a) -1 (b) 0 (c) 1 (d) -1 and 1 (e) None of these

6. Determine the vertical asymptote(s) for the graph of $f(x) = \dfrac{x^2 + 4}{x^2 - 4x - 12}$.

   (a) $x = -2$ (b) $x = 6$ (c) $x = -2, x = 6$

   (d) $x = -6$ (e) None of these

7. Find $\displaystyle\lim_{x \to \infty} \dfrac{2x^3 + 6x^2 + 5}{x^3 + 3}$

   (a) $\frac{2}{3}$ (b) ∞ (c) 1 (d) 2 (e) None of these

8. Evaluate: $\displaystyle\lim_{x \to -\infty} \dfrac{6x - x^3}{x^2 + 2x + 3}$.

   (a) ∞ (b) $-\infty$ (c) -1 (d) 0 (e) None of these

9. Find the horizontal asymptote, if any, for the graph of $y = \dfrac{2x}{x^2 - 4}$.

(a) $y = 0$ (b) $y = 1$ (c) $y = 2$ (d) $x = 2$ (e) None of these

10. The graph of the function $y = x^3 - 4x + 5$ has:

(a) Two relative extrema and one inflection point.   (b) One relative extremum and one inflection point.

(c) One relative extremum and two inflection points. (d) No extrema and two inflection points.

(e) None of these

11. Which of the following is the correct sketch of the graph of the function $f(x) = \dfrac{1}{(x - 2)^2}$?

(a) 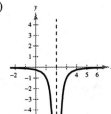   (b) 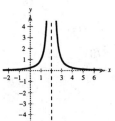   (c) 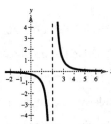   (d) 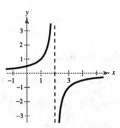   (e) None of these

12. Find the positive number such that the sum of the number and its reciprocal is a minimum.

(a) 3   (b) $\frac{1}{2}$ (c) $\frac{1}{3}$ (d) 1   (e) None of these

13. Find the number of units, x, that will minimize the average cost function if the total cost function is $C = \frac{1}{2}x^2 - 5x + 5000$.

(a) 100   (b) 5   (c) 1000   (d) 50   (e) None of these

14. If the cost function is $C = 100 + 40x$ and the revenue function is $R = 200x - 10x^2$, find the price p that maximizes the profit.

(a) $8   (b) $120   (c) $20   (d) $540   (e) None of these

15. Calculate the differential dy for the function $y = (x^2 + 1)^{3/2}$.

(a) $dy = \frac{3}{2}(x^2 + 1)^{1/2}dx$ (b) $dy = 3(x^2 + 1)^{1/2}dx$ (c) $y' = 3x\sqrt{x^2 + 1}$

(d) $dy = 3x\sqrt{x^2 + 1}\, dx$ (e) None of these

Test Form C   Name _____ Date _____

Chapter 3   Class _____ Section _____

1. Find all critical numbers for the function $f(x) = x + \dfrac{36}{x}$.

2. Find all open intervals on which the function $f(x) = \sqrt[3]{x^2 - 1}$ is decreasing.

3. Find the point(s) of relative extrema for the graph of the function $f(x) = x(x - 4)^3$.

4. Find all intervals on which $y = \dfrac{4x^2 - x}{x^4}$ is concave up.

5. Let $f(x) = x^3 - x^2 + 3$. Use the Second-Derivative Test to determine which critical numbers, if any, give relative extrema.

6. Evaluate: $\lim\limits_{x \to \infty} \dfrac{6x}{x^3 + 3}$.

7. Find $\lim\limits_{x \to \infty} \left(\dfrac{2x}{x + 2} + \dfrac{x}{x - 1} \right)$.

8. Find all horizontal and vertical asymptotes for the graph of the function $f(x) = \dfrac{6x^2}{8 - x^3}$.

9. Determine where the graph of $y = x(x^2 - 12)$ is increasing/decreasing, if it has any relative extrema, where it is concave up/down and whether it has any points of inflection. Then draw a rough sketch of the graph of $f(x)$.

10. Use the techniques learned in this chapter to sketch a graph of $y = f(x) = \dfrac{1}{x^3}$.

11. Find all inflection points for the graph of the function $f(x) = x^4 - 4x^3 + 16x + 8$.

12. If the cost function is $C = 100 + 40x$ and the revenue function is $R = 200x - 10x^2$, find the price p that maximizes the profit.

    (a) $8   (b) $120   (c) $20   (d) $540   (e) None of these

13. Find the number of units, x, that will minimize the average cost function if the total cost function is
    $C = 3x^2 + 7x + 75$.

14. Find the x–coordinate of the point of diminishing returns for the revenue function

$$R(x) = \frac{300x^2 - x^3}{10,000},$$

where R is the revenue (in thousands of dollars) and x is the amount spent on advertising (in thousands of dollars).

15. Calculate the differential of p for the demand function $p(x) = \sqrt{200 - 3x}$.

16. In a complete sentence, explain what must be true for a function $y = f(x)$ to have a maximum point at the point (a, c) if $f(x)$ is differentiable on an open interval containing $x = a$.

Test Form D

Chapter 3

Name _____ Date _____

Class _____ Section _____

1. Find all open intervals on which the function is increasing: $f(x) = \begin{cases} 7 - x^2, & x < 3 \\ 2x - 8, & x \geq 3 \end{cases}$.

   (a) $(-\infty, 0), (3, \infty)$ (b) $(-\infty, 7), (-2, \infty)$ (c) $(0, 2)$

   (d) $(-\infty, \infty)$ (e) None of these

2. Use calculus to locate the actual relative extrema for $f(x) = 4.5x^4 + 2x^3 - 18x^2 - 12x + 5$.

   (a) Relative minimum at $x = -\frac{1}{3}$; Relative maxima at $x = \sqrt{2}$

   (b) Relative maximum at $x = \frac{1}{3}$; Relative minimum at $x = \sqrt{2}$

   (c) Relative maximum at $x = -\frac{1}{3}$; Relative minimum at $x = \pm\sqrt{2}$

   (d) Relative minima at $x = \pm\sqrt{3}$

   (e) None of these

3. Given that $f(x) = -\dfrac{3}{x + 2}$, choose the correct statement.

   (a) The graph of $f(x)$ is concave down on $(-\infty, -2)$.

   (b) The graph of $f(x)$ is concave down on $(-2, \infty)$.

   (c) The graph of $f(x)$ is concave up on $(-2, \infty)$.

   (d) The graph of $f(x)$ is concave up on $(-\infty, \infty)$.

   (e) None of these

4. Find all intervals on which $y = \dfrac{x - 1}{x^2 + 3}$ is increasing.

   (a) $(-1, 3)$ (b) $(3, \infty)$ (c) $(-\infty, -1)$ (d) $(-3, 1)$ (e) None of these

5. Let $f''(x) = 3x^2 - 2x - 3$ and let $f(x)$ have critical numbers $x = -1$ and $x = \sqrt{3}$. Use the Second-Derivative Test to determine which of these critical numbers, if any, give a relative maximum.

   (a) $x = -1$ (b) $x = \sqrt{3}$ (c) Both

   (d) Neither   (e) Second-Derivative Test fails

6. The function $f(x) = \dfrac{3x^2}{x^2 + 4}$ has:

   (a) A horizontal asymptote at $y = 3$ (b) A vertical asymptote at $x = 2$

   (c) No vertical asymptotes   (d) Both (a) and (c)

   (e) Both (a) and (b)

7. Find $\lim\limits_{x \to -\infty} \dfrac{2x^2 + 6x + 5}{4x^3 + 3}$.

(a) $\frac{1}{2}$ (b) $-\infty$ (c) 0   (d) $-\frac{1}{2}$ (e) None of these

8. Evaluate: $\lim\limits_{x \to \infty} \dfrac{6 + x^2}{x^2 + 2x + 3}$.

(a) 6   (b) 1   (c) 0   (d) ∞ (e) None of these

9. Use a graphing utility to locate any vertical asymptotes for the function $y = \dfrac{x^2 + 3x + 2}{x^3 + x^2 - 5x - 5}$.

(a) $x = -2.2$ (b) $x = -2.2, x = 2.2$ (c) $x = -2.2, x = -1.0\, x = 2.2$

(d) $x = -1.0$ (e) None of these

10. Given the revenue function $R(x) = 40x^3 - 2x^4 - 100x^2 + 4000x$ and the cost function $C = 1000x + 2000$; find the number of units x to produce in order to maximize the profit.

(a) 10.2   (b) 20.7   (c) 100.6   (d) 15.0   (e) None of these

11. If the demand function for a product is $p = 20 - 4x^2$, determine the elasticity of demand and whether the demand function is elastic or inelastic at the price of \$2.

(a) 1; neither elastic or inelastic   (b) $\frac{1}{2}$; elastic   (c) $\frac{1}{2}$; inelastic

(d) $-\frac{1}{8}$; inelastic   (e) None of these

12. An open box is constructed from cardboard by cutting out squares of equal size in the corners and then folding up the sides. If the cardboard is 5 in. by 10 in., determine the volume of the largest box which can be so constructed.

(a) 24.0 in.^{3} (b) 1.1 in.^{3} (c) 14.7 in.^{3} (d) 3.4 in.^{3} (e) None of these

13. Find the x value, accurate to the nearest 0.1, of the point on the graph of $y = x^3$ that lies closest to the point $(2, 0)$.

(a) $(1.2, 1.728)$ (b) $(0.8, 0.512)$ (c) $(1.8, 5.832)$ (d) $(1, 1)$ (e) None of these

14. Using a graphing utility, graph the function $y = x^3 - 2x^2 + 3$ and its tangent line at $x = 1$. Determine the approximate discrepancy between dy at $x = 1$ and Δy on $[1, 2]$.

(a) $dy = 1, \Delta y = 1$ (b) $dy = -1, \Delta y = 1$ (c) $dy = -1, \Delta y = -1$

(d) $dy = 1, \Delta y = -1$ (e) None of these

15. Calculate the differential of p for the demand function $p(x) = \sqrt{100 - x}$.

(a) $dp = \dfrac{dx}{2\sqrt{100 - x}}$

(b) $dp = \dfrac{-1}{2\sqrt{100 - x}}$

(c) $dp = \dfrac{-1}{2\sqrt{100 - x}}\, dx$

(d) $dp = \dfrac{-dx}{\sqrt{100 - x}}$

(e) None of these

16. Determine any x values (to the nearest 0.1) where the graph of

$$f(x) = \frac{x^5}{20} - \frac{x^4}{6} + \frac{7}{6}x^3 - 7x^2$$

has any points of inflection by using a graphing utility to find the zeros of the second derivative.

(a) $x = -2.6$

(b) $x = 2.6$

(c) $x = 2.0$

(d) $x = -2.6, 2.0, 2.6$

(e) None of these

Test Form E   Name _____ Date _____

Chapter 3   Class _____ Section _____

1. Use a graphing utility to estimate the x-values of the relative extrema of the function

   $f(x) = 4.5x^4 + 3x^3 - 1.8x^2 - 12x + 10.$

2. For the function $y = f(x) = 2x^3 - 10x^2$, compare the actual change in y on $[1, 2]$ with the value of the differential of y when $x = 1$ and $dx = 1$.

3. Given that $f(x) = -\dfrac{4}{x + 2}$, find the intervals where y is concave up or down and any inflection points.

4. Find all intervals on which $y = f(x) = \dfrac{x + 1}{x^2 + 3}$ is increasing.

5. Given $f(x) = 3x^4 - 4x^3 - 18x^2$, find any critical numbers and use the Second-Derivative Test to determine which of these critical numbers, if any, give a relative maximum.

6. Find any vertical and/or horizontal asymptotes for the function $f(x) = \dfrac{3x^2}{x^2 + 4}$.

7. Find $\displaystyle\lim_{x \to \infty} \dfrac{3x^2 + 7x + 5}{6x^3 + 3}$.

8. Evaluate: $\displaystyle\lim_{x \to \infty} \dfrac{10 + x^3}{-x^2 + 2x + 3}$.

9. Use a graphing utility to locate any vertical asymptotes for the function $y = \dfrac{3x + 2}{2x^3 - 4x^2 + 14x - 28}$.

10. Given the demand function $p(x) = \sqrt{16 - x}$ and the cost function $C = 0.2x + 1.0$; find the number of units x to produce in order to maximize the profit by using a graphing utility to draw the graph of the profit function.

11. Use the differential of C to approximate the change in cost if the cost function is

    $C(x) = \dfrac{10{,}000x}{50 - x}$,

    and production is increased from 100 to 101 units.

12. An open box is to be constructed from cardboard by cutting out squares of equal size in the corners and then folding up the sides. If the cardboard is 6 in. by 11 in., determine the volume of the largest box which can be so constructed.

13. Find the x value, accurate to the nearest 0.1, of the point on the graph of $y = x^3$ that lies closest to the point $(1, 0)$.

14. Calculate the differential of p for the demand function $p(x) = \sqrt{200 - 3x}$.

15. Determine any x values, to the nearest 0.1, where the graph of $f(x) = 3x^5 - 10x^4 + 70x^3 - 420x^2$ has any points of inflection by using a graphing utility to find the zeros of the second derivative.

16. Explain in a complete sentence the significance of the sign of the derivative of a function $y = f(x)$ with respect to the increasing or decreasing behavior of the function $y = f(x)$.

Test Form A   Name _____ Date _____

Chapter 4   Class _____ Section _____

1. Evaluate: $\left(\frac{1}{16}\right)^{3/4}$

   (a) $\frac{3}{64}$ (b) $\frac{1}{8}$ (c) 12   (d) $\frac{1}{12}$ (e) None of these

2. Solve for x: $4^{3x+1} = \frac{1}{16}$.

   (a) $-\frac{1}{3}$ (b) $\frac{1}{3}$ (c) $-\frac{1}{2}$ (d) -1 (e) None of these

3. Identify the correct sketch of the graph of $y = e^x$.

   (a)   (b)   (c)   (d)

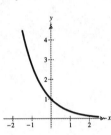
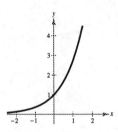
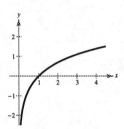
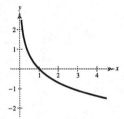

4. Find the amount of an investment of \$2000 invested at a rate of 4% for three years if the interest is compounded monthly.

   (a) $2000(1 + 0.04)^{36}$ (b) $2000\left(1 + \frac{0.04}{12}\right)^{36}$ (c) $200\left(1 + \frac{0.04}{12}\right)^{3}$

   (d) $2000\left(1 + \frac{0.04}{3}\right)^{36}$ (e) None of these

5. Find the derivative: $y = e^{-x^2}$.

   (a) $-x^2 e^{-x^2-1}$ (b) $-2xe^{-x^2}$ (c) $\frac{1}{x^2 e^{x^2-1}}$ (d) e^{-2x} (e) None of these

6. Find $f'(x)$ if $f(x) = \sqrt{x + e^{-2x}}$.

   (a) $\frac{1 + e^{-2x}}{2\sqrt{x + e^{-2x}}}$ (b) $\frac{1 - 2e^{-2x}}{\sqrt{x + e^{-2x}}}$ (c) $\frac{1}{2\sqrt{1 - 2e^{-2x}}}$ (d) $\frac{1 - 2e^{-2x}}{2\sqrt{x + e^{-2x}}}$ (e) None of these

7. Find $\frac{dy}{dx}$ for $y = \ln\sqrt{x^2 + 4}$.

   (a) $\frac{x}{\sqrt{x^2 + 4}}$ (b) $\frac{2x}{\sqrt{x^2 + 4}}$ (c) $\frac{x}{x^2 + 4}$ (d) $\frac{1}{x}$ (e) None of these

8. Find $\frac{dy}{dx}$ using implicit differentiation: $y^2 + e^y = \ln x^2 + 4x$.

   (a) $\frac{2 + 4x - xe^y}{2xy}$ (b) $\frac{2 + 4x - 2yx}{xe^y}$ (c) $\frac{\frac{2}{x} + 4 - e^y}{2y}$ (d) $\frac{2 + 4x}{2xy + xe^y}$ (e) None of these

9. Find the slope of the tangent line to the graph of $y = \ln(xe^x)$ at the point where $x = 3$.

(a) $\ln 3 + 3$ (b) $e^3 + \ln 3$ (c) $\frac{4}{3}$ (d) $\frac{1}{3}$ (e) None of these

10. Find $\dfrac{dy}{dx}$ if $y = \ln(x^2 + 1)$.

(a) $\dfrac{dy}{dx} = \dfrac{2x}{x^2 + 1}$ (b) $\dfrac{dy}{dx} = \dfrac{1}{x^2 + 1}$ (c) $\dfrac{dy}{dx} = \dfrac{1}{(x^2 + 1)\ln^2(x^2 + 1)}$

(d) $\dfrac{dy}{dx} = \dfrac{2x}{(x^2 + 1)\ln^2(x^2 + 1)}$ (e) None of these

11. The number of fruit flies increases according to the law of exponential growth. If initially there are 10 fruit flies and after 5 hours there are 24, find the number of fruit flies after t hours.

(a) $y = 10e^{[\ln(12/5)]t}$ (b) $y = 10e^{[\ln(12/5)](t/5)}$ (c) $y = 10e^{[-\ln(12/5)](t/5)}$

(d) $y = 10e^{(\ln 12)(t/5)}$ (e) None of these

12. A radioactive isotope has a half–life of 20 years. At $t = 0$, there are 100 grams of this substance. Find the amount of this isotope present at time t using an exponential model of decay.

(a) $y = 100e^{(\ln 2)t/20}$ (b) $y = 100e^{-[\ln(1/2)]t/20}$ (c) $y = 20e^{-(\ln 2)t/100}$

(d) $y = 100e^{-(\ln 2)t/20}$ (e) None of these

13. Find any critical numbers for the function $f(x) = x^2 - \ln x$.

(a) $x = \pm\sqrt{2}$ (b) $x = 0$ (c) $x = \sqrt{2}$

(d) $x = -\sqrt{2}, 0, \sqrt{2}$ (e) None of these

14. Determine where the graph of $f(x) = e^{-x^2}$ is concave up.

(a) $\left(-\dfrac{\sqrt{2}}{2}, \dfrac{\sqrt{2}}{2}\right)$ (b) $\left(-\infty, -\dfrac{\sqrt{2}}{2}\right), \left(\dfrac{\sqrt{2}}{2}, \infty\right)$ (c) $(-8, 0)$

(d) $(0, \infty)$ (e) None of these

15. The temperature T in degrees Fahrenheit at which water boils at selected pressures p (in pounds per square inch) can be modeled by the equation

$$T = 87.97 + 34.96 \ln p + 7.91\sqrt{p}.$$

Find the rate of change of the temperature, accurate to the nearest 0.01, when the pressure is 50 pounds per square inch.

(a) 1.26 degrees/pound   (b) 12.6 degrees/pound   (c) 140.63 degrees/pound

(d) 280.67 degrees/pound   (e) None of these

Test Form B

Chapter 4

Name _____ Date _____

Class _____ Section _____

1. Evaluate: $\left(\frac{1}{64}\right)^{2/3}$.

   (a) $\frac{1}{16}$ (b) $\frac{1}{96}$ (c) 96   (d) $\frac{1}{2}$ (e) None of these

2. Solve for x: $\left(\frac{1}{3}\right)^{2x-1} = 81$.

   (a) $\frac{3}{2}$ (b) $-\frac{3}{2}$ (c) $\frac{5}{2}$ (d) $-\frac{5}{2}$ (e) None of these

3. Identify the correct sketch of the graph of $y = \ln x$.

   (a)   (b) 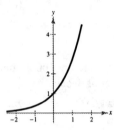   (c) 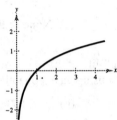   (d)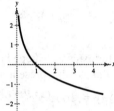

   (e) None of these

4. Find the amount of an investment of $1000 invested at a rate of 6% for three years if the interest is compounded quarterly.

   (a) $2000(1 + 0.06)^{12}$ (b) $1000\left(1 + \frac{0.06}{4}\right)^{12}$ (c) $1000\left(1 + \frac{0.06}{4}\right)^{3}$

   (d) $1000\left(1 + \frac{0.06}{3}\right)^{12}$ (e) None of these

5. Find the derivative $\frac{dy}{dx}$ if $y = e^{x^2 + 4x}$.

   (a) $(2x)e^{x^2+4x}$ (b) $(2x+4)e^{x^2+4x}$ (c) $\frac{1}{(2x+4)e^{x^2+4x}}$

   (d) e^{-2x} (e) None of these

6. Find $f'(x)$ if $f(x) = \frac{3}{4x - e^{3x}}$.

   (a) $\frac{3}{(4x - e^{3x})^2}$ (b) $\frac{3(3e^{3x} - 4)}{(e^{3x} - 4x)^2}$ (c) $\frac{3}{4 - 3e^{3x}}$ (d) $\frac{(4 + 3e^{3x})}{(4x - e^{3x})^2}$ (e) None of these

7. Find $\frac{dy}{dx}$ for $y = \ln(5 - x)^6$.

   (a) $\frac{1}{(5 - x)^6}$ (b) $\frac{6}{x - 5}$ (c) $-6(5 - x)^5$ (d) $6(5 - x)^5$ (e) None of these

8. Find $\dfrac{dy}{dx}$ using implicit differentiation: $\ln\sqrt{y} + e^x = \ln(2y) + 4x$.

(a) $\dfrac{dy}{dx} = 2y(e^x - 4)$

(b) $\dfrac{dy}{dx} = 2y(e^2 + 4)$

(c) $\dfrac{e^x + 4}{2y}$

(d) $\dfrac{dy}{dx} = \dfrac{e^x - 4}{2y}$

(e) None of these

9. Find the slope of the tangent line to the graph of $y = (\ln x)e^x$ at the point where $x = 2$.

(a) $\frac{1}{2}e^2$
(b) $e^2\!\left(\ln 2 + \frac{1}{2}\right)$
(c) e
(d) $e(2\ln 2 + 1)$
(e) None of these

10. Find $\dfrac{dy}{dx}$ if $y = \ln(x^3 + 1)$.

(a) $\dfrac{dy}{dx} = \dfrac{1}{x^3 + 1}$

(b) $\dfrac{dy}{dx} = \dfrac{3x^2}{x^3 + 1}$

(c) $\dfrac{dy}{dx} = \dfrac{1}{(x^3 + 1)\ln^2(x^3 + 1)}$

(d) $\dfrac{dy}{dx} = \dfrac{3x^2}{(x^3 + 1)\ln^2(x^3 + 1)}$

(e) None of these

11. The number of fruit flies increases according to the law of exponential growth. If initially there are 10 fruit flies and after 6 hours there are 24, find the number of fruit flies after t hours.

(a) $y = 10e^{[\ln(12/5)](t/6)}$

(b) $y = 10e^{[\ln(12/5)]t}$

(c) $y = 10e^{[-\ln(12/5)](t/6)}$

(d) $y = 10e^{(\ln 12)(t/6)}$

(e) None of these

12. A radioactive isotope has a half–life of 30 years. At $t = 0$, there are 100 grams of this substance. Find the amount of this isotope present at time t using an exponential model of decay.

(a) $y = 100e^{(\ln 2)t/30}$

(b) $y = 100e^{-[\ln(1/2)]t/30}$

(c) $y = 30e^{-(\ln 2)t/100}$

(d) $y = 100e^{-(\ln 2)t/30}$

(e) None of these

13. Find any critical numbers for the function $f(x) = x^2 \ln x$.

(a) $x = -\dfrac{1}{\sqrt{e}}$

(b) $x = \dfrac{1}{\sqrt{e}}$

(c) $x = 0$

(d) $x = -\dfrac{1}{\sqrt{e}}, 0, \dfrac{1}{\sqrt{e}}$

(e) None of these

14. Determine where the graph of $f(x) = \dfrac{e^x}{x^2}$ is increasing.

(a) $(-\infty, 0), (2, \infty)$

(b) $(0, 2)$

(c) $(-\infty, 2)$

(d) $(2, \infty)$

(e) None of these

15. Find the instantaneous rate of change of the demand function $x = \ln\!\left(\dfrac{100}{p^2 + 1}\right)$ when the price p is \$10.

(a) Decreasing $\frac{10}{101}$ (b) Increasing $\frac{10}{101}$ (c) Increasing $\frac{20}{101}$ (d) Decreasing $\frac{20}{101}$ (e) None of these

Test Form C   **Name** _____ **Date** _____

Chapter 4   **Class** _____ **Section** _____

1. Evaluate: $\left(\frac{8}{27}\right)^{-4/3}$.

2. Write as a single logarithm: $2\ln(x) - 3\ln(x - 2) - 5\ln(x + 1)$.

3. Sketch a graph of $y = f(x) = \ln(x - 2)$.

4. Find $\dfrac{dy}{dx}$ if $y = x^e e^x$.

5. Find the derivative: $y = e^{\sqrt{x}}$.

6. Find $f'(x)$ if $f(x) = \dfrac{e^x + e^{-x}}{2x}$.

7. Find $\dfrac{dy}{dx}$ if $y = \ln\dfrac{(x)(x + 1)}{x - 2}$.

8. Find the instantaneous rate of change of y with respect to x for the curve described implicitly by $xe^y + x = xy$.

9. Find the slope of the curve $y = e^{4 - 3/x}$ at the point where $x = 3$.

10. Find $\dfrac{dy}{dx}$ if $y = \ln\sqrt{x^2 + 4}$.

11. The number of fruit flies increases according to the law of exponential growth. If initially there are 10 fruit flies and after 8 hours there are 30, find the number of fruit flies after t hours.

12. A radioactive isotope has a half–life of 3 years. At $t = 0$, there are 100 grams of this substance. Find the amount of this isotope present at time t using an exponential model of decay.

13. Find any critical numbers for the function: $y = \dfrac{e^x}{x}$.

14. Determine where the graph of $f(x) = \dfrac{e^x}{x^3}$ is increasing.

15. Find the instantaneous rate of change of the demand function $x = \ln\left(\dfrac{200}{p^3 + 10}\right)$ when the price p is \$10.

16. Explain in a complete sentence how to differentiate a function of the form $y = f(x) = e^u$ if $u = g(x)$.

Test Form D

Chapter 4

Name _____ Date _____

Class _____ Section _____

1. Evaluate: $\left(\frac{7}{2}\right)^{3/2}$.

    (a) 3.726   (b) 6.548   (c) 5.328   (d) 4.269   (e) None of these

2. Solve for x: $3^{2x+1} = 243$.

    (a) 40   (b) 3   (c) 2   (d) 5   (e) None of these

3. Find the price per unit that will maximize the revenue function if the demand function for a certain product is $p = 42e^{-0.002x}$.

    (a) \$15.45   (b) \$500.00   (c) \$7725.47   (d) \$4321.22   (e) None of these

4. Find the amount of an investment of \$1000 invested at a rate of 9% for three years if the interest is compounded monthly.

    (a) \$270.00   (b) \$1270.00   (c) \$1309.96   (d) \$1308.65   (e) None of these

5. Find the derivative $\dfrac{dy}{dx}$ if $y = e^{-x^3}$.

    (a) $-x^3 e^{-x^3-1}$ (b) $-3x^2 e^{-x^3}$ (c) $\dfrac{1}{x^3 e^{-x^3-1}}$ (d) e^{-3x^2} (e) None of these

6. Find $f'(x)$ if $f(x) = \sqrt[3]{x + e^{-4x}}$.

    (a) $\dfrac{1 + e^{-4x}}{3\sqrt[3]{x + e^{-4x}}}$ (b) $\dfrac{1 - 4e^{-4x}}{\sqrt[3]{x + e^{-4x}}}$ (c) $\dfrac{1}{3\sqrt[3]{1 + 4e^{-4x}}}$

    (d) $\dfrac{1 - 4e^{-4x}}{3(x + e^{-4x})^{2/3}}$ (e) None of these

7. Find $\dfrac{dy}{dx}$ for $y = \ln\sqrt{x^3 + 4e^x}$.

    (a) $\dfrac{3x^2 + 4e^x}{2(x^3 + 4e^x)}$ (b) $\dfrac{1}{2\sqrt{x^3 + 4e^x}}$ (c) $\dfrac{3x^2 + 4e^x}{(x^3 + 4e^x)}$ (d) $\dfrac{3}{x} + 1$ (e) None of these

8. Find $\dfrac{dy}{dx}$ using implicit differentiation: $y^2 + e^y = \ln x^2 + 4$.

    (a) $\dfrac{2 - xe^y}{2xy}$ (b) $\dfrac{2x - 2yx}{xe^y}$ (c) $\dfrac{\dfrac{2}{x} - e^y}{2y}$ (d) $\dfrac{2}{2xy + xe^y}$ (e) None of these

9. Write the equation of the tangent line to the curve $y = \ln\left(\dfrac{2}{e^{2x}}\right)$ at the point $(0, \ln 2)$.

   (a) $2x + y + \ln 2 = 0$ (b) $2x - y + \ln 2 = 0$ (c) $2x + y - \ln 2 = 0$

   (d) $2x - y - \ln 2 + 0$ (e) None of these

10. Find $\dfrac{dy}{dx}$ if $y = \dfrac{10}{1 + e^{-(1/x)}}$.

   (a) $\dfrac{dy}{dx} = \dfrac{-10e^{-(1/x)}}{x^2(1 + e^{-(1/x)})^2}$ (b) $\dfrac{dy}{dx} = \dfrac{-10}{(1 + e^{-(1/x)})^2}$ (c) $\dfrac{dy}{dx} = \dfrac{-10e^{-(1/x)}}{x^2(1 + e^{-(1/x)})^2}$

   (d) $\dfrac{dy}{dx} = \dfrac{10e^{-(1/x)}}{(1 + e^{-(1/x)})^2}$ (e) None of these

11. The number of fruit flies increases according to the law of exponential growth. If initially there are 10 fruit flies and after 7 hours there are 24, find the number of fruit flies after t hours.

   (a) $y = 10e^{[\ln(12/5)]t}$ (b) $y = 10e^{[\ln(12/5)](t/7)}$ (c) $y = 10e^{[-\ln(12/5)](t/7)}$

   (d) $y = 10e^{(\ln 12)(t/7)}$ (e) None of these

12. A radioactive isotope has a half–life of 40 years. At $t = 0$, there are 200 grams of this substance. Find the amount of this isotope present at time t using an exponential model of decay.

   (a) $y = 200e^{(\ln 2)t/40}$ (b) $y = 200e^{-[\ln(1/2)]t/40}$ (c) $y = 200e^{-(\ln 2)t/40}$

   (d) $y = 40e^{-(\ln 2)t/200}$ (e) None of these

13. Use a graphing utility to find the number of units which maximizes the profit for a product whose demand function is $p = 1000\left(\frac{2}{3}\right)^x$ and cost function is $C = 40x + 100$.

   (a) 30.1   (b) 24.3   (c) 2.3   (d) 23.5   (e) None of these

14. Determine where the graph of $f(x) = e^{-(1/2)x^2}$ is concave down.

   (a) $(-1, 1)$ (b) $(-\infty, -1), (1, \infty)$ (c) $(-\infty, 0)$

   (d) $(0, \infty)$ (e) None of these

15. The temperature T in degrees Fahrenheit at which water boils at selected pressures p (in pounds per square inch) can be modeled by the equation

$$T = 87.97 + 34.96 \ln p + 7.91\sqrt{p}.$$

Find the rate of change of the temperature, accurate to the nearest 0.01, when the pressure is 65 pounds per square inch.

   (a) 146.43 degrees/pound   (b) 12.60 degrees/pound   (c) 2.06 degrees/pound

   (d) 1.03 degrees/pound   (e) None of these

Test Form E   Name _____ Date _____

Chapter 4   Class _____ Section _____

1. Evaluate: $\left(\frac{7}{2}\right)^{3/2}$.

   (a) 3.726   (b) 6.548   (c) 5.328   (d) 4.269   (e) None of these

2. Solve for x: $4^{7x-4} = \frac{1}{64}$.

   (a) $\frac{3}{7}$ (b) $\frac{1}{7}$ (c) $\frac{6}{7}$ (d) $-\frac{1}{7}$ (e) None of these

3. Find the price per unit that will maximize the revenue function if the demand function for a certain product is $p = 46e^{-0.003x}$.

4. Find the amount of an investment of $5000 invested at a rate of 5% for three years if the interest is compounded monthly.

5. Find $f'(x)$ if $f(x) = \dfrac{1}{\sqrt[4]{x + e^{3x}}}$.

6. Find $\dfrac{dy}{dx}$ for $y = x^2 10^{2x}$.

7. Find $\dfrac{dy}{dx}$ using implicit differentiation: $y^3 + \dfrac{1}{e^y} = \ln\sqrt{x} + 4x$.

8. Write the equation of the tangent line to the curve $y = \ln\left(\dfrac{4}{e^{3x}}\right)$ at the point $(0, \ln 4)$.

9. Find $\dfrac{dy}{dx}$ if $y = \dfrac{10}{x + e^{-2x}}$.

10. The number of fish in a lake is modeled using

$$P(t) = \frac{20,000}{1 + 19e^{-(t/10)}},$$

   where $t \geq 0$, where t is the time since the lake was stocked (in months). Use a graphing utility to determine if the population is increasing or decreasing after one year.

11. A radioactive isotope has a half–life of 50 years. At $t = 0$, there are 200 grams of this substance. Find the amount of this isotope present at time t using an exponential model of decay.

12. Use a graphing utility to find the number of units which maximizes the profit for a product whose demand function is

$$p = \frac{1000}{1 + e^{-x}}$$

and cost function is $C = e^x + 100$.

13. Determine where the graph of $f(x) = e^{-(1/2)x^2}$ has any inflection points.

14. The temperature T in degrees Fahrenheit at which water boils at selected pressures p (in pounds per square inch) can be modeled by the equation

$$T = 87.97 + 34.96 \ln p + 7.91\sqrt{p}.$$

Find the rate of change of the temperature, accurate to the nearest 0.01, when the pressure is 55 pounds per square inch.

15. In a complete sentence, describe how the rate of change of a quantity y which grows exponentially is related to the amount of the quantity itself.

Test Form A   Name _____ Date _____

Chapter 5   Class _____ Section _____

1. Evaluate $\int \frac{4}{x^3}\, dx.$

   (a) $\frac{1}{x^4} + C$ (b) $\frac{-2}{x^2} + C$ (c) $\frac{16}{x^3} + C$ (d) $\frac{-2}{x} + C$ (e) None of these

2. Evaluate $\int (4x^3 + 5)^2\, dx.$

   (a) $\frac{(4x^3 + 5)^3}{3} + C$ (b) $16x^7 + 20x^4 + 25x + C$ (c) $16x^7 - 80x^4 + 25x + C$

   (d) $\frac{16}{7}x^7 + 10x^4 + 25x + C$ (e) None of these

3. Evaluate: $\int \sqrt{4 - x}\, dx.$

   (a) $2x - \frac{2}{3}x^{3/2} + C$ (b) $(4 - x)^{3/2} + C$ (c) $-\frac{2}{3}(4 - x)^{3/2} + C$

   (d) $-\frac{3}{2}(4 - x)^{3/2} + C$ (e) None of these

4. Evaluate $\int \frac{3x^4 - 5}{x^2}\, dx.$

   (a) $x^3 + \frac{5}{x} + C$ (b) $3x^3 + \frac{5}{x} + C$ (c) $x^3 - \frac{5}{x} + C$

   (d) $x^3 - \frac{5}{3x^3} + C$ (e) None of these

5. Evaluate: $\int 3x^2(x^3 - 1)^5\, dx.$

   (a) $\frac{1}{6}x^3(x^3 - 1)^6 + C$ (b) $\frac{1}{2}x^6 - x^3 + C$ (c) $\frac{1}{2}(x^5 - x^2)^6 + C$

   (d) $\frac{1}{6}(x^3 - 1)^6 + C$ (e) None of these

6. Evaluate: $\int \frac{3y}{\sqrt{y^2 + 1}}\, dy.$

   (a) $\frac{3}{4}\sqrt{y^2 + 1} + C$ (b) $6\sqrt{y^3 + y} + C$ (c) $\frac{3}{4}y^2\sqrt{y^2 + 1} + C$

   (d) $3\sqrt{y^2 + 1} + C$ (e) None of these

7. If the marginal cost function is $\dfrac{dC}{dx} = x + 65$ and fixed costs are \$125, find the total cost function.

   (a) $C = \frac{1}{2}x^2 + 65x$
   (b) $C = x + 190$
   (c) $C = \frac{1}{2}x^2 + 65x + 125$
   (d) $C = \frac{1}{2}x^2 + 190x$
   (e) None of these

8. Use the Fundamental Theorem to evaluate $\displaystyle\int_{-2}^{1} (3x^3 - 4x^2 + 5)\, dx$.

   (a) $\frac{155}{12}$
   (b) $\frac{39}{4}$
   (c) $-\frac{39}{4}$
   (d) $\frac{79}{6}$
   (e) None of these

9. Use the Fundamental Theorem of Calculus to evaluate $\displaystyle\int_{0}^{1} \frac{x}{(1 + 2x^2)^3}\, dx$.

   (a) $-\frac{5}{36}$
   (b) $\frac{1}{9}$
   (c) $-\frac{1}{36}$
   (d) $-\frac{1}{9}$
   (e) None of these

10. Use the Midpoint Rule with $n = 3$ to approximate the area of the region bounded by the curve $y = x^2$ and the x-axis over the interval $[0, 3]$.

   (a) 5
   (b) 9
   (c) $\frac{35}{4}$
   (d) 14
   (e) None of these

11. The marginal revenue for a certain product is given by

   $$\frac{dR}{dx} = 30 - 2x.$$

   Find the change in revenue when sales increase from 5 to 10 units.

   (a) \$10
   (b) \$75
   (c) \$25
   (d) $-$\$25
   (e) None of these

12. Determine the area bounded by the graphs of $y = -x^2 + 4x$ and $y = 0$.

   (a) $\frac{16}{3}$
   (b) $\frac{32}{3}$
   (c) $\frac{8}{3}$
   (d) $\frac{128}{3}$
   (e) None of these

13. What is the average value of $f(x) = 2x^3 + 1$ on the interval $[1, 4]$?

   (a) 109
   (b) 42
   (c) $\frac{104}{3}$
   (d) $\frac{87}{2}$
   (e) None of these

14. Find the volume of the solid formed when the graph of the region bounded by $y = e^x$, $x = 0$, $x = 2$, and $y = 0$ is revolved about the x-axis.

   (a) $\frac{\pi}{2}(e^4 - 1)$
   (b) $\frac{\pi e^4}{2}$
   (c) $\pi(e^2 - 1)$
   (d) $\pi(e^2 - 1)$
   (e) None of these

15. Find $y = f(x)$ if $f''(x) = x^{1/\sqrt{x}}$, $f'(0) = 3$, and $f(1) = 4$.

   (a) $\frac{4}{3}x^{3/2} + 3x + 4$
   (b) $x^{-1/2} + 7$
   (c) $\frac{4}{3}x^{3/2} + 3x - \frac{1}{3}$
   (d) $4x^{3/2} + 9x - 1$
   (e) None of these

16. A company produces a product for which the marginal cost of producing x units is

$$\frac{dC}{dx} = 0.6x - 2$$

and fixed costs are \$250. Find the average cost of producing 50 units.

(a) \$18   (b) \$30   (c) \$90   (d) \$900   (e) None of these

Test Form B

Chapter 5

Name _____ Date _____

Class _____ Section _____

1. Evaluate $\int 5x\sqrt{x}\,dx.$

    (a) $\frac{5}{3}x^{7/2} + C$ (b) $\frac{5}{2}x^2 + C$ (c) $5x^{5/2} + C$ (d) $2x^{5/2} + C$ (e) None of these

2. Evaluate $\int 4(x^3 + 5)x^4\,dx.$

    (a) $x^5(x^3 + 5)^2 + C$ (b) $4x^5(x^3 + 5)^2 + C$ (c) $4x^8 + 20x^5 + C$

    (d) $\dfrac{x^8}{2} + 4x^5 + C$ (e) None of these

3. Evaluate $\int \dfrac{1}{(3t)^2}\,dt.$

    (a) $-\dfrac{1}{3t} + C$ (b) $-\dfrac{1}{3(3t)^3} + C$ (c) $\dfrac{1}{9}(3t)^3 + C$ (d) $-\dfrac{1}{9t} + C$ (e) None of these

4. Evaluate $\int \dfrac{3x^4 - 6}{x^2}\,dx.$

    (a) $3x^3 - \dfrac{6}{x} + C$ (b) $x^3 + \dfrac{6}{x} + C$ (c) $x^3 + \dfrac{3}{x} + C$ (d) $x^3 + \dfrac{2}{x^3} + C$ (e) None of these

5. Evaluate: $\int 3x^2(x^3 + 5)^4\,dx.$

    (a) $\frac{1}{5}x^3(x^3 + 5)^5 + C$ (b) $\frac{3}{5}(x^5 + 5x^2)^5 + C$ (c) $\frac{1}{5}(x^3 + 5)^5 + C$

    (d) $6x(7x^2 + 5)(x^3 + 5)^3 + C$ (e) None of these

6. Evaluate: $\int \dfrac{5y}{\sqrt[3]{4 - y^2}}\,dy.$

    (a) $\dfrac{-15(4 - y^2)^{2/3}}{2}$ (b) $\dfrac{15(4 - y^2)^{2/3}}{4}$ (c) $\dfrac{-15(4 - y^2)^{4/3}}{8}$

    (d) $\dfrac{-15(4 - y^2)^{2/3}}{4}$ (e) None of these

7. If the marginal cost function is $\dfrac{dC}{dx} = 2x - 15$ and fixed costs are \$75, find the total cost function.

(a) $C = x^2 - 15x + 75$ (b) $C = 2x + 60$ (c) $C = x^2 - 15x$

(d) $C = x^2 + 160x$ (e) None of these

8. Use the Fundamental Theorem to evaluate $\displaystyle\int_{-3}^{0} (2x^3 - 4x^2)\, dx$.

(a) $\dfrac{153}{2}$ (b) $-\dfrac{153}{2}$ (c) 198   (d) -198 (e) None of these

9. Use the Fundamental Theorem of Calculus to evaluate $\displaystyle\int_{1}^{2} x(1 - x^2)^2\, dx$.

(a) $\dfrac{1}{2}$ (b) $\dfrac{9}{2}$ (c) -27 (d) $-\dfrac{9}{2}$ (e) None of these

10. Use the Midpoint Rule with $n = 3$ to approximate the area of the region bounded by the curve $y = x^2 + x$ and the x-axis over the interval $[0, 3]$.

(a) $\dfrac{53}{4}$ (b) $\dfrac{27}{2}$ (c) 8   (d) 20   (e) None of these

11. The marginal profit for a certain product is given by

$$\frac{dP}{dx} = -4x + 72.$$

Find the change in profit when sales increase from 10 to 20 units.

(a) \$1560   (b) \$100   (c) \$120   (d) \$32   (e) None of these

12. Determine the area bounded by the graphs of $y = \sqrt{4 - x}$, $x = 0$, and $y = 0$.

(a) $\dfrac{32}{3}$ (b) 8   (c) $\dfrac{8}{3}$ (d) $\dfrac{16}{3}$ (e) None of these

13. What is the average value of $f(x) = 2x^2 + 3$ on the interval $[0, 2]$?

(a) $\dfrac{22}{3}$ (b) $\dfrac{17}{3}$ (c) 4   (d) 27   (e) None of these

14. Find the volume of the solid formed by revolving the region bounded by $y = \sqrt{5 - x}$, $x = 4$, and $y = 1$ about the x-axis.

(a) 6π (b) 4π (c) $\dfrac{7\pi}{2}$ (d) 10π (e) None of these

15. Find $y = f(x)$ if $f''(x) = \dfrac{1}{e^x} + 2$, $f'(0) = 3$, and $f(0) = 1$.

(a) $f(x) = -e^{-x} + 2x^2 + 4x$ (b) $f(x) = -e^{-x} + 2x + 4$ (c) $f(x) = e^{-x} + x^2 + 4x$

(d) $f(x) = -e^{-x} - x^2 + 4x + 3$ (e) None of these

Test Form C

Chapter 5

Name _____ , Date _____

Class _____ Section _____

1. Evaluate $\displaystyle\int \frac{2}{\sqrt{x}}\,dx$.

2. Evaluate $\displaystyle\int x(4x^3)\,dx$.

3. Evaluate $\displaystyle\int xe^{-x^2}\,dx$.

4. Evaluate: $\displaystyle\int \sqrt[3]{2-3x}\,dx$.

5. Evaluate $\displaystyle\int \frac{x^2}{x^3-1}\,dx$.

6. Evaluate: $\displaystyle\int 10y(3y^2+4)^5\,dy$.

7. Find y as a function of x if the slope of the graph is given by

$$\frac{dy}{dx} = \frac{2}{(x+1)}$$

   and the graph passes through the point $(0, 1)$.

8. Use the Fundamental Theorem to evaluate $\displaystyle\int_{-3}^{3} (4x^2 - x^4)\,dx$.

9. Use the Fundamental Theorem of Calculus to evaluate $\displaystyle\int_{0}^{1} \frac{x}{\sqrt{1+x^2}}\,dx$.

10. Use the Midpoint Rule with $n = 3$ to approximate the area of the region bounded by the curve

$$y = \frac{3}{x+1}$$

   and the x-axis over the interval $[0, 3]$.

11. The marginal revenue for a certain product is given by

    $$\frac{dR}{dx} = 25 - 2x.$$

    Find the change in revenue when sales increase from 7 to 10 units.

12. Determine the area of the region bounded by the graphs of $y = 4x - x^2$ and $y = x - 4$.

13. What is the average value of $y = x^3$ over the interval $[0, 2]$?

14. Find the volume of the solid formed when the graph of the region bounded by $y = e^x$, $y = 1$, and $x = 4$ is revolved about the x-axis.

15. Find $y = f(x)$ if $f''(x) = x^{1/\sqrt{x}}$, $f'(0) = 3$, and $f(1) = 4$.

16. What is the average value of $f(x) = 2x^3 + x$ on the interval $[-1, 2]$?

17. In a complete sentence, explain what the Fundamental Theorem of Calculus says about the evaluation of the definite integral

    $$\int_a^b f(x)\, dx.$$

Test Form D   Name _____ Date _____

Chapter 5   Class _____ Section _____

1. Evaluate $\displaystyle\int \frac{5}{x^2}\,dx$.

   (a) $-\dfrac{5}{x} + C$ (b) $\dfrac{5}{3x^3} + C$ (c) $\dfrac{15}{x^3} + C$ (d) $-\dfrac{5}{2x} + C$ (e) None of these

2. Evaluate $\displaystyle\int \left(\frac{2}{x} + 3\right)^2 dx$.

   (a) $-\dfrac{4}{x} + 9x + C$ (b) $\dfrac{4}{x} + 12\ln x + 9x + C$ (c) $\dfrac{4}{x^3} - \dfrac{12}{x^2} + 9x + C$

   (d) $-\dfrac{4}{x} + 12\ln x + 9x + C$ (e) None of these

3. Use the general power rule to evaluate the integral: $\displaystyle\int x\sqrt{4 - 9x^2}\,dx$.

   (a) $-\frac{1}{27}(4 - 9x^2)^{3/2} + C$ (b) $-\frac{1}{18}(4 - 9x^2)^{3/2} + C$ (c) $\frac{2}{3}(4 - 9x^2)^{3/2} + C$

   (d) $-\frac{4}{27}(4 - 9x^2)^{3/2} + C$ (e) None of these

4. Evaluate $\displaystyle\int \frac{3x^4 - 5x}{x^2}\,dx$.

   (a) $x^3 - \ln x^5 + C$ (b) $3x^3 + \dfrac{5}{x} + C$ (c) $x^3 - \dfrac{5}{x} + C$

   (d) $x^3 - \dfrac{5}{3x^3} + C$ (e) None of these

5. Evaluate $\displaystyle\int_{0.1}^{0.4} 30(x^4 - x^5)\,dx$.

   (a) 1.0495   (b) 2.3215   (c) 0.43208   (d) 0.040905   (e) None of these

6. Evaluate $\displaystyle\int \frac{10y^2}{5 + y^3}\,dy$.

   (a) $\dfrac{-10}{3(5 + y^3)^2} + C$ (b) $-\dfrac{10}{3}\ln|5 + y^3| + C$ (c) $\dfrac{10}{3}\ln|5 + y^3| + C$

   (d) $10\ln|5 + y^3| + C$ (e) None of these

7. If the marginal cost function is $\dfrac{dC}{dx} = x + 65$ and fixed costs are \$125, find the total cost function.

   (a) $C = \frac{1}{2}x^2 + 65x$ (b) $C = x + 190$ (c) $C = \frac{1}{2}x^2 + 65x + 125$

   (d) $C = \frac{1}{2}x^2 + 190x$ (e) None of these

8. Use the Fundamental Theorem to evaluate $\displaystyle\int_{-2}^{1} (3x^3 - 4x^2 + 5)\, dx$.

   (a) $\frac{155}{12}$ (b) $\frac{39}{4}$ (c) $-\frac{39}{4}$ (d) $\frac{79}{6}$ (e) None of these

9. Use the Fundamental Theorem of Calculus to evaluate $\displaystyle\int_{0}^{1} \dfrac{x}{(1 + 2x^2)^3}\, dx$.

   (a) $-\frac{5}{36}$ (b) $\frac{1}{9}$ (c) $-\frac{1}{36}$ (d) $-\frac{1}{9}$ (e) None of these

10. Use the Midpoint Rule with $n = 3$ to approximate the area of the region bounded by the curve $y = e^{x^2}$ and the x-axis over the interval $[0, 3]$.

    (a) 518.35   (b) 497.62   (c) 528.78   (d) 499.42   (e) None of these

11. The marginal revenue for a certain product is given by

    $$\dfrac{dR}{dx} = 20x + e^{-x}.$$

    Find the change in revenue when sales increase from 100 to 101 units.

    (a) \$2010.00   (b) \$1990.00   (c) \$1874.34   (d) \$2018.84   (e) None of these

12. Determine the area bounded by the graphs of $y = e^x$, $x = 0$ and $y = 3$.

    (a) $\ln 9 - 2$ (b) $3 \ln 3 - 4$ (c) $\ln 27$ (d) $3 \ln 3 - 2$ (e) None of these

13. What is the average value of the function $f(x) = \dfrac{x}{x^2 + 1}$ on the interval $[1, 4]$?

    (a) $\frac{1}{2}(\ln 17 - \ln 2)$ (b) $\frac{1}{6}\ln\left(\frac{17}{2}\right)$ (c) $\frac{1}{3}\ln\left(\frac{17}{2}\right)$

    (d) $\frac{1}{6}\ln(17)$ (e) None of these

14. Set up the integral needed to find the volume of the solid formed when the graph of the region bounded by $y = \sqrt{25 - x^2}$ and $y = 3$ is revolved about the x–axis.

    (a) $\pi \displaystyle\int_{-4}^{4} (16 - x^2)\, dx$ (b) $\pi \displaystyle\int_{0}^{4} (16 - x^2)\, dx$ (c) $\pi \displaystyle\int_{-4}^{4} (22 - x^2)\, dx$

    (d) $\pi \displaystyle\int_{-3}^{3} (16 - x^2)\, dx$ (e) None of these

15. Given the profit

$$P = 0.5\left(1 + \frac{1000}{x}\right),$$

find the average profit obtained when x varies from 4 to 7.

(a) $182.34   (b) $169.56   (c) $-$186.54   (d) $-$172.66   (e) None of these

16. Given the profit

$$P = 0.2\left(1 + \frac{1000}{3x}\right),$$

find the average profit when x varies from 12 to 18.

(a) $29.23   (b) $141.16   (c) $401.20   (d) $-$114.58   (e) None of these

Test Form E

Chapter 5

Name _____ Date _____

Class _____ Section _____

1. Evaluate $\int \dfrac{6}{x^3} \, dx$.

2. Evaluate $\int \left(\dfrac{3}{x} + 4 \right)^2 dx$.

3. Evaluate: $\int \dfrac{3}{\sqrt{2 + 3x}} \, dx$.

4. Evaluate $\int \left(\dfrac{4x^5 - 7x^2}{x^3} + e^x \right) dx$.

5. Evaluate $\int_{\sqrt{2}}^{\sqrt{3}} 20(x^5 - x^6) \, dx$.

6. Evaluate $\int \dfrac{15y^3}{6 + y^4} \, dy$.

7. If the marginal cost function is $\dfrac{dC}{dx} = \dfrac{400}{3x + 4}$ and the fixed costs are \$160, find the total cost function.

8. Use the Fundamental Theorem to evaluate $\int_{-3}^{0} (4x^4 - 5x^3 + 8) \, dx$.

9. Use the Fundamental Theorem of Calculus to evaluate $\int_{0}^{3} \dfrac{x}{(3 + 4x^2)^3} \, dx$.

10. Use the Fundamental Theorem of Calculus to evaluate $\int_{-1}^{1} (3t^2 + 2t - 5) \, dt$.

11. The marginal revenue for a certain product is given by

$$\dfrac{dR}{dx} = 30x + e^{-2x}.$$

Find the change in revenue when sales increase from 100 to 101 units.

12. Determine the area bounded by the graphs of $f(x) = e^{0.5x}$, $g(x) = e^x$ and $x = \ln 3$.

13. What is the average value of the function $f(x) = \dfrac{x^2}{x^3 + 1}$ on the interval $[2, 5]$?

14. Find the volume of the solid formed when the graph of the region bounded by $y = \sqrt{9 - x^2}$ and $y = 1$ is revolved about the x-axis.

15. Given the profit

$$P = 1.3\left(1 + \frac{1000}{x}\right),$$

find the average profit when x varies from 10 to 20.

16. For a family of four, the marginal propensity to consume income x can be modeled by

$$\frac{dQ}{dx} = \frac{0.96}{(x - 11{,}999)^{0.4}}, \quad x \geq 12{,}000.$$

Find Q, the propensity to consume, if 100% of the income is consumed when the income is \$12,000.

17. In a complete sentence, explain how to find the average value of a function $f(x)$ over an interval $[a, b]$.

Test Form A   Name _____ Date _____

Chapter 6   Class _____ Section _____

1. Find the indefinite integral using substitution: $\int \dfrac{x}{\sqrt{5x+1}}\,dx$.

   (a) $\dfrac{2}{75}\sqrt{5x+1}(5x-2)+C$ (b) $\dfrac{1}{5}x^2\sqrt{5x+1}+C$ (c) $\dfrac{1}{10}\left(5x-2\ln\sqrt{5x+1}\right)+C$

   (d) $\dfrac{2x}{5}\sqrt{5x+1}+C$ (e) None of these

2. Evaluate using integration by parts: $\int_1^2 x\ln x\,dx$.

   (a) $\ln 4-\dfrac{5}{4}$ (b) $\ln 4-1$ (c) $2\ln 2+\dfrac{3}{4}$ (d) $\ln 4-\dfrac{3}{4}$ (e) None of these

3. Find the indefinite integral using integration by parts: $\int x^2 e^x\,dx$.

   (a) $\dfrac{x^3 e^x}{3}+C$ (b) $\dfrac{x^3 e^{x+1}}{3(x+1)}+C$ (c) $e^x(x^2-2x+2)+C$

   (d) $xe^x(x+2)+C$ (e) None of these

4. Evaluate using partial fractions: $\int \dfrac{6}{x^2-25}\,dx$.

   (a) $\dfrac{18}{5}\ln\left|\dfrac{x+5}{x-5}\right|+C$ (b) $\dfrac{3}{5}\ln\left|\dfrac{x-5}{x+5}\right|+C$ (c) $\dfrac{6}{5}\ln\left|\dfrac{x-5}{x+5}\right|+C$

   (d) $\dfrac{18}{5}\ln|x^2-25|+C$ (e)

   None of these

5. Find the partial fractions for: $\dfrac{1}{x^2(x+1)}$.

   (a) $\dfrac{1}{x^2}+\dfrac{1}{x+1}$ (b) $\dfrac{1}{x^2}-\dfrac{1}{x+1}$ (c) $-\dfrac{1}{x}+\dfrac{1}{x^2}+\dfrac{1}{x+1}$

   (d) $\dfrac{1/3}{x}+\dfrac{1/3}{x^2}+\dfrac{1/3}{x+1}$ (e) None of these

6. Complete the square to express the polynomial, $2x^2 + 10x + 12$, as the sum or difference of squares.

   (a) $2\left(x + \frac{5}{2}\right)^2 + \frac{1}{2}$

   (b) $2\left(x + \frac{5}{2}\right)^2 - \frac{1}{2}$

   (c) $(2x + 5)^2 - 13$

   (d) $(2x + 5)^2 - \frac{1}{2}$

   (e) None of these

7. Select the integral form that would be used to find the indefinite integral $\displaystyle\int \frac{3}{x\sqrt{3 - 5x^2}}\,dx$, by using tables.

   (a) $\displaystyle\int \frac{1}{u^2 - a^2}\,du$

   (b) $\displaystyle\int u\sqrt{a + bu}\,du$

   (c) $\displaystyle\int \frac{1}{u\sqrt{a + bu}}\,du$

   (d) $\displaystyle\int \frac{1}{u\sqrt{a^2 - u^2}}\,du$

   (e) None of these

8. Use Simpson's Rule with $n = 2$ to approximate $\displaystyle\int_1^2 \frac{1}{x}\,dx$.

   (a) $\frac{25}{12}$

   (b) $\frac{25}{18}$

   (c) $\frac{25}{36}$

   (d) $\frac{25}{72}$

   (e) None of these

9. Determine if the following improper integral converges or diverges. If it converges, find its value. $\displaystyle\int_2^\infty \frac{1}{x - 1}\,dx$

   (a) Diverges

   (b) Converges to 1

   (c) Converges to -1

   (d) Converges to 0

   (e) None of these

10. Determine if the integral $\displaystyle\int_1^2 \frac{1}{\sqrt{x - 1}}\,dx$ converges or diverges. If it converges, find its value.

    (a) Diverges

    (b) Converges to 2

    (c) Converges to $\sqrt{2}$

    (d) Converges to $2\left(\sqrt{2} - 1\right)$

    (e) None of these

11. Find the present value of the income given by $c(t) = 3000$, measured in dollars, over five years, at an annual interest rate of 4%.

    (a) $\$75{,}000(1 - e^{-0.2})$

    (b) $\$75{,}000(1 - e^{-0.4})$

    (c) $\$75{,}000(e^{-0.2} - 1)$

    (d) $\$15{,}000$

    (e) None of these

12. For the income given by $c(t) = 3000$, the annual income over the next five years would be found by evaluating:

    (a) $\displaystyle\int_0^5 3000e^{-0.04t}\,dt$

    (b) $\displaystyle\int_0^5 3000e^{0.04t}\,dt$

    (c) $\displaystyle\int_0^5 3000\,dt$

    (d) $\displaystyle\int_0^5 3000te^{-0.04t}\,dt$

    (e) None of these

13. The integral $\displaystyle\int \frac{1}{y(400 - y)}\, dy$ would be evaluated by:

(a) u substitution   (b) Partial fractions   (c) Parts

(d) Numeric approximation only   (e) None of these

Test Form B   **Name** _____ **Date** _____

Chapter 6   **Class** _____ **Section** _____

1. Find the indefinite integral using substitution: $\int x\sqrt{2x+1}\,dx$.

    (a) $\frac{1}{6}x^2(2x+1)^{3/2} + C$ (b) $\frac{1}{15}(2x+1)^{3/2}(3x-1) + C$ (c) $\frac{2}{3}(2x^3+x)^{3/2} + C$

    (d) $\dfrac{3x+1}{\sqrt{2x+1}} + C$ (e) None of these

2. Find the indefinite integral using integration by parts: $\int \sqrt{x}\ln x\,dx$.

    (a) $x^{3/2}(\ln x)^2 + C$ (b) $\ln x^{7/2} + C$ (c) $\frac{2}{9}x^{3/2}[\ln x - 2] + C$

    (d) $\dfrac{2+\ln x}{2\sqrt{x}} + C$ (e) None of these

3. Find the indefinite integral using integration by parts: $\int x^2 e^{-x}\,dx$.

    (a) $xe^{-x}(2-x) + C$ (b) $\dfrac{-x^3 e^{-x}}{3} + C$ (c) $-xe^{-x}(x+2) + C$

    (d) $-e^{-x}(x^2+2x+2) + C$ (e) None of these

4. Evaluate using partial fractions: $\int \dfrac{10}{16-25x^2}\,dx$.

    (a) $\frac{1}{8}\ln\left|\dfrac{4+5x}{4-5x}\right| + C$ (b) $\frac{1}{4}\ln\left|\dfrac{4+5x}{4-5x}\right| + C$ (c) $\frac{1}{4}\ln\left|\dfrac{4-5x}{4+5x}\right| + C$

    (d) $\frac{5}{8}\ln\left|\dfrac{4+5x}{4-5x}\right| + C$ (e) None of these

5. Find the partial fractions for: $\dfrac{1}{x^2(x-1)}$.

    (a) $-\dfrac{1}{x} - \dfrac{1}{x^2} + \dfrac{1}{x-1}$ (b) $-\dfrac{1}{x^2} + \dfrac{1}{x-1}$ (c) $\dfrac{1}{x} + \dfrac{1}{x^2} + \dfrac{1}{x-1}$

    (d) $\dfrac{1}{x^2} - \dfrac{1}{x-1}$ (e) None of these

6. Complete the square to express the polynomial, $3x^2 + 18x + 4$, as the sum or difference of squares.

(a) $3(x + 3)^2 - 23$ (b) $3(x - 3)^2 + 23$ (c) $(3x + 3)^2 - 12$

(d) $3(x + 3)^2 - 31$ (e) None of these

7. Select the integral form that would be used to find the indefinite integral $\int x^2 \sqrt{x^2 + 9}\, dx$, by using tables.

(a) $\int u^n \sqrt{a + bu}\, du$ (b) $\int \sqrt{u^2 \pm a^2}\, du$ (c) $\int \dfrac{1}{u^2 \sqrt{u^2 \pm a^2}}\, du$

(d) $\int u^2 \sqrt{u^2 \pm a^2}\, du$ (e) None of these

8. Use the Trapezoidal Rule with $n = 4$ to approximate the definite integral: $\displaystyle\int_1^2 \dfrac{1}{x^2 + 1}\, dx$.

(a) 0.323342   (b) 0.321747   (c) 0.321750   (d) 0.323522   (e) None of these

9. Determine if the following improper integral converges or diverges. If it converges, find its value. $\displaystyle\int_2^\infty \dfrac{1}{(x - 1)^2}\, dx$

(a) Diverges   (b) Converges to 1   (c) Converges to -1

(d) Converges to 0   (e) None of these

10. Evaluate: $\displaystyle\int_0^\infty \dfrac{1}{10} e^{-t/10}\, dt$.

(a) Diverges   (b) Converges to 0   (c) Converges to $\ln 2$

(d) Converges to 2   (e) None of these

11. Which of the following would be used to find the present value of the income given by $c(t) = 4000e^{0.06t}$, measured in dollars, over four years, at an annual interest rate of 5%.

(a) $\displaystyle\int_0^4 c(t)e^{0.06t}\, dt$ (b) $\displaystyle\int_0^4 4000e^{-0.01t}\, dt$ (c) $\displaystyle\int_0^4 4000e^{0.05t}\, dt$

(d) $\displaystyle\int_0^4 c(t)e^{-0.05t}\, dt$ (e) None of these

12. Find the present value of the income given by $c(t) = 5000$, measured in dollars, over four years, at an annual interest rate of 8%.

(a) \$6600.00   (b) \$5995.24   (c) \$6885.64   (d) \$4796.19   (e) None of these

13. The integral $\int_0^4 2000te^{-0.07t}\, dt$ can be evaluated by:

(a) u substitution   (b) Partial fractions   (c) Parts

(d) Numeric approximation only   (e) None of these

Test Form C   Name _____ Date _____

Chapter 6   Class _____ Section _____

1. Find the indefinite integral: $\int \dfrac{x}{\sqrt{x-1}}\, dx.$

2. Evaluate: $\int xe^{3x}\, dx.$

3. Integrate: $\int \dfrac{1}{t^2-9}\, dt.$

4. Complete the square to express the polynomial, $-2x^2 + 8x + 40$, as the sum or difference of squares.

5. Evaluate using substitution: $\int \dfrac{x}{\sqrt[4]{x+1}}\, dx.$

6. Evaluate the definite integral: $\int_1^e \ln(2x)\, dx.$

7. Evaluate the improper integral: $\int_1^5 \dfrac{x}{\sqrt{5-x}}\, dx.$ $\left[\text{Hint: Let } u = \sqrt{5-x}.\right]$

8. Find the partial fractions for: $\dfrac{3}{(x-2)^2(x+5)}.$

9. Use Simpson's Rule with $n = 2$ to approximate the value of $\int_2^4 \dfrac{3}{2x-1}\, dx.$

10. If the annual income of a small business is given by $c(t) = 100{,}000t$, $0 \le t \le 12$, and the inflation rate is 6%, find the present value of this income over a twelve–year period.

11. Find the actual income using $c(t) = 100{,}000t$, $0 \le t \le 12$ over the first six years of operation.

12. Explain, in one complete sentence, the need for numerical integration techniques.

Test Form D   Name _____   Date _____

Chapter 6   Class _____   Section _____

1. Evaluate using substitution: $\int \dfrac{x}{\sqrt[3]{2x+1}}\,dx.$

   (a) $\dfrac{3(2x+1)^{2/3}}{40}(4x-3)+C$ (b) $\dfrac{3(2x+1)^{2/3}}{20}(4x-3)+C$ (c) $\dfrac{(2x+1)^{2/3}}{4}(4x-3)+C$

   (d) $\dfrac{(2x+1)^{2/3}}{20}(4x+3)+C$ (e) None of these

2. Evaluate using integration by parts: $\int x^2 \ln x\,dx.$

   (a) $\dfrac{x^3}{9}(\ln x^3 - 1)+C$ (b) $\dfrac{x^3}{9}(\ln x^3 - 3)+C$ (c) $\dfrac{x^3}{3}(3\ln x + 1)+C$

   (d) $\dfrac{x^3}{9}(3\ln x + 1)+C$ (e) None of these

3. Find the indefinite integral using integration by parts: $\int x^2 e^{2x}\,dx.$

   (a) $\dfrac{e^{2x}}{4}(x^2 - x + 1)+C$ (b) $\dfrac{e^{2x}}{2}(2x^2 - 2x + 1)+C$ (c) $\dfrac{e^{2x}}{4}(2x^2 + 2x + 1)+C$

   (d) $\dfrac{e^{2x}}{4}(2x^2 - 2x + 1)+C$ (e) None of these

4. Evaluate using partial fractions: $\int \dfrac{9}{x^2 - 81}\,dx.$

   (a) $\ln\sqrt{\dfrac{x+9}{x-9}}+C$ (b) $\ln\left|\dfrac{x-9}{x+9}\right|+C$ (c) $\ln\sqrt{\dfrac{x-9}{x+9}}+C$

   (d) $2\ln\left|\dfrac{x-9}{x+9}\right|+C$ (e) None of these

5. Find the partial fraction decomposition for:

$$\frac{x^2 + 6x + 1}{2x^3 - x^2 + 8x - 4}$$

by graphing the denominator on a graphing utility to find its zeros.

(a) $\dfrac{1}{2x - 1} + \dfrac{3}{x^2 + 4}$ (b) $\dfrac{3}{2x - 1} + \dfrac{2}{x^2 + 4}$ (c) $\dfrac{2}{2x - 1} + \dfrac{3x - 4}{x^2 + 4}$

(d) $\dfrac{1}{2x + 1} + \dfrac{3}{x^2 - 4}$ (e) None of these

6. Complete the square to express the polynomial, $3x^2 + 18x + 4$, as the sum or difference of squares.

(a) $3(x + 3)^2 - 23$ (b) $3(x - 3)^2 + 23$ (c) $(3x + 3)^2 - 12$

(d) $3(x + 3)^2 - 31$ (e) None of these

7. Select the integral form that would be used to find the indefinite integral $\displaystyle\int \frac{x^2}{\sqrt{x^2 + 9}}\, dx$, by using tables.

(a) $\displaystyle\int \frac{u^2}{\sqrt{u^2 \pm a^2}}\, du$ (b) $\displaystyle\int \frac{u}{\sqrt{u^2 \pm a^2}}\, du$ (c) $\displaystyle\int \frac{u^2}{\sqrt{a + bu}}\, du$

(d) $\displaystyle\int \frac{u}{\sqrt{a + bu}}\, du$ (e) None of these

8. Use the Trapezoidal Rule with $n = 4$ to approximate $\displaystyle\int_{50}^{51} e^{-0.11(x - 50)^2}\, dx$.

(a) 0.9640   (b) 0.9645   (c) 0.9635   (d) 0.9630   (e) None of these

9. Determine the divergence or convergence of the improper integral $\displaystyle\int_0^\infty xe^{-x^2/2}\, dx$. If it converges, find its value.

(a) Diverges   (b) Converges to 1   (c) Converges to -1

(d) Converges to 0   (e) None of these

10. Determine if the integral $\displaystyle\int_0^2 \frac{1}{x}\, dx$ converges or diverges. If it converges, find its value.

(a) Diverges   (b) Converges to $\ln 2$ (c) Converges to $\ln 2 - 1$

(d) Converges to $\ln 3$ (e) None of these

11. Find the present value of the income given by $c(t) = 1000e^{0.02t}$, measured in dollars, over four years, at an annual interest rate of 4%.

(a) \$3814.25   (b) \$50,000.00   (c) \$3844.18   (d) \$52,366.53   (e) None of these

Test Form E   **Name** _____ **Date** _____

Chapter 6   **Class** _____ **Section** _____

1. Evaluate using substitution: $\displaystyle\int \frac{x}{\sqrt[4]{x+1}}\,dx$.

2. Evaluate: $\displaystyle\int x^3 \ln x\,dx$.

3. Evaluate the definite integral: $\displaystyle\int_1^e \ln x\,dx$.

4. Evaluate using partial fractions: $\displaystyle\int \frac{x+1}{x^2+4x+3}\,dx$.

5. Find the partial fraction decomposition for:

   $$\frac{14x^2 - 9x + 10}{4x^3 - 3x^2 + 20x - 15}$$

   by graphing the denominator on a graphing utility to find its zeros.

6. Complete the square to express the polynomial, $-2x^2 + 8x + 40$, as the sum or difference of squares.

7. Complete the square, then use integration tables to evaluate the indefinite integral. $\displaystyle\int \sqrt{x^2 - 8x}\,dx$.

8. Use the Trapezoidal Rule with $n = 4$ to approximate $\displaystyle\int_{60}^{61} e^{-0.11(x-60)^2}\,dx$.

9. Determine if the following improper integral converges or diverges. If it converges, find its value. $\displaystyle\int_2^\infty \frac{1}{(x-1)^2}\,dx$

10. Evaluate the improper integral: $\displaystyle\int_1^2 \frac{1}{(x-1)^{3/2}}\,dx$.

11. Find the present value of the income given by $c(t) = 1000 + 60e^{t/2}$ over 6 years at the annual interest rate of 10%.

12. Evaluate the improper integral: $\displaystyle\int_0^\infty xe^{-x^2}\,dx.$

13. In a complete sentence, describe the two different types of improper integrals.

Test Form A

Chapter 7

Name _____ Date _____

Class _____ Section _____

1. Find the distance between the points $(4, 2, -1)$ and $(-2, 3, -2)$.

   (a) $2\sqrt{2}$ (b) $\sqrt{34}$ (c) $2\sqrt{10}$ (d) $\sqrt{38}$ (e) None of these

2. Find the center and radius of the sphere whose equation is $x^2 + y^2 + z^2 - 4x - 6y + 4z + 3 = 0$.

   (a) Center $(2, 3, -2)$; radius $\sqrt{14}$ (b) Center $(-2, -3, 2)$; radius 14

   (c) Center $(4, 9, 4)$; radius $2\sqrt{5}$ (d) Center $(-4, -9, -4)$; radius 20

   (e) None of these

3. Find the intercepts of the plane $x + 2y - 3z = 6$.

   (a) $(0, 0, 0)$ (b) $(6, 0, 0), (0, 3, 0), (0, 0, -2)$

   (c) $(-6, 0, 0), (0, -3, 0), (0, 0, 2)$ (d) $(6, 3, 2)$

   (e) None of these

4. Identify the quadric surface: $z = \dfrac{x^2}{9} - \dfrac{y^2}{25}$.

   (a) Elliptic paraboloid   (b) Hyperboloid paraboloid   (c) Ellipsoid

   (d) Elliptic cone   (e) None of these

5. Find $f(-2, 3, 1)$ for $f(x, y, z) = \dfrac{xyz - x^2}{y}$.

   (a) $-\frac{10}{3}$ (b) $\frac{2}{3}$ (c) $-\frac{2}{3}$ (d) 5   (e) None of these

6. Find $\dfrac{\partial f}{\partial y}$ for $f(x, y) = \dfrac{4x^2 - y^2}{xy}$.

   (a) $\dfrac{4x^2 - y^2}{xy^2}$ (b) $\dfrac{4y^2 - x^2}{xy^2}$ (c) $\dfrac{4y^2 - x^2}{x^2y^2}$ (d) $-\dfrac{4x^2 + y^2}{xy^2}$ (e) None of these

7. Find the slope in the y-direction of the surface $z = xy^2$ at the point $(3, -2, 12)$.

   (a) -12 (b) 4   (c) 12   (d) -4 (e) None of these

8. Find the minimum value of the function $f(x, y) = x^2 + y^2 + xy + 6x + 4$.

   (a) 40   (b) 0   (c) -4 (d) 8   (e) None of these

9. Use Lagrange Multipliers to find three positive numbers whose sum is 36 and whose product is a maximum.

   (a) 10, 12, 14   (b) 8, 12, 16   (c) 12, 12, 12   (d) 9, 12, 15   (e) None of these

8. Find the minimum value of the function $f(x, y) = x^2 + y^2 + xy + 6x + 4$.

(a) 40   (b) 0   (c) -4 (d) 8   (e) None of these

9. Use Lagrange Multipliers to find three positive numbers whose sum is 36 and whose product is a maximum.

(a) 10, 12, 14   (b) 8, 12, 16   (c) 12, 12, 12   (d) 9, 12, 15   (e) None of these

10. Evaluate $\displaystyle\iint_R (x^2 + 4y)\, dA$ where R is the region bounded by $y = 2x$ and $y = x^2$.

(a) $\frac{77}{30}$ (b) $-\frac{152}{15}$ (c) $\frac{16}{3}$ (d) $\frac{152}{15}$ (e) None of these

11. Evaluate $\displaystyle\int_0^2 \int_{y/2}^1 e^{x^2}\, dx\, dy$ by reversing the order of integration.

(a) $e - 1$ (b) $e + 1$ (c) e^2 (d) $e^4 - 1$ (e) None of these

12. Find the least squares regression line for the points $(0, 1), (1, 3), (2, 2), (3, 4), (4, 5)$.

(a) $y = 1.2x + 0.8$ (b) $y = 0.8x + 0.9$ (c) $y = 0.9x + 1.2$

(d) $y = 1.2x + 0.9$ (e) None of these

Test Form B

Chapter 7

Name _____ Date _____

Class _____ Section _____

1. Find the distance between the points $(1, -2, 3)$ and $(4, 1, -3)$.

   (a) $3\sqrt{6}$ (b) $3\sqrt{2}$ (c) $\sqrt{26}$ (d) $2\sqrt{3}$ (e) None of these

2. Find the center and radius of the sphere whose equation is $x^2 + y^2 + z^2 - 3x - 2y + 6z = 4$.

   (a) Center $\left(-\frac{3}{2}, -1, 3\right)$; radius $\frac{\sqrt{65}}{2}$ (b) Center $\left(\frac{3}{2}, 1, 3\right)$; radius 2

   (c) Center $\left(-\frac{3}{2}, -1, 3\right)$; radius $\frac{\sqrt{55}}{2}$ (d) Center $\left(\frac{3}{2}, -1, -3\right)$; radius $\frac{\sqrt{65}}{2}$

   (e) None of these

3. Find the intercepts of the plane $2x - 3y + z = 6$.

   (a) $(0, 0, 0)$ (b) $(-3, 0, 0), (0, 2, 0), (0, 0, -6)$

   (c) $(3, 0, 0), (0, -2, 0), (0, 0, 6)$ (d) $(3, -2, 6)$

   (e) None of these

4. Identify the quadric surface: $z = \frac{x^2}{9} + \frac{y^2}{25}$.

   (a) Elliptic paraboloid   (b) Hyperbolic paraboloid   (c) Ellipsoid

   (d) Elliptic cone   (e) None of these

5. Find $f(-1, 3, 5)$ for the function $f(x, y, z) = \frac{xz - x^3}{y^2}$.

   (a) $-\frac{10}{3}$ (b) $\frac{2}{3}$ (c) $-\frac{4}{9}$ (d) 5   (e) None of these

6. Find $\frac{\partial f}{\partial x}$ for $f(x, y) = \frac{e^{y^2}}{xy}$.

   (a) $\frac{e^{y^2}}{x^2 y}$ (b) $-\frac{e^{y^2}}{x^2 y}$ (c) $-\frac{2e^{y^2}}{y}$ (d) $\frac{e^{y^2} \ln x}{y}$ (e) None of these

7. Find the slope in the x-direction of the surface $z = xy^2 + x^2 y$ at the point $(2, -3, 6)$.

   (a) -8 (b) -3 (c) 24 (d) 21 (e) None of these

8. Find the saddle point for $f(x, y) = x^2 - y^2 - 3x - 8y + 5$.

   (a) $\left(\frac{3}{2}, -4, \frac{33}{2}\right)$ (b) $\left(-4, \frac{3}{2}, \frac{33}{2}\right)$ (c) $(0, 0, 5)$ (d) $\left(\frac{3}{2}, 4, \frac{75}{4}\right)$ (e) None of these

9. Use Lagrange Multipliers to maximize $f(x, y, z) = 4x^2 + y^2 + z^2$ with the constraint that $2x - y + z = 4$.

(a) $\frac{16}{3}$ (b) $\left(\frac{2}{3}, -\frac{4}{3}, \frac{4}{3}\right)$ (c) 36   (d) $\frac{16}{9}$ (e) None of these

10. Evaluate $\int\int_R \frac{x}{\sqrt{1 + y^2}} \, dA$ where R is the region in the first quadrant bounded by $y = x^2$, $y = 4$, and $x = 0$.

(a) $\frac{1}{2}\sqrt{17} - 1$ (b) $4\sqrt{17} - \frac{10\sqrt{5}}{3} + 1$ (c) $68\sqrt{17}$

(d) $34\sqrt{17}$ (e) None of these

11. Evaluate $\int_0^1 \int_{2x}^2 e^{y^2} \, dy \, dx$ by reversing the order of integration.

(a) 0   (b) $\frac{1}{4}(e^4 - 1)$ (c) $\frac{3e^4 + 1}{8}$ (d) $\frac{1}{4}e^4$ (e) None of these

12. Find the least squares regression line for the points $(0, 2), (1, 4), (2, 5), (3, 7), (4, 9)$.

(a) $y = 1.8x + 3$ (b) $y = 1.7x + 2$ (c) $y = 1.9x + 1.8$

(d) $y = 2.1x + 1$ (e) None of these

Test Form C   Name _____   Date _____

Chapter 7   Class _____   Section _____

1. Find the center and radius of the sphere whose equation is $x^2 + y^2 + z^2 - 3x + 9y - 6z + 2 = 0$.

2. Identify the quadric surface: $3x^2 + y^2 - z = 0$.

3. Find the distance between the points $(2, 1, 0)$ and $(-1, 2, 4)$.

4. Determine the domain of the function $f(x, y) = \sqrt{4 - x^2 - y^2}$.

5. Find $\dfrac{\partial w}{\partial x}$ for the function given by $w = xye^{xyz}$.

6. Find the slope in the y-direction of the surface $f(x, y) = \dfrac{xy^2}{1 + x^2}$ at the point $\left(1, 1, \dfrac{1}{2}\right)$.

7. Determine the relative extrema of the function $f(x, y) = x^2 - 4x + 6xy + 2y^3 - 6$.

8. Use a Lagrange Multiplier to maximize the function $f(x, y) = x + 2xy + 2y$ with the constraint $x + 2y = 80$.

9. Evaluate $\displaystyle\iint_R (x^2 + 4y)\, dA$ where R is the region bounded by $y = 2x$ and $y = x^2$.

   (a) $\dfrac{77}{30}$ (b) $-\dfrac{152}{15}$ (c) $\dfrac{16}{3}$ (d) $\dfrac{152}{15}$ (e) None of these

10. Evaluate $\displaystyle\int_0^1 \int_0^{\sqrt{1-x}} xy^2\, dy\, dx$ by reversing the order of integration.

    (a) $\dfrac{3}{32}$ (b) $\dfrac{4}{105}$ (c) $\dfrac{2}{15}$ (d) $\dfrac{7}{30}$ (e) None of these

11. Find the least squares regression line for the points $(0, 400)$, $(1, 200)$, $(2, 0)$, $(3, -100)$ and $(4, -300)$.

12. Find any critical points and classify them for the function $z = f(x, y) = x^3 + y^3 - 9xy + 10$.

13. Describe, in a complete sentence, what must be true for the point $(a, b, f(a, b))$ to be a critical point for the function $f(x, y)$.

Test Form D   Name _____   Date _____

Chapter 7   Class _____   Section _____

1. Find the distance between the points $(5, -3, 2)$ and $(-3, 4, 6)$. Approximate your answer to the nearest 0.01.

   (a) 9.00   (b) 13.30   (c) 11.36   (d) 8.31   (e) None of these

2. Find the equation of the sphere whose center is $(1, -2, -4)$ and radius is $\sqrt{3}$.

   (a) $x^2 + y^2 + z^2 + 2x + 4y + 8z + 18 = 0$ (b) $x^2 + y^2 + z^2 - 2x - 4y - 8z + 18 = 0$

   (c) $x^2 + y^2 + z^2 + 2x - 4y - 8z + 18 = 0$ (d) $x^2 + y^2 + z^2 - 2x + 4y + 8z + 18 = 0$

   (e) None of these

3. Find the domain of the function $f(x, y) = \dfrac{3x^2 - 2y}{x - y}$.

   (a) All (x, y) such that $x \neq y$ (b) All (x, y) such that $x \neq 1$

   (c) All (x, y) such that $x \neq 1$ and $y \neq 0$ (d) All (x, y)

   (e) None of these

4. Identify the quadric surface: $z^2 = \dfrac{x^2}{4} + \dfrac{y^2}{16}$.

   (a) Elliptic cone   (b) Elliptic paraboloid   (c) Hyperbolic paraboloid

   (d) Hyperboloid of one sheet   (e) Hyperboloid of two sheets

5. Find $A(1000, 0.06, 10)$ when $A(P, r, t) = Pe^{rt}$.

   (a) \$10,618.67   (b) \$1986.82   (c) \$1822.11   (d) \$114.97   (e) None of these

6. Find $f_y(x, y)$ for $f(x, y) = \dfrac{xy}{x^2 - y^2}$.

   (a) $\dfrac{-y}{x^2 - y^2}$ (b) $\dfrac{y}{2x}$ (c) $\dfrac{-y(y^2 - x^2)}{(y^2 - x^2)^2}$ (d) $\dfrac{x(x^2 + y^2)}{(x^2 - y^2)^2}$ (e) None of these

7. Find the slope in the x-direction of the surface

$$z = \frac{1}{x^2} \ln(x + y^2)$$

at the point $\left(2, 2, \frac{1}{4} \ln 6\right)$. Approximate your answer to the nearest 0.01.

(a) -0.41 (b) -0.17 (c) 0.17 (d) 0.45 (e) None of these

8. Find the maximum profit if the profit function is $P(x, y) = 30x + 90y - 0.5x^2 - 2y^2 - xy$.

(a) $1050.00   (b) $1020.00   (c) $2010.00   (d) $967.23   (e) None of these

9. A manufacturer has an order for 1500 units that can be produced at two locations. Let x_1 and x_2 be the number of units produced at the two plants. Find the minimum cost for producing this order if the cost function is

$$C = 0.125x_1{}^2 - 14x_1 + 0.25x_2{}^2 - 227x_2.$$

(a) $44,110   (b) $35,419   (c) $31,488   (d) $29,754   (e) None of these

10. Evaluate $\displaystyle\int_0^1 \int_{x^3}^{x^2} (x^2 - xy)\, dy\, dx$.

(a) $-\frac{9}{80}$ (b) $\frac{1}{5}$ (c) $\frac{1}{80}$ (d) $-\frac{7}{40}$ (e) None of these

11. Evaluate $\displaystyle\int_0^1 \int_{2x}^2 e^{y^2}\, dy\, dx$ by reversing the order of integration.

(a) 0 (b) $\dfrac{e^4 - 1}{4}$ (c) $\dfrac{3e^4 + 1}{8}$ (d) $\dfrac{e^4 + 1}{8}$ (e) None of these

12. Find the least squares regression line for the points $(4, 1)$, $(-3, -1)$, $(2, -4)$ and $(-4, 7)$.

(a) $y = -0.7542x + 1.0615$ (b) $y = -0.3520x + 3.1620$

(c) $y = 0.5809x^2 - 0.6536x - 5.4482$ (d) $y = 0.0397x^2 - 0.3451x + 2.2715$

(e) None of these

Test Form E

Chapter 7

Name _____ Date _____

Class _____ Section _____

1. Find the distance between the points $(4, 3, 5)$ and $(-3, -3, 6)$. Approximate your answer to the nearest 0.01.

2. Find the equation of the sphere whose center is $\left(-1, \frac{5}{2}, 2\right)$ and whose radius is $\frac{9}{2}$.

3. Determine the domain of the function defined by $f(x, y) = \sqrt{1 - x^2 - y^2}$.

4. Find all intercepts: $2x + 4y - 5z = -20$.

5. Find $f(0, 2)$ if $f(x, y) = x^3 - y \ln(x + 3)$. Approximate your answer to the nearest 0.01.

6. Find $\dfrac{\partial w}{\partial x}$ if $w = x^2 + y\sqrt{z - x^2}$.

7. Find the slope in the y-direction of the surface $f(x, y) = xy^2 + x^2y$ at the point $(2, -3, 6)$.

8. Determine the maximum revenue obtained by a furniture store that sells two competitive products, the prices of which are p_1 and p_2.

$$R = 300p_1 + 900p_2 + 1.8p_1p_2 - 1.5p_1^2 - p_2^2.$$

9. Use Lagrange Multipliers to find three positive numbers whose sum is 33 and whose product is a maximum.

10. Evaluate $\displaystyle\int_0^3 \int_0^{\sqrt{9-y^2}} (y + x)\, dx\, dy$.

11. Evaluate $\displaystyle\int_0^1 \int_{y^2}^1 ye^{x^2}\, dx\, dy$ by reversing the order of integration.

12. Find the least squares regression line for the points $(1, 3)$, $(-5, -5)$, $(-3, -2)$ and $(5, 7)$.

13. Explain, in a complete sentence, what must be true about the first and second partial derivatives of a function $z = f(x, y)$ if the function has a saddle point at the point $P(a, b)$.

Test Form A   **Name** _____ **Date** _____

Chapter 8   **Class** _____ **Section** _____

1. Find the $\csc\theta$ if the angle θ is in standard position and the terminal side of θ passes through the point $(-2, 3)$.

(a) 3   (b) $-\dfrac{\sqrt{13}}{2}$ (c) $\dfrac{\sqrt{13}}{3}$ (d) $\dfrac{1}{3}$ (e) None of these

2. Find $\sec\theta$ given that $\tan\theta = \dfrac{1}{\sqrt{14}}$ and $\sin\theta < 0$.

(a) $\dfrac{1}{\sqrt{15}}$ (b) $-\dfrac{\sqrt{14}}{\sqrt{15}}$ (c) $\dfrac{\sqrt{14}}{\sqrt{15}}$ (d) $-\dfrac{1}{\sqrt{15}}$ (e) None of these

3. Find the area of the equilateral triangle, each of whose sides has a length of two inches.

(a) 2 in.^{2} (b) $\sqrt{3}$ in.^{2} (c) 1 in.^{2} (d) 6 in.^{2} (e) None of these

4. Find all angles in the interval $[0, 2\pi)$ that satisfy the equation $2\cos^2\theta - 3\cos\theta + 1 = 0$.

(a) $\theta = 0, \dfrac{2\pi}{3}, \dfrac{4\pi}{3}$ (b) $\theta = 0, \dfrac{\pi}{3}, \dfrac{5\pi}{3}$ (c) $\theta = 0, \dfrac{\pi}{6}, \dfrac{5\pi}{6}$

(d) $\theta = 0, \dfrac{2\pi}{3}, \dfrac{5\pi}{3}$ (e) None of these

5. Differentiate: $f(x) = \sec(2x - \pi)$.

(a) $\sec(2x - \pi)\tan(2x - \pi)$ (b) $2\tan^2(2x - \pi)$ (c) $2\sec(2x - \pi)\tan(2x - \pi)$

(d) $2\sec 2x \tan 2x + 1$ (e) None of these

6. Find $\dfrac{dy}{dx}$ for the function $y = \dfrac{\cos(x^2 - 1)}{2x + 5}$.

(a) $\dfrac{2[2x + 5)\sin(x^2 - 1) + \cos(x^2 - 1)]}{(2x + 5)^2}$ (b) $\dfrac{-2[(2x^2 + 5x)\sin(x^2 - 1) + \cos(x^2 - 1)]}{(2x + 5)^2}$

(c) $\dfrac{2[(2x^2 + 5x)\cos(x^2 - 1) + \sin(x^2 - 1)]}{(2x + 5)^2}$ (d) $\dfrac{2[(2x^2 + 5x)\sin(x^2 - 1) - \cos(x^2 - 1)]}{(2x + 5)^2}$

(e) None of these

7. Find $f'\left(\dfrac{\pi}{4}\right)$ for $f(x) = e^{\tan x}$.

(a) $2e$ (b) $\dfrac{\pi}{4}e^{\tan x}$ (c) $\sqrt{2}e$ (d) 1   (e) None of these

8. Find the derivative of the given function and simplify the answer: $y = \ln(\sec x)$.

(a) $\sec x \tan x$ (b) $\tan x$ (c) $2 \tan x$ (d) $-\cot x$ (e) None of these

9. Use implicit differentiation to find $\dfrac{dy}{dx}$ for $x = \cos x + \sin y$.

(a) $-\dfrac{1 + \sin x}{\sin y}$ (b) $\sec x \tan x - 1$ (c) $1 + \sin x$

(d) $-\csc(x + y) - 1$ (e) None of these

10. Find an equation for the tangent line to the graph of $y = \sin^2 x$ at the point $\left(\dfrac{\pi}{6}, \dfrac{1}{4}\right)$.

(a) $y = \dfrac{\sqrt{3}}{2}x - \dfrac{1}{4} + \dfrac{\sqrt{3}\pi}{12}$ (b) $y = \dfrac{\sqrt{3}}{2}x + \dfrac{1}{4} - \dfrac{\sqrt{3}\pi}{12}$ (c) $y = \dfrac{\sqrt{3}}{4}x + \dfrac{1}{4} - \dfrac{\sqrt{3}\pi}{12}$

(d) $y = \dfrac{\sqrt{3}}{2}x + \dfrac{1}{4} + \dfrac{\sqrt{3}\pi}{12}$ (e) None of these

11. Evaluate $\displaystyle\int \sec 3x \, dx$.

(a) $3 \sec 3x \tan 3x + C$ (b) $\frac{1}{3} \ln|\sec 3x + \tan 3x| + C$ (c) $\frac{1}{3} \csc 3x + C$

(d) $\frac{1}{3} \tan^2 3x + C$ (e) None of these

12. Evaluate $\displaystyle\int \sin^2 x \cos x \, dx$.

(a) $\sin^3 x \cos x + C$ (b) $\dfrac{\sin^3 x}{3} + C$ (c) $-\dfrac{\sin^3 x}{3} + C$

(d) $\dfrac{\sin^3 x \cos^2 x}{6} + C$ (e) None of these

13. Evaluate $\displaystyle\int \dfrac{\cos 2x}{1 - \sin 2x} \, dx$.

(a) $\frac{1}{2}[\sin 2x - \ln|\sin 2x|] + C$ (b) $-\dfrac{1}{2} \ln|1 - \sin 2x| + C$ (c) $\dfrac{\sin 2x}{2x + \cos 2x} + C$

(d) $\dfrac{1}{2} \sin 2x + C$ (e) None of these

14. Evaluate $\displaystyle\int_0^\pi (x + \sin x) \, dx$.

(a) $\dfrac{\pi^2}{2}$ (b) $\dfrac{\pi^2}{2} - 2$ (c) $\dfrac{\pi^2}{2} + 1$ (d) $\dfrac{\pi^2}{2} + 2$ (e) None of these

15. Determine the area of the region bounded by $y = -\cos\left(\dfrac{x}{2}\right)$ and $y = 0$ for

$0 \le x \le \pi$.

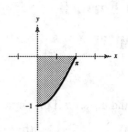

(a) $-\dfrac{1}{2}$ (b) $\dfrac{1}{2}$

(c) $2\sqrt{2}$ (d) 2

(e) None of these

16. Evaluate: $\displaystyle\lim_{x \to \infty} \dfrac{e^{2x}}{3x}$.

(a) $\dfrac{2}{3}$ (b) $\dfrac{1}{3}$ (c) 0   (d) ∞ (e) None of these

Test Form B   Name _____ Date _____

Chapter 8   Class _____ Section _____

1. Find the $\sec\theta$ if the angle θ is in standard position and the terminal side of θ passes through the point $(-3, 4)$.

   (a) $\frac{5}{4}$ (b) $-\frac{5}{3}$ (c) $-\frac{4}{3}$ (d) $-\frac{3}{4}$ (e) None of these

2. Find $\tan\theta$ given that $\sec\theta = \frac{3}{2}$ and $\sin\theta < 0$.

   (a) $\frac{\sqrt{5}}{2}$ (b) $-\frac{\sqrt{5}}{2}$ (c) $\frac{2}{\sqrt{5}}$ (d) $-\frac{2}{\sqrt{5}}$ (e) None of these

3. Find the area of the equilateral triangle, each of whose sides has a length of three centimeters.

   (a) 4.5 cm^2 (b) $\frac{9}{4}$ cm^2 (c) $\frac{9\sqrt{3}}{4}$ cm^2 (d) 9 cm^2 (e) None of these

4. Find all angles in the interval $[0, \pi]$ that satisfy the equation $\sin^2\theta + \left(\frac{\sqrt{3}}{2} - 1\right)\sin\theta - \frac{\sqrt{3}}{2} = 0$.

   (a) $\theta = \frac{\pi}{2}, \frac{2\pi}{3}$ (b) $\theta = \frac{\pi}{2}$ (c) $\theta = \frac{\pi}{2}, \frac{5\pi}{6}$ (d) $\theta = \frac{2\pi}{3}$ (e) None of these

5. Differentiate: $f(x) = \cot(\pi - 2x)$.

   (a) $2\csc^2(\pi - 2x)$ (b) $2\csc^2 2x$ (c) $-\csc^2(\pi - 2x)$

   (d) $2\csc(\pi - 2x)\cot(\pi - 2x)$ (e) None of these

6. Find $\frac{dy}{dx}$ for the function $y = \frac{x^2 - \sin x}{x}$.

   (a) $\frac{x^2 + x\cos x - \sin x}{x^2}$ (b) $\frac{x^2 - x\cos x + \sin x}{x^2}$ (c) $\frac{x^2 + x\cos x - \sin x}{x^2}$

   (d) $\frac{x^2 - \cos x + \sin x}{x^2}$ (e) None of these

7. Find $f'\left(\frac{\pi}{5}\right)$ for the function $f(x) = e^{\sin x}$.

   (a) 1.3591 (b) 1.7800 (c) 1.4562 (d) 1 (e) None of these

8. Find the derivative of the given function and simplify your answer by using trigonometric identities: $y = \ln(\sin^2 x)$.

   (a) $2\tan x$ (b) $2\cos x\cot x$ (c) $2\cot x$

   (d) $-2\cot x$ (e) None of these

9. Evaluate $\int \dfrac{\sec^2 x}{\tan x}\, dx.$

(a) $\ln|\tan x| + C$

(b) $\tan x + \ln|\tan x| + C$

(c) $\dfrac{\tan x}{\ln|\cos x|} + C$

(d) $x \tan x + C$

(e) None of these

10. Evaluate $\displaystyle\int_0^{\pi/6} \sec^2 (2x)\, dx.$

(a) $\dfrac{\pi^2}{2}$

(b) $\dfrac{\pi^2}{2} - 2$

(c) $\dfrac{\pi^2}{2} + 1$

(d) $\dfrac{\sqrt{3}}{2}$

(e) None of these

11. Use implicit differentiation to find $\dfrac{dy}{dx}$ for $x = \cos x + \cos y.$

(a) $-\dfrac{1 + \sin x}{\sin y}$

(b) $\sec x \tan x - 1$

(c) $1 + \sin x$

(d) $-\csc(x + y) - 1$

(e) None of these

12. Find an equation for the tangent line to the graph of $y = \csc(2x)$ at the point $\left(\dfrac{\pi}{6}, \dfrac{2\sqrt{3}}{3}\right)$.

(a) $y = -\dfrac{4}{\sqrt{3}}x + \dfrac{2\pi\sqrt{3}}{9} + \dfrac{2\sqrt{3}}{3}$

(b) $y = -\dfrac{4}{3}x + \dfrac{2\pi}{9} + \dfrac{2\sqrt{3}}{3}$

(c) $y = -\dfrac{1}{3}x + \dfrac{2\sqrt{3}}{3} + \dfrac{\pi}{18}$

(d) $y = \dfrac{4}{3}x + \dfrac{2\pi}{9} + \dfrac{2\sqrt{3}}{3}$

(e) None of these

13. Evaluate $\int \csc \dfrac{x}{2}\, dx.$

(a) $-\dfrac{1}{2} \csc \dfrac{x}{2} \cos \dfrac{x}{2} + C$

(b) $\sin(\ln x^2) + C$

(c) $2 \sec \dfrac{x}{2} + C$

(d) $2 \ln\left|\csc \dfrac{x}{2} - \cot \dfrac{x}{2}\right| + C$

(e) None of these

14. Evaluate $\int \cot^2 x \csc^2 x\, dx.$

(a) $\sin^3 x \cos x + C$

(b) $-\dfrac{\cot^3 x}{3} + C$

(c) $-\dfrac{\sin^3 x}{3} + C$

(d) $\dfrac{\sin^3 x \cos^2 x}{6} + C$

(e) None of these

15. Determine the area of the region bounded by $y = \cos 2x$ and $y = 0$ for
$0 \le x \le \dfrac{\pi}{4}$.

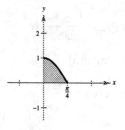

(a) -2

(b) $\frac{1}{2}$

(c) $2\sqrt{2}$

(d) 2

(e) None of these

16. Find the limit: $\lim\limits_{x \to \infty} \dfrac{e^x}{x^2}$.

(a) 2
(b) ∞
(c) 1
(d) 0
(e) None of these

Test Form C   Name _____ Date _____

Chapter 8   Class _____ Section _____

1. Evaluate: $\sec\left(\dfrac{\pi}{3}\right)$.

    (a) $\dfrac{\sqrt{2}}{2}$ (b) $\dfrac{\sqrt{3}}{2}$ (c) $\dfrac{\sqrt{3}}{3}$ (d) 2   (e) None of these

2. Sketch one period of the graph of $y = 2\cos\dfrac{x}{3}$.

3. If $\sin\theta = \frac{1}{3}$ and $\cos\theta < 0$, find $\cot\theta$.

4. Solve for θ, $(0 \le \theta < 2\pi)$: $2\cos^2\theta - 5\cos\theta = 3$.

5. Differentiate: $f(x) = 2\tan 3x$.

6. Find $\dfrac{dy}{dx}$ for the function $y = \dfrac{\sin x}{1 - \cos x}$.

7. Find $f'\left(\dfrac{\pi}{2}\right)$ for $f(x) = \csc\dfrac{t}{2}$.

8. Use implicit differentiation to find $\dfrac{dy}{dx}$ for $x = \tan y$.

9. Find the derivative of the given function and simplify your answer by using trigonometric identities: $y = \ln(\sin^2 x)$.

    (a) $2\tan x$ (b) $2\cos x \cot x$ (c) $2\cot x$

    (d) $-2\cot x$ (e) None of these

10. Find all values of x in the interval $[0, 2\pi]$ that give extrema for the function $y = \sin x + \cos x$.

11. Evaluate $\displaystyle\int 3\csc x \cot x \, dx$.

12. Evaluate $\displaystyle\int \sqrt{\tan x}\, \sec^2 x \, dx$.

13. Evaluate $\displaystyle\int \dfrac{\cos 4x}{\sin 4x}\, dx$.

14. Evaluate $\displaystyle\int_{\pi/4}^{\pi/3} \sec^2 x \, dx$.

15. Determine the area of the region bounded by the graphs of $y = \sin x$ and $y = 0$ in the interval $[0, \pi]$.

16. Find the limit: $\displaystyle\lim_{x \to \infty} \frac{\ln(x - 4)}{x^2}$.

Test Form D

Chapter 8

Name _____ Date _____

Class _____ Section _____

1. Find the $\sec\theta$ if the angle is in the standard position and the terminal side of θ passes through the point $(-5, 6)$.

   (a) $-\dfrac{6}{5}$　　　(b) $-\dfrac{5}{\sqrt{61}}$　　　(c) $-\dfrac{\sqrt{61}}{5}$　　　(d) $\dfrac{\sqrt{61}}{6}$　　　(e) None of these

2. Find $\cos\theta$ given that $\tan\theta = \dfrac{1}{\sqrt{17}}$ and $\sin\theta < 0$.

   (a) 0.9178　　　(b) 0.2357　　　(c) -0.2357　　　(d) -0.9178　　　(e) None of these

3. Solve the triangle for c.

   (a) 6　　　　　　　　(b) $3\sqrt{2}$

   (c) $3\sqrt{3}$　　　　　　(d) $\sqrt{6}$

   (e) None of these

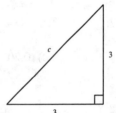

4. Find all angles in the interval $[0, \pi]$ that satisfy the equation $1 + \cos 2\theta + \cos\theta = 0$.

   (a) 0.5236, 1.5708　　　　　(b) 1.5708, 2.0944　　　　　(c) 1.5708, 2.6180

   (d) 0.7854　　　　　　　　(e) None of these

5. Differentiate: $f(x) = \tan^2(2x - \pi)$.

   (a) $4\tan(2x - \pi)\sec(2x - \pi)$　　　　　(b) $2\tan(2x - \pi)\sec^2(2x - \pi)$

   (c) $4\tan(2x - \pi)\sec^2(2x - \pi)$　　　　　(d) $4\sec^2(2x - \pi)$

   (e) None of these

6. Find $\dfrac{dy}{dx}$ for $y = \dfrac{\sin(x + 1)}{x + 1}$.

   (a) $\dfrac{\cos(x + 1) - \sin(x + 1)}{x + 1}$　　　　　(b) $\dfrac{(x + 1)\cos(x + 1) - \sin(x + 1)}{(x + 1)^2}$

   (c) $\cos(x + 1)$　　　　　　　　　(d) $\dfrac{\sin(x + 1) - (x + 1)\cos(x + 1)}{(x + 1)^2}$

   (e) None of these

7. Find $f'\left(\dfrac{\pi}{5}\right)$ for the function $f(x) = e^{\sin x}$.

   (a) 1.3591　　　(b) 1.7800　　　(c) 1.4562　　　(d) 1　　　(e) None of these

8. Find the derivative of the given function and simplify the answer: $y = \ln(\sec^2 x)$.

(a) $2 \sec x \tan x$ (b) $\tan^2 x$ (c) $2 \tan x$ (d) $-2 \cot x$ (e) None of these

9. Find the average value of the function $f(x) = \sin x$ on the interval $[0, \pi]$.

(a) 0.6366   (b) 0   (c) 0.3813   (d) 0.7283   (e) None of these

10. Find an equation of the tangent line to the graph of the function $f(x) = \tan x$ at the point $\left(\dfrac{\pi}{4}, 1\right)$.

(a) $y = 2x + 1 - \left(\dfrac{\pi}{2}\right)$ (b) $y = 2x - \left(\dfrac{\pi}{2}\right)$ (c) $y = 2x + 1$

(d) $y = \sqrt{2}x + 1 - \left(\dfrac{\sqrt{2}\pi}{4}\right)$ (e) None of these

11. Evaluate $\displaystyle\int_0^{\pi/8} \sec 2x \tan 2x \, dx$.

(a) 1.4142   (b) 1   (c) 0.2071   (d) 0   (e) None of these

12. Evaluate $\displaystyle\int \dfrac{\sec^3\theta \tan\theta}{1 + \tan^2\theta} \, d\theta$.

(a) $\frac{1}{4}\sec^4\theta + C$ (b) $\frac{1}{2}\sec^2\theta + C$ (c) $\frac{1}{4}\sec^2\theta \tan^2\theta + C$

(d) $\sec\theta + C$ (e) None of these

13. Evaluate $\displaystyle\int \sin^3 3x \cos 3x \, dx$.

(a) $\frac{1}{8}\sin^4 3x \cos^2 3x + C$ (b) $\frac{1}{4}\sin^4 3x + C$ (c) $3\sin^2 3x(3\cos^2 3x - \sin^2 3x) + C$

(d) $\frac{1}{12}\sin^4 3x + C$ (e) None of these

14. Evaluate $\displaystyle\int_{\pi/2}^{\pi} (x + \cos x) \, dx$.

(a) $1 - \left(\dfrac{\pi}{2}\right)$ (b) 0   (c) π (d) $\dfrac{\pi}{2}$ (e) None of these

15. Find the volume of the solid formed by revolving the region bounded by $y = \sin x$ and $y = 0$ in the interval $[0, \pi]$ about the y-axis.

(a) π^3 (b) $\frac{1}{2}\pi^2$ (c) $2\pi^2$ (d) π (e) None of these

16. Find the limit: $\displaystyle\lim_{x \to 0} \dfrac{3\sin(2x)}{\sin(4x)}$.

(a) $\frac{1}{2}$ (b) $\frac{3}{2}$ (c) 3   (d) 0   (e) None of these

Test Form E   **Name** _____ **Date** _____

Chapter 8   **Class** _____ **Section** _____

1. Find the $\csc\theta$ if the angle θ is in the standard position and the terminal side of θ passes through $(-2, 5)$. Do not approximate your answer.

2. Find $\cos\theta$ given that $\cot\theta = \dfrac{1}{\sqrt{15}}$ and $\sin\theta < 0$.

3. Using a graphing utility, find $\displaystyle\lim_{x\to 0} \dfrac{\sin(3x)}{\sin(5x)}$.

4. Find all angles θ such that $2\sin^2\theta - 5\cos\theta - 3 = 0$, in the interval $[0, \pi]$.

5. Find the derivative of $y = \sin x^2$.

6. Find $\dfrac{dy}{dx}$ for $y = \dfrac{1 + \cos x}{1 - \cos x}$.

7. Find $f'\left(\dfrac{\pi}{8}\right)$ for the function $f(x) = e^{\cos x}$. Approximate your answer to 4 decimal places.

8. Find the derivative of the given function and simplify your answer by using trigonometric identities: $y = \ln(\cos x)$.

9. Find the average value of $f(x) = \sin x$ on the interval $\left[\dfrac{\pi}{4}, \dfrac{\pi}{2}\right]$. Approximate your answer to 4 decimal places.

10. Use implicit differentiation to find $\dfrac{dy}{dx}$ for $x = \sin y$.

11. Evaluate $\displaystyle\int_{\pi/6}^{\pi/2} 3\csc x \cot x\, dx$.

12. Evaluate $\displaystyle\int \dfrac{\sec^2 x}{\sqrt{\tan x}}\, dx$.

13. Evaluate $\displaystyle\int \dfrac{\cos^3\theta}{2 - 2\sin^2\theta}\, d\theta$.

14. Evaluate $\displaystyle\int \sec 2x \tan 2x\, dx$.

15. Find the area of the region bounded by the graphs of $f(x) = \sin x$ and $g(x) = \cos x$, for $\frac{\pi}{4} \leq x \leq \frac{5\pi}{4}$.

16. Find the limit: $\lim\limits_{x \to 0} \dfrac{1 - \cos(2x)}{\sin(2x)}$.

Test Form A   Name _____ Date _____

Chapter 9   Class _____ Section _____

1. Two dice are cast. List the elements of the event A that the sum is 7.

   (a) $\{(1, 6), (2, 5), (3, 4)\}$

   (b) $\{(3, 4), (2, 5), (1, 6), (0, 7)\}$

   (c) $\{(1, 6), (2, 5), (3, 4), (4, 3), (5, 2), (6, 1)\}$

   (d) $\{(7, 0), (6, 1), (5, 2), (4, 3), (3, 4), (2, 5), (1, 6), (0, 7)\}$

   (e) None of these

2. A coin is tossed four times. What is the event that no more than one head occurs?

   (a) {HTTT, TTTT}   (b) {HTTT, TTTH, THTT, TTHT}

   (c) {TTTT}   (d) {HTTT, THTT, TTHT, TTTH, TTTT}

   (e) None of these

3. Find $P(x > 1)$ for the given probability distribution.

x	0	1	2	3
$P(x)$	0.051	0.459	0.367	0.123

   (a) 0.949   (b) 0.367   (c) 0.490   (d) 0.0451   (e) None of these

4. Find the expected value of x.

   (a) $\frac{3}{2}$ (b) $\frac{10}{32}$ (c) $\frac{5}{2}$ (d) $\frac{25}{16}$ (e) None of these

5. Find the variance of x.

   (a) 1   (b) $\frac{3}{2}$ (c) $\frac{25}{16}$ (d) $\frac{5}{4}$ (e) None of these

6. Find the standard derivation.

   (a) $\frac{\sqrt{5}}{2}$ (b) $\frac{5}{4}$ (c) $\frac{\sqrt{6}}{2}$ (d) 1   (e) None of these

7. Find the constant k so that the function $f(x) = k\sqrt{x}$ is a probability density function over the interval $[0, 9]$.

   (a) $\frac{1}{3}$ (b) $\frac{1}{18}$ (c) $\frac{1}{27}$ (d) 9   (e) None of these

8. Find $P(0 \le x \le 2)$, given the probability density function $f(x) = \dfrac{8}{(x + 2)^3}$, $x \ge 0$.

   (a) $\frac{3}{16}$ (b) $\frac{3}{8}$ (c) $\frac{3}{4}$ (d) $\frac{1}{8}$ (e) None of these

9. The daily demand, x, for a certain product is a random variable with the probability density function

$$f(x) = \frac{6x(5 - x)}{125}, [0, 5].$$

Determine the probability that the demand will be less than three.

(a) $\frac{81}{125}$ (b) $\frac{36}{125}$ (c) $\frac{96}{125}$ (d) $\frac{68}{125}$ (e) None of these

10. Determine the expected value for the probability density function, $f(x) = \dfrac{4}{3x^2}, [1, 4].$

(a) $\frac{4}{3}$ (b) 1   (c) $\frac{4}{3} \ln 4$ (d) $\frac{4}{3} \ln 3$ (e) None of these

11. Find the variance for the probability density function, $f(x) = \frac{1}{2}, 0 \le x \le 2$, if the expected value is 1.

(a) $\frac{1}{8}$ (b) $\frac{1}{4}$ (c) $\frac{1}{16}$ (d) $\frac{1}{6}$ (e) None of these

12. Determine the median for the probability density function $f(x) = 3e^{-3x}, [0, \infty).$

(a) $\frac{1}{3} \ln 2$ (b) 0   (c) $\frac{1}{3}$ (d) $\frac{1}{9}$ (e) None of these

13. Let x be a continuous random variable that is normally distributed with a mean of 35 and a standard deviation of 5. Write the integral that could be solved to find the probability that $x \ge 40$.

(a) $\displaystyle\int_0^{45} \frac{1}{5\sqrt{2\pi}} e^{-(x-35)^2/50}$ (b) $\displaystyle\int_0^{45} \frac{1}{\sqrt{2\pi}} e^{-(x-35)^2/5}$ (c) $\displaystyle\int_{45}^{\infty} \frac{1}{\sqrt{2\pi}} e^{-(x-35)^2/25}$

(d) $\displaystyle\int_{45}^{\infty} \frac{1}{5\sqrt{2\pi}} e^{-(x-35)^2/50}$ (e) None of these

14. Determine the standard deviation, σ, of the probability density function, $f(x) = \dfrac{3}{2x^2}, [1, 3].$

(a) 0.084   (b) 1   (c) 0.533   (d) 0.825   (e) None of these

15. The standard normal probability density function is:

(a) $f(x) = \dfrac{1}{\sigma\sqrt{2\pi}} e^{-(x-\mu)^2/2\sigma^2}$ (b) $f(x) = ae^{-ax}$ (c) $f(x) = \dfrac{1}{\sqrt{2\pi}} e^{-x^2/2}$

(d) $f(x) = \dfrac{1}{b - a}$ (e) None of these

Test Form B   Name _____ Date _____

Chapter 9   Class _____ Section _____

1. Three coins are tossed. Choose the event B that exactly two tails appear.

   (a) {(THT, TTT, TTH, HTT}   (b) {THT, TTH, HTT}

   (c) {THT, TTH, HTT, HTH, HHT, THH}   (d) {TTT}

   (e) None of these

2. A bag contains three red balls, two blue balls, and four green balls. If a ball is chosen at random, what is the probability that it will be blue?

   (a) $\frac{7}{9}$ (b) $\frac{2}{9}$ (c) $\frac{1}{2}$ (d) $\frac{1}{4}$ (e) None of these

3. Find $P(x \leq 2)$ for the given probability distribution.

x	0	1	2	3
$P(x)$	0.051	0.459	0.367	0.123

   (a) 0.367   (b) 0.510   (c) 0.123   (d) 0.877   (e) None of these

For problems 4 through 6, use the probability distribution for the discrete random variable x, given below.

x	0	1	2	3	4
$P(x)$	$\frac{1}{10}$	$\frac{4}{10}$	$\frac{3}{10}$	$\frac{1}{10}$	$\frac{1}{10}$

4. Find the expected value of x.

   (a) $\frac{3}{2}$ (b) $\frac{10}{17}$ (c) $\frac{17}{10}$ (d) $\frac{25}{16}$ (e) None of these

5. Find the variance of x.

   (a) 1   (b) $\frac{3}{2}$ (c) $\frac{25}{16}$ (d) $\frac{5}{4}$ (e) None of these

6. Find the standard derivation.

   (a) $\frac{11}{10}$ (b) $\frac{5}{4}$ (c) $\frac{\sqrt{6}}{2}$ (d) 1   (e) None of these

7. Find the constant k so that the function $f(x) = \dfrac{k}{x^2}$ is a probability density function over the interval $[1, 3]$.

   (a) 2   (b) $-\frac{9}{8}$ (c) $\frac{3}{2}$ (d) 3   (e) None of these

8. Find $P(0 \leq x \leq 2)$ given the probability density function $f(x) = \dfrac{8}{(x + 3)^3}, x \geq 0$.

   (a) $\frac{16}{25}$ (b) $\frac{8}{25}$ (c) $\frac{9}{50}$ (d) $\frac{18}{25}$ (e) None of these

9. The daily demand, x, for a certain product is a random variable with the probability density function

$$f(x) = \frac{3x(4 - x)}{32}, [0, 4].$$

Determine the probability that the demand will be less than three.

(a) $\frac{9}{32}$ (b) $\frac{27}{32}$ (c) $\frac{1}{2}$ (d) $\frac{3}{4}$ (e) None of these

10. Determine the expected value of the probability density function, $f(x) = \frac{1}{12}\sqrt[3]{x}, [0, 8]$.

(a) $\frac{4}{7}$ (b) 1   (c) $\frac{32}{7}$ (d) $\frac{4}{3}$ (e) None of these

11. Find the variance for the probability density function, $f(x) = \frac{1}{3}, 0 \le x \le 3$, if the expected value is $\frac{3}{2}$.

(a) $\frac{1}{2}$ (b) $\frac{1}{4}$ (c) $\frac{3}{2}$ (d) $\frac{3}{4}$ (e) None of these

12. Determine the median for the probability density function $f(x) = 4e^{-4x}, [0, \infty)$.

(a) $\frac{1}{4}\ln 2$ (b) 0   (c) $\frac{1}{4}$ (d) $\frac{1}{16}$ (e) None of these

13. Let x be a continuous random variable that is normally distributed with a mean of 12 and a standard deviation of 3. Write the integral that could be solved to find the probability that $x \ge 14$.

(a) $\displaystyle\int_{14}^{\infty} \frac{1}{3\sqrt{2\pi}} e^{-(x-12)^2/18}$ (b) $\displaystyle\int_{14}^{\infty} \frac{1}{12\sqrt{2\pi}} e^{-(x-9)^2/24}$ (c) $\displaystyle\int_{14}^{\infty} \frac{1}{3\sqrt{2\pi}} e^{-(x-12)^2/144}$

(d) $\displaystyle\int_{0}^{\infty} \frac{1}{3\sqrt{2\pi}} e^{-(x-12)^2/18}$ (e) None of these

14. Determine the standard deviation, σ, of the probability density function, $f(x) = \frac{1}{18}\sqrt{x}, [0, 9]$.

(a) 5.89   (b) 5.85   (c) 0.70   (d) 2.36   (e) None of these

15. The normal probability density function is:

(a) $f(x) = \frac{1}{\sigma\sqrt{2\pi}} e^{-(x-\mu)^2/2\sigma^2}$ (b) $f(x) = ae^{-ax}$ (c) $f(x) = \frac{1}{\sqrt{2\pi}} e^{-x^2/2}$

(d) $f(x) = \frac{1}{b - a}$ (e) None of these

Test Form C

Chapter 9

Name _____ Date _____

Class _____ Section _____

1. Three coins are tossed. List the event B that exactly two heads appear.

2. An integer is chosen at random between 10 and 29, inclusive. What is the probability that one of the digits of the integer will be a 1?

3. Find $P(x \le 2)$ for the given probability distribution.

x	0	1	2	3
$P(x)$	0.023	0.312	0.367	0.298

4. Find the expected value of x.

5. Find the variance of x.

6. Find the standard deviation.

7. Find the constant k so that the function $f(x) = \dfrac{k}{x^2}$ is a probability density function over the interval $[1, 5]$.

8. Find $P(0 \le x \le 2)$ given the probability density function $f(x) = \dfrac{8}{(x + 2)^3}, x \ge 0$.

9. The daily demand, x, for a certain product is a random variable with the probability density function

$$f(x) = \frac{3x(4 - x)}{32}, [0, 4].$$

Determine the probability that the demand will be less than three.

10. Determine the expected value for the probability density function, $f(x) = \dfrac{16}{15x^3}, [1, 4]$.

11. Find the variance for the probability density function, $f(x) = \frac{1}{6}, 0 \le x \le 6$, if the expected value is 3.

12. Determine the median for the probability density function $f(x) = 0.2e^{-0.2x}, [0, \infty)$.

For problems 13 and 14, use the probability density function $f(x) = \dfrac{6x(5 - x)}{125}, [0, 5]$.

13. Determine the mean of x.

14. Determine the standard deviation of x.

15. Explain, in a complete sentence, the difference between two normally distributed populations, where one population has a large standard deviation and the other has a very small standard deviation.

Test Form D   Name _____ Date _____

Chapter 9   Class _____ Section _____

1. A card is chosen at random from a standard 52-card deck of playing cards. If aces are low, what is the probability that the face value of the card will be less than 5?

   (a) $\frac{5}{52}$ (b) $\frac{4}{52}$ (c) $\frac{5}{13}$ (d) $\frac{1}{2}$ (e) None of these

2. A card is chosen at random from a standard 52-card deck of playing cards. If aces are low, what is the probability that the face value of the card will be less than 10?

   (a) $\frac{5}{26}$ (b) $\frac{9}{13}$ (c) $\frac{10}{13}$ (d) $\frac{5}{13}$ (e) None of these

3. Find $P(x < 2)$ for the given probability distribution.

x	0	1	2	3
$P(x)$	0.151	0.359	0.167	0.323

   (a) 0.677   (b) 0.359   (c) 0.510   (d) 0.323   (e) None of these

For problems 4 through 6, use the probability distribution for the discrete random variable x, given below.

x	0	1	2	3	4	5
$P(x)$	0.12	0.24	0.24	0.36	0.03	0.01

4. Find the expected value of x.

   (a) 1.87   (b) 2.02   (c) 1.97   (d) 1.79   (e) None of these

5. Find the variance of x.

   (a) 1   (b) 1.4789   (c) 0.6789   (d) 1.2891   (e) None of these

6. Find the standard derivation.

   (a) 1.1354   (b) 1.2161   (c) 0.8239   (d) 1   (e) None of these

7. Find the constant k so that the function $f(x) = kx(6 - x)$ is a probability density function over the interval $[0, 6]$.

   (a) $\frac{1}{6}$ (b) $\frac{1}{36}$ (c) $\frac{1}{108}$ (d) $\frac{1}{12}$ (e) None of these

8. Find $P(0 \le x \le 2)$, given the probability density function $f(x) = \dfrac{5}{4(x + 1)^2}, 0 \le x \le 4$.

   (a) $\frac{5}{36}$ (b) $\frac{5}{6}$ (c) $\frac{5}{12}$ (d) $\frac{5}{2}$ (e) None of these

9. The daily demand, x, for a certain product is a random variable with the probability density function

$$f(x) = \frac{3x(4 - x)}{32}, [0, 4].$$

Determine the probability that the demand will be greater than three.

(a) $\frac{9}{32}$ (b) $\frac{27}{32}$ (c) $\frac{1}{2}$ (d) $\frac{3}{4}$ (e) None of these

10. The usable lifetime in years of a certain product is modeled by the probability density function
$f(t) = 0.05e^{-0.05t}, t \geq 0$. Find the probability that a randomly selected unit will have a lifetime of more than four years.

(a) 0.783   (b) 0.045   (c) 0.779   (d) 0.819   (e) None of these

11. Find the expected value on the random variable x with probability density function, $f = \frac{x}{8}, 0 \leq x \leq 4$.

(a) $\frac{1}{8}$ (b) $\frac{8}{3}$ (c) $\frac{3}{16}$ (d) 2   (e) None of these

12. Determine the median for the probability density function $f(x) = 4e^{-4x}, [0, \infty)$.

(a) 0.173   (b) 0.982   (c) 0.327   (d) 0.137   (e) None of these

13. Let x be a continuous random variable that is normally distributed with a mean of 12 and a standard deviation of 3. Write the integral that could be solved to find the probability that $x \geq 14$.

(a) $\int_{14}^{\infty} \frac{1}{3\sqrt{2\pi}} e^{-(x-12)^2/18}$ (b) $\int_{14}^{\infty} \frac{1}{12\sqrt{2\pi}} e^{-(x-9)^2/24}$ (c) $\int_{14}^{\infty} \frac{1}{3\sqrt{2\pi}} e^{-(x-12)^2/144}$

(d) $\int_{0}^{\infty} \frac{1}{3\sqrt{2\pi}} e^{-(x-12)^2/18}$ (e) None of these

14. In the normal probability density function $f(x) = \frac{1}{\sigma\sqrt{2\pi}} e^{-(x-\mu)^2/2\sigma^2}$, the expected value is:

(a) σ (b) $\sqrt{\sigma}$ (c) μ (d) μ^2 (e) None of these

15. If z is a standard normal random variable, its expected value is:

(a) 1   (b) 0   (c) 0.5   (d) -1 (e) None of these

Test Form E

Chapter 9

Name _____ Date _____

Class _____ Section _____

1. Two dice are cast. List the elements of the event A that their sum is 4.

2. A card is chosen at random from a standard 52-card deck of playing cards. What is the probability that the card is red and a king?

3. Find $P(x < 2)$ for the given probability distribution.

x	0	1	2	3
$P(x)$	0.151	0.359	0.267	0.223

For problems 4 through 6, use the probability distribution for the discrete random variable x, given below.

x	0	1	2	3	4	5
$P(x)$	0.12	0.20	0.28	0.34	0.05	0.01

4. Find the expected value of x.

5. Find the variance of x.

6. Find the standard deviation.

7. Find the constant k so that the function $f(x) = kx(8 - x)$ is a probability density function over the interval $[0, 8]$.

8. Find $P(1 \leq x \leq 3)$ given the probability density function $f(x) = \dfrac{5}{4(x + 1)^2}, 0 \leq x \leq 4$.

9. The daily demand, x, for a certain product is a random variable with the probability density function

   $$f(x) = \frac{x(6 - x)}{36}, [0, 6].$$

   Determine the probability that the demand will be greater than three.

10. The usable lifetime in years of a certain product is modeled by the probability density function
    $f(t) = 0.04e^{-0.04t}, t \geq 0$. Find the probability that a randomly selected unit will have a lifetime of more than four years.

11. Use standard normal probability density function to find the probability of $x < -1.23$.

12. Determine the median for the probability density function $f(x) = 4e^{-4x}, [0, \infty)$.

13. Let x be a continuous random variable that is normally distributed with a mean of 35 and a standard deviation of 5. Write the integral that could be solved to find the probability that $x \geq 40$.

14. Describe, in a complete sentence, the difference between a discrete and a continuous random variable.

Test Form A   Name _____ Date _____

Chapter 10   Class _____ Section _____

1. Find the fourth term of the sequence: $\left\{\dfrac{(-1)^{n+1}2^n}{3n-1}\right\}, n = 1, 2, 3, \cdots$.

   (a) $\dfrac{16}{11}$ (b) $-\dfrac{16}{11}$ (c) $-\dfrac{8}{11}$ (d) $-\dfrac{16}{13}$ (e) None of these

2. Determine if the following sequence converges or diverges:

   $\left\{\dfrac{3n+1}{4n^2-3}\right\}, n = 1, 2, 3, \cdots$.

   (a) Converges to $\dfrac{3}{4}$ (b) Converges to 0   (c) Converges to $\dfrac{4}{3}$

   (d) Diverges   (e) None of these

3. Determine if the following sequence converges or diverges:

   $\left\{\dfrac{n!}{(n-2)!}\right\}, n = 2, 3, 4, \cdots$.

   If the sequence converges, find its limit.

   (a) Converges to 2   (b) Converges to 0   (c) Converges to 4

   (d) Diverges   (e) None of these

4. Find the sum of the geometric series: $\displaystyle\sum_{n=0}^{\infty} 5\left(\dfrac{3}{4}\right)^n$.

   (a) -10 (b) 5   (c) 20   (d) 15   (e) None of these

5. Find the sum of the following infinite geometric series: $\displaystyle\sum_{n=1}^{\infty} 2(-0.9)^n$.

   (a) 2   (b) 20   (c) -18 (d) $-\dfrac{18}{19}$ (e) None of these

6. Which of the following converges?

   (a) $\displaystyle\sum_{n=1}^{\infty}\dfrac{2}{n^2}$ (b) $\displaystyle\sum_{n=0}^{\infty}5\left(\dfrac{7}{3}\right)^n$ (c) $\displaystyle\sum_{n=0}^{\infty}\dfrac{(n+1)!}{2^n}$ (d) $\displaystyle\sum_{n=0}^{\infty}\dfrac{1}{n^{3/4}}$ (e) None of these

7. Which of the following diverges?

   (a) $\displaystyle\sum_{n=0}^{\infty}\dfrac{1}{2^n}$ (b) $\displaystyle\sum_{n=1}^{\infty}(4+(-1)^n)$ (c) $\displaystyle\sum_{n=0}^{\infty}\dfrac{(-1)^n}{(n+1)!}$

   (d) $\displaystyle\sum_{n=1}^{\infty}\dfrac{1}{n^2}$ (e) None of these

8. Which test would be used to prove the convergence of $\displaystyle\sum_{n=1}^{\infty} \frac{1}{n^2}$?

    (a) *p*-Series Test   (b) Geometric Series Test   (c) *n*th-Term Test

    (d) Ratio Test   (e) None of these

9. A ball is dropped from a height of 24 feet. Each time it drops h feet, it rebounds $\frac{2}{3}h$ feet. Find the total distance traveled by the ball.

    (a) 72 feet   (b) 144 feet   (c) 120 feet   (d) 84 feet   (e) None of these

10. Find the radius of convergence for the power series $\displaystyle\sum_{n=0}^{\infty} \frac{(3x)^n}{n+1}$.

    (a) 3   (b) ∞ (c) $\frac{1}{3}$ (d) 0   (e) None of these

11. Find the radius of convergence for the power series $\displaystyle\sum_{n=0}^{\infty} \left(\frac{x}{2}\right)^n$.

    (a) $\frac{1}{2}$ (b) 2   (c) ∞ (d) 0   (e) None of these

12. Find the third-degree Taylor polynomial centered at 0 for the function $f(x) = e^{2x} + 3x$.

    (a) $4 + 5x + 2x^2 + \frac{4}{3}x^3$ (b) $1 + 5x + 4x^2 + 8x^3$ (c) $1 + 5x + 2x^2 + 8x^3$

    (d) $1 + 5x + 2x^2 + \frac{4}{3}x^3$ (e) None of these

13. Find the third-degree Taylor polynomial centered at $c = 0$ for the function $f(x) = e^{3x}$.

    (a) $1 + 3x + 9x^2 + 27x^3$ (b) $e + 3ex + 9ex^2 + 27ex^3$ (c) $1 + 3x + \frac{9}{2}x^2 + \frac{9}{2}x^3$

    (d) $1 + x + \frac{x^2}{2} + \frac{x^3}{3}$ (e) None of these

Test Form B   **Name** _____ **Date** _____

Chapter 10   **Class** _____ **Section** _____

1. Find the fourth term of the sequence: $\left\{ \dfrac{(-1)^n(2^n + 1)}{n!} \right\}, n = 1, 2, 3, \cdots$.

   (a) $\dfrac{17}{4}$ (b) $\dfrac{-7}{4}$ (c) $\dfrac{9}{24}$ (d) $\dfrac{17}{24}$ (e) None of these

2. Determine if the following sequence converges or diverges:

$$\left\{ \frac{2n - 1}{3n^2 + 1} \right\}, n = 1, 2, 3, \cdots .$$

   If the sequence converges, find its limit.

   (a) Converges to $\dfrac{2}{3}$ (b) Converges to 0   (c) Converges to $-\dfrac{1}{3}$

   (d) Diverges   (e) None of these

3. Determine if the following sequence converges or diverges:

$$\left\{ \frac{n!}{(n - 2)!} \right\}, n = 2, 3, 4, \cdots .$$

   If the sequence converges, find its limit.

   (a) Converges to 2   (b) Converges to 0   (c) Converges to 4

   (d) Diverges   (e) None of these

4. Find the sum of the geometric series: $\displaystyle\sum_{n=0}^{\infty} 5\left(\frac{1}{e}\right)^n$.

   (a) 2.910   (b) 1.839   (c) 7.910   (d) 5   (e) None of these

5. Find the sum of the geometric series: $\displaystyle\sum_{n=0}^{\infty} 2\left(-\frac{1}{2}\right)^n = 2 - 1 + \frac{1}{2} - \frac{1}{4} + \cdots$.

   (a) $\dfrac{4}{3}$ (b) -1 (c) 0   (d) 4   (e) None of these

6. Which of the following converges?

   (a) $\displaystyle\sum_{n=1}^{\infty} (4 + (-1^n))$ (b) $\displaystyle\sum_{n=1}^{\infty} \frac{1}{\sqrt[3]{n}}$ (c) $\displaystyle\sum_{n=0}^{\infty} 4\left(-\frac{5}{3}\right)^n$

   (d) $\displaystyle\sum_{n=1}^{\infty} \frac{3^n}{(n + 1)!}$ (e) None of these

7. Which of the following diverges?

   (a) $\displaystyle\sum_{n=0}^{\infty} \frac{n!}{3n! - 1}$ (b) $\displaystyle\sum_{n=1}^{\infty} \frac{1}{n^6}$ (c) $\displaystyle\sum_{n=0}^{\infty} 5\left(\frac{1}{10}\right)^n$ (d) $\displaystyle\sum_{n=0}^{\infty} \frac{n}{2^n}$ (e) None of these

8. Which test would be used to prove the divergence of $\displaystyle\sum_{n=0}^{\infty}\left(1 + \frac{1}{e^n}\right)$?

    (a) *p*-Series Test   (b) Geometric Series Test   (c) *n*th-Term Test

    (d) Ratio Test   (e) None of these

9. A ball is dropped from a height of 8 feet. Each time it drops h feet, it rebounds $\frac{4}{5}h$ feet. Find the total distance traveled by the ball.

    (a) 80 feet   (b) 40 feet   (c) 32 feet   (d) 72 feet   (e) None of these

10. Find the radius of convergence for the power series $\displaystyle\sum_{n=0}^{\infty} \frac{x^n}{4(n^2 + 3)}$.

    (a) 3   (b) $\frac{1}{4}$ (c) 1   (d) 4   (e) None of these

11. Find the radius of convergence for the power series $\displaystyle\sum_{n=0}^{\infty} \left(\frac{x}{2}\right)^n$.

    (a) $\frac{1}{2}$ (b) 2   (c) ∞ (d) 0   (e) None of these

12. Find the third-degree Taylor polynomial centered at 1 for the function $f(x) = \dfrac{x + 3}{x}$.

    (a) $13 - 18 + 12x^2 - 3x^3$ (b) $4 + 3x + 3x^2 + 3x^3$ (c) $4 - 3x + 6x^2 - 18x^3$

    (d) $4 + 3x + 6x^2 + 18x^3$ (e) None of these

13. Find the Taylor polynomial of degree two for the function $f(x) = \ln(x^2 + 4)$ centered at 0.

    (a) $\ln 4 + \dfrac{5}{32}x^2$ (b) $\ln 4 + \dfrac{x}{2} + \dfrac{x^2}{4}$ (c) $\ln 4 + \dfrac{x^2}{2}$ (d) $\ln 4 + \dfrac{x^2}{4}$ (e) None of these

Test Form C   Name _____ Date _____

Chapter 10   Class _____ Section _____

1. Find the fourth term of the sequence: $\left\{\dfrac{(-1)^{n+1}2^n}{3n-1}\right\}, n = 1, 2, 3, \cdots$.

2. Determine if the following sequence converges or diverges:

$$\left\{\dfrac{5n^2 + 1}{4n^2 + 3n + 2}\right\}, n = 0, 1, 2, \cdots.$$

   If the sequence converges, find its limit.

3. Determine if the following sequence converges or diverges:

$$\left\{\dfrac{e^n}{e^n + 2}\right\}, n = 0, 1, 2, \cdots.$$

   If the sequence converges, find its limit.

4. Find the sum of the geometric series: $\displaystyle\sum_{n=0}^{\infty} 3\left(\dfrac{4}{7}\right)^n$.

5. Determine the convergence or divergence of the following series, and state the test used: $\displaystyle\sum_{n=1}^{\infty} \dfrac{1}{\sqrt[3]{n}}$.

6. Determine the convergence or divergence of the following series, and state the test used: $\displaystyle\sum_{n=0}^{\infty} \dfrac{1}{e^n}$.

7. Determine the convergence or divergence of the following series, and state the test used: $\displaystyle\sum_{n=1}^{\infty} \dfrac{5n}{2n-1}$.

8. Determine the convergence or divergence of the following series, and state the test used:

$$\sum_{n=1}^{\infty} \dfrac{1 \cdot 3 \cdot 5 \cdots (2n-1)}{n!}.$$

9. Find the radius of convergence for the power series $\displaystyle\sum_{n=0}^{\infty} \left(\dfrac{2x}{3}\right)^n$.

10. Given $f(x) = \displaystyle\sum_{n=0}^{\infty} \dfrac{3x^n}{n!}$, find a power series for $f'(x)$.

11. Find the first three nonzero terms in a Taylor Series for the function $y = \ln x$ centered at 3.

12. Find the fourth-degree Taylor polynomial for $f(x) = \ln x$, centered at $x = 1$.

13. Find an approximation for

$$f(3) \text{ where } f(x) = \frac{1}{x}$$

by using the first four terms of a Taylor polynomial centered at 2.

14. In a complete sentence, state what must be true about the series

$$\sum_{n=0}^{\infty} a_n$$

if the ratio test is used to show that it converges.

Test Form D

Chapter 10

Name _____ Date _____

Class _____ Section _____

1. Find the third term of the sequence: $\left\{\dfrac{(-2)^n(2^n+1)}{\sqrt{n}}\right\}, n = 1, 2, 3, \cdots$.

   (a) 4.619   (b) 5.196   (c) -5.196 (d) -4.619 (e) None of these

2. Determine if the following sequence converges or diverges:

   $\left\{\dfrac{4n^2+1}{6n^2-3}\right\}, n = 1, 2, 3, \cdots$.

   (a) Converges to $-\frac{1}{3}$ (b) Converges to $\frac{2}{3}$ (c) Converges to 0

   (d) Diverges   (e) None of these

3. Determine if the following sequence converges or diverges: $\{\ln(n^2+4) - \ln(n)\}, n = 2, 3, 4, \cdots$.

   (a) Converges to ln 4   (b) Converges to ln 5   (c) Converges to ln 2

   (d) Diverges   (e) None of these

4. Determine the behavior of the sequence: $\left\{\left(1+\dfrac{2}{n}\right)^n\right\}, n = 1, 2, 3, \cdots$.

   (a) Diverges   (b) Converges to 7.3891   (c) Converges to 2.7828

   (d) Converges to 4.7891   (e) None of these

5. Find the sum of the geometric series: $\displaystyle\sum_{n=0}^{\infty} 5\left(\dfrac{1}{e}\right)^n$.

   (a) 2.910   (b) 1.839   (c) 7.910   (d) 5   (e) None of these

6. Which of the following converges?

   (a) $\displaystyle\sum_{n=0}^{\infty}(5+(-2)^n)$ (b) $\displaystyle\sum_{n=1}^{\infty}\dfrac{5^n}{(2n+1)!}$ (c) $\displaystyle\sum_{n=0}^{\infty}6\left(-\dfrac{7}{2}\right)^n$

   (d) $\displaystyle\sum_{n=1}^{\infty}\dfrac{1}{\sqrt[4]{n}}$ (e) None of these

7. Which of the following diverges?

   (a) $\displaystyle\sum_{n=0}^{\infty}\dfrac{n!}{5n!-2}$ (b) $\displaystyle\sum_{n=1}^{\infty}\dfrac{1}{n^7}$ (c) $\displaystyle\sum_{n=0}^{\infty}11\left(\dfrac{3}{8}\right)^n$ (d) $\displaystyle\sum_{n=1}^{\infty}\dfrac{n^2}{3^n}$ (e) None of these

8. Which test would be used to prove the divergence of $\displaystyle\sum_{n=0}^{\infty}\left(\dfrac{1}{1+e^n}\right)$?

   (a) p-Series Test   (b) Geometric Series Test   (c) nth-Term Test

   (d) Ratio Test   (e) None of these

9. Find the radius of convergence for the power series $\displaystyle\sum_{n=0}^{\infty} \frac{x^n}{4(n^2 + 3)}$.

(a) 3   (b) $\frac{1}{4}$ (c) 1   (d) 4   (e) None of these

10. Complete two iterations of Newton's Method to approximate a zero of $f(x) = x^3 - 10$ using $x_1 = 3$ as an initial estimate. Round to four decimal places.

(a) $x_3 = 2.14$ (b) $x_3 = 2.28$ (c) $x_3 = 2.17$ (d) $x_3 = 2.71$ (e) None of these

11. Use a fourth-degree Taylor polynomial, centered at 2, for the function $f(x) = \ln(x - 2)$ to approximate $\ln(1.5)$.

(a) 0.416   (b) 0.401   (c) 0.427   (d) 0.399   (e) None of these

12. Find the first three nonzero terms in a Maclaurin Series for the function $f(x) = \dfrac{2}{x + 3}$.

(a) $\frac{2}{3} + \frac{2}{9}x + \frac{2}{27}x^2$ (b) $\frac{2}{3} - \frac{2}{9}x + \frac{4}{27}x^2$ (c) $\frac{2}{3} - \frac{2}{9}x + \frac{2}{27}x^2$

(d) $\frac{2}{3} - 2x + 2x^2$ (e) None of these

13. Find a power series centered at $x = 0$ for $f(x) = \dfrac{1}{x + 6}$.

(a) $\displaystyle\sum_{n=0}^{\infty} \frac{(-1)^n}{6^{n+1}}(x + 6)^n$ (b) $\displaystyle\sum_{n=0}^{\infty} \frac{(-1)^n n!}{(x + 6)^n}$ (c) $\displaystyle\sum_{n=0}^{\infty} \frac{(-1)^n}{6^{n+1}}x^n$

(d) $\displaystyle\sum_{n=0}^{\infty} \frac{(-1)^n n!}{6^{n+1}}x^n$ (e) None of these

Test Form E   Name _____ Date _____

Chapter 10   Class _____ Section _____

1. Find the third term of the sequence: $\left\{ \dfrac{(-2)^n(2^n + 1)}{\sqrt{n}} \right\}, n = 1, 2, 3, \cdots$.

2. Determine if the following sequence converges or diverges:

   $$\left\{ \dfrac{3n^2 + 1}{n} \right\}.$$

   If the sequence converges, find its limit.

3. Determine if the following sequence converges or diverges:

   $$\left\{ \left(\dfrac{n + 1}{n} \right)^n \right\}, n = 1, 2, 3, \cdots.$$

   If the sequence converges, find its limit.

4. Determine the behavior of the sequence: $\left\{ 3\left(1 + \dfrac{4}{n} \right)^n \right\}, n = 0, 1, 2, \cdots$.

5. Find the sum of the geometric series: $\displaystyle\sum_{n=0}^{\infty} 5\left(\dfrac{1}{e^2} \right)^n$.

6. Give a reason for the convergence of the series $\displaystyle\sum_{n=1}^{\infty} \dfrac{5^n}{(2n + 1)!}$.

7. Give a reason for the divergence of the series $\displaystyle\sum_{n=0}^{\infty} \dfrac{n!}{5n! - 2}$.

8. Apply any appropriate test to show that the series $\displaystyle\sum_{n=0}^{\infty} \left(\dfrac{1}{1 + e^n} \right)$ diverges.

9. Find the radius of convergence for the power series $\displaystyle\sum_{n=0}^{\infty} \dfrac{x^n}{3(n^2 + 4)}$.

10. Complete two iterations of Newton's Method to approximate a zero of $f(x) = 3x^3 - 7$ using $x_1 = 1.2$ as an initial estimate. Round to four decimal places.

11. Use a fourth-degree Taylor polynomial to approximate e^2.

12. Find the fourth term of the Taylor Series for $f(x) = \ln x$ centered at $x = 1$.

13. Use a power series, centered at 0, to get a degree two approximation for $\sqrt[3]{1.5}$ using the function $f(x) = \sqrt[3]{x + 1}$.

14. Explain, in a complete sentence, how a convergent series converges by explaining what must happen to the corresponding sequence of partial sums.

A N S W E R   K E Y S

Answers to Mid-Chapter Quizzes

Chapter 0

1. d	**2.** b	**3.** a	**4.** c	**5.** b
6. a	**7.** b	**8.** e	**9.** a	**10.** c

Chapter 1

1. b	**2.** e	**3.** a	**4.** c	**5.** a
6. c	**7.** a	**8.** b	**9.** d	**10.** b

Chapter 2

1. a	**2.** d	**3.** a	**4.** a	**5.** c
6. c	**7.** b	**8.** a	**9.** d	**10.** d

Chapter 3

1. c	**2.** d	**3.** b	**4.** d	**5.** c
6. c	**7.** c	**8.** d	**9.** c	**10.** a

Chapter 4

1. a	**2.** d	**3.** c	**4.** a	**5.** c
6. d	**7.** c	**8.** a	**9.** a	**10.** b

Chapter 5

1. c	**2.** a	**3.** d	**4.** a	**5.** a
6. d	**7.** d	**8.** b	**9.** c	**10.** d

Chapter 6

1. d	**2.** a	**3.** a	**4.** c	**5.** c
6. a	**7.** c	**8.** e	**9.** b	**10.** b

Chapter 7

1. b	**2.** b	**3.** c	**4.** e	**5.** a
6. c	**7.** d	**8.** b	**9.** c	**10.** c
11. a	**12.** b			

Chapter 8

1. b	**2.** a	**3.** c	**4.** d	**5.** b
6. e	**7.** d	**8.** d	**9.** b	**10.** a
11. c	**12.** c			

Chapter 9

| 1. b | 2. d | 3. b | 4. a | 5. d |
| 6. c | 7. d | 8. a | 9. a | 10. e |

Chapter 10

| 1. d | 2. c | 3. a | 4. d | 5. a |
| 6. c | 7. a | 8. b | 9. c | 10. a |

Answers to Cumulative Tests

Chapters 0–3

1. c	2. d	3. c	4. c	5. e
6. b	7. d	8. d	9. a	10. d
11. c	12. a	13. e	14. a	15. c

Chapters 0–7

1. d	2. a	3. b	4. c	5. b
6. a	7. d	8. b	9. d	10. b
11. b	12. a	13. c	14. e	15. d

Chapters 0–10

1. b	2. c	3. b	4. a	5. c
6. c	7. b	8. d	9. b	10. d
11. e	12. c	13. b	14. c	15. a

Answers to Final Exams

Final Exam A

1. e	2. c	3. c	4. b	5. c
6. a	7. b	8. d	9. b	10. b
11. b	12. c	13. d	14. a	15. a
16. a	17. b	18. b	19. c	20. c
21. e	22. b	23. a	24. a	25. a
26. c	27. d	28. a	29. d	30. e
31. c	32. c	33. b	34. b	35. a
36. b	37. d	38. b	39. c	40. e

Final Exam B

1. (a) $\dfrac{5}{x^4 - 1}$ **(b)** $(-\infty, -1)(-1, 1)(1, \infty)$ **2.** $-\dfrac{14}{x^3}$ **3.** $y = -20x + 31$

4. $\dfrac{31}{4}$ m/sec   **5.** $\dfrac{6x^2 + 2}{(1 - 3x^2)^2}$ **6.** $\dfrac{72x^2}{(1 - 4x^3)^3}$ **7.** $6(5x^2 + 1)(x^2 + 1)$ **8.** 4

9. $\dfrac{-2x - y}{x + 2y}$ **10.** $y = 2$ **11.** 20,000 units   **12.** $\left(-\infty, \dfrac{8}{3}\right)$ **13.** $(4, 0)(2, -32)$

14. $\dfrac{1 + 8x}{6xy^2 - 2xe^{-y}}$ **15.** $10e^{[(\ln 3)/8]t}$ **16.** $\dfrac{(2x + 1)e^{1/x}}{x^4}$ **17.** $\dfrac{x^2}{2} - x + C$ **18.** $41

19. $-\dfrac{1}{3(x^3 - 1)^3}$ **20.** $2\sqrt{e^x + 1} + C$ **21.** $\dfrac{8192\pi}{15}$ **22.** $-\dfrac{2}{5}(5 - x)^{3/2}(3x + 10) + C$

23. $\dfrac{3}{x - 1} - \dfrac{1}{(x - 1)^2} + \dfrac{9}{x + 3}$ **24.** $\dfrac{e^{3x}}{3}\left(x^2 - \dfrac{2}{3}x + \dfrac{2}{9}\right) + C$ **25.** Diverges

26. $2x^2 + 2xy - 3y^2$ **27.** Relative minimum at $(1, 1)$ **28.** $\displaystyle\int_{-1}^{1}\int_{x^2}^{2-x^2} dy \, dx$ **29.** $\dfrac{9}{2}$

30. $2\theta \sec \theta^2 \tan \theta^2$ **31.** $-2 \cos x + \ln |\csc x + \cot x| + C$ **32.** 0   **33.** $\dfrac{1}{e^2} - \dfrac{1}{e^4}$

34. 4   **35.** Diverges, nth-Term Test   **36.** $1 + x + \dfrac{x^2}{2} + \dfrac{x^3}{3!}$

37. 2   **38.** ± 0.001 **39.** $\dfrac{1}{\pi}$ in./sec   **40.** $\dfrac{1}{4}(e - 1)$

Final Exam C

1. 27   **2.** $\dfrac{4(8x + 3)}{3x^{2/3}}$ **3.** $(1, -2), (-1, 2)$ **4.** 9.3   **5.** $\dfrac{8x}{(x + 2)^2}$

6. $\dfrac{2}{3}$ **7.** 42 ft/sec^2 **8.** $\dfrac{2(5x^2 + 3x + 1)}{(1 - x^2)^4}$ **9.** $\left(-\dfrac{4}{3}, \infty\right)$ **10.** -36.0 cm^3/hr

11. Max: $(0, 10)$, Min: $(2, 2)$ **12.** $(-\infty, 0), \left(\dfrac{1}{2}, \infty\right)$ **13.** 37.2 in.^{2} **14.** $\dfrac{5}{(x + 3)^2} \, dx$

15. 3   **16.** $\dfrac{1}{6}$ **17.** $x = 6.9$ **18.** $675.79   **19.** $\dfrac{1}{2x} + \dfrac{1}{5 + x}$

20. 16.09 years   **21.** $Q(t) = 10e^{-0.023t}$ **22.** $x - 4 \ln |x + 1| + C$ **23.** $\dfrac{5}{16}(2y^2 + 1)^3 \, dy$

24. $y = x^2 - x + 3$ **25.** 5   **26.** $\dfrac{423}{5}\pi$ **27.** $\dfrac{16}{105}$

28. $\dfrac{4}{x + 1} - \dfrac{1}{(x + 1)^2} - \dfrac{1}{x - 8}$ **29.** $2,527,973.85   **30.** 0.9635   **31.** $\dfrac{16}{\sqrt{29}} \approx 2.971$

32. $2909.98   **33.** 3   **34.** $52,000   **35.** $y = 0.4205x^2 + 2.7x + 0.5568$

36. $\dfrac{993}{10}$ **37.** $2x \sec^2\left(x^2 - \dfrac{\pi}{4}\right)$ **38.** $\dfrac{125}{128} \approx 0.976562$ **39.** 0.4864   **40.** 1.1015625

41. Diverges, Ratio Test   **42.** 40 cm

Answers to Chapter Tests

Chapter 0

Test Form A

1. d	**2.** d	**3.** a	**4.** c	**5.** b
6. b	**7.** c	**8.** b	**9.** c	**10.** a
11. a	**12.** c	**13.** e	**14.** d	**15.** a

Test Form B

1. b	**2.** b	**3.** d	**4.** c	**5.** d
6. a	**7.** a	**8.** e	**9.** c	**10.** e
11. d	**12.** d	**13.** b	**14.** d	**15.** a

Test Form C

1. $x \leq \frac{3}{2}$ **2.** $x > -\frac{8}{5}$ **3.** $-\frac{4}{3}$ **4.** $\dfrac{7y^4}{3z^4 x^{7/2}}$ **5.** $\dfrac{3x + 2}{\sqrt{x + 1}}$

6. $(x - 3)(x + 2)(x + 3)(x^2 - 2x + 4)$ **7.** $-2, 4$ **8.** $-4, -3, 0$

9. $\dfrac{(A + C)x^2 + (2A + B)x + 2B}{x^2(x + 2)}$ **10.** $6x + \Delta x - 4$ **11.** $2 - \sqrt{x}$ **12.** $\dfrac{4x - 7}{\sqrt{x - 1}}$

13. $100 \leq x \leq 161$ **14.** A number x is less than 4 units from the number 2.

Test Form D

1. b	**2.** b	**3.** a	**4.** e	**5.** c
6. a	**7.** a	**8.** c	**9.** b	**10.** a
11. d	**12.** c	**13.** b	**14.** e	**15.** b
16. a	**17.** d			

Test Form E

1. $(-\infty, -1)$ or $(6, \infty)$ **2.** $x < -1.1$ or $x > 6.1$

3. $(-\infty, -1] \cup [5, \infty)$ **4.** $\left[-\frac{2}{3}, \infty\right)$ **5.** \$53,496.01   **6.** \$418.83

7. -3.375 **8.** $\dfrac{26y^{9/2}w^3}{x^7 z^{1/2}}$ **9.** 49   **10.** $(3, \infty)$ **11.** $\dfrac{2x + 9}{(x - 5)^{2/3}}$

12. $-2.3, 0.6$ **13.** $\frac{4}{3}$ **14.** $\dfrac{x^2 - 8x + 14}{x - 3}$ **15.** $\dfrac{x - 9}{2x\sqrt{x} + 6x}$ **16.** $\dfrac{2(2x - 3)}{3x^3(3 - x)}$

17. $x^2 - 3x + 2 - \dfrac{9}{x + 2}$ **18.** A rational number is any real number that can be written as a fraction.

Chapter 1

Test Form A

1. c	**2.** c	**3.** d	**4.** a	**5.** a
6. d	**7.** c	**8.** d	**9.** c	**10.** b
11. c	**12.** a	**13.** c	**14.** a	**15.** c
16. a	**17.** c	**18.** b	**19.** b	**20.** e

Test Form B

1. d	**2.** b	**3.** a	**4.** b	**5.** b
6. e	**7.** c	**8.** a	**9.** c	**10.** a
11. d	**12.** d	**13.** a	**14.** a	**15.** d
16. e	**17.** b	**18.** c	**19.** b	**20.** d

Test Form C

1. $2\sqrt{10}$ **2.** 3   **3.** $\left(0, -\frac{1}{3}\right), \left(\frac{1}{2}, 0\right)$ **4.** $x^2 + y^2 - 6x + 8y = 0$

5. $3x - 4y - 10 = 0$ **6.** $5x - 2y - 10 = 0$ **7.** 25

8.

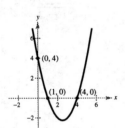

9. $(0, 0), (3, 3)$ **10.** $\left(-\infty, \frac{4}{3}\right]$ **11.** $-\frac{8}{5}$

12. $-x^2 - 2x\Delta x - (\Delta x)^2 + 4x + 4\Delta x + 5$ **13.** $\dfrac{x^2 + 1}{x^2}$ **14.** $f^{-1}(x) = \dfrac{2x^2 - 4}{x^2}$

15. $\frac{1}{3}$ **16.** 0   **17.** 2   **18.** 3

19. $x = 6$, <u>nonremovable</u>   **20.** 3

Test Form D

1. b	**2.** c	**3.** a	**4.** d	**5.** c
6. d	**7.** d	**8.** b	**9.** a	**10.** c
11. c	**12.** a	**13.** b	**14.** a	**15.** a
16. a	**17.** b	**18.** e	**19.** c	**20.** d

Test Form E

1. $\sqrt{41}$ **2.** Yes   **3.** $(0, 5), (-2.7, 0)$ **4.** $x^2 + y^2 + 2x - 6y + 1 = 0$

5. $(0.8, 0.2), (-1.8, 2.8)$ **6.** $3x - 2y + 11 = 0$ **7.** 47.9

8.   **9.** $(0, 0), (2, 4)$ **10.** $x \le \frac{2}{3}$ **11.** 2

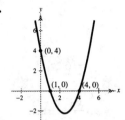

12. $-x^2 - 2x\Delta x - (\Delta x)^2 + 4x + 4\Delta x + 5$ **13.** $\frac{1}{x} - 5$ **14.** $\frac{9 - 2x^2}{x^2}$ **15.** 0

16. 2   **17.** -3 removable; 2 nonremovable   **18.** 3

19. $(-\infty, -3)(-3, \infty)$ **20.** Answers will vary.

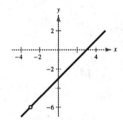

Chapter 2

Test Form A

1. d   **2.** c   **3.** c   **4.** c   **5.** c

6. d   **7.** c   **8.** c   **9.** d   **10.** e

11. d   **12.** a   **13.** c

Test Form B

1. c   **2.** c   **3.** b   **4.** e   **5.** a

6. d   **7.** d   **8.** Answers will vary. **9.** c   **10.** d

11. b   **12.** b   **13.** b

Test Form C

1. $-3x^2 + 4x - 1$ **2.** $\frac{4x}{(x^2 + 2)^2}$ **3.** $\frac{-10(4x^3 - 3)}{(x^4 - 3x)^3}$ **4.** $\frac{1}{(x^2 + 1)^{3/2}}$ **5.** $\frac{3x^2 - 4xy + 3y^2}{2x^2 - 6xy}$

6. $y = 2$ **7.** Average rate of change: -1, instantaneous rate of change: 0   **8.** 2.75 m/sec.

9. $\frac{x^2(7x + 6)}{2\sqrt{x + 1}}$ **10.** 23 units/month   **11.** $\frac{1}{3}$, 1   **12.** 42 ft/sec^2 **13.** Answers will vary.

Test Form D

1. a	**2.** c	**3.** d	**4.** b	**5.** c
6. c	**7.** b	**8.** c	**9.** a	**10.** a
11. b	**12.** b	**13.** c		

Test Form E

1. $-4(3x^3 - 3x^2 + 6x - 4)$
2. $\dfrac{12x^2 + 8x}{(1 + 3x)^2}$
3. $36x^2(x^3 - 1)^3$
4. $\dfrac{-6}{x^3}$

5. $\dfrac{2\sqrt{y} - 2y}{2y\sqrt{y} + x}$
6. $(1, 2)$
7. \$0.26
8. \$2.68
9. $\dfrac{x^2(7x + 3)}{\sqrt{2x + 1}}$

10. $-36.0 \text{ cm}^3/\text{hr}$
11. $0.0, 1.3$
12. 42 ft/sec^2
13. Answers will vary.

Chapter 3

Test Form A

1. d	**2.** c	**3.** a	**4.** b	**5.** c
6. d	**7.** e	**8.** b	**9.** e	**10.** b
11. a	**12.** d	**13.** b	**14.** b	**15.** c

Test Form B

1. c	**2.** b	**3.** b	**4.** a	**5.** a
6. c	**7.** d	**8.** b	**9.** a	**10.** a
11. b	**12.** d	**13.** a	**14.** b	**15.** d

Test Form C

1. $6, -6$
2. $(-\infty, 0)$
3. Relative minimum: $(1, -27)$
4. $(-\infty, 0), \left(\frac{1}{2}, \infty\right)$

5. $x = 0$, relative maximum; $x = \frac{2}{3}$, relative minimum
6. 0
7. 3

8. Vertical asymptote: $x = 2$. Horizontal asymptote: $y = 0$.

9. Increasing on $(-\infty, -2), (2, \infty)$

Decreasing on $(-2, 2)$
Concave up on $(0, \infty)$
Concave down on $(-\infty, 0)$
Relative maximum at $(-2, 16)$
Relative minimum at $(2, -16)$
Inflection point at $(0, 0)$

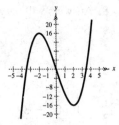

10.

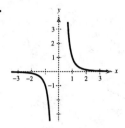

11. $(0, 8)$ and $(2, 24)$ **12.** $120   **13.** 5

14. $x = 100$ **15.** $dp = \dfrac{-3\,dx}{2\sqrt{200 - 3x}}$ **16.** Answers will vary.

Test Form D

1. a   **2.** c   **3.** b   **4.** a   **5.** d

6. d   **7.** c   **8.** b   **9.** b   **10.** d

11. d   **12.** a   **13.** b   **14.** b   **15.** c

16. c

Test Form E

1. Relative minimum: $(0.8, 2.6)$ **2.** $dy = -14$, $\Delta y = -16$

3. Concave upward: $(-\infty, -2)$; Concave downward: $(-2, \infty)$; No inflection points   **4.** $(-3, 1)$

5. Critical numbers: $0, \dfrac{\sqrt{13}}{2} + \dfrac{1}{2}, \dfrac{1}{2} - \dfrac{\sqrt{13}}{2}$; Relative maximum at $x = 0$

6. Horizontal asymptote: $y = 3$. No vertical asymptotes.   **7.** 0   **8.** $-\infty$

9. $x = 2$ **10.** 10 units   **11.** $200   **12.** 37.2 in.³   **13.** $(0.7, 0.3)$

14. $dp = \dfrac{-3\,dx}{2\sqrt{200 - 3x}}$ **15.** $x = 2$ **16.** Answers will vary.

Chapter 4

Test Form A

1. b   **2.** d   **3.** b   **4.** b   **5.** b

6. d   **7.** c   **8.** d   **9.** c   **10.** a

11. b   **12.** d   **13.** c   **14.** b   **15.** a

Test Form B

1. a   **2.** b   **3.** c   **4.** b   **5.** b

6. b   **7.** e   **8.** a   **9.** b   **10.** b

11. a   **12.** d   **13.** b   **14.** a   **15.** d

Test Form C

1. $\frac{81}{16}$

2. $\ln \dfrac{x^2}{(x-2)^3(x+1)^5}$

3.

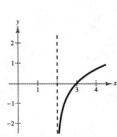

4. $e^x x^{e-1}(x+1)$

5. $\dfrac{e^{\sqrt{x}}}{2\sqrt{x}}$

6. $\dfrac{x(e^x - e^{-x}) - (e^x + e^{-x})}{2x^2}$

7. $\dfrac{x^2 - 4x - 2}{x^3 - x^2 - 2x}$

8. $\dfrac{y - 1 - e^y}{xe^y - x}$

9. $\frac{1}{3}e^3$

10. $\dfrac{x}{x^2 + 4}$

11. $y = 10e^{[(\ln 3)/8]t}$

12. $y = 100e^{-t(\ln 2)/3}$

13. $x = 1$

14. $(3, \infty)$

15. $-\frac{30}{101}$

16. The derivative of $y = e^u$ where $u = g(x)$ is the function e^u times the derivative of the exponent.

Test Form D

1. b   **2.** c   **3.** a   **4.** d   **5.** b

6. d   **7.** a   **8.** d   **9.** c   **10.** a

11. b   **12.** c   **13.** c   **14.** a   **15.** a

Test Form E

1. 6.548

2. $\frac{1}{7}$

3. $16.92

4. $5807.36

5. $\dfrac{-(1 + 3e^{3x})}{4(x + e^{3x})^{5/4}}$

6. $2x(1 + x \ln 10)10^{2x}$

7. $\dfrac{1 + 8x}{6xy^2 - 2xe^{-y}}$

8. $y = -3x + \ln 4$

9. $\dfrac{10(2e^{-2x} - 1)}{(x + e^{-2x})^2}$

10. Increasing   **11.** $y = 200e^{-t(\ln 2)/50}$ **12.** $x = 6.9$ **13.** $-1, 1$

14. 1.17 degrees/pound

15. The rate of change of the quantity is the multiple of a constant, a power of e, and the quantity itself.

Chapter 5

Test Form A

1. b   **2.** d   **3.** c   **4.** a   **5.** d

6. d   **7.** c   **8.** e   **9.** b   **10.** c

11. b   **12.** b   **13.** d   **14.** a   **15.** c

16. a

Test Form B

1. d	2. d	3. d	4. b	5. c
6. d	7. a	8. b	9. b	10. a
11. c	12. d	13. b	14. e	15. c

Test Form C

1. $4\sqrt{x} + C$ 2. $\frac{4}{5}x^5 + C$ 3. $-\frac{1}{2}e^{-x^2} + C$ 4. $-\frac{1}{4}(2 - 3x)^{4/3} + C$

5. $\frac{1}{3}\ln|x^3 - 1| + C$ 6. $\frac{5}{18}(3y^2 + 4)^6 + C$ 7. $2\ln|x + 1| + 1$ 8. $-\frac{126}{5}$ 9. $\sqrt{2} - 1$

10. $\frac{142}{35}$ 11. 24 12. $\frac{125}{6} \approx 20.83$ 13. 2   14. $\frac{\pi}{2}(e^8 - 9)$

15. $\frac{4}{3}x^{3/2} + 3x - \frac{1}{3}$ 16. 3   17. Answers will vary.

Test Form D

1. a	2. d	3. a	4. a	5. d
6. c	7. c	8. e	9. b	10. c
11. a	12. d	13. b	14. a	15. e
16. a				

Test Form E

1. $\frac{-3}{x^2} + C$ 2. $-\frac{9}{x} + 24\ln|x| + 16x + C$ 3. $\frac{2}{3}\sqrt{2 + 3x} + C$

4. $\frac{4}{3}x^3 - 7\ln|x| + e^x + C$ 5. $\frac{190}{3} + \frac{160\sqrt{2}}{7} - \frac{540\sqrt{3}}{7} \approx -37.957$

6. $\frac{15}{4}\ln(6 + y^4) + C$ 7. $C = \frac{400}{3}\ln|3x + 4| - 24.84$ 8. $\frac{6393}{20} = 319.65$ 9. $\frac{17}{1014} \approx 0.0069$

10. -8 11. 3015 12. $4 - 2\sqrt{3}$ 13. $\frac{1}{9}\ln(14)$ 14. $\frac{64\sqrt{2}\pi}{3}$

15. 91.41 16. $Q = (x - 11{,}999)^{0.96} + 11{,}999$ 17. Answers will vary.

Chapter 6

Test Form A

1. a	2. d	3. c	4. b	5. e
6. b	7. d	8. c	9. a	10. b
11. a	12. c	13. b		

Test Form B

1. b	2. c	3. d	4. b	5. a
6. a	7. d	8. d	9. b	10. e
11. d	12. b	13. c		

Test Form C

1. $\frac{2}{3}\sqrt{x-1}(x+2) + C$
2. $\frac{e^{3x}(3x-1)}{9} + C$
3. $\frac{1}{6}\ln\left|\frac{t-3}{t+3}\right| + C$

4. $48 - 2(x-2)^2 = 2[24 - (x-2)^2]$
5. $\frac{4(3x-4)(x+1)^{3/4}}{21} + C$
6. $e\ln 2 - \ln 2 + 1$

7. $\frac{44}{3}$
8. $\frac{3/49}{(x+5)} + \frac{3/7}{(x-2)^2} - \frac{3/49}{(x-2)}$
9. 1.27619
10. $4,521,836.67

11. $7,200,000
12. Answers will vary.

Test Form D

1. a	2. a	3. d	4. c	5. a
6. a	7. a	8. c	9. b	10. a
11. c				

Test Form E

1. $\frac{4(3x-4)(x+1)^{3/4}}{21} + C$
2. $\frac{1}{4}x^4 \ln x - \frac{1}{16}x^4 + C$
3. 1

4. $\ln|x+3| + C$
5. $\frac{2}{4x-3} + \frac{3x}{x^2+5}$
6. $48 - 2(x-2)^2 = 2[24 - (x-2)^2]$

7. $\frac{1}{2}\left[(x-4)\sqrt{x^2-8x} - 16\ln|(x-4) + \sqrt{x^2-8x}|\right] + C$
8. 0.9635
9. Converges to 1

10. The integral diverges.
11. $6015.35
12. $\frac{1}{2}$
13. Answers will vary.

Chapter 7

Test Form A

1. d	2. a	3. b	4. b	5. a
6. d	7. a	8. e	9. c	10. d
11. a	12. c			

Test Form B

1. a	2. a	3. c	4. a	5. c
6. b	7. b	8. e	9. a	10. e
11. b	12. b			

Test Form C

1. $\left(-\dfrac{3}{2}, -\dfrac{9}{2}, 3\right); r = \dfrac{\sqrt{118}}{2}$

2. Elliptic paraboloid

3. $\sqrt{26}$

4. $\{(x, y): x^2 + y^2 \leq 4\}$

5. $y(xyz + 1)e^{xyz}$

6. 1

7. Relative minimum at $(-4, 2, -6)$
   Saddlepoint at $(-1, -1, 5)$

8. $f(40, 20) = 1680$

9. $\dfrac{152}{15}$

10. $\dfrac{4}{105}$

11. $y = -170x + 380$

12. Relative minimum at $(3, 3, -17)$
   Saddlepoint at $(0, 0, 10)$

13. Answers will vary.

Test Form D

1. b   **2.** d   **3.** a   **4.** a   **5.** c

6. d   **7.** b   **8.** a   **9.** d   **10.** c

11. b   **12.** a

Test Form E

1. 9.27

2. $x^2 + y^2 + z^2 + 10x - 5y - 8z + 9 = 0$

3. $\{(x, y): x^2 + y^2 \leq 1\}$

4. $(0, 0, 4), (0, -5, 0), (-10, 0, 0)$

5. -2.20

6. $2x - \dfrac{xy}{\sqrt{z - x^2}}$

7. -8

8. \$52,000

9. 11, 11, 11

10. 18

11. $\dfrac{1}{4}(e - 1)$

12. $y = 1.1949x + 1.3475$

13. Answers will vary.

Chapter 8

Test Form A

1. c   **2.** b   **3.** b   **4.** b   **5.** c

6. b   **7.** a   **8.** b   **9.** e   **10.** b

11. b   **12.** b   **13.** b   **14.** d   **15.** d

16. d

Test Form B

1. b   **2.** b   **3.** c   **4.** b   **5.** a

6. b   **7.** c   **8.** c   **9.** a   **10.** b

11. d   **12.** b   **13.** a   **14.** d   **15.** b

16. b

Test Form C

1. 2

2.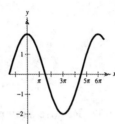

3. $-2\sqrt{2}$

4. $\dfrac{2\pi}{3}, \dfrac{4\pi}{3}$

5. $6\sec^2 3x$

6. $\dfrac{1}{\cos x - 1}$

7. $-\dfrac{1}{\sqrt{2}}$

8. $\cos^2 y$

9. $2\cot x$

10. $\dfrac{\pi}{4}, \dfrac{5\pi}{4}$

11. $-3\csc x + C$

12. $\frac{2}{3}(\tan x)^{3/2} + C$

13. $\frac{1}{4}\ln|\sin 4x| + C$

14. $\sqrt{3} - 1$

15. 2

16. 0

Test Form D

1. d　　　**2.** c　　　**3.** b　　　**4.** b　　　**5.** c

6. b　　　**7.** c　　　**8.** c　　　**9.** a　　　**10.** a

11. c　　　**12.** d　　　**13.** d　　　**14.** e　　　**15.** c

16. b

Test Form E

1. $\dfrac{\sqrt{29}}{5}$

2. $-\frac{1}{4}$

3. $\frac{3}{5}$

4. 1.79181

5. $2x\cos x^2$

6. $\dfrac{-2\sin x}{(1 - \cos x)^2}$

7. -0.9640

8. $-\tan x$

9. 0.9003

10. $\sec y$

11. 3

12. $2\sqrt{\tan x} + C$

13. $\frac{1}{2}\sin\theta + C$

14. $\frac{1}{2}\ln|\tan x| + C$

15. $2\sqrt{2}$

16. 0

Chapter 9

Test Form A

1. c　　　**2.** d　　　**3.** c　　　**4.** c　　　**5.** a

6. a　　　**7.** b　　　**8.** c　　　**9.** a　　　**10.** c

11. e　　　**12.** a　　　**13.** d　　　**14.** c　　　**15.** c

Test Form B

1. b　　　**2.** b　　　**3.** d　　　**4.** c　　　**5.** e

6. a　　　**7.** c　　　**8.** a　　　**9.** b　　　**10.** c

11. d　　　**12.** a　　　**13.** a　　　**14.** d　　　**15.** a

Test Form C

1. {HHT, HTH, THH}   2. $\frac{11}{20}$ 3. 0.702   4. 1.6

5. 1.44   6. 1.2   7. $\frac{5}{4}$ 8. $\frac{3}{4}$ 9. $\frac{27}{32}$

10. 2.4   11. 3   12. 5 ln 2   13. $\frac{5}{2}$ 14. $\frac{\sqrt{5}}{2}$

15. Answers will vary.

Test Form D

1. e   2. b   3. c   4. c   5. d

6. a   7. b   8. b   9. e   10. d

11. b   12. a   13. a   14. c   15. b

Test Form E

1. {(1, 3), (3, 1), (2, 2)}   2. $\frac{1}{26}$ 3. 0.777   4. 2.03

5. 1.3091   6. 1.144   7. $\frac{3}{256}$ 8. $\frac{5}{16}$ 9. 0.5

10. $e^{-4/25} \approx 0.852143$ 11. 0.1093   12. $\frac{1}{4}$ ln 2

13. $\displaystyle\int_{45}^{\infty} \frac{1}{5\sqrt{2\pi}} e^{-(x-35)^2/50}$ 14. Answers will vary.

Chapter 10

Test Form A

1. b   2. b   3. d   4. c   5. d

6. a   7. b   8. a   9. c   10. c

11. b   12. d   13. c

Test Form B

1. d   2. b   3. d   4. c   5. a

6. d   7. a   8. c   9. d   10. c

11. b   12. a   13. d

Test Form C

1. $-\frac{16}{11}$ 2. Converges to $\frac{5}{4}$ 3. Converges to 1   4. 7   5. Diverges, p-Series

6. Converges, Ratio Test   7. Diverges, nth-Term Test

8. Diverges, Ratio Test   9. $\frac{3}{2}$ 10. $f'(x) = \sum_{n=0}^{\infty} \frac{3x^n}{n!}$

11. $\ln 3 + \frac{1}{3}(x - 3) - \frac{1}{18}(x - 3)^2$ 12. $P_4(x) = (x - 1) - \frac{(x - 1)^2}{2} + \frac{(x - 1)^3}{3} - \frac{(x - 1)^4}{4}$

13. $\frac{5}{16}$ 14. Answers will vary.

Test Form D

1. c   2. b   3. d   4. b   5. c

6. b   7. a   8. d   9. c   10. c

11. b   12. c   13. c

Test Form E

1. -5.196 2. Diverges   3. Converges to e 4. Converges to 163.8

5. 5.783   6. Ratio Test; $L = 0 < 1$ 7. Ratio Test; $L > 1$

8. Ratio Test; $L = \frac{1}{e} < 1$ 9. 1   10. $x_3 = 1.3265$

11. 7   12. $-\frac{1}{4}(x - 1)^4$ 13. 1.139   14. Answers will vary.